# A Century of Writers

## *1855–1955*

*A CENTENARY VOLUME*

CHOSEN BY D. M. LOW & OTHERS

*With an Introduction by*

OLIVER WARNER

THE REPRINT SOCIETY
LONDON

FIRST PUBLISHED 1955
THIS EDITION PUBLISHED BY THE REPRINT SOCIETY LTD
BY ARRANGEMENT WITH CHATTO & WINDUS LTD 1957

Printed in Great Britain
at the University Press, Oxford
by Charles Batey
Printer to the University

# A CENTURY OF WRITERS

# Contents

*There are illustrations and decorations in the text by the following artists: George Cruikshank, p. 45; Gilbert Spencer, p. 505; George A. Fothergill, p. 515; McKnight Kauffer, p. 521; Ray Garnett, p. 554; Mervyn Peake, p. 587; George Plank, p. 611; Edward Bawden, p. 645; Lynton Lamb, p. 650*

# CHATTO AND WINDUS

## A BRIEF ACCOUNT OF THE FIRM'S ORIGIN HISTORY AND DEVELOPMENT

BY

## OLIVER WARNER

### I

FOR over eighty years the imprint 'Chatto and Windus' has been associated with varying kinds of books, and for a full century, ever since the foundation of the business by John Camden Hotten, the firm has had vigorous direction. Although the value of the Hotten and, later, of the Chatto and Windus trade-mark has altered over the decades, the firm's name has seldom been placed on writing which, at the time of publication, did not appear to be good of its kind. Much has stood the test of years, as will be seen in this anthology; some proportion may have survival quality as long as English is read.

Any sketch of the history of the business itself will be, from the very nature of publishing, largely one of personalities, for the good publisher habitually exercises his own individual taste and judgement. It may therefore be appropriate to consider the more vivid figures of the past, and some of the changes in emphasis in the products of the firm.

Chatto and Windus are not the only London publishers whose founder has been thought worthy of inclusion in *The Dictionary of National Biography*, but the honour is sufficiently uncommon to be worth pondering. Hotten was a remarkable and in some respects a puzzling character, but he built to endure, and it is probable that he knew it. He never did anything without purpose, and he had skill in creating lasting values, in a sphere which has always demanded acumen. A firm which can span a century, and remain as vital as it was in its childhood, with its imprint honoured today as much as at any time in the past, will in fact have been guided by a succession of astute people. Astute—and stable: for it is an impressive fact that during the ninety-eight years in which the firm was a private partnership, there were only five successive senior partners. And in every single instance, apart from Hotten himself, these heads of the firm took up their position after much experience with their predecessors.

The founder, John Camden Hotten, was born in 1832, in the reign of William IV. He lived only to be forty-three, yet he crowded much into his brief life. Both his parents were Cornish: perhaps his fire and energy were Celtic: but he was brought up as a Londoner, at Clerkenwell, where his father had become established as a master-carpenter. At fourteen he was apprenticed to John Petheram, a bookseller of

Chancery Lane, and soon discovered his vocation. A contributor to *Notes and Queries* once estimated that Hotten had a hand, often the sole hand, in not less than twenty-five books, mainly, though not exclusively, of an antiquarian sort, and the full list may never now be agreed.

He used pseudonyms, including the singular one of Titus A. Brick, and his gifts to the world included a *Slang Dictionary*. His most ambitious work, which a modern collector described as being, in his opinion, 'next to Lowndes's *Bibliographers' Manual*, probably the largest work of labour of its kind performed by one man during the last century', was an annotated catalogue of 20,000 books relating to the Topography and Family History of England and Wales. Like almost everything Hotten put a hand to, it is still worth consulting.

Hotten's interests were diverse. When in due time he came to publish in a large way, his list included not only a fine edition of *The Book of Common Prayer*, but a *Romance of the Rod; an Anecdotal History of the Birch in Ancient and Modern Times*, compiled, it is true, by a clergyman. There was not only *Songs of the Nativity* but a *History of Playing Cards*, with coloured illustrations: and there was an illustrated *Modern Confectioner*, written from data supplied by William Jeanes, chief confectioner at the delectable Messrs. Gunter's, then of Berkeley Square. The summit of elegance in production, in which Hotten took some pride, was reached in 1869: in that year he issued a version of Alban Butler's *Lives of the Saints*. It cost £7, 'enriched with fifty-one exquisite Full-page Miniatures, in gold silk velvet, preserved in a case', to quote the special announcement.

While still in his teens, Hotten went with his brother to America. The fruits of this visit became apparent soon after 1855, when he set up his business, first as bookseller, then as bookseller and publisher, at 151*b* Piccadilly, which surviving photographs show as a two-storied Georgian building, in brick. The premises have since disappeared, along with many others, in favour of the Ritz Hotel. Though small, Hotten's enterprise prospered: his 'literary knowledge and shrewd intelligence collected around him a large circle of acquaintances,' says *The Dictionary of National Biography*. In those few words are expressed much of the secret of successful book trafficking; and they refer to a time when Piccadilly was a centre for the book trade to a far greater extent than it has since been.

Hotten began his business in the year that the well-known publisher, William Pickering, also of Piccadilly, was gathered to his fathers, and it is significant that Hotten's earliest surviving trade-list contains many items bearing the beautiful anchor and dolphin design of Pickering's Aldine Edition of the poets. Other catalogues followed in quick succession, including an extensive offer of Tracts, Manuscripts, and Pamphlets, and a selection from the libraries of Samuel Rogers, the banker-poet, and of Lord Alvanley. Hotten had a percipient touch, where books were concerned. All he did bears signs of that. By the end of the fifties he was busily introducing American work to English readers. In time his list came to include Mark Twain, Bret Harte, Artemus Ward, Oliver Wendell Holmes, C. G. Leland, J. R. Lowell, Edgar Allan Poe, Walt Whitman, Ambrose Bierce, and others important in the history of American letters.

Alas, Hotten's rôle in the reciprocal literary traffic between the United States and this country was not altruistic. Although a long line of illustrious English writers, Dickens among them, suffered from piracy of their work in the United States, and complained of it in no meek terms, yet the founder of the firm of Chatto and Windus, along with others, did his best to see that the business was not all one way. In his time, very few Americans took such steps as they could, or were necessary, to copyright their work in this country, and they suffered much. Where Hotten had the advantage over his confrères was that he knew the American field better than they did, and made unscrupulous use of that knowledge. These are strong words, but evidence of their truth is contained in an important though forgotten letter which Mark Twain published in *The Spectator* for 20 September 1872. This was a sally against Hotten, who, though within the law, had apparently published the writer's books without paying him a penny. That was not all!

> My books are bad enough [said Mark Twain] just as they are written; then what must they be after Mr. John Camden Hotten has composed half a dozen chapters and added the same to them? Sometimes, when I read one of these additional chapters constructed by Mr. John Camden Hotten, I feel as if I wanted to take a broom-stick and go and knock that man's brains out. Not in anger, for I feel none. Oh! not in anger; but only to see, that is all. Mere idle curiosity.

Apparently one of Hotten's beliefs was that 'Carl Byng' was, like 'Mark Twain', a pseudonym for Samuel Clemens. If so, he was wrong. Mark Twain said so, adding:

> How would this sinful aborigine feel if I were to call him John Camden Hottentot? I do honestly believe it would throw him into a brain fever, if there was not an insuperable obstacle in the way.

Mark Twain ended by saying that the firm of George Routledge were the only British publishers who paid him for his work. It should be added that when Andrew Chatto took on Hotten's business, the year after the letter appeared, relations with Mark Twain were established on the happiest basis, and remained so ever afterwards.

II

In 1866 various landmarks stood out in Hotten's business life. He published his beautiful Chiswick Press edition of the Prayer Book. He also issued a *History of Signboards*, which was in regular demand for many years, and which has recently been reprinted. This book is interesting for many reasons. The title-page states that it was written by Jacob Larwood and John Camden Hotten, and the dedication is to Thomas Wright, the author of a *Caricature History of the Georges* which, with its colour plates and its large and small editions, was long popular on Hotten's list. Larwood was the pseudonym of a Dutchman, Herman Diederik Johan van Schevichaven, who numbered among his gifts an ability in simple line drawing. Many of his illustrations enliven the pages. One more notable fact about this book is that it appears to have been printed by (not *for*) the publisher. As the same notice occurs in one or two others of the Hotten series, it is possible that he combined a printing press with his other activities.

Another event in this memorable year was the publication of *Poems and Ballads* by Algernon Charles Swinburne. The event demands more than passing reference, since it permanently affected the nature of Hotten's business. Hitherto he had been known mainly as a specialist in certain lines—Americana, books with an antiquarian flavour, and what might be called historical oddities. Now, entirely of his own volition, he became publisher to a young creative artist of genius. He had ceased to be merely the 'astute purveyor', in the cold phrase of Swinburne's biographer, Sir Edmund Gosse, with a 'somewhat dingy imprint'. He had transformed himself into what every publisher must become if he wishes his name to mean anything in literary history—a vital collaborator, willing to finance and to market wares which possess inspiring, experimental, and even explosive qualities.

The issue of *Poems and Ballads* was in fact the most important single event since the foundation of the firm, and it may well have appeared so at the time. It took courage, and this was, in the long run, thoroughly rewarded. Meanwhile Hotten experienced the difficulties as well as the excitements of issuing the work of a man who possessed, pre-eminently, the artistic temperament.

The detailed circumstances of the first transaction were as follows. Swinburne, who was then just under thirty, with a reputation gained through his poetic plays and through *Atalanta in Calydon*, which had appeared in 1865, had sent *Poems and Ballads* to the firm of Moxon, who had published his earlier work. Moxon himself was dead, but the sage advice once given him by Wordsworth was remembered by his successor, Bertrand Payne: 'first acquire a competence, then practise virtue'. Payne had already sent early copies of *Poems and Ballads* to the newspapers for review, when he suddenly began to hear whispers. They grew. *The Saturday Review* was known to be ready to print a fierce attack on the morals of the poet. Worse still, *The Times* was said to be preparing a broadside which would include a demand for the criminal prosecution of the publisher.

Payne was horrified. On 5 August 1866 he withdrew the book from sale, 'without consulting me, without warning, and without compensation', in Swinburne's words, 'a victim of sudden and craven panic' in those of Gosse.

It was at this point that Hotten stepped in. He paid £200 for the existing copies of *Poems and Ballads*, acquiring the sheets of Swinburne's essay on Blake, which appeared two years later 'with facsimile Paintings, coloured by hand', and also his earlier work. In fact, he took over the poet as a going concern.

The success of *Poems and Ballads* was immediate, though it had violent denunciators, and not long after publication Swinburne wrote to Sir Richard Burton, of the *Arabian Nights*, to say that 'one anonymous letter from Dublin threatened me, if I did not suppress my book within six weeks from that date, with castration'.

By 1869 *Poems and Ballads* was advertised as being in its third edition, though Swinburne's bibliographer, the late T. J. Wise, went so far as to say: 'I have been forced to the conclusion that Hotten repeatedly reprinted *Poems and Ballads* without any notification of the fact appearing upon the title-page.' He found it 'impossible to imagine that one single edition, following the first (which consisted of 1,000 copies only) would have sufficed to meet the circulation that undoubtedly existed'. Hotten, at any rate, was pushing Swinburne in no half-hearted way.

It would be pleasant to record that the relationship, begun with such enterprise, thenceforward blossomed. Alas, it was not so. From the outset it was uneasy. Swinburne chafed in Hotten's care, and as early as 1871 he had *Songs Before Sunrise* published elsewhere. Hotten was so angry that he threatened legal action, but the matter was temporarily smoothed, and the book was taken over three years later by Chatto and Windus. In fact Swinburne's relations with the firm (though never with Hotten personally) in the end became easier. When the poet came under the care of Watts-Dunton at The Pines, Putney, in his later years, he allowed his mentor to transact all his business for him, except that with Hotten's pupil and successor, Andrew Chatto.

For seven years after his dramatic appropriation of Swinburne, Hotten continued to prosper, and to build up his list. The episode seems to have imbued him with even more vigour than before, and he flourished in strength right up to the time of his death, on 14 June 1873. He was then living at Maitland Park Villas, Haverstock Hill, Hampstead.

There is now no exact means of telling what manner of man Hotten was. His industry is indisputable. His boldness was shown first in his setting up so early in life in the heart of the West End, then by his sustained success, and finally in the matter of Swinburne. There were stories long current of authors, in search of their due, seeking him out at his private address, to be met with a dusty answer; but the fact remains that when he died, at an age when many men are only just beginning to find themselves, he had built up a sturdy business which showed every sign that it would last.

Nearly thirty years after Hotten's death, *The Daily News*, in the issue of 27 July 1901, announced that 'an Indianapolis literary Society are about to place a tablet to J. C. Hotten, the famous Piccadilly publisher, in their library, as an acknowledgement of his services in introducing certain famous American authors to the British reading public'. No irony was intended: and it is true that even today Hotten's own books, and many that bear his imprint, are sought for and cherished.

III

During his eighteen years' reign Hotten had moved from No. 151*b* to Nos. 74 and 75 Piccadilly, premises nearly opposite the first site. His successor, Andrew Chatto, who had been with the firm since the age of fifteen, had a literary background. His father, William Andrew Chatto, was a versatile writer, author of a standard work on wood-engraving which was reissued, in due time, as an act of filial piety. When Hotten died, Andrew Chatto bought the business from the widow for £25,000. He was joined in not very active partnership by W. E. Windus, who wrote narrative and lyric verses. Windus's first book, *Under Dead Leaves*, was published by Hotten in 1871, and his second, *Broadstone Hall and Other Poems*, appeared with his own name and that of Chatto on the title-page. It is as well to add that the last of the three volumes recorded as from him in the catalogue of the British Museum, *Elizabeth Stuart* (a dramatic sketch), was issued by the firm of Gubbins in the Isle of Wight—perhaps a pointer to publishers not to risk their more recondite verse on their own list.

W. E. Windus is sometimes confused with W. L. Windus, an historical painter who exhibited in the forties and fifties of the last century. W. E. is now scarcely quotable, though his appreciation of the good things of life may be illustrated by an unexpected Bacchanalian from *Broadstone Hall*:

Come fill another bumper, lad,
The wine is old and mellow.
The toast I'll give shall not be sad—
'Here's to our friends', old fellow!
For life's too short to fret and pine,
Or brood too much in sorrow;
Our foes we'll drown in generous wine,
And leave them till tomorrow.

At the end of Windus's book of verse was a catalogue, forty pages long, still full of Hotteniana. The date was 1875, and it was in fact the second or third issued by the newly named firm. The first which is now in the archives, dated July 1874, had as its principal item Maclise's *Gallery of Illustrious Literary Characters*, a demy quarto of over 400 pages. It was priced at 31*s*. 6*d*. in cloth, 'or in morocco elegant, 70/-'. There followed announcements of Cruikshank's *Comic Almanack*, Poems by Charles and Mary Lamb, Mayhew's *London Characters*, Theodore Hook's *Humorous Works*, Swinburne's *Bothwell: a Tragedy*, and a large assortment of American items.

In the year 1876 Percy Spalding brought a breeze into the business. Spalding, who is affectionately remembered by many still reasonably young, was the son of H. B. Spalding, of the firm of Spalding and Hodge, well known as paper merchants. Four years after his arrival the partnership moved to 214 Piccadilly, a few yards from the Circus, where it continued for nineteen years. It has been settled since 1897 in the neighbourhood of St. Martin's Lane, first at No. 111, then after 1918 at Nos. 97 and 99, and finally, for the last two decades, just round the Coliseum corner at 40 and 42 William IV Street. The move to 214 Piccadilly coincides very roughly with the change-over from bookselling and publishing to publishing pure and simple.

If Windus, as a man of business, remains shadowy, there is charming evidence about both Andrew Chatto and Percy Spalding. These two men, between them, could have claimed credit for establishing the firm not merely on a respectable but an assured basis.

Chatto was his own reader. He was a man of wide interests, an amateur scientist and astronomer, a 'cellist and a yachtsman. Mr. Swinnerton recalls him in *The Bookman's London* (1951), from which he has kindly given leave to quote, as:

a gentle elderly man with a rolling walk, genially sweet in manner to every member of his staff, and much loved.

Almost better loved still was his partner, Percy Spalding, who did not pretend to any literary taste, but put his hands in his pockets, jingled his keys and coppers, whistled *Meet Me To-Night in Dreamland* and said to all authors, whatever their pretensions, 'Nce, give us a rattling good story!'

Another account of Andrew Chatto senior is given in a letter from Mr. George Frommholz, for long production manager of the firm. He remembers him as looking, what indeed he must have been,

a typical English gentleman. Rather under average height, heavily built, bearded, and with pince-nez. He, with Mr. Spalding sitting opposite to him at the huge desk they used to occupy, simply oozed confidence. I don't wonder they published for so many eminent authors.

Mr. Chatto himself always went to Smith's and Mudie's for subscription orders for new books. This duty was never delegated to the travellers. The same hansom cabby drove him to and fro.

Chatto's two sons followed him into the bookselling line. Tom, the younger, joined the well-known antiquarian firm of Pickering and Chatto, now of Orange Street; the elder, Andrew, was at least a nominal partner of his father from 1893 onwards to 1919, though his real interests were out-doors.

It was in fact the elder Chatto and Percy Spalding who guided the long and prosperous middle era of the firm. In the year that Spalding became a partner, much of the stock and copyright formerly belonging to Henry Bohn was acquired in consideration of £20,000, and from the seventies to the early years of the present century the firm was eminent both as general and as fiction publishers. The list in due time came to include the works of Sir Walter Besant, Wilkie Collins, Justin McCarthy, Ouida, Charles Reade, R. L. Stevenson, and many others important in their era. It also included at least one or two books by others of the more notable writers of the later Victorian and the Edwardian age, including Hardy's *Under the Greenwood Tree* and some vintage Trollope. Moreover, the firm won the good-will both of the trade and of its writers. Besant, the first President of the Society of Authors, once remarked: 'I should like to see my friend Chatto driving in a gilded coach!'; while perhaps the best-known tribute ever paid to the concern came in the form of a letter to Andrew Chatto from R. L. Stevenson, sent from Bournemouth on 3 October 1884:

> If you don't know that you have a good author [wrote Stevenson] I know that I have a good publisher. Your fair, open and handsome dealings are a good point in my life, and do more for my crazy health than has yet been done by any doctor.

This letter was written two years after the publication by Cassell of *Treasure Island*, a book which first brought Stevenson fame, and one which has been a big seller ever since. Tradition long maintained that Andrew Chatto lost this jewel through suggesting to Stevenson that he should set aside an earlier effort in fiction which he had proposed for publication. The facts do not seem to support this. Stevenson wrote *Treasure Island* as a serial for *Young Folks*, and was delighted when he was offered £100 for it by Cassell. But the result of his success was that his father bought back R.L.S.'s earlier copyrights and transferred the stocks to Chatto and Windus. Although the firm did not, indeed, publish all Stevenson's later books, the association was long, close, and profitable. Chatto crowned his services in a way which touched the author's heart. In 1890 Stevenson wrote, in white-hot passion, a defence of the memory of Father Damien of the Molokai leper colony, whose good name had been assailed in Australia by a Presbyterian parson of the name of Hyde. It was a splendid piece of prose, and the invective demolished his victim. Stevenson presented the pamphlet to Chatto, refusing all payment, saying that 'he was not a cannibal, and could not eat the flesh of Dr. Hyde'. Chatto, not to be outdone in generosity, sent the author's share of the profits to Molokai.

## IV

It was D. H. Lawrence who, in an apt phrase, once spoke of the Victorian heads of the firm as 'old-flavoured folk'. They conducted a large business without aid of telephone or typewriter. They made outright agreements on half sheets of notepaper, and they tended to view office routine almost as an extension of home. Percy Spalding, for instance, regularly rode in the Park during what would now be termed 'office hours'. There is much to be said for such a felicitous way of life, but publishing has always been a competitive activity, and from time to time strong injections of new people, ideas, and capital become necessary. It was so with Chatto and Windus.

Seeking vigour, the firm imported a whirlwind in the person of Philip Lee-Warner. He arrived in 1905.

A long whisking figure [Mr. Swinnerton recalls], his eyes always blinking, and little tufts of cotton wool dotting his face where he had cut his skin while shaving. He curved as he whisked, and he had a sweet grin. Really brilliant, but a gambler. . . . He sniffed his speeches: 'Look here, P. Spolding. . . .' He always called Spalding Spolding.

He was liked by everybody, and the memory long lingered in the office of how he would dictate his letters, lying on the floor with a cushion at the back of his head. So startling were Lee-Warner's projects that, within three years, he had shaken the partnership to its roots, and brought it within sight of disaster. The horrid vision receded: so did the dazzling newcomer, who continued onwards in his zestful career to found the Medici Society.

He left a varied legacy. His interest in art had led him to acquire excellent but expensive books on that subject. He made use of the services of that great scholar, Sir Israel Gollancz, as general editor of the 'King's Classics' and the 'Medieval Library'. He set standards in book production—exemplified in the fine Florence Press editions—which have been maintained ever since; and he introduced into the firm two young men, Geoffrey Whitworth and Frank Swinnerton, who served it for twenty years apiece, brought in many new authors, and gained renown later in other fields, Whitworth as founder of the British Drama League, Swinnerton as novelist, critic, broadcaster, and author of a highly individual work on a subject of which he knew much: *The Georgian Literary Scene*.

Andrew Chatto senior did not long survive Lee-Warner's departure. He retired in 1911 and died two years later. He was the strongest link with the past, but there was no abrupt break with tradition, for after he had gone affairs were conducted by Percy Spalding and, less enthusiastically, by the younger Chatto. Early in 1914 Charles Prentice arrived from Oxford, but he had little time to become familiar with the problems of publishing before being caught up into the military machine and finding himself in line of battle in Flanders.

Of the days at the earlier St. Martin's Lane premises, when the firm was in the magazine as well as the book-publishing field, Mr. Frommholz writes:

Looking back, it seems to me that authors, budding and otherwise, would float in and out almost at will. I think the most frequent visitor was George R. Sims, who seemed to make a habit of arriving just as the partners were going upstairs to lunch. In those days the firm employed a man and wife as caretakers, and the caretaker's wife always prepared lunch, which was taken on the second floor. Those were the days!—and if old Jack Smith the housekeeper was caught napping when George R. Sims bowled in, he could always run out for a steak or a dozen oysters and a pint of stout.

George R. Sims is almost forgotten, but his prodigious output included the verses 'It Was Christmas Day in the Workhouse' (assuredly not based on his experience in St. Martin's Lane), and he paid his old friend Andrew Chatto a left-handed compliment in calling his hair-restorer Tatcho, which was an anagram on his name.

It was chiefly in his capacity as a journalist that Sims grew familiar to the firm, though they also published his novels. Chatto and Windus were then prominent in the field of magazine publishing. For many years they handled the old-established *Gentleman's Magazine*, which survived, with breaks, from 1731 to 1922; the *Belgravia*, in which Hardy's *The Return of the Native* first appeared and to which Ouida contributed, which was extant from 1866 to 1899; and the *Idler*, associated with Jerome K. Jerome, which ran from 1892 to 1911. Geoffrey Whitworth's bi-monthly *Drama* had a year's run, from July 1919 to July 1920, in the firm's catalogue, after which there came a long break with the tradition of journal publishing, which was to be revived in the thirties.

The older way of life must have had good moments. For instance, there was a period when profusely illustrated catalogues came annually from the great London stores. One applicant from the Gold Coast, who perhaps looked to Chatto and Windus to produce a similar type of article, wrote as follows:

> Dear Sirs; I have the honour to inform you. Please send me your books, and you have the greatest honour. O death, where is thy sting! Yours etc.

A final recollection by Mr. Frommholz from the pre-1914 years concerns a sporting event, comparatively rare in the firm's annals owing to its modest size. A challenge to a football match was offered: it came from either Messrs. Heinemann or Messrs. James Burn, the binders.

> Jerseys were bought for the occasion [says Mr. Frommholz], and in due course the team turned out in full regalia at Wormholt Farm, Shepherd's Bush. Mr. Swinnerton was in the side, but despite his and everybody else's efforts we were beaten by a large margin. Nobody appeared anxious to referee the game, but the situation was saved by an under-sized little fellow, a proper Cockney, coming up and asking us if he could officiate. He was a rough diamond, but he controlled the game well, and when it was over both sides made a collection for him. I don't know what the other team collected, but it must have been a much smaller amount than ours, for when we handed him the three or four shillings we had subscribed he looked at it, spat on the silver and said, 'Gawd, if I'd only known!'

## V

In the history of businesses there is a point of time, shortly after a major change of direction has taken place, when both past and future are illuminated. It seemed that it had been reached, in the instance of

Chatto and Windus, in 1926. The past lingered; Percy Spalding still hung his glossy top-hat in the partners' cloakroom, though it was the last year in which he did so; the present was strong in personalities; something of the future could be discerned. Fresh standards were apparent; policy was forward-looking; younger men were in charge.

The guiding spirits were Charles Prentice and Harold Raymond. Ian Parsons, who was to succeed Prentice as typographer, was even then editing the *Cambridge Review*, and in less than two years took Geoffrey Whitworth's place as art editor. Among the executives were a few who had been engaged by the historic Andrew Chatto; others were but recently from school. Evidences of Lee-Warner's three electric years as partner could still be perceived on the walls in the shape of coloured prints.

Spalding's successor as senior partner, Charles Prentice, was a remarkable man. One of the neatest attempts to describe him was made by Mr. John Fothergill of *An Innkeeper's Diary*. He called him 'a genius in eiderdown clothing'. Probably no publisher ever had more books dedicated to him than Prentice. Like many Scots, he was generous in the extreme, though like every man of sense he hated waste.

Prentice had an air of Mr. Pickwick, who was in fact one of his favourite characters in fiction. There was, however, a sharp difference. Prentice was shrewd; he had no illusions about life in general—he felt, like Conrad's Winnie Verloc, that it didn't bear looking into; he was a scholar; and both in literary matters and in book design he had wonderful taste. That is to say much. Proof resides in the firm's catalogues during the years in which he was most active—from 1919 to 1934. In proportion to its yearly output, Chatto and Windus maintained what was probably the most distinguished list in London, both in content and appearance. Lest this seems to be hyperbole, the words of a typographer of wide reputation may be called in evidence.

> Chatto and Windus [writes Mr. Ruari McLean in *Modern Book Design* (1951)] have probably the longest unbroken record of excellence in book design of any London publishers still in business. They were good before 1900 . . . after the 1914 war, Chatto and Windus books were designed by Charles Prentice. Typical and familiar examples of his work are the first editions of C. E. Montague, R. H. Mottram, and Aldous Huxley. They have a quiet and unpretentious excellence; and like all well-made books they feel just right in the hand even before they are opened—a combination of size, thickness, weight of paper and the texture of the binding cloth.

'Quiet and unpretentious excellence' helps to describe Prentice, a man of silences. It was due to Harold Raymond that his discriminating books were more than collectors' pieces, were in fact merchandise widely distributed throughout the literate world.

Prentice and Raymond were heirs to an accumulation of fiction and miscellaneous works which had been swelling the catalogue for a great number of years. Grant Allen, Frank Barrett, Sir Hall Caine, B. M.

Croker, Dick Donovan with his detective stories, Manville Fenn, Florence Marryat, D. Christie Murray, James Payn, these are a random choice of names from lists in the decline of the Chatto era. One of Raymond's earliest problems, which he described in the Dent Memorial Lecture for 1938, was 'to job off an accumulation of works which had long ceased to sell. Those who regard Penguins as a modern portent may be surprised to hear that I found a stock of over three-quarters of a million sixpenny paper-covered works lying dormant on Chatto's shelves.' Upwards of eighty titles were concerned, and, as Raymond said: 'it was a *very* long fiction list that could produce that number of works which would pay to be re-set and sold at sixpence.'

If the past lay dormant on shelves, future sunlight was promised with the publication of Lytton Strachey's *Eminent Victorians* (1918) followed by *Queen Victoria* (1921). The effect of these books was considerable, and lasting. Strachey was a prominent member of the Bloomsbury Group, among whom were E. M. Forster, J. M. Keynes, Virginia and Leonard Woolf, G. E. Moore, Duncan Grant, Roger Fry, Clive Bell, and G. Lowes Dickinson. Many of them were associated either with Chatto and Windus or the Hogarth Press.

'Keynes and Strachey did not want to bring down the Victorian house', says Mr. J. K. Johnstone, the historian of the group, 'they wanted to sweep out some trash, move in some new furniture and re-arrange the rooms.' It was precisely this revivifying effort which Strachey achieved, not only on the outlook of his time but on the list of the firm with whom he chose to publish. His spirit was infectious. That they were ready to seize the opportunity offered by such writers as Strachey to revitalize the list is a measure of the skill of the new partners.

Prentice, having seen the firm increase in stature, had himself no wish to die in harness, and he was fortunate enough to have no reason for so doing. He ended his twenty years of partnership in 1934 and travelled in Greece, which had long been his wish. Alas, illness pursued him. He recovered sufficiently to make a brief return during the earlier part of the Second World War, when Raymond was alone, and later still did some typographical work for Penguin Books. Indeed, in his later years he seemed so much more his earlier self that his death, while on a visit to East Africa in 1949, came as a very great shock to those who knew him best.

After Prentice had retired, Mr. J. W. McDougall joined Harold Raymond and Ian Parsons in a triumvirate which guided important events in the firm's history. The first was re-entry into the sphere of journal publishing. The second was the move to William IV Street.

It began with the publication of a review called *World*, edited by Mr. Vernon Bartlett, which, uniting later with *Review of Reviews*, was given new vigour as *World Review of Reviews*, at a time when foreign affairs were mounting towards the climax of European war. The paper at first appeared from the old premises at 97 and 99 St. Martin's Lane. Shortly after the move, which was made in 1935, came the launching of *The Geographical Magazine* by Mr. Michael Huxley. In its earlier years this journal was run from the publisher's premises. It was a magazine which filled a clear need in a thorough way.

Less success attended a lone but exciting excursion into weekly journalism. *Night and Day* ran—if 'raced' is not a more appropriate word—from July to December 1937. It was a humorous paper of a kind which John Camden Hotten would surely have approved, since it had the poker-faced wit which is one of America's pleasures. Like a firework, *Night and Day* coruscated and went out. There are those who cherish their bound volumes, for it was years before anything remotely comparable was sponsored in this country. A very great number of leading writers and artists of today appeared in its columns during that rip-roaring half-year. Since the sad demise of *Night and Day* the firm has added two journals to its catalogue, *The Use of English*, an educational quarterly taken over in 1951, and *The London Magazine* happily revived in 1954 and edited by John Lehmann.

Book publishing during the few years between the establishment of the new pattern of partnership and the outbreak of war became increasingly difficult. The general output of the trade continued to rise, without a corresponding response from the book-buying public. Times were hard, and war, which dispersed the personnel of the firm—Ian Parsons went into the Royal Air Force and McDougall into the Admiralty—brought its own sharp problems. On the other hand, it resolved others. Trade gradually boomed. Towards the end of the war, almost any book could find a purchaser. It had been so in World War I. History was merely repeating itself. So were the inevitable shortages in materials, particularly paper.

Afterwards the partnership was re-formed. McDougall left to become head of a still older concern, Chapman and Hall Ltd. Mrs. Norah Smallwood, who had been in charge of the firm's typography during the war years, became a partner in 1945, and in the following year Chatto and Windus invited Mr. C. Day Lewis to become their literary adviser.

In 1946 the firm took under its management the Hogarth Press, which had been founded at Richmond in 1917 by Leonard and Virginia Woolf. In 1953 the firm ceased to be a private partnership and became a limited company, with Mr. Harold Raymond as Chairman. The Board of Directors as at present constituted has Ian Parsons as Chairman and Managing Director; the other members are Mr. Harold Raymond, Mrs. Smallwood, Mr. Piers Raymond, who continues a family tradition, Mr. C. Day Lewis, Mr. P. J. A. Calvocoressi, and Mr. Leonard Woolf, who retains his paramount interest in the affairs of the Hogarth Press.

There were those who, for sentimental reasons, regretted the disappearance of the old-style partnership, with its Dickensian flavour. It was perhaps an achievement to have preserved it for close upon a century. Chatto and Windus Ltd. still retains many of the advantages of a private business. It has not become impersonal, and it will be a sad day if it ever does so.

## VI

As the fame of a publishing firm, to say nothing of its solvency, depends upon the writers for whom it markets, it is well to consider some of the works which have helped to give the imprint of Chatto and Windus its flavour. Time is the surest winnower, and it is interesting to note those whose writings had survived, in the general catalogue, from Victorian and Edwardian days, right up to that period in the Second World War when so much good work became unobtainable, either through enemy action or material shortages.

Among general works, selections from Theodore Hook and Thomas Hood were still in print, together with some Richard Jefferies, George Macdonald, and Justin McCarthy, whose *History of Our Own Times* had once been a great money-spinner. There was still much Stevenson; W. N. P. Barbellion's *Journal of a Disappointed Man* was typical of the many fine books which were given continued life in the Phoenix Library, which Prentice had designed in 1927 to replace the earlier St. Martin's Library of pocket reprints. There were some specialist works; there were landmarks like Clive Bell's *Art* and F. R. Leavis's *New Bearings in English Poetry*; some Belloc and Chesterton; Arnold Bennett's plays; Sir W. S. Gilbert's comic operas; and some great translations—Constance Garnett's Tchehov and Gogol, C. K. Scott Moncrieff's Proust and Stendhal, Vizetelly's Zola. And there were a few doughty old stand-bys like Dr. E. C. Brewer's *Reader's Handbook*, invaluable to puzzle addicts.

In fiction there was some more Arnold Bennett; there was Besant, both alone and in collaboration with James Rice; Wilkie Collins in force; Mrs. B. M. Croker in force; Bret Harte in force; Ouida likewise. Ouida was extravagant, and soon spent the large sums which according to current practice were paid outright for her novels. Then there were warning notes from Chatto or Spalding, and she curbed her pace for a while. There was Charles Reade in quantity; Mark Twain in quantity; there were juveniles perpetually in demand, prominent among them Helen Bannerman's *Little Black Sambo*, first published in 1899 and going strong today, and E. V. Lucas's invaluable *Three Hundred Games and Pastimes for Children*. There was that phenomenal best-seller of the early twenties, Daisy Ashford's *The Young Visiters*. There could indeed be no complaint that the firm's products did not last, and a number of books, such as F. L. Lucas's four-volume edition of John Webster and Leonard King's *History of Babylonia* were evidence of that respect for scholarship without which no publisher of standing and reputation may be said to have done his whole duty.

Among contemporaneous books, Lytton Strachey's earlier biographies were the precursors of a succession of distinguished modern works, including a long and varied list, begun in 1920 with *Leda* and *Limbo*, by Aldous Huxley, who is one of the small band of current English writers with an international reputation. There were books by Julian Huxley, by Roger Fry, David Garnett, J. B. S. Haldane, Norman Douglas, Richard Hughes, and the Nobel Prize winners Pär Lagerkvist and William Faulkner, the latter an American novelist of striking originality whose appearance on the list would have delighted John Camden Hotten, as would that of Clarence Day, author of *Life With Father*. There were the earlier novels of Rosamond Lehmann; Wyndham Lewis's polemics; A. A. Milne's plays; C. E. Montague; the *Spanish Farm* series of R. H. Mottram; Wilfred Owen's war poems; the entire range of works by T. F. Powys; the works of Sylvia Townsend Warner, whose first story, *Lolly Willowes*, was one of the most graceful books that Prentice ever designed, and the novels of Margaret Irwin and Ann Bridge. To continue would be to catalogue; much will be discoverable from the pages that follow.

More recent additions to the list include works of infinite variety by Sir Compton Mackenzie, scholarship and criticism by such authorities as E. M. W. Tillyard and Basil Willey, lively books for the young, poetry, good fiction, and a number of impressive war books such as F. Spencer Chapman's *The Jungle is Neutral*. Moreover, just as in the First World War the firm produced one of the first books on air fighting, the war letters of Harold Rosher, written while serving in the Royal Naval Air Service, after the second they published the enthralling narratives of Pierre Clostermann, outstanding among French pilots. And today, as in an earlier epoch, there are few serious writers who have not either themselves contributed items to the list or who do not owe stimulus to some who adorn it.

Nor have wider obligations been forgotten. The firm has always supported, actively, every means by which the use of books generally could be increased. In this connection Harold Raymond will be particularly remembered in the annals of the book trade for his origination of the Book Token scheme. For over twenty years this has proved itself to be one of the most successful and extensive co-operative efforts for increasing the sale of books.

If maxims and morals may be perceived through such a story as is outlined herein, it is that good writers attract other good writers; that it is sound to develop along regular lines of interest; and that it rarely pays to lower standards in the hope of passing success.

Conditions in publishing remain difficult. Counter-attractions to reading become more and more pervasive. An active policy was never so necessary. But from the ever fresh appearance of the seasonal lists, an observer, however cautious, might well be disposed to prophesy that the history of Chatto and Windus would continue far into the future, that its high summer was by no means over. The accumulated harvest of pleasure, profit, and interest already gathered into the catalogue is so rich that any historian of the firm's activities is faced not with lack of material but with the need for selecting, pruning, leaving out. In a way, it is a fortunate problem. It is one which may daunt a successor when, in the fullness of time, he comes to survey the century which now lies ahead.

# ALGERNON CHARLES SWINBURNE

## *The Garden of Proserpine*

FROM 'POEMS AND BALLADS'

HERE, where the world is quiet;
  Here, where all trouble seems
Dead winds' and spent waves' riot
  In doubtful dreams of dreams;
I watch the green field growing
For reaping folk and sowing,
For harvest-time and mowing,
  A sleepy world of streams.

I am tired of tears and laughter,
  And men that laugh and weep;
Of what may come hereafter
  For men that sow to reap;
I am weary of days and hours,
Blown buds of barren flowers,
Desires and dreams and powers
  And everything but sleep.

Here life has death for neighbour,
  And far from eye or ear
Wan waves and wet winds labour,
  Weak ships and spirits steer;
They drive adrift, and whither
They wot not who make thither;
But no such winds blow hither,
  And no such things grow here.

No growth of moor or coppice,
  No heather-flower or vine,
But bloomless buds of poppies,
  Green grapes of Proserpine,
Pale beds of blowing rushes
Where no leaf blooms or blushes
Save this whereout she crushes
  For dead men deadly wine.

Pale, without name or number,
In fruitless fields of corn,
They bow themselves and slumber
All night till light is born;
And like a soul belated,
In hell and heaven unmated,
By cloud and mist abated
Comes out of darkness morn.

Though one were strong as seven,
He too with death shall dwell,
Nor wake with wings in heaven,
Nor weep for pains in hell;
Though one were fair as roses,
His beauty clouds and closes;
And well though love reposes,
In the end it is not well.

Pale, beyond porch and portal,
Crowned with calm leaves, she stands
Who gathers all things mortal
With cold immortal hands;
Her languid lips are sweeter
Than love's who fears to greet her
To men that mix and meet her
From many times and lands.

She waits for each and other,
She waits for all men born;
Forgets the earth her mother,
The life of fruits and corn;
And spring and seed and swallow
Take wing for her and follow
Where summer song rings hollow
And flowers are put to scorn.

There go the loves that wither,
The old loves with wearier wings;
And all dead years draw thither,
And all disastrous things;
Dead dreams of days forsaken,
Blind buds that snows have shaken,
Wild leaves that winds have taken,
Red strays of ruined springs.

We are not sure of sorrow,
And joy was never sure;
To-day will die to-morrow;
Time stoops to no man's lure;
And love, grown faint and fretful,
With lips but half regretful
Sighs, and with eyes forgetful
Weeps that no loves endure.

From too much love of living,
From hope and fear set free,
We thank with brief thanksgiving
Whatever gods may be
That no life lives for ever;
That dead men rise up never;
That even the weariest river
Winds somewhere safe to sea.

Then star nor sun shall waken,
Nor any change of light:
Nor sound of waters shaken,
Nor any sound or sight:
Nor wintry leaves nor vernal,
Nor days nor things diurnal;
Only the sleep eternal
In an eternal night.

*1866*

# *Obscenity in Books*

FROM 'NOTES ON POEMS AND REVIEWS'

I HAVE now gone over the poems which, as I hear, have incurred most blame; whether deservedly or not, I have shown. For the terms in which certain critics have clothed their sentiments I bear them no ill-will: they are welcome for me to write unmolested, as long as they keep to simple ribaldry. I hope it gives them amusement; I presume it brings them profit; I know it does not affect me. Absolute falsehood may, if it be worth while, draw down contradiction and disproof; but the mere calling of bad names is a child's trick, for which the small fry of the press should have a child's correction at the hands of able editors; standing as these gentlemen ought to do in a parental or pedagogic relation to their tender charges. They have, by all I see and hear, been sufficiently scurrilous—one or two in particular.

However, from one crime they are exempt;  
They do not strike a brother, striking *me*.

I will only throw them one crumb of advice in return; I fear the alms will be of no avail, but it shall not be withheld:

Why grudge them lotus-leaf and laurel,  
O toothless mouth or swinish maw,  
Who never grudged you bells and coral,  
Who never grudged you troughs and straw?

Lie still in kennel, sleek in stable,  
Good creatures of the stall or sty;  
Shove snouts for crumbs below the table;  
Lie still; and rise not up to lie.

To all this, however, there is a grave side. The question at issue is wider than any between a single writer and his critics, or it might well be allowed to drop. It is this: whether or not the first and last requisite of art is to give no offence; whether or not all that cannot be lisped in the nursery or fingered in the schoolroom is therefore to be cast out of the library; whether or not the domestic circle is to be for all men and writers the outer limit and extreme horizon of their world of work. For to this we have come; and all students of art must face the matter as it stands. Who has not heard it asked, in a final and triumphant tone, whether this book or that can be read aloud by her mother to a young girl? whether such and such a picture can properly be exposed to the eyes of young persons? If you reply that this is nothing to the point, you fall at once into the ranks of the immoral. Never till now, and nowhere but in England, could so monstrous an absurdity rear for one moment its deformed and eyeless head. In no past century were artists ever bidden to work on these terms; nor are they now, except among us. The disease, of course, afflicts the meanest members of the body with most virulence. Nowhere is cant at once so foul-mouthed and so tight-laced as in the penny, twopenny, threepenny, or sixpenny press. Nothing is so favourable to the undergrowth of real indecency as this overshadowing foliage of fictions, this artificial network of proprieties. *L'Arioste rit au soleil, l'Arétin ricane à l'ombre.* The whiter the sepulchre without, the ranker the rottenness within. Every touch of plaster is a sign of advancing decay. The virtue of our critical journals is a dowager of somewhat dubious antecedents: every day that thins and shrivels her cheek thickens and hardens the paint on it; she consumes more chalk and ceruse than would serve a whole courtful of crones. 'It is to be presumed,' certainly, that in her case 'all is not sweet, all is not sound.' The taint on her fly-blown reputation is hard to overcome by patches and perfumery. Literature, to be worthy of men, must be large, liberal, sincere; and cannot be chaste if it be prudish. Purity and prudery cannot keep house together. Where free speech and fair play are interdicted, foul hints and evil suggestions are hatched into fetid life. And if literature indeed is not to deal with the full life of man and the whole nature of things, let it be cast aside with the rod and rattles of childhood. Whether it affect to teach or to amuse, it is equally trivial and contemptible to us; only less so than the charge of immorality. Against how few really great names has not this small and dirt-encrusted pebble been thrown! A reputation seems imperfect without this tribute also: one jewel is wanting to the crown. It is good to be praised by those whom all men should praise; it is better to be reviled by those whom all men should scorn.

Various chances and causes must have combined to produce a state of faith or feeling which would turn all art and literature 'into the line of children.' One among others may be this: where the heaven of invention holds many stars at once, there is no fear that the highest and largest will either efface or draw aside into its orbit all lesser lights. Each of these takes its own way and sheds its proper lustre. But where one alone is dominant in heaven, it is encircled by a pale procession of satellite moons, filled with shallow and stolen radiance. Thus, with English versifiers now, the idyllic form is alone in fashion. The one great and prosperous poet of the time has given out the tune, and the hoarser choir takes it up. His highest lyrical work remains unimitated, being in the main inimitable. But the trick of tone which suits an idyl is easier to assume; and the note has been struck so often that the shrillest songsters can affect to catch it up. We have idyls good and bad, ugly and pretty; idyls of the farm and the mill; idyls of the dining-room and the deanery; idyls of the gutter and the gibbet. If the Muse of the minute will not feast with 'gig-men' and their wives, she must mourn with costermongers and their trulls. I fear the more ancient Muses are guests at neither house of mourning nor house of feasting.

For myself, I begrudge no man his taste or his success; I can enjoy and applaud all good work, and would always, when possible, have the workman paid in full. There is much excellent and some admirable verse among the poems of the day: to none has it given more pleasure than to me, and from none, had I been a man of letters to whom the ways were open, would it have won heartier applause. I have never been able to see what should attract men to the profession of criticism but the noble pleasure of praising. But I have no right to claim a place in the silver flock of idyllic swans. I have never worked for praise or pay, but simply by impulse, and to please myself; I must therefore, it is to be feared, remain where I am, shut out from the communion of these. At all events, I shall not be hounded into emulation of other men's work by the baying of unleashed beagles. There are those with whom I do not wish to share the praise of their praisers. I am content to abide a far different judgment:—

> I write as others wrote
> On Sunium's height.

I need not be over-careful to justify my ways in other men's eyes; it is enough for me that they also work after their kind, and earn the suffrage, as they labour after the law, of their own people. The idyllic form is best for domestic and pastoral poetry. It is naturally on a lower level than that of tragic or lyric verse. Its gentle and maidenly lips are somewhat narrow for the stream and somewhat cold for the fire of song. It is very fit for the sole diet of girls; not very fit for the sole sustenance of men.

When England has again such a school of poetry, so headed and so followed, as she has had at least twice before, or as France has now; when all higher forms of the various arts are included within the larger limits of a stronger race; then, if such a day should ever rise or return upon us, it will be once more remembered that the office of adult art is neither puerile nor feminine, but virile; that its purity is not that of the cloister or the harem; that all things are good in its sight, out of which good work may be produced. Then the press will be as impotent as the pulpit to dictate the laws and remove the landmarks of art; and those will be laughed at who demand from one thing the qualities of another—who seek for sermons in sonnets and morality in music. Then all accepted work will be noble and chaste in the wider masculine sense, not truncated and curtailed, but outspoken and full-grown; art will be pure by instinct and fruitful by nature, no clipped and forced growth of unhealthy heat and unnatural air; all baseness and all triviality will fall off from it, and be forgotten; and no one will then need to assert, in defence of work done for the work's sake, the simple laws of his art which no one will then be permitted to impugn.

*1866*

# BRET HARTE

## *Tennessee's Partner*

FROM 'THE LUCK OF ROARING CAMP'

I DO not think that we ever knew his real name. Our ignorance of it certainly never gave us any social inconvenience, for at Sandy Bar in 1854 most men were christened anew. Sometimes these appellatives were derived from some distinctiveness of dress, as in the case of 'Dungaree Jack;' or from some peculiarity of habit, as shown in 'Saleratus Bill,' so called from an undue proportion of that chemical in his daily bread; or from some unlucky slip, as exhibited in 'The Iron Pirate,' a mild, inoffensive man, who earned that baleful title by his unfortunate mispronunciation of the term 'iron pyrites.' Perhaps this may have been the beginning of a rude heraldry; but I am constrained to think that it was because a man's real name in that day rested solely upon his own unsupported statement. 'Call yourself Clifford, do you?' said Boston, addressing a timid new-comer with infinite scorn; 'hell is full of such Cliffords!' He then introduced the unfortunate man, whose name happened to be really Clifford, as 'Jay-bird Charley,'—an unhallowed inspiration of the moment, that clung to him ever after.

But to return to Tennessee's Partner, whom we never knew by any other than this relative title; that he had ever existed as a separate and distinct individuality we only learned later. It seems that in 1853 he left Poker Flat to go to San Francisco, ostensibly to procure a wife. He never got any farther than Stockton. At that place he was attracted by a young person who waited upon the table at the hotel where he took his meals. One morning he said something to her which caused her to smile not unkindly, to somewhat coquettishly break a plate of toast over his upturned, serious, simple face, and to retreat to the kitchen. He followed her, and emerged a few moments later, covered with more toast and victory. That day week they were married by a Justice of the Peace, and returned to Poker Flat. I am aware that something more might be made of this episode, but I prefer to tell it as it was current at Sandy Bar—in the gulches and bar rooms—where all sentiment was modified by a strong sense of humour.

Of their married felicity but little is known, perhaps for the reason that Tennessee, then living with his partner, one day took occasion to say something to the bride on his own account, at which, it is said, she smiled not unkindly and chastely retreated,—this time as far as Marysville, where Tennessee followed her, and where they went to housekeeping without the aid of a Justice of the Peace. Tennessee's Partner took the loss of his wife simply and seriously, as was his fashion. But to everybody's surprise, when Tennessee one day returned from Marysville, without his partner's wife,—she having smiled and retreated with somebody else,—Tennessee's Partner was the first man to shake his hand and greet him with affection. The boys who had gathered in the cañon to see the shooting were naturally indignant. Their indignation might have found vent in sarcasm but for a certain look in Tennessee's Partner's eye that indicated a lack of humorous appreciation. In fact, he was a grave man, with a steady application to practical detail which was unpleasant in a difficulty.

Meanwhile a popular feeling against Tennessee had grown up on the Bar. He was known to be a gambler; he was suspected to be a thief. In these suspicions Tennessee's Partner was equally compromised; his continued intimacy with Tennessee after the affair above quoted could only be accounted for on the hypothesis of a co-partnership of crime. At last Tennessee's guilt became flagrant. One day he overtook a stranger on his way to Red Dog. The stranger afterwards related that Tennessee beguiled the time with interesting anecdote and reminiscence, but illogically concluded the interview in the following words: 'And now, young man, I'll trouble you for your knife, your pistols, and your money. You see your weppings might get you into trouble at Red Dog, and your money's a temptation to the evilly disposed. I think you said your address was San Francisco. I shall endeavour to call.' It may be stated here that Tennessee had a fine flow of humour, which no business preoccupation could wholly subdue.

This exploit was his last. Red Dog and Sandy Bar made common cause against the highwayman. Tennessee was hunted in very much the same fashion as his prototype, the grizzly. As the toils closed around him, he made a desperate dash through the Bar, emptying his revolver at the crowd before the Arcade Saloon, and so on up Grizzly Cañon; but at its farther extremity he was stopped by a small man on a grey horse. The men looked at each other a moment in silence. Both were fearless, both self-possessed and independent; and both types of a civilization that in the seventeenth century would have been called heroic, but, in the nineteenth, simply 'reckless.' 'What have you got there?—I call,' said Tennessee, quietly. 'Two bowers and an ace,' said the stranger, as quietly, showing two revolvers and a bowie knife. 'That takes me,' returned Tennessee; and with this gambler's epigram, he threw away his useless pistol, and rode back with his captor.

It was a warm night. The cool breeze which usually sprang up with the going down of the sun behind the *chaparral*-crested mountain was that evening withheld from Sandy Bar. The little cañon was stifling with heated resinous odours, and the decaying drift-wood on the Bar sent forth faint sickening exhalations. The feverishness of day, and its fierce passions, still filled the camp. Lights moved restlessly along the bank of the river, striking no answering reflection from its tawny current. Against the blackness of the pines the windows of the old loft above the express-office stood out staringly bright; and through their curtainless panes the loungers below could see the forms of those who were even then deciding the fate of Tennessee. And above all this, etched on the dark firmament, rose the Sierra, remote and passionless, crowned with remoter passionless stars.

The trial of Tennessee was conducted as fairly as was consistent with a judge and jury who felt themselves to some extent obliged to justify, in their verdict, the previous irregularities of arrest and indictment. The law of Sandy Bar was implacable, but not vengeful. The excitement and personal feeling of the chase were over; with Tennessee safe in their hands they were ready to listen patiently to any defence, which they were already satisfied was insufficient. There being no doubt in their own minds, they were willing to give the prisoner the benefit of any that might exist. Secure in the hypothesis that he ought to be hanged, on general principles, they indulged him with more latitude of defence than his reckless hardihood seemed to ask. The Judge appeared to be more anxious than the prisoner, who, otherwise unconcerned, evidently took a grim pleasure in the responsibility he had created. 'I don't take any hand in this yer game,' had been his invariable, but good-humoured reply to all questions. The Judge—who was also his captor—for a moment vaguely regretted that he had not shot him 'on sight,' that morning, but presently dismissed this human weakness as unworthy of the judicial mind. Nevertheless, when there was a tap at the door, and it was said that Tennessee's Partner was there on behalf of the prisoner, he was admitted at once without question. Perhaps the younger members of the jury, to whom the proceedings were becoming irksomely thoughtful, hailed him as a relief.

For he was not, certainly, an imposing figure. Short and stout, with a square face, sunburned into a preternatural redness, clad in a loose duck 'jumper,' and trousers streaked and splashed with red soil, his aspect under any circumstances would have been quaint, and was now even ridiculous. As he stooped to deposit at his feet a heavy carpet-bag he was carrying, it became obvious, from partially developed regions and inscriptions, that the material with which his trousers had been patched had been originally intended for a less ambitious covering. Yet he advanced with great gravity, and after having shaken the hand of each person in the room with laboured cordiality, he wiped his serious, perplexed face on a red bandanna handkerchief, a shade lighter than his complexion, laid his powerful hand upon the table to steady himself, and thus addressed the Judge:—

'I was passin' by,' he began, by way of apology, 'and I thought I'd just step in and see how things was gittin' on with Tennessee thar—my pardner. It's a hot night. I disremember any sich weather before on the Bar.'

He paused a moment, but nobody volunteering any other meteorological recollection, he again had recourse to his pocket-handkerchief, and for some moments mopped his face diligently.

'Have you anything to say in behalf of the prisoner?' said the Judge, finally.

'That's it,' said Tennessee's Partner, in a tone of relief. 'I come yar as Tennessee's pardner—knowing him nigh on four year, off and on, wet and dry, in luck and out o' luck. His ways ain't allers my ways, but thar ain't any p'ints in that young man, thar ain't any liveliness as he's been up to, as I don't know. And you sez to me, sez you—confidential-like, and between man and man—sez you, "Do you know anything in his behalf?" and I sez to you, sez I—confidential-like, as between man and man—"What should a man know of his pardner?" '

'Is this all you have to say?' asked the Judge, impatiently, feeling, perhaps, that a dangerous sympathy of humour was beginning to humanize the Court.

'Thet's so,' continued Tennessee's Partner. 'It ain't for me to say anything agin' him. And now what's the case? Here's Tennessee wants money, wants it bad, and doesn't like to ask it of his old pardner. Well, what does Tennessee do? He lays for a stranger, and he fetches that stranger. And you lays for *him*, and you fetches *him*; and the honours is easy. And I put it to you, bein' a fair-minded man, and to you, gentlemen, all, as fair-minded men, ef this isn't so.'

'Prisoner,' said the Judge, interrupting, 'have you any questions to ask this man?'

'No! no!' continued Tennessee's Partner, hastily. 'I play this yer hand alone. To come down to the bed-rock, it's just this: Tennessee, thar, has played it pretty rough and expensive-like on a stranger, and on this yer camp. And now, what's the fair thing? Some would say more; some would say less. Here's seventeen hundred dollars in coarse gold and a watch,—it's about all my pile,—and call it square!' And before a hand could be raised to prevent him, he had emptied the contents of the carpet-bag upon the table.

For a moment his life was in jeopardy. One or two men sprang to their feet, several hands groped for hidden weapons, and a suggestion to 'throw him from the window' was only overridden by a gesture from the Judge. Tennessee laughed. And apparently oblivious of the excitement, Tennessee's Partner improved the opportunity to mop his face again with his handkerchief.

When order was restored, and the man was made to understand, by the use of forcible figures and rhetoric, that Tennessee's offence could not be condoned by money, his face took a more serious and sanguinary hue, and those who were nearest to him noticed that his rough hand trembled slightly on the table. He hesitated a moment as he slowly returned the gold to the carpet-bag, as if he had not yet entirely caught the elevated sense of justice which swayed the tribunal, and was perplexed with the belief that he had not offered enough. Then he turned to the Judge, and saying, 'This yer is a lone hand, played alone, and without my pardner,' he bowed to the jury and was about to withdraw, when the Judge called him back. 'If you have anything to say to Tennessee, you had better say it now.' For the first time that evening the eyes of the prisoner and his strange advocate met. Tennessee smiled, showed his white teeth, and saying, 'Euchred, old man!' held out his hand. Tennessee's Partner took it in his own, and saying, 'I just dropped in as I was passin' to see how things was gettin' on,' let the hand passively fall, and adding that 'it was a warm night,' again mopped his face with his handkerchief, and without another word withdrew.

The two men never again met each other alive. For the unparalleled insult of a bribe offered to Judge Lynch—who, whether bigoted, weak, or narrow, was at least incorruptible—firmly fixed in the mind of that mythical personage any wavering determination of Tennessee's fate; and at the break of day he was marched, closely guarded, to meet it at the top of Marley's Hill.

How he met it, how cool he was, how he refused to say anything, how perfect were the arrangements of the committee, were all duly reported, with the addition of a warning moral and example to all future evil-doers, in the Red Dog Clarion, by its editor, who was present, and to whose vigorous English I cheerfully refer the reader. But the beauty of that midsummer morning, the blessed amity of earth and air and sky, the awakened life of the free woods and hills, the joyous renewal and promise of Nature, and above all, the infinite serenity that thrilled through each, was not reported, as not being a part of the social lesson. And yet, when the weak and foolish deed was done, and a life, with its possibilities and responsibilities, had passed out of the misshapen thing that dangled between earth and sky, the birds sang, the flowers bloomed, the sun shone, as cheerily as before; and possibly the Red Dog Clarion was right.

Tennessee's Partner was not in the group that surrounded the ominous tree. But as they turned to disperse, attention was drawn to the singular appearance of a motionless donkey-cart halted at the side of the road. As they approached, they at once recognised the venerable 'Jenny' and the two-wheeled cart as the property of Tennessee's Partner—used by him in carrying dirt from his claim; and a few paces distant the owner of the equipage himself, sitting under a buckeye-tree, wiping the perspiration from his glowing face. In answer to an inquiry, he said he had come for the body of the 'diseased' 'if it was all the same to the committee.' He didn't wish to 'hurry anything;' he could 'wait.' He was not working that day; and when the gentlemen were done with the 'diseased,' he would take him. 'Ef thar is any present,' he added, in his simple, serious way, 'as would care to jine in the fun'l, they kin come.' Perhaps it was from a sense of humour, which I have already intimated was a feature of Sandy Bar,—perhaps it was from something even better than that; but two-thirds of the loungers accepted the invitation at once.

It was noon when the body of Tennessee was delivered into the hands of his partner. As the cart drew up to the fatal tree, we noticed that it contained a rough oblong box, apparently made from a section of sluicing,—and half filled with bark and the tassels of pine. The cart was further decorated with slips of willow, and made fragrant with buckeye-blossoms. When the body was deposited in the box, Tennessee's Partner drew over it a piece of tarred canvas, and gravely mounting the narrow seat in front, with his feet upon the shafts, urged the little donkey forward. The equipage moved slowly on, at that decorous pace which was habitual with 'Jenny,' even under less solemn circumstances. The men—half-curiously, half-jestingly, but all good-humouredly—strolled along beside the cart; some in advance, some a little in the rear of the homely catafalque. But, whether from the narrowing of the road or some present sense of decorum, as the cart passed on the company fell to the rear in couples, keeping step, and otherwise assuming the external show of a formal procession. Jack Folinsbee, who had at the outset played a funeral march in dumb show upon an imaginary trombone, desisted, from a lack of sympathy and appreciation,—not having, perhaps, your true humorist's capacity to be content with the enjoyment of his own fun.

The way led through Grizzly Cañon—by this time clothed in funereal drapery and shadows. The red-woods, burying their moccasined feet in the red soil, stood in Indian file along the track, trailing an uncouth benediction from their bending boughs upon the passing bier. A hare, surprised into helpless activity, sat upright and pulsating in the ferns by the roadside as the *cortège* went by. Squirrels hastened to gain a secure outlook from higher boughs; and the blue-jays, spreading their wings, fluttered before them like outriders, until the outskirts of Sandy Bar were reached, and the solitary cabin of Tennessee's Partner.

Viewed under more favourable circumstances, it would not have been a cheerful place. The unpicturesque site, the rude and unlovely outlines, the unsavoury details, which distinguish the nest-building of the California miner, were all here, with the dreariness of decay superadded. A few paces from the cabin there was a rough enclosure, which, in the brief days of Tennessee's Partner's matrimonial felicity, had been used as a garden, but was now overgrown with fern. As we approached it, we were surprised to find that what we had taken for a recent attempt at cultivation was the broken soil about an open grave.

The cart was halted before the enclosure; and rejecting the offers of assistance with the same air of simple self-reliance he had displayed throughout, Tennessee's Partner lifted the rough coffin on his back, and deposited it, unaided, within the shallow grave. He then nailed down the board which served as a lid; and mounting the little mound of earth beside it, took off his hat, and slowly mopped his face with his handkerchief. This the crowd felt was a preliminary to speech; and they disposed themselves variously on stumps and boulders, and sat expectant.

'When a man,' began Tennessee's Partner, slowly, 'has been running free all day, what's the natural thing for him to do? Why, to come home. And if he ain't in a condition to go home, what can his best friend do? Why, bring him home! And here's Tennessee has been running free, and we brings him home from his wandering.' He paused, and picked up a fragment of quartz, rubbed it thoughtfully on his sleeve, and went on: 'It ain't the first time that I've packed him on my back, as you see'd me now. It ain't the first time that I brought him to this yer cabin when he couldn't help himself; it ain't the first time that I and "Jinny" have waited for him on yon hill, and picked him up and so fetched him home, when he couldn't speak and didn't know me. And now that it's the last time, why—' he paused, and rubbed the quartz gently on his sleeve—'you see it's a sort of rough on his partner. And now, gentlemen,' he added, abruptly, picking up his long-handled shovel, 'the fun'l's over; and my thanks, and Tennessee's thanks to you for your trouble.'

Resisting any proffers of assistance, he began to fill in the grave, turning his back upon the crowd, that after a few moments' hesitation gradually withdrew. As they crossed the little ridge that hid Sandy Bar from view, some, looking back, thought they could see Tennessee's Partner, his work done, sitting upon the grave, his shovel between his knees, and his face buried in his red bandanna handkerchief. But it was argued by others that you couldn't tell his face from his handkerchief at that distance; and this point remained undecided.

In the reaction that followed the feverish excitement of that day, Tennessee's Partner was not forgotten. A secret investigation had cleared him of any complicity in Tennessee's guilt, and left only a suspicion of his general sanity. Sandy Bar made a point of calling on him, and proffering various uncouth, but well-meant kindnesses. But from that day his rude health and great strength seemed visibly to decline; and when the rainy season fairly set in, and the tiny grass-blades were beginning to peep from the rocky mound above Tennessee's grave, he took to his bed.

One night, when the pines beside the cabin were swaying in the storm, and trailing their slender fingers over the roof, and the roar and rush of the swollen river were heard below, Tennessee's Partner lifted his head from the pillow, saying, 'It is time to go for Tennessee; I must put "Jinny" in the cart;' and would have risen from his bed but for the restraint of his attendant. Struggling, he still pursued his singular fancy: 'There, now, steady, "Jinny,"—steady, old girl. How dark it is! Look out for the ruts,—and look out for him, too, old gal. Sometimes, you know, when he's blind drunk, he drops down right in the trail. Keep on straight up to the pine on the top of the hill. Thar—I told you so!—thar he is,—coming this way, too,—all by himself, sober, and his face a-shining. Tennessee! Pardner!'

And so they met.

*1869*

# EDGAR ALLAN POE

## *The Tell-Tale Heart*

FROM 'TALES OF MYSTERY AND IMAGINATION'

TRUE!—nervous—very, very dreadfully nervous I had been and am; but why *will* you say that I am mad? The disease had sharpened my senses—not destroyed—not dulled them. Above all was the sense of hearing acute. I heard all things in the heaven and in the earth. I heard many things in hell. How, then, am I mad? Hearken! and observe how healthily—how calmly I can tell you the whole story.

It is impossible to say how first the idea entered my brain; but once conceived, it haunted me day and night. Object there was none. Passion there was none. I loved the old man. He had never wronged me. He had never given me insult. For his gold I had no desire. I think it was his eye! yes, it was this! One of his eyes resembled that of a vulture—a pale blue eye, with a film over it. Whenever it fell upon me, my blood ran cold; and so by degrees—very gradually—I made up my mind to take the life of the old man, and thus rid myself of the eye for ever.

Now this is the point. You fancy me mad. Madmen know nothing. But you should have seen *me*. You should have seen how wisely I proceeded—with what caution—with what foresight—with what dissimulation I went to work! I was never kinder to the old man than during the whole week before I killed him. And every night, about midnight, I turned the latch of his door and opened it—oh, so gently! And then when I had made an opening sufficient for my head, I put in a dark lantern, all closed, closed, so that no light shone out, and then

I thrust in my head. Oh, you would have laughed to see how cunningly I thrust it in! I moved it slowly—very, very slowly, so that I might not disturb the old man's sleep. It took me an hour to place my whole head within the opening so far that I could see him as he lay upon his bed. Ha!—would a madman have been so wise as this? And then, when my head was well in the room, I undid the lantern cautiously—oh, so cautiously—cautiously (for the hinges creaked)—I undid it just so much that a single thin ray fell upon the vulture eye. And this I did for seven long nights—every night just at midnight—but I found the eye always closed; and so it was impossible to do the work; for it was not the old man who vexed me, but his Evil Eye. And every morning, when the day broke, I went boldly into the chamber, and spoke courageously to him, calling him by name in a hearty tone, and inquiring how he had passed the night. So you see he would have been a very profound old man, indeed, to suspect that every night, just at twelve, I looked in upon him while he slept.

Upon the eighth night I was more than usually cautious in opening the door. A watch's minute hand moves more quickly than did mine. Never before that night had I *felt* the extent of my own powers—of my sagacity. I could scarcely contain my feelings of triumph. To think that there I was, opening the door, little by little, and he not even to dream of my secret deeds or thoughts. I fairly chuckled at the idea; and perhaps he heard me; for he moved on the bed suddenly, as if startled. Now you may think that I drew back—but no. His room was as black as pitch with the thick darkness (for the shutters were close fastened, through fear of robbers), and so I knew that he could not see the opening of the door, and I kept pushing it on steadily, steadily.

I had my head in, and was about to open the lantern, when my thumb slipped upon the tin fastening, and the old man sprang up in the bed, crying out—'Who's there?'

I kept quite still and said nothing. For a whole hour I did not move a muscle, and in the meantime I did not hear him lie down. He was still sitting up in the bed, listening;—just as I have done, night after night, hearkening to the death-watches in the wall.

Presently I heard a slight groan, and I knew it was the groan of mortal terror. It was not a groan of pain or of grief—oh, no!—it was the low stifled sound that arises from the bottom of the soul when over-charged with awe. I knew the sound well. Many a night, just at mid-night, when all the world slept, it has welled up from my own bosom, deepening, with its dreadful echo, the terrors that distracted me. I say I knew it well. I knew what the old man felt, and pitied him, although I chuckled at heart. I knew that he had been lying awake ever since the first slight noise, when he had turned in the bed. His fears had been ever since growing upon him. He had been trying to fancy them cause-less, but could not. He had been saying to himself—'It is nothing but the wind in the chimney—it is only a mouse crossing the floor,' or, 'it is merely a cricket which has made a single chirp.' Yes, he had been trying to comfort himself with these suppositions: but he had found all in vain. *All in vain*; because Death, in approaching him, had stalked with his black shadow before him, and enveloped the victim. And it was the mournful influence of the unperceived shadow that caused him to feel,—although he neither saw nor heard—to *feel* the presence of my head within the room.

When I had waited a long time, very patiently, without hearing him lie down, I resolved to open a little—a very, very little crevice in the lantern. So I opened it—you cannot imagine how stealthily, stealthily—until, at length, a single dim ray, like the thread of the spider, shot from out the crevice and fell upon the vulture eye.

It was open—wide, wide open—and I grew furious as I gazed upon it. I saw it with perfect distinctness—all a dull blue, with a hideous veil over it that chilled the very marrow in my bones; but I could see nothing else of the old man's face or person: for I had directed the ray, as if by instinct, precisely upon the damned spot.

And now have I not told you that what you mistake for madness is but over acuteness of the senses?—now, I say, there came to my ears a low, dull, quick sound, such as a watch makes when enveloped in cotton. I knew *that* sound well, too. It was the beating of the old man's heart. It increased my fury, as the beating of a drum stimulates the soldier into courage.

But even yet I refrained and kept still. I scarcely breathed. I held the lantern motionless. I tried how steadily I could maintain the ray upon the eye. Meantime the hellish tattoo of the heart increased. It grew quicker and quicker, and louder and louder every instant. The old man's terror *must* have been extreme! It grew louder, I say, louder every moment!—do you mark me well? I have told you that I am nervous: so I am. And now, at the dead hour of the night, amid the dreadful silence of that old house, so strange a noise as this excited me to uncontrollable terror. Yet, for some minutes longer, I refrained and stood still. But the beating grew louder, louder! I thought the heart must burst. And now a new anxiety seized me—the sound would be heard by a neighbour! The old man's hour had come! With a loud yell I threw open the lantern and leaped into the room. He shrieked once—once only. In an instant I dragged him to the floor, and pulled the heavy bed over him. I then smiled gaily, to find the deed so far done. But, for many minutes, the heart beat on with a muffled sound. This, however, did not vex me; it would not be heard through the wall. At length it ceased. The old man was dead. I removed the bed and examined the corpse. Yes, he was stone, stone dead. I placed my hand upon the heart and held it there many minutes. There was no pulsation. He was stone dead. His eye would trouble me no more.

If still you think me mad, you will think so no longer when I describe the wise precautions I took for the concealment of the body. The night waned, and I worked hastily, but in silence. First of all I dismembered the corpse. I cut off the head and the arms and the legs.

I then took up three planks from the flooring of the chamber and deposited all between the scantlings. I then replaced the boards so cleverly, so cunningly, that no human eye—not even *his*—could have detected anything wrong. There was nothing to wash out—no stain of any kind—no blood-spot whatever. I had been too wary for that. A tub had caught all—ha! ha!

When I had made an end of these labours, it was four o'clock—still dark as midnight. As the bell sounded the hour, there came a knocking at the street door. I went down to open it with a light heart,—for what had I *now* to fear? There entered three men, who introduced themselves with perfect suavity, as officers of the police. A shriek had been heard by a neighbour during the night; suspicion of foul play had been aroused; information had been lodged at the police office, and they (the officers) had been deputed to search the premises.

I smiled—for *what* had I to fear? I bade the gentlemen welcome. The shriek, I said, was my own in a dream. The old man, I mentioned, was absent in the country. I took my visitors all over the house. I bade them search—search *well*. I led them, at length, to *his* chamber. I showed them his treasures, secure, undisturbed. In the enthusiasm of my confidence, I brought chairs into the room, and desired them *here* to rest from their fatigues, while I myself, in the wild audacity of my perfect triumph, placed my own seat upon the very spot beneath which reposed the corpse of the victim.

The officers were satisfied. My *manner* had convinced them. I was singularly at ease. They sat, and while I answered cheerily, they chatted of familiar things. But, ere long, I felt myself getting pale and wished them gone. My head ached, and I fancied a ringing in my ears: but still they sat and still chatted. The ringing became more distinct:—it continued and became more distinct: I talked more freely to get rid of the feeling: but it continued and gained definitiveness—until, at length, I found that the noise was *not* within my ears.

No doubt I now grew *very* pale;—but I talked more fluently, and with a heightened voice. Yet the sound increased—and what could I do? It was *a low, dull, quick sound—much such a sound as a watch makes when enveloped in cotton*. I gasped for breath—and yet the officers heard it not. I talked more quickly—more vehemently; but the noise steadily increased. I arose and argued about trifles, in a high key and with violent gesticulations; but the noise steadily increased. Why *would* they not be gone? I paced the floor to and fro with heavy strides, as if excited to fury by the observations of the men—but the noise steadily increased. Oh God! what *could* I do? I foamed—I raved—I swore! I swung the chair upon which I had been sitting, and grated it upon the boards, but the noise arose over all and continually increased. It grew louder—louder—*louder!* And still the men chatted pleasantly, and smiled. Was it possible they heard not? Almighty God!—no, no! They heard!—they suspected!—they *knew!*—they were making a mockery of my horror!—this I thought, and this I think. But anything was better than this agony! Anything was more tolerable than this derision! I could bear those hypocritical smiles no longer! I felt that I must scream or die!—and now—again! hark! louder! louder! louder! *louder!*—

'Villains!' I shrieked, 'dissemble no more! I admit the deed!—tear up the planks!—here, here!—it is the beating of his hideous heart!'

*1872*

'MY WIFE IS A WOMAN OF MIND'

From George Cruikshank's *Comic Almanack*, 1844–53. Chatto & Windus, 1874

# ARTEMUS WARD

## *Introduced at the Club*

FROM 'ARTEMUS WARD IN LONDON'

MR PUNCH,—MY DEAR SIR,—It is seldom that the Commercial relations between Great Britain and the United States is mar'd by Games.

It is Commerce, after all, which will keep the two countries friendly to'ards each other rather than statesmen.

I look at your last Parliament, and I can't see that a single speech was encored during the entire session.

Look at Congress—but no, I'd rather not look at Congress.

Entertainin this great regard for Commerce, 'whose sales whiten every sea,' as everybody happily observes every chance he gets, I learn with disgust and surprise that a British subjeck bo't a Barril of Apple Sass in America recently, and when he arrove home he found under a few deloosiv layers of sass nothin but saw-dust. I should have instantly gone into the City and called a meetin of the leadin commercial men to condemn and repudiate, as a American, this gross frawd, if I hadn't learned at the same time that the draft given by the British subjeck in payment for this frawdylent sass was drawd onto a Bankin House in London which doesn't have a existence, but far otherwise, and never did.

There is those who larf at these things, but to me they merit rebooks and frowns.

With the exception of my Uncle Wilyim—who, as I've before stated, is a uncle by marriage only, who is a low cuss, and filled his coat pockets with pies and biled eggs at his weddin breakfast, given to him by my father, and made the clergyman as united him a present of my father's new overcoat, and when my father, on discoverin it, got in a rage and denounced him, Uncle Wilyim said the old man (meanin my parent) hadn't any idee of first-class Humer!—with the exception of this wretched Uncle, the escutchin of my fam'ly has never been stained by Games. The little harmless deceptions I resort to in my perfeshion I do not call Games. They are sacrifisses to Art.

I come of a very clever fam'ly.

The Wards is a very clever fam'ly indeed.

I believe we are descendid from the Puritins, who nobly fled from a land of despitism to a land of freedim, where they could not only enjoy their own religion, but prevent everybody else from enjoyin *his*.

As I said before, we are a very clever fam'ly.

I was strolling up Regent Street the other day, thinkin what a clever fam'ly I come of, and looking at the gay shop-winders. I've got some new close since you last saw me. I saw them others wouldn't do. They carrid the observer too far back into the dim vister of the past, and I gave 'em to a Orfun Asylum. The close I wear now I bo't of Mr. Moses, in the Commercial Road. They were expressly made, Mr. Moses informed me, for a nobleman; but as they fitted him too muchly, partic'ly the trows'rs (which is blue, with large red and white checks), he had said:

'My dear feller, make me some more, only mind—be sure you sell these to some genteel old feller.'

I like to saunter thro' Regent Street. The shops are pretty, and it does the old man's heart good to see the troops of fine healthy girls which one may always see there at certain hours in the afternoon, who don't spile their beauty by devouring cakes and sugar things, as too many of the American and French lasses do. It's a mistake about everybody being out of town, I guess. Regent Street is full. I'm here; and, as I said before, I come of a very clever fam'ly.

As I was walking along, amoosin myself by stickin my penknife into the calves of the footmen who stood waitin by the swell coaches (not one of whom howled with angwish), I was accosted by a man of about thirty-five summers, who said, 'I have seen that face somewheres afore!'

He was a little shabby in his wearin apparil. His coat was one of those black, shiny garments, which you can always tell have been burnished by adversity; but he was very gentlemanly.

'Was it in the Crimea, comrade? Yes, it was. It was at the stormin of Sebastopol, where I had a narrow escape from death, that we met!'

I said, 'No, it wasn't at Sebastopol. I escaped a fatal wound by not bein there. It was a healthy old fortress,' I added.

'It was. But it fell. It came down with a crash.'

'And plucky boys they was who brought her down,' I added; 'and hurrah for 'em!'

The man graspt me warmly by the hand, and said he had been in America, Upper Canada, Africa, Asia Minor, and other towns, and he'd never met a man he liked so much as he did me.

'Let us,' he added, 'let us to the shrine of Bachus!'

And he dragged me into a public-house. I was determined to pay, so I said, 'Mr. Bachus, giv this gen'l'man what he calls for.'

We conversed there in a very pleasant manner till my dinner-time arrove, when the agree'ble gentleman insisted that I should dine with him. 'We'll have a banquet, sir, fit for the gods!'

I told him good plain vittles would soot me. If the gods wanted to have the dispepsy, they was welcome to it.

We had soop and fish, and a hot jint, and growsis, and wines of rare and costly vintige. We had ices, and we had froots from Greenland's icy mountains and Injy's coral strands; and when the sumptoous reparst was over, the agree'ble man said he'd unfortnitly left his pocket-book at home on the marble center-table.

'But, by Jove!' he said, 'it was a feast fit for the gods!'

I said, 'Oh, never mind,' and drew out my puss; tho' I in'ardly wished the gods, as the dinner was fit for 'em, was there to pay for it.

I come of a very clever fam'ly.

The agree'ble gentleman then said, 'Now I will show you our Club. It dates back to the time of William the Conqueror.'

'Did Bill belong to it?' I inquired.

'He did.'

'Wall,' I said, 'if Billy was one of 'em, I need no other endorsement as to its respectfulness; and I'll go with you, my gay trooper boy!' And we went off arm-in-arm.

On the way the agree'ble man told me that the Club was called the Sloshers. He said I would notice that none of 'em appeared in evenin dress. He said it was agin the rools of the Club. In fack, if any member appeared there in evenin dress, he'd be instantly expeld. 'And yit,' he added, 'there's geneyus there, and lorfty emotions, and intelleck. You'll be surprised at the quantities of intelleck you'll see there.'

We reached the Sloshers in due time, and I must say they was a shaky-looking lot, and the public-house where they convened was certingly none of the best.

The Sloshers crowded round me, and said I was welcome.

'What a beautiful brestpin you've got,' said one of 'em. 'Permit me,' and he took it out of my neckercher. 'Isn't it luvly?' he said, parsin it to another, who passed it to another.

It was given me by my aunt, on my promisin her I'd never swear profanely; and I never have, except on very special occasions. I see that beautiful boosum-pin a parsin from one Slosher to another, and I'm reminded of them sad words of the poit, 'parsin away! parsin away!' I never saw it no more.

Then in comes a athletic female, who no sooner sees me than she utters a wild yell, and cries:

'At larst! at larst! My Wilyim, from the seas!'

I said, 'Not at all, Marm. Not on no account. I have heard the boatswain pipe to quarters; but a voice in my heart didn't whisper Seu-zan! I've belayed the marlin-spikes on the upper jibpoop, but Seu-zan's eye wasn't on me, much. Young woman, I am not your Saler boy. Far different.'

'Oh yes, you are!' she howled, seizin me round the neck. 'Oh, how I've lookt forwards to this meetin!'

'And you'll presently,' I said, 'have a opportunity of lookin backwards to it, because I'm on the point of leavin this institution.'

I will here observe that I come of a very clever fam'ly. A very clever fam'ly, indeed.

'Where,' I cried, as I struggled in vain to release myself from the eccentric female's claws, 'where is the Capting—the man who was into the Crimea, amidst the cannon's thunder? I want him.'

He came forward, and cried, 'What do I see? Me Sister! me sweet Adulaide! and in teers! Willim!' he screamed, 'and you're the serpent I took to my boosum, and borrowed money of, and went round with, and was cheerful with, are you?—You ought to be ashamed of yourself.'

Somehow my coat was jerked off, the brest-pocket of which contained my pocket-book, and it parsed away like the brestpin. Then they sorter quietly hustled me into the street.

It was about 12 at night when I reached the Green Lion.

'Ha! ha! you sly old rascal, you've been up to larks!' said the lan'lord, larfin loudly, and digging his fist into my ribs.

I said, 'Bigsby, if you do that agin, I shall hit you! Much as I respect you and your excellent fam'ly, I shall disfigger your beneverlent countenance for life!'

'What has ruffled your spirits, friend?' said the lan'lord.

'My spirits has been ruffled,' I ansered in a bittur voice, 'by a viper who was into the Crimea. What good was it,' I cried, 'for Sebastopol to fall down without enwelopin in its ruins that viper?'

I then went to bed. I come of a very clever fam'ly.

*1872*

# ARTHUR WILLIAM EDGAR O'SHAUGHNESSY

## *Ode*

WE are the music makers,
  And we are the dreamers of dreams,
Wandering by lone sea-breakers,
  And sitting by desolate streams;—
World-losers and world-forsakers,
  On whom the pale moon gleams:
Yet we are the movers and shakers
  Of the world for ever, it seems.

With wonderful deathless ditties
We build up the world's great cities,

And out of a fabulous story
 We fashion an empire's glory:
One man with a dream, at pleasure,
 Shall go forth and conquer a crown;
And three with a new song's measure
 Can trample a kingdom down.

We, in the ages lying
 In the buried past of the earth,
Built Nineveh with our sighing,
 And Babel itself in our mirth;
And o'erthrew them with prophesying
 To the old of the new world's worth;
For each age is a dream that is dying,
 Or one that is coming to birth.

A breath of our inspiration
Is the life of each generation;
 A wondrous thing of our dreaming
 Unearthly, impossible seeming—
The soldier, the king, and the peasant
 Are working together in one,
Till our dream shall become their present,
 And their work in the world be done.

They had no vision amazing
Of the goodly house they are raising;
 They had no divine foreshowing
 Of the land to which they are going:
But on one man's soul it hath broken,
 A light that doth not depart;
And his look, or a word he hath spoken,
 Wrought flame in another man's heart.

And therefore to-day is thrilling
With a past day's late fulfilling;
 And the multitudes are enlisted
 In the faith that their fathers resisted,
And, scorning the dream of to-morrow,
 Are bringing to pass, as they may,
In the world, for its joy or its sorrow,
 The dream that was scorned yesterday.

But we, with our dreaming and singing,
Ceaseless and sorrowless we!
The glory about us clinging
Of the glorious futures we see,
Our souls with high music ringing:
O men! it must ever be
That we dwell, in our dreaming and singing,
A little apart from ye.

For we are afar with the dawning
And the suns that are not yet high,
And out of the infinite morning
Intrepid you hear us cry—
How, spite of your human scorning,
Once more God's future draws nigh,
And already goes forth the warning
That ye of the past must die.

Great hail! we cry to the comers
From the dazzling unknown shore;
Bring us hither your sun and your summers,
And renew our world as of yore;
You shall teach us your song's new numbers,
And things that we dreamed not before:
Yea, in spite of a dreamer who slumbers,
And a singer who sings no more.

*1874*

# W. H. MALLOCK

## *Culture in an English Country House*

FROM 'THE NEW REPUBLIC'

MR. ROSE's soft lulling tone harmonised well with the scene and hour, and the whole party seemed willing to listen to him; or at any rate no one felt any prompting to interrupt him.

'I can show you an example, Mr. Herbert,' he said, 'of culture demanding a finer climate, in—if you will excuse my seeming egoism—in myself. For instance (to take the widest matter I can fix upon—the general outward surroundings of our lives), often, when I walk about London, and see how hideous its whole external aspect is, and what a dissonant population throngs it, a chill feeling of despair comes over me. Consider how the human eye delights in form and colour, and the ear in tempered and harmonious sounds; and then think for a moment of a London street! Think of the shapeless houses, the forest of ghastly chimney-pots, of the hell of distracting noises made by the carts, the cabs, the carriages—think of the bustling, commonplace, careworn crowds that jostle you—think of an omnibus—think of a four-wheeler——'

'I often ride in an omnibus,' said Lord Allen, with a slight smile, to Miss Merton.

'It is true,' replied Mr. Rose, only overhearing the tone in which these words were said, 'that one may ever and again catch some touch of sunlight that will for a moment make the meanest object beautiful with its furtive alchemy. But that is Nature's work, not man's; and we must never confound the accidental beauty that Nature will bestow on man's work, even at its worst, with the rational and designed beauty of man's work at its best. It is this rational human beauty that I say our modern city life is so completely wanting in; nay, the look of out-of-door London seems literally to stifle the very power of imagining such beauty possible. Indeed, as I wander along our streets, pushing my way among the throngs of faces—faces puckered with misdirected thought, or expressionless with none—barbarous faces set towards Parliament, or Church, or scientific lecture-rooms, or Government offices, or counting-houses—I say, as I push my way amongst all the sights and sounds of the streets of our great city, only one thing ever catches my eye, that breaks in upon my mood, and warns me I need not despair.'

'And what is that?' asked Allen, with some curiosity.

'The shops,' Mr. Rose answered, 'of certain of our upholsterers and dealers in works of art. Their windows, as I look into them, act like a sudden charm on me—like a splash of cold water dashed on my forehead when I am fainting. For I seem there to have got a glimpse of the real heart of things; and as my eyes rest on the perfect pattern (many of which are really quite delicious; indeed, when I go to ugly houses, I often take a scrap of some artistic cretonne with me in my pocket as a kind of aesthetic smelling salts), I say, when I look in at their windows, and my eyes rest on the perfect pattern of some new fabric for a chair or for a window-curtain, or on some new design for a wall-paper, or on some old china vase, I become at once sharply conscious, Mr. Herbert, that, despite the ungenial mental climate of the present age, strange yearnings for, and knowledge of, true beauty are beginning to show themselves like flowers above the weedy soil; and I remember, amidst the roar and clatter of our streets, and the mad noises of our own times, that there is amongst us a growing number who have deliberately turned their backs on all these things, and have thrown their whole souls and sympathies into the happier art-ages of the past. They have gone back,' said Mr. Rose, raising his voice a little, 'to Athens and to Italy, to the Italy of Leo and to the Athens of Pericles. To such men the clamour, the interests, the struggles of our own times, become as meaningless as they really are. To them the boyhood of Bathyllus is of more moment than the manhood of Napoleon. Borgia is a more familiar name than Bismarck. I know, indeed—and I really do not blame them—several distinguished artists who, resolving to make their whole lives consistently perfect, will, on principle, never admit a newspaper into their houses that is of later date than the times of Addison; and I have good trust that the number of such men is on the increase—men I mean,' said Mr. Rose, toying tenderly with an exquisite wine-glass of Salviati's, 'who with a steady and set purpose follow art for the sake of art, beauty for the sake of beauty, love for the sake of love, life for the sake of life.'

Mr. Rose's slow gentle voice, which was apt at certain times to become peculiarly irritating, sounded now like the evening air grown articulate, and had secured him hitherto a tranquil hearing, as if by a kind of spell. This however seemed here in sudden danger of snapping.

'What, Mr. Rose!' exclaimed Lady Ambrose, 'do you mean to say, then, that the number of people is on the increase who won't read the newspapers?'

'Why, the men must be absolute idiots!' said Lady Grace, shaking her grey curls, and putting on her spectacles to look at Mr. Rose.

Mr. Rose, however, was imperturbable.

'Of course,' he said, 'you may have newspapers if you will: I myself always have them; though in general they are too full of public events to be of much interest. I was merely speaking just now of the spirit of the movement. And of that we must all of us here have some knowledge. We must all of us have friends whose houses more or less embody it.

And even if we had not, we could not help seeing signs of it—signs of how true and earnest it is, in the enormous sums that are now given for really good objects.'

'That,' said Lady Grace, with some tartness, 'is true enough, thank God.'

'But I can't see,' said Lady Ambrose, whose name often figured in *The Times*, in the subscription-lists of advertised charities—'I can't see, Mr. Rose, any reason in that why we should not read the newspapers.'

'The other day, for instance,' said Mr. Rose reflectively, 'I heard of eight Chelsea shepherdesses, picked up by a dealer, I really forget where—in some common cottage, if I recollect aright, covered with dirt, giving no pleasure to anyone—and these were all sold in a single day, and not one of them fetched less than two hundred and twenty pounds.'

'*I* can't help thinking they must have come from Cremorne,' said Mrs. Sinclair softly.

'But why,' said Mr. Rose, 'should I speak of particular instances? We *must* all of us have friends whose houses are full of priceless treasures such as these—the whole atmosphere of whose rooms really seems impregnated with art—seems in fact, Mr. Herbert, such an atmosphere as we should dream of for our new Republic.'

'To be sure,' exclaimed Lady Ambrose, feeling that she had at last got upon solid ground. 'By the way, Mr. Rose,' she said, with her most gracious of smiles, 'I suppose you have hardly seen Lady Julia Hayman's new house in Belgrave Square? I'm sure that would delight you. I should like to take you there some day, and show it to you.'

'I have seen it,' said Mr. Rose, with languid condescension. 'It was very pretty, I thought—some of it really quite nice.'

This and the slight rudeness of manner it was said with, raised Mr. Rose greatly in Lady Ambrose's estimation, and she began to think with respect of his late utterances.

*1877*

NOTE

*By Mr. Rose Walter Pater is clearly intended. Mr. Herbert is John Ruskin while it is believed that Mrs. Sinclair is 'Violet Fane' and Lady Grace Mrs. Mark Pattison.* D.M.L.

# ROBERT LOUIS STEVENSON

## *The Royal Sport Nautique*

FROM 'AN INLAND VOYAGE'

THE rain took off near *Laeken*. But the sun was already down; the air was chill; and we had scarcely a dry stitch between the pair of us. Nay, now we found ourselves near the end of the *Allée Verte*, and on the very threshold of *Brussels* we were confronted by a serious difficulty. The shores were closely lined by canal boats waiting their turn at the lock. Nowhere was there any convenient landing-place; nowhere so much as a stable-yard to leave the canoes in for the night. We scrambled ashore and entered an estaminet where some sorry fellows were drinking with the landlord. The landlord was pretty round with us; he knew of no coach-house or stable-yard, nothing of the sort; and seeing we had come with no mind to drink, he did not conceal his impatience to be rid of us. One of the sorry fellows cam e to the rescue. Somewhere in the corner of the basin there was a slip,he informed us, and something else besides, not very clearly defined by him, but hopefully construcd by his hearers.

Sure enough thcre was the slip in the corner of the basin; and at the top of it two nice-looking lads in boating clothes. The *Arethusa* addressed himself to these. One of them said there would be no difficulty about a night's lodging for our boats; and the other, taking a cigarette from his lips, inquired if they were made by Searle & Son. The name was quite an introduction. Half-a-dozen other young men came out of a boat-house bearing the superscription ROYAL SPORT NAUTIQUE, and joined in the talk. They were all very polite, voluble and enthusiastic; and their discourse was interlarded with English boating terms, and the names of English boat-builders and English clubs. I do not know, to my shame, any spot in my native land where I should have been so warmly received by the same number of people. We were English boating-men, and the Belgian boating-men fell upon our necks. I wonder if French Huguenots were as cordially greeted by English Protestants when they came across the Channel out of great tribulation. But after all, what religion knits people so closely as a common sport?

The canoes were carried into the boat-house; they were washed down for us by the Club servants, the sails were hung out to dry, and everything made as snug and tidy as a picture. And in the meanwhile we were led upstairs by our new-found brethren, for so more than one of them stated the relationship, and made free of their lavatory. This one lent us soap, that one a towel, a third and fourth helped us to undo our bags. And all the time such questions, such assurances of respect and sympathy! I declare I never knew what glory was before.

'Yes, yes, the *Royal Sport Nautique* is the oldest club in Belgium.'

'We number two hundred.'

'We'—this is not a substantive speech, but an abstract of many speeches, the impression left upon my mind after a great deal of talk; and very youthful, pleasant, natural and patriotic it seems to me to be—'We have gained all races, except those where we were cheated by the *French*.'

'You must leave all your wet things to be dried.'

'O! *entre frères*! In any boat-house in *England* we should find the same.' (I cordially hope they might.)

'*En Angleterre, vous employez des sliding seats, n'est-ce pas?*'

'We are all employed in commerce during the day; but in the evening, *voyez-vous, nous sommes sérieux*.'

These were the words. They were all employed over the frivolous mercantile concerns of Belgium during the day; but in the evening they found some hours for the serious concerns of life. I may have a wrong idea of wisdom but I think that was a very wise remark. People connected with literature and philosophy are busy all their days in getting rid of second-hand notions and false standards. It is their profession, in the sweat of their brows, by dogged thinking, to recover their old fresh view of life, and distinguish what they really and originally like, from what they have only learned to tolerate perforce. And these Royal Nautical Sportsmen had the distinction still quite legible in their hearts. They had still those clean perceptions of what is nice and nasty, what is interesting and what is dull, which envious old gentlemen refer to as illusions. The nightmare illusion of middle age, the bear's hug of custom gradually squeezing the life out of a man's soul, had not yet begun for these happy-star'd young Belgians. They still knew that the interest they took in their business was a trifling affair compared to their spontaneous, long-suffering affection for nautical sports. To know what you prefer, instead of humbly saying Amen to what the world tells you you ought to prefer, is to have kept your soul alive. Such a man may be generous; he may be honest in something more than the commercial sense; he may love his friends with an elective, personal sympathy, and not accept them as an adjunct of the station to which he has been called. He may be a man, in short, acting on his own instincts, keeping his own shape that God made him in; and not a mere crank in the social engine house, welded on principles that he does not understand, and for purposes that he does not care for.

For will anyone dare to tell me that business is more entertaining than fooling among boats? He must have never seen a boat, or never seen an office, who says so. And for certain the one is a great deal better for the health. There should be nothing so much a man's business as his amusements. Nothing but money-grubbing can be put forward to the contrary; no one but

> Mammon, the least erected spirit that fell
> From Heaven,

durst risk a word in answer. It is but a lying cant that would represent the merchant and the banker as people disinterestedly toiling for mankind, and then most useful when they are most absorbed in their transactions; for the man is more important than his services. And when my Royal Nautical Sportsman shall have so far fallen from his hopeful youth that he cannot pluck up an enthusiasm over anything but his ledger, I venture to doubt whether he will be near so nice a fellow, and whether he would welcome, with so good a grace, a couple of drenched Englishmen paddling into Brussels in the dusk.

When we had changed our wet clothes and drunk a glass of pale ale to the Club's prosperity, one of their number escorted us to an hotel. He would not join us at our dinner, but he had no objection to a glass of wine. Enthusiasm is very wearing; and I begin to understand why prophets were unpopular in Judæa, where they were best known. For three stricken hours did this excellent young man sit beside us to dilate on boats and boat-races; and before he left he was kind enough to order our bed-room candles.

We endeavoured now and again to change the subject; but the diversion did not last a moment, the Royal Nautical Sportsman bridled, shied, answered the question, and then breasted once more into the swelling tide of his subject. I call it his subject; but I think it was he who was subjected. The *Arethusa*, who holds all racing as a creature of the devil, found himself in a pitiful dilemma. He durst not own his ignorance for the honour of Old England, and spoke away about English clubs and English oarsmen whose fame had never before come to his ears. Several times, and, once above all, on the question of sliding-seats, he was within an ace of exposure. As for the *Cigarette*, who has rowed races in the heat of his blood, but now disowns these slips of his wanton youth, his case was still more desperate; for the *Royal Nautical* proposed that he should take an oar in one of their eights on the morrow, to compare the English with the Belgian stroke. I could see my friend perspiring in his chair whenever that particular topic came up. And there was yet another proposal which had the same effect on both of us. It appeared that the champion canoeist of Europe (as well as most other champions) was a Royal Nautical Sportsman. And if we would only wait until the Sunday, this infernal paddler would be so condescending as to accompany us on our next stage. Neither of us had the least desire to drive the coursers of the sun against Apollo.

When the young man was gone, we countermanded our candles, and ordered some brandy and water. The great billows had gone over our head. The Royal Nautical Sportsmen were as nice young fellows as a man would wish to see, but they were a trifle too young and a thought too nautical for us. We began to see that we were old and cynical; we liked ease and the agreeable rambling of the human mind about this and the other subject; we did not want to disgrace our native land by messing an eight, or toiling pitifully in the wake of the champion canoeist. In short, we had recourse to flight. It seemed ungrateful, but we tried to make that good on a card loaded with sincere compliments. And indeed it was no time for scruples; we seemed to feel the hot breath of the champion on our necks.

*1884*

## *To S. R. Crockett*

FROM 'SONGS OF TRAVEL'

BLOWS the wind to-day, and the sun and the rain are flying,
Blows the wind on the moors to-day and now,
Where about the graves of the martyrs the whaups are crying,
My heart remembers how!

Grey recumbent tombs of the dead in desert places,
Standing-stones on the vacant wine-red moor,
Hills of sheep, and the homes of the silent vanished races,
And winds, austere and pure:

Be it granted me to behold you again in dying,
Hills of home! and to hear again the call;
Hear about the graves of the martyrs the peewees crying,
And hear no more at all.

VAILIMA *1896*

# CHARLES READE

## *The Storm*

### FROM 'THE CLOISTER AND THE HEARTH'

ABOUT two months before this scene in Eli's home, the natives of a little maritime place between Naples and Rome might be seen flocking to the sea beach, with eyes cast seaward at a ship, that laboured against a stiff gale blowing dead on the shore.

At times she seemed likely to weather the danger, and then the spectators congratulated her aloud: at others the wind and sea drove her visibly nearer, and the lookers-on were not without a secret satisfaction they would not have owned even to themselves.

Non quia vexari quemquam est jucunda voluptas
Sed quibus ipse malis careas quia cernere suave est.

And the poor ship, though not scientifically built for sailing, was admirably constructed for going ashore, with her extravagant poop that caught the wind, and her lines like a cocked hat reversed. To those on the beach that battered labouring frame of wood seemed alive, and struggling against death with a panting heart. But could they have been transferred to her deck they would have seen she had not one beating heart but many, and not one nature but a score were coming out clear in that fearful hour.

The mariners stumbled wildly about the deck, handling the ropes as each thought fit, and cursing and praying alternately.

The passengers were huddled together round the mast, some sitting, some kneeling, some lying prostrate, and grasping the bulwarks as the vessel rolled and pitched in the mighty waves. One comely young man, whose ashy cheek, but compressed lips, showed how hard terror was battling in him with self-respect, stood a little apart, holding tight by a shroud, and wincing at each sea. It was the ill-fated Gerard.

Meantime prayers and vows rose from the trembling throng amidships, and to hear them, it seemed there were almost as many gods about as men and women. The sailors, indeed, relied on a single goddess. They varied her titles only, calling on her as 'Queen of Heaven,' 'Star of the Sea,' 'Mistress of the World,' 'Haven of Safety.' But among the landsmen Polytheism raged. Even those who by some strange chance hit on the same divinity did not hit on the same edition of that divinity.

An English merchant vowed a heap of gold to our lady of Walsingham. But a Genoese merchant vowed a silver collar of four pounds to our lady of Loretto; and a Tuscan noble promised ten pounds of wax lights to our lady of Ravenna; and with a similar rage for diversity they pledged themselves, not on the true Cross, but on the true Cross in this, that, or the other modern city.

Suddenly a more powerful gust than usual catching the sail at a disadvantage, the rotten shrouds gave way, and the sail was torn out with a loud crack, and went down the wind smaller and smaller, blacker, and blacker, and fluttered into the sea, half a mile off, like a sheet of paper, and ere the helmsman could put the ship's head before the wind, a wave caught her on the quarter, and drenched the poor wretches to the bone, and gave them a foretaste of chill death. Then one vowed aloud to turn Carthusian monk, if St. Thomas would save him. Another would go a pilgrim to Compostella, bareheaded, barefooted, with nothing but a coat of mail on his naked skin, if St. James would save him. Others invoked Thomas, Dominic, Denys, and above all, Catherine of Sienna.

Two petty Neapolitan traders stood shivering.

One shouted at the top of his voice—

'I vow to St. Christopher at Paris a waxen image of his own weight, if I win safe to land.'

On this the other nudged him, and said—

'Brother, brother, take heed what you vow. Why, if you sell all you have in the world by public auction, 'twill not buy his weight in wax.'

'Hold your tongue, you fool,' said the vociferator.

Then in a whisper—

'Think ye I am in earnest? Let me but win safe to land, I'll not give him a rush dip.'

Others lay flat and prayed to the sea.

'Oh, most merciful sea! oh, sea most generous! oh, bountiful sea! oh, beautiful sea! be gentle, be kind, preserve us in this hour of peril.'

And others wailed and moaned in mere animal terror each time the ill-fated ship rolled or pitched more terribly than usual; and she was now a mere plaything in the arms of the tremendous waves.

A Roman woman of the humbler class sat with her child at her half-bared breast, silent amid that wailing throng: her cheek ashy pale; her eye calm; and her lips moved at times in silent prayer, but she neither wept, nor lamented, nor bargained with the gods. Whenever the ship seemed really gone under their feet, and bearded men squeaked, she kissed her child; but that was all. And so she sat patient, and suckled him in death's jaws; for why should he lose any joy she could give him; *moribundo?* Ay, there I do believe, sat Antiquity among those mediævals. Sixteen hundred years had not tainted the old Roman blood in her veins; and the instinct of a race she had perhaps scarce heard of taught her to die with decent dignity.

A gigantic friar stood on the poop with feet apart, like the Colossus of Rhodes, not so much defying, as ignoring, the peril that surrounded him. He recited verses from the Canticles with a loud unwavering voice;

and invited the passengers to confess to him. Some did so on their knees, and he heard them, and laid his hands on them, and absolved them as if he had been in a snug sacristy, instead of a perishing ship. Gerard got nearer and nearer to him, by the instinct that takes the wavering to the side of the impregnable. And in truth, the courage of heroes facing fleshly odds might have paled by the side of that gigantic friar, and his still more gigantic composure. Thus, even here, two were found who maintained the dignity of our race; a woman, tender, yet heroic, and a monk steeled by religion against mortal fears.

And now, the sail being gone, the sailors cut down the useless mast a foot above the board, and it fell with its remaining hamper over the ship's side. This seemed to relieve her a little.

But now the hull, no longer impelled by canvas, could not keep ahead of the sea. It struck her again and again on the poop, and the tremendous blows seemed given by a rocky mountain, not by a liquid.

The captain left the helm and came amidships pale as death.

'Lighten her,' he cried. 'Fling all overboard, or we shall founder ere we strike, and lose the one little chance we have of life.'

While the sailors were executing this order, the captain, pale himself, and surrounded by pale faces that demanded to know their fate, was talking as unlike an English skipper in like peril as can well be imagined.

'Friends,' said he, 'last night when all was fair, too fair, alas! there came a globe of fire close to the ship. When a pair of them come it is good luck, and nought can drown her that voyage. We mariners call these fiery globes Castor and Pollux. But if Castor come without Pollux, or Pollux without Castor, she is doomed. Therefore, like good Christians, prepare to die.'

These words were received with a loud wail.

To a trembling inquiry how long they had to prepare, the captain replied—

'She may, or may not, last half-an-hour; over that, impossible; she leaks like a sieve; bustle, men, lighten her.'

The poor passengers seized on everything that was on deck and flung it overboard. Presently they laid hold of a heavy sack; an old man was lying on it, sea sick. They lugged it from under him. It rattled. Two of them drew it to the side; up started the owner, and with an unearthly shriek, pounced on it.

'Holy Moses! what would you do? 'Tis my all; 'tis the whole fruits of my journey; silver candlesticks, silver plates, brooches, hanaps——'

'Let go, thou hoary villain,' cried the others; 'shall all our lives be lost for thy ill-gotten gear?'

'Fling him in with it,' cried one; ''tis this Ebrew we Christian men are drowned for.'

Numbers soon wrenched it from him, and heaved it over the side. It splashed into the waves. Then its owner uttered one cry of anguish, and stood glaring, his white hair streaming in the wind, and was going to leap after it, and would, had it floated, But it sank, and was gone for ever; and he staggered to and fro, tearing his hair, and cursed them and the ship, and the sea, and all the powers of heaven and hell alike.

And now the captain cried out—

'See, there is a church in sight. Steer for that church, mate, and you, friends, pray to the saint, whoe'er he be.'

So they steered for the church and prayed to the unknown god it was named after. A tremendous sea pooped them, broke the rudder, and jammed it immovable, and flooded the deck.

Then wild with superstitious terror some of them came round Gerard. 'Here is the cause of all,' they cried. 'He has never invoked a single saint. He is a heathen; here is a pagan aboard.'

'Alas, good friends, say not so,' said Gerard, his teeth chattering with cold and fear. 'Rather call these heathens, that lie a praying to the sea. Friends, I do honour the saints—but I dare not pray to them now—there is no time—(oh!) what avail me Dominic, and Thomas, and Catherine? Nearer God's throne than these St. Peter sitteth; and if I pray to him, it's odd, but I shall be drowned ere he has time to plead my cause with God. Oh! oh! oh! I must need go straight to Him that made the sea, and the saints, and me. Our Father, which art in heaven, save these poor souls and me that cry for the bare life! Oh, sweet Jesus, pitiful Jesus, that didst walk Genezaret when Peter sank, and wept for Lazarus dead when the apostles' eyes were dry, oh, save poor Gerard—for dear Margaret's sake!'

At this moment the sailors were seen preparing to desert the sinking ship in the little boat, which even at that epoch every ship carried; then there was a rush of egotists; and thirty souls crowded into it. Remained behind three who were bewildered, and two who were paralysed, with terror. The paralysed sat like heaps of wet rags, the bewildered ones ran to and fro, and saw the thirty egotists put off, but made no attempt to join them: only kept running to and fro, and wringing their hands.

Besides these there was one on his knees, praying over the wooden statue of the Virgin Mary, as large as life, which the sailors had reverently detached from the mast. It washed about the deck, as the water came slushing in from the sea, and pouring out at the scuppers; and this poor soul kept following it on his knees, with his hands clasped at it, and the water playing with it. And there was the Jew palsied, but not by fear. He was no longer capable of so petty a passion. He sat cross-legged bemoaning his bag, and whenever the spray lashed him, shook his fist at where it came from, and cursed the Nazarenes, and their gods, and their devils, and their ships, and their waters, to all eternity.

And the gigantic Dominican, having shriven the whole ship, stood calmly communing with his own spirit. And the Roman woman sat pale and patient, only drawing her child closer to her bosom as death came nearer.

Gerard saw this, and it awakened his manhood.

'See! see!' he said, 'they have ta'en the boat and left the poor woman and her child to perish.'

His heart soon set his wit working.

'Wife, I'll save thee yet, please God.'

And he ran to find a cask or a plank to float her. There was none.

Then his eye fell on the wooden image of the Virgin. He caught it up in his arms, and heedless of a wail that issued from its worshipper like a child robbed of its toy, ran aft with it.

'Come, wife,' he cried. 'I'll lash thee and the child to this. 'Tis sore worm eaten, but 'twill serve.'

She turned her great dark eye on him and said a single word—

'Thyself?!'

But with wonderful magnanimity and tenderness.

'I am a man, and have no child to take care of.'

'Ah!' said she, and his words seemed to animate her face with a desire to live. He lashed the image to her side. Then with the hope of life she lost something of her heroic calm; not much: her body trembled a little, but not her eye.

The ship was now so low in the water that by using an oar as a lever he could slide her into the waves.

'Come,' said he, 'while yet there is time.'

She turned her great Roman eyes, wet now, upon him.

'Poor youth!—God forgive me!—My child!'

And he launched her on the surge, and with his oar kept her from being battered against the ship.

A heavy hand fell on him; a deep sonorous voice sounded in his ear: ''Tis well. Now come with me.'

It was the gigantic friar.

Gerard turned, and the friar took two strides, and laid hold of the broken mast. Gerard did the same, obeying him instinctively. Between them, after a prodigious effort, they hoisted up the remainder of the mast, and carried it off.

'Fling it in,' said the friar, 'and follow it.'

They flung it in; but one of the bewildered passengers had run after them, and jumped first and got on one end. Gerard seized the other, the friar the middle.

It was a terrible situation. The mast rose and plunged with each wave like a kicking horse, and the spray flogged their faces mercilessly, and blinded them: to help knock them off.

Presently was heard a long grating noise ahead. The ship had struck, and soon after, she being stationary now, they were hurled against her with tremendous force. Their companion's head struck against the upper part of the broken rudder with a horrible crack, and was smashed like a cocoa-nut by a sledge-hammer. He sunk directly, leaving no trace but a red stain on the water, and a white clot on the jagged rudder, and a death cry ringing in their ears, as they drifted clear under the lee of the black hull. The friar uttered a short Latin prayer for the safety of his soul, and took his place composedly. They rolled along ὑπὲκ θανάτοιο; one moment they saw nothing, and seemed down in a mere basin of watery hills: the next they caught glimpses of the shore speckled bright with people, who kept throwing up their arms with wild Italian gestures to encourage them, and the black boat driving bottom upwards, and between it and them the woman rising and falling like themselves. She had come across a paddle, and was holding her child tight with her left arm, and paddling gallantly with her right.

When they had tumbled along thus a long time, suddenly the friar said quietly—

'I touched the ground.'

'Impossible, father,' said Gerard; 'we are more than a hundred yards from shore. Prithee, prithee, leave not our faithful mast.'

'My son,' said the friar, 'you speak prudently. But know that I have business of Holy Church on hand, and may not waste time floating when I can walk, in her service. There, I felt it with my toes again; see the benefit of wearing sandals, and not shoon. Again; and sandy. Thy stature is less than mine: keep to the mast! I walk.'

He left the mast accordingly, and extending his powerful arms, rushed through the water. Gerard soon followed him. At each overpowering wave the monk stood like a tower, and closing his mouth, threw his head back to encounter it, and was entirely lost under it awhile: then emerged and ploughed lustily on. At last they came close to the shore; but the suction outward baffled all their attempts to land. Then the natives sent stout fishermen into the sea, holding by long spears in a triple chain; and so dragged them ashore.

The friar shook himself, bestowed a short paternal benediction on the natives, and went on to Rome, with eyes bent on earth according to his rule, and without pausing. He did not even cast a glance back upon that sea, which had so nearly engulfed him, but had no power to harm him, without his Master's leave.

*1882*

# RICHARD JEFFERIES

## *A London Trout*

### FROM 'NATURE NEAR LONDON'

THERE is a beech in the plantation standing so near the verge of the stream that its boughs droop over. It has a number of twigs around the stem—as a rule the beechbole is clear of boughs, but some which are of rather stunted growth are fringed with them. The leaves on the longer boughs above fall off and voyage down the brook, but those on the lesser twigs beneath, and only a little way from the ground, remain on, and rustle, dry and brown, all through the winter.

Under the shelter of these leaves, and close to the trunk, there grew a plant of flag—the tops of the flags almost reached to the leaves—and all the winter through, despite the frosts for which it was remarkable, despite the snow and the bitter winds which followed, this plant remained green and fresh. From this beech in the morning a shadow stretches to a bridge across the brook, and in that shadow my trout used to lie. The bank under the drooping boughs forms a tiny cliff a foot high, covered with moss, and here I once observed shrew mice diving and racing about. But only once, though I frequently passed the spot; it is curious that I did not see them afterwards.

Just below the shadow of the beech there is a sandy, oozy shore, where the footprints of moorhens are often traceable. Many of the trees of the plantation stand in water after heavy rain; their leaves drop into it in autumn, and, being away from the influence of the current, stay and soak, and lie several layers thick. Their edges overlap, red, brown, and pale yellow, with the clear water above and shadows athwart it, and dry white grass at the verge. A horse-chestnut drops its fruit in the dusty road; high above its leaves are tinted with scarlet.

It was at the tail of one of the arches of the bridge over the brook that my favourite trout used to lie. Sometimes the shadow of the beech came as far as his haunts, that was early in the morning, and for the rest of the day the bridge itself cast a shadow. The other parapet faces south, and looking down from it the bottom of the brook is generally visible, because the light is so strong. At the bottom a green plant may be seen waving to and fro in summer as the current sways it. It is not a weed or flag, but a plant with pale green leaves, and looks as if it had come there by some chance; this is the water-parsnip.

By the shore on this, the sunny side of the bridge, a few forget-me-nots grow in their season, water crow'sfoot flowers, flags lie along the surface and slowly swing from side to side like a boat at anchor. The breeze brings a ripple, and the sunlight sparkles on it; the light reflected dances up the piers of the bridge. Those that pass along the road are naturally drawn to this bright parapet where the brook winds brimming full through green meadows. You can see right to the bottom; you can see where the rush of the water has scooped out a deeper channel under the arches, but look as long as you like there are no fish.

The trout I watched so long, and with such pleasure, was always on the other side, at the tail of the arch, waiting for whatever might come through to him. There in perpetual shadow he lay in wait, a little at the side of the arch, scarcely ever varying his position except to dart a yard up under the bridge to seize anything he fancied, and drifting out again to bring up at his anchorage. If people looked over the parapet that side they did not see him; they could not see the bottom there for the shadow, or if the summer noonday cast a strong beam even then it seemed to cover the surface of the water with a film of light which could not be seen through. There are some aspects from which even a picture hung on the wall close at hand cannot be seen. So no one saw the trout; if any one more curious leant over the parapet he was gone in a moment under the arch.

Folk fished in the pond about the verge of which the sedge-birds chattered, and but a few yards distant; but they never looked under the arch on the northern and shadowy side, where the water flowed beside the beech. For three seasons this continued. For three summers I had the pleasure to see the trout day after day whenever I walked that way, and all that time, with fishermen close at hand, he escaped notice, though the place was not preserved. It is wonderful to think how difficult it is to see anything under one's very eyes, and thousands of people walked actually and physically right over the fish.

However, one morning in the third summer, I found a fisherman standing in the road and fishing over the parapet in the shadowy water. But he was fishing at the wrong arch, and only with paste for roach. While the man stood there fishing, along came two navvies; naturally enough they went quietly up to see what the fisherman was doing, and one instantly uttered an exclamation. He had seen the trout. The man who was fishing with paste had stood so still and patient that the trout, re-assured, had come out, and the navvy—trust a navvy to see anything of the kind—caught sight of him.

The navvy knew how to see through water. He told the fisherman, and there was a stir of excitement, a changing of hooks and bait. I could not stay to see the result, but went on, fearing the worst. But he did not succeed; next day the wary trout was there still, and the next, and the next. Either this particular fisherman was not able to come again, or was discouraged; at any rate, he did not try again. The fish escaped, doubtless more wary than ever.

In the spring of the next year the trout was still there, and up to the summer I used to go and glance at him. This was the fourth season, and still he was there; I took friends to look at this wonderful fish, which defied all the loafers and poachers, and above all, surrounded himself not only with the shadow of the bridge, but threw a mental shadow over the minds of passers-by, so that they never thought of the possibility of such a thing as trout. But one morning something happened. The brook was dammed up on the sunny side of the bridge, and the water let off by a side-hatch, that some accursed main or pipe or other horror might be laid across the bed of the stream somewhere far down.

Above the bridge there was a brimming broad brook, below it the flags lay on the mud, the weeds drooped, and the channel was dry. It was dry up to the beech tree. There, under the drooping boughs of the beech, was a small pool of muddy water, perhaps two yards long, and very narrow—a stagnant muddy pool, not more than three or four inches deep. In this I saw the trout. In the shallow water, his back came up to the surface (for his fins must have touched the mud sometimes)—once it came above the surface, and his spots showed as plain as if you had held him in your hand. He was swimming round to try and find out the reason of this sudden stinting of room.

Twice he heaved himself somewhat on his side over a dead branch that was at the bottom, and exhibited all his beauty to the air and sunshine. Then he went away into another part of the shallow and was hidden by the muddy water. Now under the arch of the bridge, his favourite arch, close by there was a deep pool, for, as already mentioned, the scour of the current scooped away the sand and made a hole there. When the stream was shut off by the dam above this hole remained partly full. Between this pool and the shallow under the beech there was sufficient connection for the fish to move into it.

My only hope was that he would do so, and as some showers fell, temporarily increasing the depth of the narrow canal between the two pools, there seemed every reason to believe that he had got to that under the arch. If now that accursed pipe or main, or whatever repair it was, could only be finished quickly, even now the trout might escape! Every day my anxiety increased, for the intelligence would soon get about that the brook was dammed up, and any pools left in it would be sure to attract attention.

Sunday came, and directly the bells had done ringing four men attacked the pool under the arch. They took off shoes and stockings and waded in, two at each end of the arch. Stuck in the mud close by was an eel-spear. They churned up the mud, wading in, and thickened and darkened it as they groped under. No one could watch these barbarians longer.

Is it possible that he could have escaped? He was a wonderful fish, wary and quick. Is it just possible that they may not even have known that a trout was there at all; but have merely hoped for perch, or tench, or eels? The pool was deep and the fish quick—they did not bale it, might he have escaped? Might they even, if they did find him, have mercifully taken him and placed him alive in some other water nearer their homes? Is it possible that he may have almost miraculously made his way down the stream into other pools?

There was very heavy rain one night, which might have given him such a chance. These 'mights,' and 'ifs,' and 'is it possible' even now keep alive some little hope that some day I may yet see him again. But that was in the early summer. It is now winter, and the beech has brown spots. Among the limes the sedges are matted and entangled, the sword-flags rusty; the rooks are at the acorns, and the plough is at work in the stubble. I have never seen him since. I never failed to glance over the parapet into the shadowy water. Somehow it seemed to look colder, darker, less pleasant than it used to do. The spot was empty, and the shrill winds whistled through the poplars.

*1883*

## THE GOOD OLD DAYS

April 25th 1882.

| | | | |
|---|---|---|---|
| Chatto & Windus London. | 2251 | 5 | 0 |
| 750 Crown 8vo 308pp | | | |
| Buchanan's Poems. | | | |
| Composition in long Primer, old style | | | |
| leaded assimilations equal 9 5/ths | | | |
| sheets of 32pp @ £2 19 6 Ch 25/- 1508/15 finished. | 28 | 12 | 8 |
| Extra on adds & appendix | | 19 | 6 |

An extract from the ledgers of Messrs. Butler and Tanner; one of the firm's oldest printing accounts, showing the cost of setting up a 308-page book in 1882—£28 - 12 - 8.

# WILKIE COLLINS

## *The Duel*

FROM 'THE BLACK ROBE'

THE doctors could do no more for the Dowager Lady Berrick.

When the medical advisers of a lady who has reached seventy years of age recommend the mild climate of the South of France, they mean in plain language that they have arrived at the end of their resources. Her ladyship gave the mild climate a fair trial, and then decided (as she herself expressed it) to 'die at home.' Travelling slowly, she had reached Paris at the date when I last heard of her. It was then the beginning of November. A week later, I met with her nephew, Lewis Romayne, at the club.

'What brings you to London at this time of year? I asked.

'The fatality that pursues me,' he answered grimly 'I am one of the unluckiest men living.'

He was thirty years old; he was not married; he was the enviable possessor of the fine old country seat, called Vange Abbey; he had no poor relations; and he was one of the handsomest men in England. When I add that I am, myself, a retired army officer, with a wretched income, a disagreeable wife, four ugly children, and a burden of fifty years on my back, no one will be surprised to hear that I answered Romayne, with bitter sincerity, in these words:

'I wish to Heaven I could change places with you!'

'I wish to Heaven you could!' he burst out, with equal sincerity on his side. 'Read that.'

He handed me a letter addressed to him by the travelling medical attendant of Lady Berrick. After resting in Paris, the patient had continued her homeward journey as far as Boulogne. In her suffering condition, she was liable to sudden fits of caprice. An insurmountable horror of the Channel passage had got possession of her: she positively refused to be taken on board the steamboat. In this difficulty, the lady who held the post of her 'companion' had ventured on a suggestion. Would Lady Berrick consent to make the Channel passage if her nephew came to Boulogne expressly to accompany her on the voyage? The reply had been so immediately favourable, that the doctor lost no time in communicating with Mr. Lewis Romayne. This was the substance of the letter.

It was needless to ask any more questions—Romayne was plainly on his way to Boulogne. I gave him some useful information. 'Try the oysters,' I said, 'at the restaurant on the pier.'

He never even thanked me. He was thinking entirely of himself.

'Just look at my position,' he said. 'I detest Boulogne; I cordially share my aunt's horror of the Channel passage; I had looked forward to some months of happy retirement in the country among my books—and what happens to me? I am brought to London in this season of fogs, to travel by the tidal train at seven to-morrow morning—and all for a woman with whom I have no sympathies in common. If I am not an unlucky man—who is?'

He spoke in a tone of vehement irritation which seemed to me, under the circumstances, to be simply absurd. But *my* nervous system is not the irritable system—sorely tried by night study and strong tea—of my friend Romayne. 'It's only a matter of two days,' I remarked, by way of reconciling him to his situation.

'How do I know that?' he retorted. 'In two days the weather may be stormy. In two days she may be too ill to be moved. Unfortunately, I am her heir; and I am told I must submit to any whim that seizes her. I'm rich enough already; I don't want her money. Besides, I dislike all travelling—and especially travelling alone. You are an idle man. If you were a good friend, you would offer to go with me.' He added, with the delicacy which was one of the redeeming points in his wayward character, 'Of course as my guest.'

I had known him long enough not to take offence at his reminding me, in this considerate way, that I was a poor man. The proposed change of scene tempted me. What did I care for the Channel passage? Besides, there was the irresistible attraction of getting away from home. The end of it was that I accepted Romayne's invitation.

II

Shortly after noon, on the next day, we were established at Boulogne—near Lady Berrick, but not at her hotel. 'If we live in the same house,' Romayne reminded me, 'we shall be bored by the companion and the doctor. Meetings on the stairs, you know, and exchanging bows and small talk.' He hated those trivial conventionalities of society, in which other people delight. When somebody once asked him in what company he felt most at ease? he made a shocking answer—he said, 'In the company of dogs.'

I waited for him on the pier while he went to see her ladyship. He joined me again with his bitterest smile. 'What did I tell you? She is not well enough to see me to-day. The doctor looks grave, and the companion puts her handkerchief to her eyes. We may be kept in this place for weeks to come.'

The afternoon proved to be rainy. Our early dinner was a bad one. This last circumstance tried his temper sorely. He was no gourmand; the question of cookery was (with him) purely a matter of digestion. Those late hours of study and that abuse of tea to which I have already alluded, had sadly injured his stomach. The doctors warned him of serious consequences to his nervous system, unless he altered his habits. He had little faith in medical science, and he greatly overrated the restorative capacity of his constitution. So far as I know, he had always neglected the doctors' advice.

The weather cleared towards evening, and we went out for a walk. We passed a church—a Roman Catholic church, of course—the doors of which were still open. Some poor women were kneeling at their prayers in the dim light. 'Wait a minute,' said Romayne. 'I am in a vile temper. Let me try to put myself into a better frame of mind.'

I followed him into the church. He knelt down in a dark corner by himself. I confess I was surprised. He had been baptised in the Church of England; but, so far as outward practice was concerned, he belonged to no religious community. I had often heard him speak with sincere reverence and admiration of the spirit of Christianity—but he never, to my knowledge, attended any place of public worship. When we met again outside the church, I asked if he had been converted to the Roman Catholic faith.

'No,' he said. 'I hate the inveterate striving of that priesthood after social influence and political power as cordially as the fiercest Protestant living. But let us not forget that the Church of Rome has great merits to set against great faults. Its system is administered with an admirable knowledge of the higher needs of human nature. Take as one example what you have just seen. The solemn tranquillity of that church, the poor people praying near me, the few words of prayer by which I silently united myself to my fellow-creatures have calmed me, and done me good. In *our* country I should have found the church closed, out of service hours.' He took my arm, and abruptly changed the subject. 'How will you occupy yourself,' he asked, 'if my aunt receives me to-morrow?'

I assured him that I should easily find ways and means of getting through the time. The next morning a message came from Lady Berrick, to say that she would see her nephew after breakfast. Left by myself, I walked towards the pier, and met with a man who asked me to hire his boat. He had lines and bait, at my service. Most unfortunately, as the event proved, I decided on occupying an hour or two by sea fishing.

The wind shifted while we were out, and before we could get back to the harbour, the tide had turned against us. It was six o'clock when I arrived at the hotel. A little open carriage was waiting at the door. I found Romayne impatiently expecting me, and no signs of dinner on the table. He informed me that he had accepted an invitation, in which I was included, and promised to explain everything in the carriage.

Our driver took the road that led towards the High Town. I subordinated my curiosity to my sense of politeness, and asked for news of his aunt's health.

'She is seriously ill, poor soul,' he said. 'I am sorry I spoke so petulantly and so unfairly when we met at the club. The near prospect of death has developed qualities in her nature which I ought to have seen before this. No matter how it may be delayed, I will patiently wait her time for the crossing to England.'

So long as he believed himself to be in the right, he was, as to his actions and opinions, one of the most obstinate men I ever met with. But once let him be convinced that he was wrong, and he rushed into the other extreme—became needlessly distrustful of himself, and needlessly eager in seizing his opportunity of making atonement. In this latter mood he was capable (with the best intentions) of committing acts of the most childish imprudence. With some misgivings, I asked how he had amused himself in my absence.

'I waited for you,' he said, 'till I lost all patience, and went out for a walk. First, I thought of going to the beach, but the smell of the harbour drove me back into the town; and there, oddly enough, I met with a man, a certain Captain Peterkin, who had been a friend of mine at college.'

'A visitor to Boulogne?' I inquired.

'Not exactly.'

'A resident?'

'Yes. The fact is, I lost sight of Peterkin when I left Oxford—and since that time he seems to have drifted into difficulties. We had a long talk. He is living here, he tells me, until his affairs are settled.'

I needed no further enlightenment—Captain Peterkin stood as plainly revealed to me as if I had known him for years. 'Isn't it a little imprudent,' I said, 'to renew your acquaintance with a man of that sort? Couldn't you have passed him, with a bow?'

Romayne smiled uneasily. 'I dare say you're right,' he answered. 'But, remember, I had left my aunt, feeling ashamed of the unjust way in which I had thought and spoken of her. How did I know that I mightn't be wronging an old friend next, if I kept Peterkin at a distance? His present position may be as much his misfortune, poor fellow, as his fault. I was half inclined to pass him, as you say—but I distrusted my own judgment. He held out his hand, and he was so glad to see me. It can't be helped now. I shall be anxious to hear your opinion of him.'

'Are we going to dine with Captain Peterkin?'

'Yes. I happened to mention that wretched dinner yesterday at our hotel. He said, "Come to my boarding-house. Out of Paris, there isn't such a table d'hôte in France." I tried to get off it—not caring, as you know, to go among strangers—I said I had a friend with me. He invited you most cordially to accompany me. More excuses on my part only led to a painful result. I hurt Peterkin's feelings. "I'm down in the world," he said, "and I'm not fit company for you and your friends. I beg your pardon for taking the liberty of inviting you!" He turned away with the tears in his eyes. What could I do?'

I thought to myself, 'You could have lent him five pounds, and got rid of his invitation without the slightest difficulty.' If I had returned in reasonable time to go out with Romayne, we might not have met the captain—or, if we had met him, my presence would have prevented the confidential talk and the invitation that followed. I felt I was to blame —and yet, how could I help it? It was useless to remonstrate: the mischief was done.

We left the Old Town on our right hand, and drove on, past a little colony of suburban villas, to a house standing by itself, surrounded by a stone wall. As we crossed the front garden on our way to the door, I noticed against the side of the house two kennels, inhabited by two large watch-dogs. Was the proprietor afraid of thieves?

### III

The moment we were introduced to the drawing-room, my suspicions of the company we were likely to meet with were fully confirmed.

'Cards, billiards, and betting'—there was the inscription legibly written on the manner and appearance of Captain Peterkin. The bright-eyed yellow old lady who kept the boarding-house would have been worth five thousand pounds in jewellery alone, if the ornaments which profusely covered her had been genuine precious stones. The younger ladies present had their cheeks as highly rouged and their eyelids as elaborately pencilled in black as if they were going on the stage, instead of going to dinner. We found these fair creatures drinking Madeira as a whet to their appetites. Among the men, there were two who struck me as the most finished and complete blackguards whom I had ever met with in all my experience, at home and abroad. One, with a brown face and a broken nose, was presented to us by the title of 'Commander,' and was described as a person of great wealth and distinction in Peru, travelling for amusement. The other wore a military uniform and decorations, and was spoken of as 'the General.' A bold bullying manner, a fat sodden face, little leering eyes, and greasy-looking hands, made this man so repellent to me that I privately longed to kick him. Romayne had evidently been announced, before our arrival, as a landed gentleman with a large income. Men and women vied in servile attentions to him. When we went into the dining-room, the fascinating creature who sat next to him held her fan before her face, and so made a private interview of it between the rich Englishman and herself. With regard to the dinner, I shall only report that it justified Captain Peterkin's boast, in some degree at least. The wine was good, and the conversation became gay to the verge of indelicacy. Usually the most temperate of men, Romayne was tempted by his neighbours into drinking freely. I was unfortunately seated at the opposite extremity of the table, and I had no opportunity of warning him.

The dinner reached its conclusion, and we all returned together, on the foreign plan, to coffee and cigars in the drawing-room. The women smoked, and drank liqueurs as well as coffee, with the men. One of them went to the piano, and a little impromptu ball followed, the ladies dancing with their cigarettes in their mouths. Keeping my eyes and ears on the alert, I saw an innocent-looking table, with a surface of rosewood, suddenly develop a substance of green cloth. At the same time, a neat little roulette-table made its appearance from a hiding-place in a sofa. Passing near the venerable landlady, I heard her ask the servant, in a whisper, 'if the dogs were loose?' After what I had observed, I could only conclude that the dogs were used as a patrol, to give the alarm in case of a descent of the police. It was plainly high time to thank Captain Peterkin for his hospitality, and to take our leave.

'We have had enough of this,' I whispered to Romayne in English. 'Let us go.'

In these days it is a delusion to suppose that you can speak confidentially in the English language, when French people are within hearing. One of the ladies asked Romayne, tenderly, if he was tired of her already. Another reminded him that it was raining heavily (as we could all hear), and suggested waiting until it cleared up. The hideous General waved his greasy hand in the direction of the card table, and said, 'The game is waiting for us.'

Romayne was excited, but not stupefied, by the wine he had drunk. He answered, discreetly enough, 'I must beg you to excuse me; I am a poor card player.'

The General suddenly looked grave. 'You are speaking, sir, under a strange misapprehension,' he said. 'Our game is lansquenet—essentially a game of chance. With luck, the poorest player is a match for the whole table.'

Romayne persisted in his refusal. As a matter of course, I supported him, with all needful care to avoid giving offence. The General took offence, nevertheless. He crossed his arms on his breast, and looked at us fiercely.

'Does this mean, gentlemen, that you distrust the company?' he asked.

The broken-nosed Commander, hearing the question, immediately joined us, in the interests of peace—bearing with him the elements of persuasion, under the form of a lady on his arm.

The lady stepped briskly forward, and tapped the General on the shoulder with her fan. '*I* am one of the company,' she said, 'and I am sure Mr. Romayne doesn't distrust *me*.' She turned to Romayne with her most irresistible smile. 'A gentleman always plays cards,' she resumed, 'when he has a lady for a partner. Let us join our interests at the table—and, dear Mr. Romayne, don't risk too much!' She put her pretty little purse into his hand, and looked as if she had been in love with him for half her lifetime.

The fatal influence of the sex, assisted by wine, produced the inevitable result. Romayne allowed himself to be led to the card table. For a moment the General delayed the beginning of the game. After what had happened, it was necessary that he should assert the strict sense of justice that was in him. 'We are all honourable men,' he began.

'And brave men,' the Commander added, admiring the General.

'And brave men,' the General admitted, admiring the Commander. 'Gentlemen, if I have been led into expressing myself with unnecessary warmth of feeling, I apologise, and regret it.'

'Nobly spoken!' the Commander pronounced. The General put his hand on his heart and bowed. The game began.

As the poorest man of the two, I had escaped the attentions lavished by the ladies on Romayne. At the same time, I was obliged to pay for my dinner, by taking some part in the proceedings of the evening. Small stakes were allowed, I found, at roulette; and, besides, the heavy chances in favour of the table made it hardly worth while to run the risk of cheating in this case. I placed myself next to the least rascally-looking man in the company, and played roulette.

For a wonder, I was successful at the first attempt. My neighbour handed me my winnings. 'I have lost every farthing I possess,' he whispered to me, piteously, 'and I have a wife and children at home.' I lent the poor wretch five francs. He smiled faintly as he looked at the money. 'It reminds me,' he said, 'of my last transaction, when I borrowed of that gentleman there, who is betting on the General's luck at the card table. Beware of employing him as I did. What do you think I got for my note of hand of four thousand francs? A hundred bottles of champagne, fifty bottles of ink, fifty bottles of blacking, three dozen handkerchiefs, two pictures by unknown masters, two shawls, one hundred maps, *and*—five francs.'

We went on playing. My luck deserted me; I lost, and lost, and lost again. From time to time I looked round at the card table. The 'deal' had fallen early to the General, and it seemed to be indefinitely prolonged. A heap of notes and gold (won mainly from Romayne, as I afterwards discovered) lay before him. As for my neighbour, the unhappy possessor of the bottles of blacking, the pictures by unknown masters, and the rest of it, he won, and then rashly presumed on his good fortune. Deprived of his last farthing, he retired into a corner of the room, and consoled himself with a cigar. I had just risen, to follow his example, when a furious uproar burst out at the card table.

I saw Romayne spring up, and snatch the cards out of the General's hand. 'You scoundrel!' he shouted, 'you are cheating!' The General started to his feet in a fury. 'You lie!' he cried. I attempted to interfere, but Romayne had already seen the necessity of controlling himself. 'A gentleman doesn't accept an insult from a swindler,' he said coolly. 'Accept this, then!' the General answered—and spat on him. In an instant Romayne knocked him down.

The blow was dealt straight between his eyes: he was a gross big-boned man, and he fell heavily. For the time he was stunned. The women ran, screaming, out of the room. The peaceable Commander trembled from head to foot. Two of the men present, who, to give them their due, were no cowards, locked the doors. 'You don't go,' they said, 'till we see whether he recovers or not.' Cold water, assisted by the landlady's smelling salts, brought the General to his senses after a while. He whispered something to one of his friends, who immediately turned to me. 'The General challenges Mr. Romayne,' he said. 'As one of his seconds, I demand an appointment for to-morrow morning.' I refused to make any appointment unless the doors were first unlocked, and we were left free to depart. 'Our carriage is waiting outside,' I added. 'If it returns to the hotel without us, there will be an inquiry.' This latter consideration had its effect. On their side, the doors were opened. On our side, the appointment was made. We left the house.

* * * * *

V

We were punctual to the appointed hour—eight o'clock.

The second who acted with me was a French gentleman, a relative of one of the officers who had brought the challenge. At his suggestion, we had chosen the pistol as our weapon. Romayne, like most Englishmen at the present time, knew nothing of the use of the sword. He was almost equally inexperienced with the pistol.

Our opponents were late. They kept us waiting for more than ten minutes. It was not pleasant weather to wait in. The day had dawned damp and drizzling. A thick white fog was slowly rolling in on us from the sea.

When they did appear, the General was not among them. A tall, well-dressed young man saluted Romayne with stern courtesy, and said to a stranger who accompanied him, 'Explain the circumstances.'

The stranger proved to be a surgeon. He entered at once on the necessary explanation. The General was too ill to appear. He had been attacked that morning by a fit—the consequence of the blow that he had received. Under these circumstances, his eldest son (Maurice) was now on the ground to fight the duel, on his father's behalf; attended by the General's seconds, and with the General's full approval.

We instantly refused to allow the duel to take place, Romayne loudly declaring that he had no quarrel with the General's son. Upon this, Maurice broke away from his seconds; drew off one of his gloves; and stepping close up to Romayne, struck him on the face with the glove. 'Have you no quarrel with me now?' the young Frenchman asked. 'Must I spit on you, as my father did?' His seconds dragged him away, and apologised to us for the outbreak. But the mischief was done.

Romayne's fiery temper flashed in his eyes. 'Load the pistols,' he said. After the insult publicly offered to him, and the outrage publicly threatened, there was no other course to take.

It had been left to us to produce the pistols. We therefore requested the seconds of our opponent to examine, and to load them. While this was being done, the advancing sea-fog so completely enveloped us, that the duellists were unable to see each other. We were obliged to wait for the chance of a partial clearing in the atmosphere. Romayne's temper had become calm again. The generosity of his nature spoke in the words which he now addressed to his seconds.

'After all,' he said, 'the young man is a good son—he is bent on redressing what he believes to be his father's wrong. Does his flipping his glove in my face matter to me? I think I shall fire in the air.'

'I shall refuse to act as your second if you do,' answered the French gentleman who was assisting us. 'The General's son is famous for his skill with the pistol. If you didn't see it in his face just now, I did—he means to kill you. Defend your life, sir!' I spoke quite as strongly, to the same purpose, when my turn came. Romayne yielded—he placed himself unreservedly in our hands.

In a quarter of an hour the fog lifted a little. We measured the distance, having previously arranged (at my suggestion) that the two men should both fire at the same moment, at a given signal. Romayne's composure, as they faced each other, was, in a man of his irritable nervous temperament, really wonderful. I placed him sideways, in a position which in some degree lessened his danger, by lessening the surface exposed to the bullet. My French colleague put the pistol into his hand, and gave him the last word of advice. 'Let your arm hang loosely down, with the barrel of the pistol pointing straight to the ground. When you hear the signal, only lift your arm as far as the elbow; keep the elbow pressed against your side—and fire.' We could do no more for him. As we drew aside—I own it—my tongue was like a cinder in my mouth, and a horrid inner cold crept through me to the marrow of my bones.

The signal was given, and the two shots were fired at the same time.

My first look was at Romayne. He took off his hat, and handed it to me with a smile. His adversary's bullet had cut a piece out of the brim of his hat, on the right side. He had literally escaped by a hairbreadth.

While I was congratulating him, the fog gathered again more thickly than ever. Looking anxiously towards the ground occupied by our adversaries, we could only see vague, shadowy forms hurriedly crossing and re-crossing each other in the mist. Something had happened! My French colleague took my arm and pressed it significantly. 'Leave *me* to inquire,' he said. Romayne tried to follow; I held him back—we neither of us exchanged a word.

The fog thickened and thickened, until nothing was to be seen. Once we heard the surgeon's voice, calling impatiently for a light to help him.

No light appeared that *we* could see. Dreary as the fog itself, the silence gathered round us again. On a sudden it was broken, horribly broken, by another voice, strange to both of us, shrieking hysterically through the impenetrable mist. 'Where is he?' the voice cried, in the French language. 'Assassin! Assassin! where are you?' Was it a woman? or was it a boy? We heard nothing more. The effect upon Romayne was terrible to see. He who had calmly confronted the weapon lifted to kill him, shuddered dumbly like a terror-stricken animal. I put my arm round him, and hurried him away from the place.

We waited at the hotel until our French friend joined us. After a brief interval he appeared, announcing that the surgeon would follow him.

The duel had ended fatally. The chance course of the bullet, urged by Romayne's unpractised hand, had struck the General's son just above the right nostril—had penetrated to the back of his neck—and had communicated a fatal shock to the spinal marrow. He was a dead man before they could take him back to his father's house.

So far, our fears were confirmed. But there was something else to tell, for which our worst presentiments had not prepared us.

A younger brother of the fallen man (a boy of thirteen years old) had secretly followed the duelling party, on their way from his father's house—had hidden himself—and had seen the dreadful end. The seconds only knew of it when he burst out of his place of concealment, and fell on his knees by his dying brother's side. His were the frightful cries which we had heard from invisible lips. The slayer of his brother was the 'assassin' whom he had vainly tried to discover through the fathomless obscurity of the mist.

We both looked at Romayne. He silently looked back at us, like a man turned to stone. I tried to reason with him.

'Your life was at your opponent's mercy,' I said. 'It was *he* who was skilled in the use of the pistol; your risk was infinitely greater than his. Are you responsible for an accident? Rouse yourself, Romayne! Think of the time to come, when all this will be forgotten.'

'Never,' he said, 'to the end of my life.'

He made that reply in dull monotonous tones. His eyes looked wearily and vacantly straight before him. I spoke to him again. He remained impenetrably silent; he appeared not to hear, or not to understand me. The surgeon came in, while I was still at a loss what to say or do next. Without waiting to be asked for his opinion, he observed Romayne attentively, and then drew me away into the next room.

'Your friend is suffering from a severe nervous shock,' he said. 'Can you tell me anything of his habits of life?'

I mentioned the prolonged night studies, and the excessive use of tea. The surgeon shook his head.

'If you want my advice,' he proceeded, 'take him home at once.

Don't subject him to further excitement, when the result of the duel is known in the town. If it ends in our appearing in a court of law, it will be a mere formality in this case, and you can surrender when the time comes. Leave me your address in London.'

I felt that the wisest thing I could do was to follow his advice. The boat crossed to Folkestone at an early hour that day—we had no time to lose. Romayne offered no objection to our return to England; he seemed perfectly careless of what became of him. 'Leave me quiet,' he said: 'and do as you like.' I wrote a few lines to Lady Berrick's medical attendant, informing him of the circumstances. A quarter of an hour afterwards we were on board the steamboat.

*1883*

# ANTHONY TROLLOPE

## *Irish M.F.H.*

FROM 'THE LAND LEAGUERS'

HE not only knew every hound in his pack, but he knew their ages, their sires and their dams; and the sires and the dams of most of their sires and dams. He knew the constitution of each, and to what extent their noses were to be trusted. 'It's a very heavy scent to-day,' he would say, 'because Gaylap carries it over the plough. It's only a catching scent because the drops don't hang on the bushes.' His lore on all such matters was incredible, but he would never listen to any argument. A man had a right to his own opinion; but then the man who differed from him knew nothing. He gave out his little laws to favoured individuals; not by way of conversation, for which he cared nothing, but because it might be well that the favoured individual should know the truth on that occasion.

As a man to ride he was a complete master of his art. There was nothing which a horse could do with a man on his back, which Daly could not make him do; and when he had ridden a horse he would know exactly what was within his power. But there was no desire with him for the showing off of a horse. He often rode to sell a horse, but he never seemed to do so. He never rode at difficult places unless driven to do so by the exigencies of the moment. He was always quiet in the field, unless when driven to express himself as to the faults of some young man. Then he could blaze forth in his anger with great power. He was constantly to be seen trotting along a road when hounds were running, because he had no desire to achieve for himself a character for hard riding. But he was always with his hounds when he was wanted, and it was boasted of him that he had ridden four days a week through the season on three horses, and had never lamed one of them. He was rarely known to have a second horse out, and when he did so, it was for some purpose peculiar to the day's work. On such days he had generally a horse to sell.

It is hardly necessary to say that Black Daly was an unmarried man. No one who knew him could conceive that he should have had a wife. His hounds were his children, and he could have taught no wife to assist him in looking after them, with the constant attention and tender care which was given to them by Barney Smith, his huntsman. A wife, had she seen to the feeding of the numerous babies, would have given them too much to eat, and had she not undertaken this care, she would have been useless at Daly's Bridge. But Barney Smith was invaluable; double the amount of work got usually from a huntsman was done by him. There was no kennel man, no second horseman, no stud-groom at the Ahaseragh kennels. It may be said that Black Daly filled all these positions himself, and that in each Barney Smith was his first lieutenant. Circumstances had given him the use of the Ahaseragh kennels, which had been the property of his cousin, and circumstances had not enabled him to build others at Daly's Bridge. Gradually he had found it easier to move himself than the hounds. And so it had come to pass that two rooms had been prepared for him close to the kennels, and that Mr. Barney Smith gave him such attendance as was necessary. Of strictly personal attendance Black Daly wanted very little; but the discomforts of that home, while one pair of breeches were supposed to be at Daly's Bridge, and the others at Ahaseragh, were presumed by the world at large to be very grievous.

But the personal appearance of Mr. Daly on hunting mornings was not a matter of indifference. It was not that he wore beautiful pink tops, or came out guarded from the dust by little aprons, or had his cravat just out of the bandbox, or his scarlet coat always new, and in the latest fashion, nor had his hat just come from the shop in Piccadilly with the newest twist to its rim. But there was something manly, and even powerful about his whole apparel. He was always the same, so that by men even in his own county, he would hardly have been known in other garments. The strong, broad-brimmed high hat, with the cord passing down his back beneath his coat, that had known the weather of various winters; the dark, red coat, with long swallow tails, which had grown nearly black under many storms; the dark, buff striped waistcoat, with the stripes running downwards, long, so as to come well down over his breeches; the breeches themselves, which were always of leather, but which had become nearly brown under the hands of Barney Smith or his wife, and the mahogany top-boots, of which the tops seemed to be a foot in length, could none of them have been worn by any but Black Daly. His very spurs must have surely been made for him, they were in length and weight, and general strength of leather, so peculiarly his own. He was unlike other masters of hounds in this, that he never carried a horn; but he spoke to his hounds in a loud, indistinct chirruping voice, which all County Galway believed to be understood by every hound in the pack.

*1884*

# MARK TWAIN

## *The Adventures of Huckleberry Finn*

### *Chapter 1*

CIVILIZING HUCK—MOSES AND THE 'BULRUSHERS'—
MISS WATSON—TOM SAWYER WAITS

YOU don't know about me, without you have read a book by the name of *The Adventures of Tom Sawyer*, but that ain't no matter. That book was made by Mr. Mark Twain, and he told the truth, mainly. There was things which he stretched, but mainly he told the truth. That is nothing. I never seen anybody but lied, one time or another, without it was Aunt Polly, or the widow, or maybe Mary. Aunt Polly—Tom's Aunt Polly, she is—and Mary, and the Widow Douglas, is all told about in that book—which is mostly a true book; with some stretchers, as I said before.

Now the way that the book winds up, is this: Tom and me found the money that the robbers hid in the cave, and it made us rich. We got six thousand dollars apiece—all gold. It was an awful sight of money when it was piled up. Well, Judge Thatcher, he took it and put it out at interest, and it fetched us a dollar a day apiece, all the year round—more than a body could tell what to do with. The Widow Douglas, she took me for her son, and allowed she would sivilize me; but it was rough living in the house all the time, considering how dismal regular and decent the widow was in all her ways; and so when I couldn't stand it no longer, I lit out. I got into my old rags and my sugar-hogshead again, and was free and satisfied. But Tom Sawyer he hunted me up and said he was going to start a band of robbers, and I might join if I would go back to the widow and be respectable. So I went back.

The widow she cried over me, and called me a poor lost lamb, and she called me a lot of other names, too, but she never meant no harm by it. She put me in them new clothes again, and I couldn't do nothing but sweat and sweat, and feel all cramped up. Well, then, the old thing commenced again. The widow rung a bell for supper, and you had to come to time. When you got to the table you couldn't go right to eating, but you had to wait for the widow to tuck down her head and grumble a little over the victuals, though there warn't really anything the matter with them. That is, nothing only everything was cooked by itself. In a barrel of odds and ends it is different; things get mixed up, and the juice kind of swaps around, and the things go better.

After supper she got out her book and learned me about Moses and the 'Bulrushers'; and I was in a sweat to find out all about him; but by-and-by she let it out that Moses had been dead a considerable long time; so then I didn't care no more about him; because I don't take no stock in dead people.

Pretty soon I wanted to smoke, and asked the widow to let me. But she wouldn't. She said it was a mean practice and wasn't clean, and I must try to not do it any more. That is just the way with some people. They get down on a thing when they don't know nothing about it. Here she was a-bothering about Moses, which was no kin to her, and no use to anybody, being gone, you see, yet finding a power of fault with me for doing a thing that had some good in it. And she took snuff too; of course, that was all right, because she done it herself.

Her sister, Miss Watson, a tolerable slim old maid, with goggles on, had just come to live with her, and took a set at me now, with a spelling-book. She worked me middling hard for about an hour, and then the widow made her ease up. I couldn't stood it much longer. Then for an hour it was deadly dull, and I was fidgety. Miss Watson would say, 'Don't put your feet up there, Huckleberry'; and, 'don't scrunch up like that, Huckleberry—set up straight'; and pretty soon she would say, 'Don't gap and stretch like that, Huckleberry—why don't you try to behave?' Then she told me all about the bad place, and I said I wished I was there. She got mad, then, but I didn't mean no harm. All I wanted was to go somewheres; all I wanted was a change, I warn't particular. She said it was wicked to say what I said; said she wouldn't say it for the whole world; *she* was going to live so as to go to the good place. Well, I couldn't see no advantage in going where she was going, so I made up my mind I wouldn't try for it. But I never said so, because it would only make trouble, and wouldn't do no good.

Now she had got a start, and she went on and told me all about the good place. She said all a body would have to do there was to go around all day long with a harp and sing for ever and ever. So I didn't think much of it. But I never said so. I asked her if she reckoned Tom Sawyer would go there, and she said, not by a considerable sight. I was glad about that, because I wanted him and me to be together.

Miss Watson she kept pecking at me, and it got tiresome and lonesome. By-and-by they fetched the niggers in and had prayers, and then everybody was off to bed. I went up to my room with a piece of candle and put it on the table. Then I set down in a chair by the window and tried to think of something cheerful, but it warn't no use. I felt so lonesome I most wished I was dead. The stars was shining, and the leaves rustled in the woods ever so mournful; and I heard an owl, away off, who-whooing about somebody that was dead, and a whippowill and a dog crying about somebody that was going to die; and the wind was trying to whisper something to me and I couldn't make out what it was, and so it made the cold shivers run over me. Then away out in the woods I heard that kind of a sound that a ghost makes when it wants to tell about something that's on its mind and can't make itself understood, and so can't rest easy in its grave and has to go about that way every night grieving. I got so downhearted and scared, I did wish I had some company. Pretty soon a spider went crawling up my shoulder, and I flipped it off and it lit in the candle; and before I could budge it was all shrivelled up. I didn't need anybody to tell me that that was an awful bad sign and would fetch me some bad luck, so I was scared and most shook the clothes off of me. I got up and turned around in my tracks three times and crossed my breast every time; and then I tied up a little lock of my hair with a thread to keep witches away. But I hadn't no confidence. You do that when you've lost a horse-shoe that you've found, instead of nailing it up over the door, but I hadn't ever heard anybody say it was any way to keep off bad luck when you'd killed a spider.

I set down again, a-shaking all over, and got out my pipe for a smoke; for the house was all as still as death, now, and so the widow wouldn't know. Well, after a long time I heard the clock away off in the town go boom—boom—boom—twelve licks—and all still again—stiller than ever. Pretty soon I heard a twig snap, down in the dark amongst the trees—something was a-stirring. I set still and listened. Directly I could just barely hear a '*me-yow! me-yow!*' down there. That was good! Says I, '*me-yow! me-yow!*' as soft as I could, and then I put out the light and scrambled out of the window on to the shed. Then I slipped down to the ground and crawled in amongst the trees, and sure enough there was Tom Sawyer waiting for me.

## *Chapter 2*

### THE BOYS ESCAPE JIM—JIM!—TOM SAWYER'S GANG—DEEP-LAID PLANS

WE went tip-toeing along a path amongst the trees back towards the end of the widow's garden, stooping down so as the branches wouldn't scrape our heads. When we was passing by the kitchen I fell over a root and made a noise. We scrouched down and laid still. Miss Watson's big nigger, named Jim, was setting in the kitchen door; we could see him pretty clear, because there was a light behind him. He got up and stretched his neck out about a minute, listening. Then he says:

'Who dah?'

He listened some more; then he come tip-toeing down and stood right between us; we could a touched him, nearly. Well, likely it was minutes and minutes that there warn't a sound, and we all there so close together. There was a place on my ankle that got to itching; but I dasn't scratch it; and then my ear begun to itch; and next my back, right between my shoulders. Seemed like I'd die if I couldn't scratch. Well, I've noticed that thing plenty of times since. If you are with the quality, or at a funeral, or trying to go to sleep when you ain't sleepy—if you are anywheres where it won't do for you to scratch, why you will itch all over in upwards of a thousand places. Pretty soon Jim says:

'Say—who is you? Whar is you? Dog my cats ef I didn' hear sumf'n. Well, I knows what I's gwyne to do. I's gwyne to set down here and listen tell I hears it agin.'

So he set down on the ground betwixt me and Tom. He leaned his back up against a tree, and stretched his legs out till one of them most touched one of mine. My nose begun to itch. It itched till the tears come into my eyes. But I dasn't scratch. Then it begun to itch on the inside. Next I got to itching underneath. I didn't know how I was going to set still. This miserableness went on as much as six or seven minutes; but it seemed a sight longer than that. I was itching in eleven different places now. I reckoned I couldn't stand it more'n a minute longer, but I set my teeth hard and got ready to try. Just then Jim begun to breathe heavy; next he begun to snore—and then I was pretty soon comfortable again.

Tom he made a sign to me—kind of a little noise with his mouth—and we went creeping away on our hands and knees. When he was ten foot off, Tom whispered to me and wanted to tie Jim to the tree for fun; but I said no; he might wake and make a disturbance, and then they'd find out I warn't in. Then Tom said he hadn't got candles enough, and he would slip in the kitchen and get some more. I didn't want him to try. I said Jim might wake up and come. But Tom wanted to resk it; so we slid in there and got three candles, and Tom laid five cents on the table for pay. Then we got out, and I was in a sweat to get away; but nothing would do Tom but he must crawl to where Jim was, on his hands and knees, and play something on him. I waited, and it seemed a good while, everything was so still and lonesome.

As soon as Tom was back, we cut along the path, around the garden fence, and by and by fetched up on the steep top of the hill the other side of the house. Tom said he slipped Jim's hat off of his head and hung it on a limb right over him, and Jim stirred a little, but he didn't wake. Afterwards Jim said the witches bewitched him and put him in a trance, and rode him all over the State, and then set him under the trees again and hung his hat on a limb to show who done it. And next time Jim told it he said they rode him down to New Orleans; and after that, every time he told it he spread it more and more, till by and by he said they rode him all over the world, and tired him most to death, and his back was all over saddle-boils. Jim was monstrous proud about it, and he got so he wouldn't hardly notice the other niggers. Niggers would come miles to hear Jim tell about it, and he was more looked up to than any nigger in that country. Strange niggers would stand with their mouths open and look him all over, same as if he was a wonder. Niggers is always talking about witches in the dark by the kitchen fire; but whenever one was talking and letting on to know all about such things, Jim would happen in and say, 'Hm! What you know 'bout witches?' and that nigger was corked up and had to take a back seat. Jim always kept that five-center piece around his neck with a string, and said it was a charm the devil give to him with his own hands and told him he could cure anybody with it and fetch witches whenever he wanted to, just by saying something to it; but he never told what it was he said to it. Niggers would come from all around there and give Jim anything they had, just for a sight of that five-center piece; but they wouldn't touch it, because the devil had had his hands on it. Jim was most ruined, for a servant, because he got so stuck up on account of having seen the devil and been rode by witches.

Well, when Tom and me got to the edge of the hill-top, we looked away down into the village and could see three or four lights twinkling, where there was sick folks, maybe; and the stars over us was sparkling ever so fine; and down by the village was the river, a whole mile broad, and awful still and grand. We went down the hill and found Jo Harper, and Ben Rogers, and two or three more of the boys, hid in the old tanyard. So we unhitched a skiff and pulled down the river two mile and a half, to the big scar on the hill-side, and went ashore.

We went to a clump of bushes, and Tom made everybody swear to keep the secret, and then showed them a hole in the hill, right in the thickest part of the bushes. Then we lit the candles and crawled in on our hands and knees. We went about two hundred yards, and then the cave opened up. Tom poked about amongst the passages and pretty soon ducked under a wall where you wouldn't a noticed that there was a hole. We went along a narrow place and got into a kind of room, all damp and sweaty and cold, and there we stopped. Tom says:

'Now we'll start this band of robbers and call it Tom Sawyer's Gang. Everybody that wants to join has got to take an oath, and write his name in blood.'

Everybody was willing. So Tom got out a sheet of paper that he had wrote the oath on, and read it. It swore every boy to stick to the band, and never tell any of the secrets; and if anybody done anything to any boy in the band, whichever boy was ordered to kill that person and his family must do it, and he mustn't eat and he mustn't sleep till he had killed them and hacked a cross in their breasts, which was the sign of the band. And nobody that didn't belong to the band could use that mark, and if he did he must be sued; and if he done it again he must be killed. And if anybody that belonged to the band told the secrets, he must have his throat cut, and then have his carcass burnt up and the ashes scattered all around, and his name blotted off of the list with blood and never mentioned again by the Gang, but have a curse put on it and be forgot, for ever.

Everybody said it was a real beautiful oath, and asked Tom if he got it out of his own head. He said, some of it, but the rest was out of pirate books, and robber books, and every gang that was high-toned had it.

Some thought it would be good to kill the *families* of boys that told the secrets. Tom said it was a good idea, so he took a pencil and wrote it in. Then Ben Rogers says:

'Here 's Huck Finn, he hain't got no family—what you going to do 'bout him?'

'Well, hain't he got a father?' says Tom Sawyer.

'Yes, he's got a father, but you can't never find him, these days. He used to lay drunk with the hogs in the tanyard, but he hain't been seen in these parts for a year or more.'

They talked it over, and they was going to rule me out, because they said every boy must have a family or somebody to kill, or else it wouldn't be fair and square for the others. Well, nobody could think of anything to do—everybody was stumped, and set still. I was most ready to cry; but all at once I thought of a way, and so I offered them Miss Watson—they could kill her. Everybody said:

'Oh, she'll do, she'll do. That's all right. Huck can come in.'

Then they all stuck a pin in their fingers to get blood to sign with, and I made my mark on the paper.

'Now,' says Ben Rogers, 'what's the line of business of this Gang?'

'Nothing only robbery and murder,' Tom said.

'But who are we going to rob? Houses—or cattle—or——'

'Stuff! Stealing cattle and such things ain't robbery, it's burglary,' says Tom Sawyer. 'We ain't burglars. That ain't no sort of style. We are highwaymen. We stop stages and carriages on the road, with masks on, and kill the people and take their watches and money.'

'Must we always kill the people?'

'Oh, certainly. It's best. Some authorities think different, but mostly it's considered best to kill them. Except some that you bring to the cave here and keep them till they're ransomed.'

'Ransomed? What's that?'

'I don't know. But that's what they do. I've seen it in books; and so, of course, that's what we've got to do.'

'But how can we do it if we don't know what it is?'

'Why blame it all, we've *got* to do it. Don't I tell you it's in the books? Do you want to go to doing different from what's in the books, and get things all muddled up?'

'Oh, that's all very fine to *say*, Tom Sawyer, but how in the nation are these fellows going to be ransomed if we don't know how to do it to them? That's the thing *I* want to get at. Now, what do you *reckon* it is?'

'Well, I don't know. But per'aps if we keep them till they're ransomed, it means that we keep them till they're dead.'

'Now, that's something *like.* That'll answer. Why couldn't you said that before? We'll keep them till they're ransomed to death—and a bothersome lot they'll be, too, eating up everything and always trying to get loose.'

'How you talk, Ben Rogers. How can they get loose when there's a guard over them, ready to shoot them down if they move a peg?'

'A guard. Well, that *is* good. So somebody's got to set up all night and never get any sleep, just so as to watch them. I think that's foolishness. Why can't a body take a club and ransom them as soon as they get here?'

'Because it ain't in the books so—that's why. Now, Ben Rogers, do you want to do things regular, or don't you?—that's the idea. Don't you reckon that the people that made the books knows what's the correct thing to do? Do you reckon *you* can learn 'em anything? Not by a good deal. No, sir, we'll just go on and ransom them in the regular way.'

'All right. I don't mind; but I say it's a fool way, anyhow. Say—do we kill the women, too?'

'Well, Ben Rogers, if I was as ignorant as you I wouldn't let on. Kill the women? No—nobody ever saw anything in the books like that. You fetch them to the cave, and you're always as polite as pie to them; and by-and-by they fall in love with you and never want to go home any more.'

'Well, if that's the way, I'm agreed, but I don't take no stock in it. Mighty soon we'll have the cave so cluttered up with women, and fellows waiting to be ransomed, that there won't be no place for the robbers. But go ahead, I ain't got nothing to say.'

Little Tommy Barnes was asleep, now, and when they waked him up he was scared, and cried, and said he wanted to go home to his ma, and didn't want to be a robber any more.

So they all made fun of him, and called him cry-baby, and that made him mad, and he said he would go straight and tell all the secrets. But Tom give him five cents to keep quiet, and said we would all go home and meet next week and rob somebody and kill some people.

Ben Rogers said he couldn't get out much, only Sundays, and so he wanted to begin next Sunday; but all the boys said it would be wicked to do it on Sunday, and that settled the thing. They agreed to get together and fix a day as soon as they could, and then we elected Tom Sawyer first captain and Jo Harper second captain of the Gang, and so started home.

I clumb up the shed and crept into my window just before day was breaking. My new clothes was all greased up and clayey, and I was dog-tired.

## *Chapter 3*

### A GOOD GOING-OVER—GRACE TRIUMPHANT—PLAYING ROBBERS—THE GENIES—'ONE OF TOM SAWYER'S LIES'

WELL, I got a good going-over in the morning, from old Miss Watson, on account of my clothes; but the widow she didn't scold, but only cleaned off the grease and clay, and looked so sorry that I thought I would behave a while if I could. Then Miss Watson she took me in the closet and prayed, but nothing come of it. She told me to pray every day, and whatever I asked for I would get it. But it warn't so. I tried it. Once I got a fish-line, but no hooks. It warn't any good to me without hooks. I tried for the hooks three or four times, but somehow I couldn't make it work. By-and-by, one day, I asked Miss Watson to try for me, but she said I was a fool. She never told me why, and I couldn't make it out no way.

I set down, one time, back in the woods, and had a long think about it. I says to myself, if a body can get anything they pray for, why don't Deacon Winn get back the money he lost on pork? Why can't the widow get back her silver snuff-box that was stole? Why can't Miss Watson fat up? No, says I to myself, there ain't nothing in it. I went and told the widow about it, and she said the thing a body could get by praying for it was 'spiritual gifts.' This was too many for me, but she told me what she meant—I must help other people, and do everything I could for other people, and look out for them all the time, and never think about myself. This was including Miss Watson, as I took it. I went out in the woods and turned it over in my mind a long time, but I couldn't see no advantage about it—except for the other people—so at last I reckoned I wouldn't worry about it any more, but just let it go. Sometimes the widow would take me one side and talk about Providence in a way to make a body's mouth water; but maybe next day Miss Watson would take hold and knock it all down again. I judged I could see that there was two Providences, and a poor chap would stand considerable show with the widow's Providence, but if Miss Watson's got him there warn't no help for him any more. I thought it all out, and reckoned I would belong to the widow's, if he wanted me, though I couldn't make out how he was agoing to be any better off then than what he was before, seeing I was so ignorant and so kind of low-down and ornery.

Pap he hadn't been seen for more than a year, and that was comfortable for me; I didn't want to see him no more. He used to always whale me when he was sober and could get his hands on me; though I used to take to the woods most of the time when he was around. Well, about this time he was found in the river drowned, about twelve mile above town, so people said. They judged it was him, anyway;

said this drowned man was just his size, and was ragged, and had uncommon long hair—which was all like pap—but they couldn't make nothing out of the face, because it had been in the water so long it warn't much like a face at all. They said he was floating on his back in the water. They took him and buried him on the bank. But I warn't comfortable long, because I happened to think of something. I knowed mighty well that a drownded man don't float on his back, but on his face. So I knowed, then, that this warn't pap, but a woman dressed up in a man's clothes. So I was uncomfortable again. I judged the old man would turn up again by-and-by, though I wished he wouldn't.

We played robbers now and then about a month, and then I resigned. All the boys did. We hadn't robbed nobody, we hadn't killed any people, but only just pretended. We used to hop out of the woods and go charging down on hog-drovers and women in carts taking garden stuff to market, but we never hived any of them. Tom Sawyer called the hogs 'ingots,' and he called the turnips and stuff 'julery,' and we would go to the cave and pow-wow over what we had done and how many people we had killed and marked. But I couldn't see no profit in it. One time Tom sent a boy to run about town with a blazing stick, which he called a slogan (which was the sign for the Gang to get together), and then he said he had got secret news by his spies that next day a whole parcel of Spanish merchants and rich A-rabs was going to camp in Cave Hollow with two hundred elephants, and six hundred camels, and over a thousand 'sumter' mules, all loaded down with di'monds, and they didn't have only a guard of four hundred soldiers, and so we would lay in ambuscade, as he called it, and kill the lot and scoop the things. He said we must slick up our swords and guns, and get ready. He never could go after even a turnip-cart but he must have the swords and guns all scoured up for it; though they was only lath and broom-sticks, and you might scour at them till you rotted, and then they warn't worth a mouthful of ashes more than what they was before. I didn't believe we could lick such a crowd of Spaniards and A-rabs, but I wanted to see the camels and elephants, so I was on hand next day, Saturday, in the ambuscade; and when we got the word, we rushed out of the woods and down the hill. But there warn't no Spaniards and A-rabs, and there warn't no camels nor no elephants. It warn't anything but a Sunday-school picnic, and only a primer-class at that. We busted it up, and chased the children up the hollow; but we never got anything but some doughnuts and jam, though Ben Rogers got a rag doll, and Jo Harper got a hymn-book and a tract; and then the teacher charged in and made us drop everything and cut. I didn't see no di'monds, and I told Tom Sawyer so. He said there was loads of them there, anyway; and he said there was A-rabs there too, and elephants and things. I said, why couldn't we see them, then? He said if I warn't so ignorant, but had read a book called *Don Quixote*, I would know without asking. He said it was all done by enchantment.

He said there was hundreds of soldiers there, and elephants and treasure, and so on, but we had enemies which he called magicians, and they had turned the whole thing into an infant Sunday-school, just out of spite. I said all right, then the thing for us to do was to go for the magicians. Tom Sawyer said I was a numskull.

'Why,' says he, 'a magician could call up a lot of genies, and they would hash you up like nothing before you could say Jack Robinson. They are as tall as a tree and as big around as a church.'

'Well,' I says, 's'pose we got some genies to help *us*—can't we lick the other crowd then?'

'How you going to get them?'

'I don't know. How do *they* get them?'

'Why, they rub an old tin lamp or an iron ring, and then the genies come tearing in, with the thunder and lightning a-ripping around and the smoke a-rolling, and everything they're told to do they up and do it. They don't think nothing of pulling a shot-tower up by the roots, and belting a Sunday-school superintendent over the head with it—or any other man.'

'Who makes them tear around so?'

'Why, whoever rubs the lamp or the ring. They belong to whoever rubs the lamp or the ring, and they've got to do whatever he says. If he tells them to build a palace forty miles long, out of di'monds, and fill it full of chewing-gum, or whatever you want, and fetch an emperor's daughter from China for you to marry, they've got to do it—and they've got to do it before sun-up next morning too. And more—they've got to waltz that palace around over the country wherever you want it, you understand.'

'Well,' says I, 'I think they are a pack of flatheads for not keeping the palace themselves 'stead of fooling them away like that. And what's more—if I was one of them I would see a man in Jericho before I would drop my business and come to him for the rubbing of an old tin lamp.'

'How you talk, Huck Finn. Why, you'd *have* to come when he rubbed it, whether you wanted to or not.'

'What, and I as high as a tree and as big as a church? All right, then; I *would* come; but I lay I'd make that man climb the highest tree there was in the country.'

'Shucks, it ain't no use to talk to you, Huck Finn. You don't seem to know anything, somehow—perfect sap-head.'

I thought all this over for two or three days, and then I reckoned I would see if there was anything in it. I got an old tin lamp and an iron ring and went out in the woods and rubbed and rubbed till I sweat like an Injun, calculating to build a palace and sell it; but it warn't no use, none of the genies come. So then I judged that all that stuff was only just one of Tom Sawyer's lies. I reckoned he believed in the A-rabs and the elephants, but as for me I think different. It had all the marks of a Sunday-school.

## *Chapter 4*

### 'SLOW BUT SURE'—HUCK AND THE JUDGE—SUPERSTITION

WELL, three or four months run along, and it was well into the winter, now. I had been to school most all the time, and could spell, and read, and write just a little, and could say the multiplication table up to six times seven is thirty-five, and I don't reckon I could ever get any further than that if I was to live for ever. I don't take no stock in mathematics, anyway.

At first I hated the school, but by and by I got so I could stand it. Whenever I got uncommon tired I played hookey, and the hiding I got next day done me good and cheered me up. So the longer I went to school the easier it got to be. I was getting sort of used to the widow's ways too, and they warn't so raspy on me. Living in a house, and sleeping in a bed, pulled on me pretty tight, mostly, but before the cold weather I used to slide out and sleep in the woods, sometimes, and so that was a rest to me. I liked the old ways best, but I was getting so I liked the new ones too, a little bit. The widow said I was coming along slow but sure, and doing very satisfactory. She said she warn't ashamed of me.

One morning I happened to turn over the salt-cellar at breakfast. I reached for some of it as quick as I could, to throw over my left shoulder and keep off the bad luck, but Miss Watson was in ahead of me, and crossed me off. She says, 'Take your hands away, Huckleberry—what a mess you are always making!' The widow put in a good word for me, but that warn't going to keep off the bad luck, I knowed that well enough. I started out, after breakfast, feeling worried and shaky, and wondering where it was going to fall on me, and what it was going to be. There is ways to keep off some kinds of bad luck, but this wasn't one of them kind; so I never tried to do anything, but just poked along low-spirited and on the watch-out.

I went down the front garden and clumb over the stile, where you go through the high board fence. There was an inch of new snow on the ground, and I seen somebody's tracks. They had come up from the quarry and stood around the stile a while, and then went on around the garden fence. It was funny they hadn't come in, after standing around so. I couldn't make it out. It was very curious, somehow. I was going to follow around, but I stooped down to look at the tracks first. I didn't notice anything at first, but next I did. There was a cross in the left boot-heel made with big nails, to keep off the devil.

I was up in a second and shinning down the hill. I looked over my shoulder every now and then, but I didn't see nobody. I was at Judge Thatcher's as quick as I could get there. He said:

'Why, my boy, you are all out of breath. Did you come for your interest?'

'No, sir', I says. 'Is there some for me?'

'Oh, yes, a half-yearly is in, last night. Over a hundred and fifty dollars. Quite a fortune for you. You better let me invest it along with your six thousand, because if you take it you'll spend it.'

'No, sir,' I says, 'I don't want to spend it. I don't want it at all—nor the six thousand, nuther. I want you to take it; I want to give it to you—the six thousand and all.'

He looked surprised. He couldn't seem to make it out. He says:

'Why, what can you mean, my boy?'

I says, 'Don't you ask me no questions about it, please. You'll take it—won't you?'

He says:

'Well, I'm puzzled. Is something the matter?'

'Please take it,' says I, 'and don't ask me nothing—then I won't have to tell no lies.'

He studied a while, and then he says:

'Oho-o. I think I see. You want to *sell* all your property to me—not give it. That's the correct idea.'

Then he wrote something on a paper and read it over, and says:

'There—you see it says "for a consideration." That means I have bought it of you and paid you for it. Here's a dollar for you. Now, you sign it.'

So I signed it, and left.

Miss Watson's nigger, Jim, had a hair-ball as big as your fist, which had been took out of the fourth stomach of an ox, and he used to do magic with it. He said there was a spirit inside of it, and it knowed everything. So I went to him that night and told him pap was here again, for I found his tracks in the snow. What I wanted to know, was, what he was going to do, and was he going to stay? Jim got out his hair-ball, and said something over it, and then he held it up and dropped it on the floor. It fell pretty solid, and only rolled about an inch. Jim tried it again, and then another time, and it acted just the same. Jim got down on his knees and put his ear against it and listened. But it warn't no use; he said it wouldn't talk. He said sometimes it wouldn't talk without money. I told him I had an old slick counterfeit quarter that warn't no good because the brass showed through the silver a little, and it wouldn't pass nohow, even if the brass didn't show, because it was so slick it felt greasy, and so that would tell on it every time. (I reckoned I wouldn't say nothing about the dollar I got from the judge.) I said it was pretty bad money, but maybe the hair-ball would take it, because maybe it wouldn't know the difference. Jim smelt it, and bit it, and rubbed it, and said he would manage so the hair-ball would think it was good. He said he would split open a raw Irish potato and stick the quarter in between and keep it there all night, and next morning you couldn't see no brass, and it wouldn't feel greasy no more, and so anybody in town would take it in a minute, let alone a hair-ball. Well, I knowed a potato would do that, before, but I had forgot it.

Jim put the quarter under the hair-ball and got down and listened again. This time he said the hair-ball was all right. He said it would tell my whole fortune if I wanted it to. I says, go on. So the hair-ball talked to Jim, and Jim told it to me. He says:

'Yo' ole father doan' know, yit, what he's a-gwyne to do. Sometimes he spec he'll go 'way, en den agin he spec he'll stay. De bes' way is to res' easy en let de ole man take his own way. Dey's two angels hoverin' roun' 'bout him. One uv 'em is white en shiny, en t'other one is black. De white one gits him to go right, a little while, den de black one sail in en bust it all up. A body can't tell, yit, which one gwyne to fetch him at de las'. But you is all right. You gwyne to have considable trouble in yo' life, en considable joy. Sometimes you gwyne to git hurt, en sometimes you gwyne to git sick; but every time you 's gwyne to git well agin. Dey 's two gals flyin' 'bout you in yo' life. One uv 'em 's light en t'other one is dark. One is rich en t'other is po'. You 's gwyne to marry de po' one fust en de rich one by-en-by. You want to keep 'way fum de water as much as you kin, en don't run no resk, 'kase it's down in de bills dat you 's gwyne to git hung.'

When I lit my candle and went up to my room that night, there set pap, his own self!

## *Chapter 5*

### HUCK'S FATHER—THE FOND PARENT—REFORM

I HAD shut the door to. Then I turned around, and there he was. I used to be scared of him all the time, he tanned me so much. I reckoned I was scared now, too; but in a minute I see I was mistaken. That is, after the first jolt, as you may say, when my breath sort of hitched—he being so unexpected; but right away after, I see I warn't scared of him worth bothering about.

He was most fifty, and he looked it. His hair was long and tangled and greasy, and hung down, and you could see his eyes shining through like he was behind vines. It was all black, no grey; so was his long, mixed-up whiskers. There warn't no colour in his face, where his face showed; it was white; not like another man's white, but a white to make a body sick, a white to make a body's flesh crawl—a tree-toad white, a fish-belly white. As for his clothes—just rags, that was all. He had one ankle resting on t'other knee; the boot on that foot was busted, and two of his toes stuck through, and he worked them now and then. His hat was laying on the floor; an old black slouch with the top caved in, like a lid.

I stood a-looking at him; he set there a-looking at me, with his chair tilted back a little. I set the candle down. I noticed the window was up; so he had clumb in by the shed. He kept a-looking me all over. By-and-by he says:

'Starchy clothes—very. You think you're a good deal of a big-bug, *don't* you?'

'Maybe I am, maybe I ain't,' I says.

'Don't you give me none o' your lip,' says he. 'You've put on considerble many frills since I been away. I'll take you down a peg before I get done with you. You're educated, too, they say; can read and write. You think you're better'n your father, now, don't you, because he can't? *I*'ll take it out of you. Who told you you might meddle with such hifalut'n foolishness, hey?—who told you you could?'

'The widow. She told me.'

'The widow, hey?—and who told the widow she could put in her shovel about a thing that ain't none of her business?'

'Nobody never told her.'

'Well, I'll learn her how to meddle. And looky here—you drop that school, you hear? I'll learn people to bring up a boy to put on airs over his own father and let on to be better'n what *he* is. You lemme catch you fooling around that school again, you hear? Your mother couldn't read, and she couldn't write, nuther, before she died. None of the family couldn't, before *they* died. *I* can't; and here you're a-swelling yourself up like this. I ain't the man to stand it—you hear? Say—lemme hear you read.'

I took up a book and begun something about General Washington and the wars. When I'd read about a half-minute, he fetched the book a whack with his hand and knocked it across the house. He says:

'It's so. You can do it. I had my doubts when you told me. Now looky here; you stop that putting on frills. I won't have it. I'll lay for you, my smarty; and if I catch you about that school I'll tan you good. First you know you'll get religion, too. I never see such a son.'

He took up a little blue and yaller picture of some cows and a boy, and says:

'What's this?'

'It's something they give me for learning my lessons good.'

He tore it up, and says:

'I'll give you something better—I'll give you a cowhide.'

He set there a-mumbling and a-growling a minute, and then he says:

'*Ain't* you a sweet-scented dandy, though? A bed; and bedclothes; and a look'n-glass; and a piece of carpet on the floor—and your own father got to sleep with the hogs in the tanyard. I never see such a son. I bet I'll take some o' these frills out o' you before I'm done with you. Why, there ain't no end to your airs—they say you're rich. Hey?—how's that?'

'They lie—that's how.'

'Looky here—mind how you talk to me; I'm a-standing about all I can stand, now—so don't gimme no sass. I've been in town two days, and I hain't heard nothing but about you bein' rich. I heard about it away down the river, too. That's why I come. You git me that money to-morrow—I want it.'

'I hain't got no money.'

'It's a lie. Judge Thatcher's got it. You git it. I want it.'

'I hain't got no money, I tell you. You ask Judge Thatcher; he'll tell you the same.'

'All right. I'll ask him; and I'll make him pungle, too, or I'll know the reason why. Say—how much you got in your pocket? I want it.'

'I hain't got only a dollar, and I want that to——'

'It don't make no difference what you want it for—you just shell it out.'

He took it and bit it to see if it was good, and then he said he was going down town to get some whisky; said he hadn't had a drink all day. When he had got out on the shed, he put his head in again, and cussed me for putting on frills and trying to be better than him; and when I reckoned he was gone, he came back and put his head in again, and told me to mind about that school, because he was going to lay for me and lick me if I didn't drop that.

Next day he was drunk, and he went to Judge Thatcher's and bully-ragged him and tried to make him give up the money, but he couldn't, and then he swore he'd make the law force him.

The judge and the widow went to law to get the court to take me away from him and let one of them be my guardian; but it was a new judge that had just come, and he didn't know the old man; so he said courts mustn't interfere and separate families if they could help it; said he'd druther not take a child away from its father. So Judge Thatcher and the widow had to quit on the business.

That pleased the old man till he couldn't rest. He said he'd cowhide me till I was black and blue if I didn't raise some money for him. I borrowed three dollars from Judge Thatcher, and pap took it and got drunk and went a-blowing around and cussing and whooping and carrying on; and he kept it up all over town, with a tin pan, till most midnight; then they jailed him, and next day they had him before court, and jailed him again for a week. But he said *he* was satisfied; said he was boss of his son, and he'd make it warm for *him*.

When he got out the new judge said he was agoing to make a man of him. So he took him to his own house, and dressed him up clean and nice, and had him to breakfast and dinner and supper with the family, and was just old pie to him, so to speak. And after supper he talked to him about temperance and such things till the old man cried, and said he'd been a fool, and fooled away his life; but now he was agoing to turn over a new leaf and be a man nobody wouldn't be ashamed of, and he hoped the judge would help him and not look down on him. The judge said he could hug him for them words; so *he* cried, and his wife she cried again; pap said he'd been a man that had always been misunderstood before, and the judge said he believed it. The old man said that what a man wanted that was down, was sympathy; and the judge said it was so; so they cried again. And when it was bedtime, the old man rose up and held out his hand, and says:

'Look at it, gentlemen, and ladies all; take ahold of it; shake it. There's a hand that was the hand of a hog; but it ain't so no more; it's the hand of a man that 's started in on a new life, and 'll die before he'll go back. You mark them words—don't forget I said them. It's a clean hand now; shake it—don't be afeard.'

So they shook it, one after the other, all around, and cried. The judge's wife she kissed it. Then the old man he signed a pledge—made his mark. The judge said it was the holiest time on record, or something like that. Then they tucked the old man into a beautiful room, which was the spare room, and in the night sometime he got powerful thirsty and clumb out on to the porch-roof and slid down a stanchion and traded his new coat for a jug of forty-rod, and clumb back again and had a good old time; and towards daylight he crawled out again, drunk as a fiddler, and rolled off the porch and broke his left arm in two places and was most froze to death when somebody found him after sun-up. And when they come to look at that spare room, they had to take soundings before they could navigate it.

The judge he felt kind of sore. He said he reckoned a body could reform the old man with a shot-gun, maybe, but he didn't know no other way.

## *Chapter 6*

### HE WENT FOR JUDGE THATCHER—HUCK DECIDES TO LEAVE—THINKING IT OVER—POLITICAL ECONOMY—THRASHING AROUND

WELL, pretty soon the old man was up and around again, and then he went for Judge Thatcher in the courts to make him give up that money, and he went for me, too, for not stopping school. He catched me a couple of times and thrashed me, but I went to school just the same, and dodged him or out-run him most of the time. I didn't want to go to school much, before, but I reckoned I'd go now to spite pap. That law trial was a slow business; appeared like they warn't ever going to get started on it; so every now and then I'd borrow two or three dollars off of the judge for him, to keep from getting a cowhiding. Every time he got money he got drunk; and every time he got drunk he raised Cain around town; and every time he raised Cain he got jailed. He was just suited—this kind of thing was right in his line.

He got to hanging around the widow's too much, and so she told him at last, that if he didn't quit using around there she would make trouble for him. Well, *wasn't* he mad? He said he would show who was Huck Finn's boss. So he watched out for me one day in the spring, and catched me, and took me up the river about three mile, in a skiff, and crossed over to the Illinois shore where it was woody and there warn't no houses but an old log hut in a place where the timber was so thick you couldn't find it if you didn't know where it was.

He kept me with him all the time, and I never got a chance to run off. We lived in that old cabin, and he always locked the door and put the key under his head, nights. He had a gun which he had stole, I reckon, and we fished and hunted, and that was what we lived on. Every little while he locked me in and went down to the store, three miles to the ferry, and traded fish and game for whisky and fetched it home and got drunk and had a good time, and licked me. The widow she found out where I was by-and-by, and she sent a man over to try to get hold of me, but pap drove him off with the gun, and it warn't long after that till I was used to being where I was, and liked it, all but the cowhide part.

It was kind of lazy and jolly, laying off comfortable all day, smoking and fishing, and no books nor study. Two months or more run along, and my clothes got to be all rags and dirt, and I didn't see how I'd ever got to like it so well at the widow's, where you had to wash, and eat on a plate, and comb up, and go to bed and get up regular, and be for ever bothering over a book and have old Miss Watson pecking at you all the time. I didn't want to go back no more. I had stopped cussing, because the widow didn't like it; but now I took to it again because pap hadn't no objections. It was pretty good times up in the woods there, take it all around.

But by-and-by pap got too handy with his hick'ry, and I couldn't stand it. I was all over welts. He got to going away so much, too, and locking me in. Once he locked me in and was gone three days. It was dreadful lonesome. I judged he had got drowned and I wasn't ever going to get out any more. I was scared. I made up my mind I would fix up some way to leave there. I had tried to get out of that cabin many a time, but I couldn't find no way. There warn't a window to it big enough for a dog to get through. I couldn't get up the chimbly, it was too narrow. The door was thick solid oak slabs. Pap was pretty careful not to leave a knife or anything in the cabin when he was away; I reckon I had hunted the place over as much as a hundred times; well, I was most all the time at it, because it was about the only way to put in the time. But this time I found something at last; I found an old rusty wood-saw without any handle; it was laid in between a rafter and the clapboards of the roof. I greased it up and went to work. There was an old horse-blanket nailed against the logs at the far end of the cabin behind the table, to keep the wind from blowing through the chinks and putting the candle out. I got under the table and raised the blanket and went to work to saw a section of the big bottom log out, big enough to let me through. Well, it was a good long job, but I was getting towards the end of it when I heard pap's gun in the woods. I got rid of the signs of my work, and dropped the blanket and hid my saw, and pretty soon pap come in.

Pap warn't in a good humour—so he was his natural self. He said he was down to town, and everything was going wrong. His lawyer said he reckoned he would win his lawsuit and get the money, if they ever got started on the trial; but then there was ways to put it off a long time, and Judge Thatcher knowed how to do it. And he said people allowed there'd be another trial to get me away from him and give me to the widow for my guardian, and they guessed it would win, this time. This shook me up considerable, because I didn't want to go back to the widow's any more and be so cramped up, and sivilized, as they called it. Then the old man got to cussing, and cussed everything and everybody he could think of, and then cussed them all over again to make sure he hadn't skipped any, and after that he polished off with a kind of a general cuss all round, including a considerable parcel of people which he didn't know the names of, and so called them what's-his-name, when he got to them, and went right along with his cussing.

He said he would like to see the widow get me. He said he would watch out, and if they tried to come any such game on him he knowed of a place six or seven mile off, to stow me in, where they might hunt till they dropped and they couldn't find me. That made me pretty uneasy again, but only for a minute; I reckoned I wouldn't stay on hand till he got that chance.

The old man made me go to the skiff and fetch the things he had got. There was a fifty-pound sack of corn-meal, and a side of bacon, ammunition, and a four-gallon jug of whisky, and an old book and two newspapers for wadding, besides some tow. I toted up a load, and went back and set down on the bow of the skiff to rest. I thought it all over, and I reckoned I would walk off with the gun and some lines, and take to the woods when I run away. I guessed I wouldn't stay in one place, but just tramp right across the country, mostly night-times, and hunt and fish to keep alive, and so get so far away that the old man nor the widow couldn't ever find me any more. I judged I would saw out and leave that night if pap got drunk enough, and I reckoned he would. I got so full of it I didn't notice how long I was staying, till the old man hollered and asked me whether I was asleep or drownded.

I got the things all up to the cabin, and then it was about dark. While I was cooking supper the old man took a swig or two and got sort of warmed up, and went to ripping again. He had been drunk over in town, and laid in the gutter all night, and he was a sight to look at. A body would a thought he was Adam, he was just all mud. Whenever his liquor begun to work, he most always went for the govment. This time he says:

'Call this a govment! why, just look at it and see what it's like.

Here's the law a-standing ready to take a man's son away from him—a man's own son, which he has had all the trouble and all the anxiety and all the expense of raising. Yes, just as that man has got that son raised at last, and ready to go to work and begin to do suthin' for *him* and give him a rest, the law up and goes for him. And they call *that* govment! That ain't all, nuther. The law backs that old Judge Thatcher up and helps him to keep me out o' my property. Here's what the law does. The law takes a man worth six thousand dollars and upards, and jams him into an old trap of a cabin like this, and lets him go round in clothes that ain't fitten for a hog. They call that govment! A man can't get his rights in a govment like this. Sometimes I've a mighty notion to just leave the country for good and all. Yes, and I *told* 'em so; I told old Thatcher so to his face. Lots of 'em heard me, and can tell what I said. Says I, for two cents I'd leave the blamed country and never come anear it agin. Them's the very words. I says, look at my hat—if you call it a hat—but the lid raises up and the rest of it goes down till it's below my chin, and then it ain't rightly a hat at all, but more like my head was shoved up through a jint o' stove-pipe. Look at it, says I—such a hat for me to wear—one of the wealthiest men in this town, if I could git my rights.

'Oh, yes, this is a wonderful govment, wonderful. Why, looky here. There was a free nigger there, from Ohio; a mulatter, most as white as a white man. He had the whitest shirt on you ever see, too, and the shiniest hat; and there ain't a man in that town that's got as fine clothes as what he had; and he had a gold watch and chain, and a silver-headed cane—the awfullest old grey-headed nabob in the State. And what do you think? they said he was a p'fessor in a college, and could talk all kinds of languages, and knowed everything. And that ain't the wust. They said he could *vote*, when he was at home. Well, that let me out. Thinks I, what is the country a-coming to? It was 'lection day, and I was just about to go and vote, myself, if I warn't too drunk to get there; but when they told me there was a State in this country where they'd let that nigger vote, I drawed out. I says I'll never vote agin. Them's the very words I said; they all heard me; and the country may rot for all me—I'll never vote agin as long as I live. And to see the cool way of that nigger—why, he wouldn't a give me the road if I hadn't shoved him out o' the way. I says to the people, why ain't this nigger put up at auction and sold?—that's what I want to know. And what do you reckon they said? Why, they said he couldn't be sold till he'd been in the State six months, and he hadn't been there that long yet. There, now—that's a specimen. They call that a govment that can't sell a free nigger till he's been in the State six months. Here's a govment that calls itself a govment, and lets on to be a govment, and thinks it is a govment, and yet's got to set stock-still for six whole months before it can take ahold of a prowling, thieving, infernal, white-shirted free nigger, and——'

Pap was agoing on so, he never noticed where his old limber legs was taking him to, so he went head over heels over the tub of salt pork, and barked both shins, and the rest of his speech was all the hottest kind of language—mostly hove at the nigger and the govment, though he give the tub some, too, all along, here and there. He hopped around the cabin considerable, first on one leg and then on the other, holding first one shin and then the other one, and at last he let out with his left foot all of a sudden and fetched the tub a rattling kick. But it warn't good judgment, because that was the boot that had a couple of his toes leaking out of the front end of it; so now he raised a howl that fairly made a body's hair raise, and down he went in the dirt, and rolled there, and held his toes; and the cussing he done then laid over anything he had ever done previous. He said so his own self, afterwards. He had heard old Sowberry Hagan in his best days, and he said it laid over him, too; but I reckon that was sort of piling it on, maybe.

After supper pap took the jug, and said he had enough whisky there for two drunks and one delirium tremens. That was always his word. I judged he would be blind drunk in about an hour, and then I would steal the key, or saw myself out, one or t'other. He drank and drank, and tumbled down on his blankets, by-and-by; but luck didn't run my way. He didn't go sound asleep, but was uneasy. He groaned, and moaned, and thrashed around this way and that, for a long time. At last I got so sleepy I couldn't keep my eyes open, all I could do, and so before I knowed what I was about I was sound asleep, and the candle burning.

I don't know how long I was asleep, but all of a sudden there was an awful scream and I was up. There was pap, looking wild and skipping around every which way and yelling about snakes. He said they was crawling up his legs; and then he would give a jump and scream, and say one had bit him on the cheek—but I couldn't see no snakes. He started and run round and round the cabin hollering 'Take him off! take him off! he's biting me on the neck!' I never see a man look so wild in the eyes. Pretty soon he was all fagged out, and fell down panting; then he rolled over and over, wonderful fast, kicking things every which way, and striking and grabbing at the air with his hands, and screaming, and saying there was devils ahold of him. He wore out, by-and-by, and laid still a while, moaning. Then he laid stiller, and didn't make a sound. I could hear the owls and the wolves, away off in the woods, and it seemed terrible still. He was laying over by the corner. By-and-by he raised up, part way, and listened, with his head to one side. He says very low:

'Tramp—tramp—tramp; that's the dead; tramp—tramp—tramp; they're coming after me; but I won't go——Oh, they're here! don't touch me—don't! hands off—they're cold; let go—— Oh, let a poor devil alone!'

Then he went down on all fours and crawled off begging them to let him alone, and he rolled himself up in his blanket and wallowed in under the old pine table, still a-begging; and then he went to crying. I could hear him through the blanket.

By-and-by he rolled out and jumped up on his feet, looking wild, and he see me and went for me. He chased me round and round the place with a clasp-knife, calling me the Angel of Death, and saying he would kill me, and then I couldn't come for him no more. I begged, and told him I was only Huck, but he laughed *such* a screechy laugh, and roared and cussed, and kept on chasing me up. Once when I turned short and dodged under his arm he made a grab and got me by the jacket between my shoulders, and I thought I was gone; but I slid out of the jacket quick as lightning, and saved myself. Pretty soon he was all tired out, and dropped down with his back against the door, and said he would rest a minute and then kill me. He put his knife under him, and said he would sleep and get strong, and then he would see who was who.

So he dozed off, pretty soon. By-and-by I got the old split-bottom chair and clumb up, as easy as I could, not to make any noise, and got down the gun. I slipped the ramrod down it to make sure it was loaded, and then I laid it across the turnip barrel, pointing towards pap, and set down behind it to wait for him to stir. And how slow and still the time did drag along.

## *Chapter 7*

LAYING FOR HIM—LOCKED IN THE CABIN—PREPARING TO START—SINKING THE BODY—PROJECTING A PLAN—RESTING

'GIT up! what you 'bout!'

I opened my eyes and looked around, trying to make out where I was. It was after sun-up, and I had been sound asleep. Pap was standing over me, looking sour—and sick, too. He says:

'What you doin' with this gun?'

I judged he didn't know nothing about what he had been doing, so I says:

'Somebody tried to get in, so I was laying for him.'

'Why didn't you roust me out?'

'Well, I tried to, but I couldn't; I couldn't budge you.'

'Well, all right. Don't stand there palavering all day, but out with you and see if there's a fish on the lines for breakfast. I'll be along in a minute.'

He unlocked the door and I cleared out, up the river bank. I noticed some pieces of limbs and such things floating down, and a sprinkling of bark; so I knowed the river had begun to rise. I reckoned I would have great times, now, if I was over at the town. The June rise used to be always luck for me; because as soon as that rise begins, here comes cord-wood floating down, and pieces of log rafts—sometimes a dozen logs together; so all you have to do is to catch them and sell them to the wood-yards and the saw-mill.

I went along up the bank with one eye out for pap and t'other one out for what the rise might fetch along. Well, all at once, here comes a canoe; just a beauty, too, about thirteen or fourteen foot long, riding high like a duck. I shot head first off of the bank, like a frog, clothes and all on, and struck out for the canoe. I just expected there'd be somebody laying down in it, because people often done that to fool folks, and when a chap had pulled a skiff out most to it they'd raise up and laugh at him. But it warn't so this time. It was a drift-canoe, sure enough, and I clumb in and paddled her ashore. Thinks I, the old man will be glad when he sees this—she's worth ten dollars. But when I got to shore pap wasn't in sight yet, and as I was running her into a little creek like a gully, all hung over with vines and willows, I struck another idea; I judged I'd hide her good, and then, stead of taking to the woods when I run off, I'd go down the river about fifty mile and camp in one place for good, and not have such a rough time tramping on foot.

It was pretty close to the shanty, and I thought I heard the old man coming, all the time; but I got her hid; and then I out and looked around a bunch of willows, and there was the old man down the path apiece just drawing a bead on a bird with his gun. So he hadn't seen anything.

When he got along, I was hard at it taking up a 'trot' line. He abused me a little for being so slow, but I told him I fell in the river and that was what made me so long. I knowed he would see I was wet, and then he would be asking questions. We got five cat-fish off of the lines and went home.

While we laid off, after breakfast, to sleep up, both of us being about wore out, I got to thinking that if I could fix up some way to keep pap and the widow from trying to follow me, it would be a certainer thing than trusting to luck to get far enough off before they missed me; you see, all kinds of things might happen. Well, I didn't see no way for a while, but by-and-by pap raised up a minute, to drink another barrel of water, and he says:

'Another time a man comes a-prowling round here, you roust me out, you hear? That man warn't here for no good. I'd a shot him. Next time, you roust me out, you hear?'

Then he dropped down and went to sleep again—but what he had been saying give me the very idea I wanted. I says to myself, I can fix it now so nobody won't think of following me.

About twelve o'clock we turned out and went along up the bank. The river was coming up pretty fast, and lots of drift-wood going by on the rise. By-and-by, along comes part of a log raft—nine logs fast together. We went out with the skiff and towed it ashore. Then we had dinner. Anybody but pap would a waited and seen the day through, so as to catch more stuff; but that warn't pap's style. Nine logs was enough for one time; he must shove right over to town and sell. So he locked me in and took the skiff and started off towing the raft about half-past three. I judged he wouldn't come back that night. I waited till I reckoned he had got a good start, then I out with my saw and went to work on that log again. Before he was t'other side of the river I was out of the hole; him and his raft was just a speck on the water away off yonder.

I took the sack of corn-meal and took it to where the canoe was hid, and shoved the vines and branches apart and put it in; then I done the same with the side of bacon; then the whisky jug; I took all the coffee and sugar there was, and all the ammunition; I took the wadding; I took the bucket and gourd; I took a dipper and a tin cup, and my old saw and two blankets, and the skillet and the coffee-pot. I took fish-lines and matches and other things—everything that was worth a cent. I cleaned out the place. I wanted an axe, but there wasn't any, only the one out at the wood pile, and I knowed why I was going to leave that. I fetched out the gun, and now I was done.

I had wore the ground a good deal, crawling out of the hole and dragging out so many things. So I fixed that as good as I could from the outside by scattering dust on the place, which covered up the smoothness and the sawdust. Then I fixed the piece of log back into its place, and put two rocks under it and one against it to hold it there, —for it was bent up at that place, and didn't quite touch ground. If you stood four or five foot away and didn't know it was sawed, you wouldn't ever notice it; and besides, this was the back of the cabin and it warn't likely anybody would go fooling around there.

It was all grass clear to the canoe; so I hadn't left a track. I followed around to see. I stood on the bank and looked out over the river. All safe. So I took the gun and went up a piece into the woods and was hunting around for some birds, when I see a wild pig; hogs soon went wild in them bottoms after they had got away from the prairie farms. I shot this fellow and took him into camp.

I took the axe and smashed in the door. I beat it and hacked it considerable, a-doing it. I fetched the pig in and took him back nearly to the table and hacked into his throat with the axe, and laid him down on the ground to bleed—I say ground, because it *was* ground—hard packed, and no boards. Well, next I took an old sack and put a lot of big rocks in it,—all I could drag—and I started it from the pig and dragged it to the door and through the woods down to the river and dumped it in, and down it sunk, out of sight. You could easy see that something had been dragged over the ground. I did wish Tom Sawyer was there, I knowed he would take an interest in this kind of business, and throw in the fancy touches. Nobody could spread himself like Tom Sawyer in such a thing as that.

Well, last I pulled out some of my hair, and bloodied the axe good, and stuck it on the back side, and slung the axe in the corner. Then I took up the pig and held him to my breast with my jacket (so he couldn't drip) till I got a good piece below the house and then dumped him into the river. Now I thought of something else. So I went and got the bag of meal and my old saw out of the canoe and fetched them to the house. I took the bag to where it used to stand, and ripped a hole in the bottom of it with the saw, for there warn't no knives and forks on the place—pap done everything with his clasp-knife, about the cooking. Then I carried the sack about a hundred yards across the grass and through the willows east of the house, to a shallow lake that was five miles wide and full of rushes—and ducks too, you might say, in the season. There was a slough or a creek leading out of it on the other side, that went miles away, I don't know where, but it didn't go to the river. The meal sifted out and made a little track all the way to the lake. I dropped pap's whetstone there too, so as to look like it had been done by accident. Then I tied up the rip in the meal-sack with a string, so it wouldn't leak no more, and took it and my saw to the canoe again.

It was about dark, now; so I dropped the canoe down the river under some willows that hung over the bank, and waited for the moon to rise. I made fast to a willow; then I took a bite to eat, and by-and-by laid down in the canoe to smoke a pipe and lay out a plan. I says to myself, they'll follow the track of that sackful of rocks to the shore and then drag the river for me. And they'll follow that meal-track to the lake and go browsing down the creek that leads out of it to find the robbers that killed me and took the things. They won't ever hunt the river for anything but my dead carcass. They'll soon get tired of that, and won't bother no more about me. All right; I can stop anywhere I want to. Jackson's Island is good enough for me; I know that island pretty well, and nobody ever comes there. And then I can paddle over to town, nights, and slink around and pick up things I want. Jackson's Island 's the place.

I was pretty tired, and the first thing I knowed, I was asleep. When I woke up I didn't know where I was, for a minute. I set up and looked around, a little scared. Then I remembered. The river looked miles and miles across. The moon was so bright I could a counted the drift logs that went a-slipping along, black and still, hundreds of yards out from shore. Everything was dead quiet, and it looked late, and *smelt* late. You know what I mean—I don't know the words to put it in.

I took a good gap and a stretch, and was just going to unhitch and start, when I heard a sound away over the water. I listened. Pretty soon I made it out. It was that dull kind of a regular sound that comes from oars working in rowlocks when it's a still night. I peeped out through the willow branches, and there it was—a skiff, away across the water. I couldn't tell how many was in it. It kept a-coming, and when it was abreast of me I see there warn't but one man in it. Thinks I, maybe it's pap, though I warn't expecting him. He dropped below me, with the current, and by-and-by he come a-swinging up-shore in the easy water, and he went by so close I could a reached out the gun and touched him. Well, it *was* pap, sure enough—and sober, too, by the way he laid to his oars.

I didn't lose no time. The next minute I was a-spinning down-stream soft but quick in the shade of the bank. I made two mile and a half, and then struck out a quarter of a mile or more towards the middle of the river, because pretty soon I would be passing the ferry landing and people might see me and hail me. I got out amongst the drift-wood and then laid down in the bottom of the canoe and let her float. I laid there and had a good rest and a smoke out of my pipe, looking away into the sky, not a cloud in it. The sky looks ever so deep when you lay down on your back in the moonshine; I never knowed it before. And how far a body can hear on the water such nights! I heard people talking at the ferry landing. I heard what they said, too, every word of it. One man said it was getting towards the long days and the short nights, now. T'other one said *this* warn't one of the short ones, he reckoned—and then they laughed, and he said it over again, and they laughed again; then they waked up another fellow and told him, and laughed, but he didn't laugh; he ripped out something brisk and said let him alone. The first fellow said he 'lowed to tell it to his old woman —she would think it was pretty good; but he said that warn't nothing to some things he had said in his time. I heard one man say it was nearly three o'clock, and he hoped daylight wouldn't wait more than about a week longer. After that, the talk got further and further away, and I couldn't make out the words any more, but I could hear the mumble; and now and then a laugh, too, but it seemed a long ways off.

I was away below the ferry now. I rose up and there was Jackson's Island, about two mile and a half down-stream, heavy-timbered and standing up out of the middle of the river, big and dark and solid, like a steamboat without any lights. There warn't any signs of the bar at the head—it was all under water now.

It didn't take me long to get there. I shot past the head at a ripping rate, the current was so swift, and then I got into the dead water and landed on the side towards the Illinois shore. I run the canoe into a deep dent in the bank that I knowed about; I had to part the willow branches to get in; and when I made fast nobody could a seen the canoe from the outside.

I went up and set down on a log at the head of the island and looked out on the big river and the black drift-wood, and away over to the town, three mile away, where there was three or four lights twinkling. A monstrous big lumber raft was about a mile up-stream, coming along down, with a lantern in the middle of it. I watched it come creeping down, and when it was most abreast of where I stood I heard a man say, 'Stern oars, there! heave her head to stabboard!' I heard that just as plain as if the man was by my side.

There was a little grey in the sky, now; so I stepped into the woods and laid down for a nap before breakfast.

## *Chapter 8*

SLEEPING IN THE WOODS—RAISING THE DEAD—ON THE WATCH!—EXPLORING THE ISLAND—A PROFITLESS SLEEP—FINDING JIM—JIM'S ESCAPE—SIGNS—'DAT ONE-LAIGGED NIGGER'—BALUM

THE sun was up so high when I waked, that I judged it was after eight o'clock. I laid there in the grass and the cool shade, thinking about things and feeling rested and ruther comfortable and satisfied. I could see the sun out at one or two holes, but mostly it was big trees all about, and gloomy in there amongst them. There was freckled places on the ground where the light sifted down through the leaves, and the freckled places swapped about a little, showing there was a little breeze up there. A couple of squirrels set on a limb and jabbered at me very friendly.

I was powerful lazy and comfortable—didn't want to get up and cook breakfast. Well, I was dozing off again, when I thinks I hears a deep sound of 'boom!' away up the river. I rouses up and rests on my elbow and listens; pretty soon I hears it again. I hopped up and went and looked out at a hole in the leaves, and I see a bunch of smoke laying on the water a long ways up—about abreast the ferry. And there was the ferry-boat full of people, floating along down. I knowed what was the matter, now. 'Boom!' I see the white smoke squirt out of the ferry-boat's side. You see, they was firing cannon over the water, trying to make my carcass come to the top.

I was pretty hungry, but it warn't going to do for me to start a fire, because they might see the smoke. So I set there and watched the cannon-smoke and listened to the boom. The river was a mile wide, there, and it always looks pretty on a summer morning—so I was having a good enough time seeing them hunt for my remainders, if I only had a bite to eat. Well, then I happened to think how they always put quicksilver in loaves of bread and float them off because they always go right to the drownded carcass and stop there. So says I, I'll keep a look-out, and if any of them's floating around after me, I'll give them a show. I changed to the Illinois edge of the island to see what luck I could have, and I warn't disappointed. A big double loaf come along, and I most got it, with a long stick, but my foot slipped and she floated out further. Of course I was where the current set in the closest to the shore—I knowed enough for that. But by-and-by along comes another one, and this time I won. I took out the plug and shook out the little dab of quicksilver, and set my teeth in. It was 'baker's bread'—what the quality eat—none of your low-down corn-pone.

I got a good place amongst the leaves, and set there on a log, munching the bread and watching the ferry-boat, and very well satisfied. And then something struck me. I says, now I reckon the widow or the parson or somebody prayed that this bread would find me, and here it has gone and done it. So there ain't no doubt but there is something in that thing. That is, there's something in it when a body like the widow or the parson prays, but it don't work for me, and I reckon it don't work for only just the right kind.

I lit a pipe and had a good long smoke and went on watching. The ferry-boat was floating with the current, and I allowed I'd have a chance to see who was aboard when she come along, because she would come in close, where the bread did. When she'd got pretty well along down towards me, I put out my pipe and went to where I fished out the bread, and laid down behind a log on the bank in a little open place. Where the log forked I could peep through.

By-and-by she come along, and she drifted in so close that they could a run out a plank and walked ashore. Most everybody was on the boat. Pap, and Judge Thatcher, and Bessie Thatcher, and Jo Harper, and Tom Sawyer, and his old Aunt Polly, and Sid and Mary, and plenty more. Everybody was talking about the murder, but the captain broke in and says:

'Look sharp, now; the current sets in the closest here, and maybe he's washed ashore and got tangled amongst the brush at the water's edge. I hope so, anyway.'

I didn't hope so. They all crowded up and leaned over the rails, nearly in my face, and kept still, watching with all their might. I could see them first-rate, but they couldn't see me. Then the captain sung out:

'Stand away!' and the cannon let off such a blast right before me that it made me deef with the noise and pretty near blind with the smoke, and I judged I was gone. If they'd a had some bullets in, I reckon they'd a got the corpse they was after. Well, I see I warn't hurt, thanks to goodness. The boat floated on and went out of sight around the shoulder of the island. I could hear the booming, now and then, further and further off, and by-and-by after an hour, I didn't hear it no more. The island was three mile long. I judged they had got to the foot, and was giving it up. But they didn't yet awhile. They turned around the foot of the island and started up the channel on the Missouri side, under steam, and booming once in a while as they went. I crossed over to that side and watched them. When they got abreast the head of the island they quit shooting and dropped over to the Missouri shore and went home to the town.

I knowed I was all right now. Nobody else would come a-hunting after me. I got my traps out of the canoe and made me a nice camp in the thick woods. I made a kind of a tent out of my blankets to put my things under so the rain couldn't get at them. I catched a cat-fish and haggled him open with my saw, and towards sundown I started my camp-fire and had supper. Then I set out a line to catch some fish for breakfast.

When it was dark I set by my camp-fire smoking, and feeling pretty satisfied; but by-and-by it got sort of lonesome, and so I went and set on the bank and listened to the currents washing along, and counted the stars and drift-logs and rafts that come down, and then went to bed; there ain't no better way to put in time when you are lonesome; you can't stay so, you soon get over it.

And so for three days and nights. No difference—just the same thing. But the next day I went exploring around down through the island. I was boss of it; it all belonged to me, so to say, and I wanted to know all about it; but mainly I wanted to put in the time. I found plenty strawberries, ripe and prime; and green summer-grapes, and green razberries; and the green blackberries was just beginning to show. They would all come handy by-and-by, I judged.

Well, I went fooling along in the deep woods till I judged I warn't far from the foot of the island. I had my gun along, but I hadn't shot nothing; it was for protection; thought I would kill some game nigh home. About this time I mighty near stepped on a good-sized snake, and it went sliding off through the grass and flowers, and I after it, trying to get a shot at it. I clipped along, and all of a sudden I bounded right on to the ashes of a camp-fire that was still smoking.

My heart jumped up amongst my lungs. I never waited for to look further, but uncocked my gun and went sneaking back on my tip-toes as fast as ever I could. Every now and then I stopped a second, amongst the thick leaves, and listened; but my breath come so hard I couldn't hear nothing else. I slunk along another piece further, then listened again; and so on, and so on; if I see a stump, I took it for a man; if I trod on a stick and broke it, it made me feel like a person had cut one of my breaths in two and I only got half, and the short half, too.

When I got to camp I warn't feeling very brash, there warn't much sand in my craw; but I says, this ain't no time to be fooling around. So I got all my traps into my canoe again so as to have them out of sight, and I put out the fire and scattered the ashes around to look like an old last year's camp, and then clumb a tree.

I reckon I was up in the tree two hours; but I didn't see nothing, I didn't hear nothing—I only *thought* I heard and seen as much as a thousand things. Well, I couldn't stay up there for ever; so at last I got down, but I kept in the thick woods and on the look-out all the time. All I could get to eat was berries and what was left over from breakfast.

By the time it was night I was pretty hungry. So when it was good and dark, I slid out from shore before moonrise and paddled over to the Illinois bank—about a quarter of a mile. I went out in the woods and cooked a supper, and I had about made up my mind I would stay there all night, when I hear a *plunkety-plunk*, *plunkety-plunk*, and says to myself, horses coming; and next I hear people's voices. I got everything into the canoe as quick as I could, and then went creeping through the woods to see what I could find out. I hadn't got far when I hear a man say:

'We better camp here, if we can find a good place; the horses is about beat out. Let's look around.'

I didn't wait, but shoved out and paddled away easy. I tied up in the old place, and reckoned I would sleep in the canoe.

I didn't sleep much. I couldn't, somehow, for thinking. And every time I waked up I thought somebody had me by the neck. So the sleep didn't do me no good. By-and-by I says to myself, I can't live this way; I'm agoing to find out who it is that's here on the island with me; I'll find it out or bust. Well, I felt better, right off.

So I took my paddle and slid out from shore just a step or two, and then let the canoe drop along down amongst the shadows. The moon was shining, and outside of the shadows it made it most as light as day. I poked along well on to an hour, everything still as rocks and sound asleep. Well, by this time I was most down to the foot of the island. A little ripply, cool breeze begun to blow, and that was as good as saying the night was about done. I give her a turn with the paddle and brung her nose to shore; then I got my gun and slipped out and into the edge of the woods. I set down there on a log and looked out through the leaves. I see the moon go off watch and the darkness begin to blanket the river. But in a little while I see a pale streak over the tree-tops, and knowed the day was coming. So I took my gun and slipped off towards where I had run across that camp-fire, stopping every minute or two to listen. But I hadn't no luck, somehow; I couldn't seem to find the place. But by-and-by, sure enough, I catched a glimpse of fire, away through the trees. I went for it, cautious and slow. By-and-by I was close enough to have a look, and there laid a man on the ground. It most give me the fan-tods. He had a blanket around his head, and his head was nearly in the fire. I set there behind a clump of bushes, in about six foot of him, and kept my eyes on him steady. It was getting grey daylight, now. Pretty soon he gapped, and stretched himself, and hove off the blanket, and it was Miss Watson's Jim! I bet I was glad to see him. I says:

'Hello, Jim!' and skipped out.

He bounced up and stared at me wild. Then he drops down on his knees, and puts his hands together and says:

'Doan' hurt me—don't! I hain't ever done no harm to a ghos'. I awluz liked dead people, en done all I could for 'em. You go en git in de river agin, whah you b'longs, en doan' do 'nuffn to Ole Jim, 'at 'uz awluz yo' fren'.'

Well, I warn't long making him understand I warn't dead. I was ever so glad to see Jim. I warn't lonesome, now. I told him I warn't afraid of *him* telling the people where I was. I talked along, but he only set there and looked at me; never said nothing. Then I says:

'It's good daylight. Le's get breakfast. Make up your camp-fire good.'

'What's de use er makin' up de camp-fire to cook strawbries en sich truck? But you got a gun, hain't you? Den we kin git sumfn' better den strawbries.'

'Strawberries and such truck,' I says. 'Is that what you live on?'

'I couldn' git nuffn' else,' he says.

'Why, how long you been on the island, Jim?'

'I come heah de night arter you's killed.'

'What, all that time?'

'Yes-indeedy.'

'And ain't you had nothing but that kind of rubbage to eat?'

'No, sah—nuffn' else.'

'Well, you must be most starved, ain't you?'

'I reck'n I could eat a hoss. I think I could. How long you ben on de islan'?'

'Since the night I got killed.'

'No! W'y, what has you lived on? But you got a gun? Oh, yes, you got a gun. Dat's good. Now you kill sumfn' en I'll make up de fire.'

So we went over to where the canoe was, and while he built a fire in a grassy open place amongst the trees, I fetched meal and bacon and coffee, and coffee-pot and frying-pan, and sugar and tin cups, and the nigger was set back considerable, because he reckoned it was all done with witchcraft. I catched a good big cat-fish, too, and Jim cleaned him with his knife, and fried him.

When breakfast was ready, we lolled on the grass and eat it smoking hot; Jim laid it in with all his might, for he was most about starved. Then when we had got pretty well stuffed, we laid off and lazied.

By-and-by Jim says:

'But looky here, Huck, who wuz it dat 'uz killed in dat shanty, ef it warn't you?'

Then I told him the whole thing, and he said it was smart. He said Tom Sawyer couldn't get up no better plan than what I had. Then I says:

'How do you come to be here, Jim, and how'd you get here?'

He looked pretty uneasy, and didn't say nothing for a minute. Then he says:

'Maybe I better not tell.'

'Why, Jim?'

'Well, dey 's reasons. But you wouldn't tell on me ef I 'uz to tell you, would you, Huck?'

'Blamed if I would, Jim.'

'Well, I b'lieve you, Huck. I—I *run off*.'

'Jim!'

'But mind, you said you wouldn't tell—you know you said you wouldn't tell, Huck.'

'Well, I did. I said I wouldn't, and I'll stick to it. Honest *injun* I will. People would call me a low-down Ablitionist and despise me for keeping mum—but that don't make no difference. I ain't agoing to tell, and I ain't agoing back there anyways. So now, le's know all about it.'

'Well, you see, its 'uz dis way. Ole Missus—dat's Miss Watson—she pecks on me all de time, en treats me pooty rough, but she awluz said she wouldn' sell me down to Orleans. But I noticed dey wuz a nigger trader roun' de place considable, lately, en I begin to git oneasy. Well, one night I creeps to de do', pooty late, en de do' warn't quite shet, en I hear ole missus tell the widder she gwyne to sell me down to Orleans, but she didn' want to, but she could git eight hund'd dollars for me, en it 'uz sich a big stack o' money she couldn' resis'. De widder she try to git her to say she wouldn' do it, but I never waited to hear de res'. I lit out mighty quick, I tell you.

'I tuck out en shin down de hill en 'spec to steal a skift 'long de sho' som'ers 'bove de town, but dey wuz people a-stirrin' yit, so I hid in de ole tumble-down cooper shop on de bank to wait for everybody to go 'way. Well, I wuz dah all night. Dey wuz somebody roun' all de time. 'Long 'bout six in the mawnin', skifts begin to go by, en 'bout eight er nine every skift dat went 'long wuz talkin' 'bout how yo' pap come over to de town en say you's killed. Dese las' skifts wuz full o' ladies en genlmen agoin' over for to see de place. Sometimes dey'd pull up at de sho' en take a res' b'fo' dey started acrost, so by de talk I got to know all 'bout de killin'. I 'uz powerful sorry you's killed, Huck, but I ain't no mo', now.

'I laid dah under de shavins all day. I 'uz hungry, but I warn't afeared; bekase I knowed ole missus en de widder wuz goin' to start to de camp-meetn' right arter breakfas' en be gone all day, en dey knows I goes off wid de cattle 'bout daylight, so dey wouldn' 'spec to see me roun' de place, en so dey wouldn' miss me tell arter dark in de evenin'. De yuther servants wouldn' miss me, kase dey'd shin out en take holiday, soon as de ole folks 'uz out'n de way.

'Well, when it come dark I tuck out up de river road, en went 'bout two mile er more to whah dey warn't no houses. I'd made up my mine 'bout what I's agwyne to do. You see ef I kep' on tryin' to git away afoot, de dogs 'ud track me; ef I stole a skift to cross over, dey'd miss dat skift, you see, en dey'd know 'bout whah I'd lan' on de yuther side en whah to pick up my track. So I says, a raff is what I's arter; it doan' *make* no track.

'I see a light a-comin' roun' de p'int, bymeby, so I wade' in en shove' a log ahead o' me, en swum more'n half-way acrost de river, en got in 'mongst de drift-wood, en kep' my head down low, en kinder swum agin de current tell the raff come along. Den I swum to de stern uv it, en tuck aholt. It clouded up en 'uz pooty dark for a little while. So I clumb up en laid down on de planks. De men 'uz all 'way yonder in de middle, whah de lantern wuz. De river wuz arisin' en dey wuz a good current; so I reck'n'd 'at by fo' in de mawnin' I'd be twenty-five mile down de river, en den I'd slip in, jis' b'fo' daylight, en swim asho' en take to de woods on de Illinoi side.

'But I didn't have no luck. When we 'uz mos' down to de head er de islan', a man begin to come aft wid de lantern. I see it warn't no use fer to wait, so I slid overboard, en struck out fer de islan'. Well, I had a notion I could lan' mos' anywhers, but I couldn't—bank too bluff. I 'uz mos' to de foot er de islan' b'fo' I foun' a good place. I went into de woods en jedged I wouldn' fool wid raffs no mo', long as dey move de lantern roun' so. I had my pipe en a plug er dog-leg, en some matches in my cap, en dey warn't wet, so I 'uz all right.'

'And so you ain't had no meat nor bread to eat all this time? Why didn't you get mud-turkles?'

'How you gwyne to git'm? You can't slip up on um en grab um; en how 's a body gwyne to hit um wid a rock? How could a body do it in de night? en I warn't gwyne to show myself on de bank in de daytime.'

'Well, that's so. You've had to keep in the woods all the time, of course. Did you hear 'em shooting the cannon?'

'Oh, yes. I knowed dey was arter you. I see um go by heah; watched um thoo de bushes.'

Some young birds come along, flying a yard or two at a time and lighting. Jim said it was a sign it was going to rain. He said it was a sign when young chickens flew that way, and so he reckoned it was the same way when young birds done it. I was going to catch some of them, but Jim wouldn't let me. He said it was death. He said his father lay mighty sick once, and some of them catched a bird, and his old granny said his father would die, and he did.

And Jim said you mustn't count the things you are going to cook for dinner, because that would bring bad luck. The same if you shook the tablecloth after sundown. And he said if a man owned a bee-hive, and that man died, the bees must be told about it before sun-up next morning, or else the bees would all weaken down and quit work and die. Jim said bees wouldn't sting idiots; but I didn't believe that, because I had tried them lots of times myself, and they wouldn't sting me.

I had heard about some of these things before, but not all of them. Jim knowed all kinds of signs. He said he knowed most everything. I said it looked to me like all the signs was about bad luck, and so I asked him if there warn't any good-luck signs. He says:

'Mighty few—an' *dey* ain' no use to a body. What you want to know when good luck's a-comin' for? want to keep it off?' And he said: 'Ef you 's got hairy arms en a hairy breas', it 's a sign dat you 's agwyne to be rich. Well, dey's some use in a sign like dat, 'kase it's so fur ahead. You see, maybe you 's got to be po' a long time fust, en so you might git discourage' en kill yo'self 'f you didn't know by de sign dat you gwyne to be rich bymeby.'

'Have you got hairy arms and a hairy breast, Jim?'

'What's de use to axe dat question? don' you see I has?'

'Well, are you rich?'

'No, but I been rich wunst, and gwyne to be rich agin. Wunst I had foteen dollars, but I tuck to speculat'n', en got busted out.'

'What did you speculate in, Jim?'

'Well, fust I tackled stock?'

'What kind of stock?'

'Why, live stock. Cattle, you know. I put ten dollars in a cow. But I ain' gwyne to resk no mo' money in stock. De cow up 'n' died on my han's.'

'So you lost the ten dollars.'

'No, I didn' lose it all. I on'y los' 'bout nine of it. I sole de hide en taller for a dollar en ten cents.'

'You had five dollars and ten cents left. Did you speculate any more?'

'Yes. You know dat one-laigged nigger dat b'longs to old Misto Bradish? well, he sot up a bank, en say anybody dat put in a dollar would git fo' dollars mo' at de en' er de year. Well, all de niggers went in, but dey didn' have much. I wuz de on'y one dat had much. So I stuck out for mo' dan fo' dollars, en I said 'f I didn' git it I'd start a bank mysef. Well, o' course dat nigger want' to keep me out er de business, bekase he say dey warn't business 'nough for two banks, so he say I could put in my five dollars en he pay me thirty-five at de en' er de year.

'So I done it. Den I reck'n'd I'd inves' de thirty-five dollars right off en keep things a-movin'. Dey wuz a nigger name' Bob, dat had ketched a wood-flat, en his marster didn' know it; en I bought it off'n him en told him to take de thirty-five dollars when de en' er de year come; but somebody stole de wood-flat dat night, en nex' day de one-laigged nigger say de bank 's busted. So dey didn' none uv us git no money.'

'What did you do with the ten cents, Jim?'

'Well, I uz gwyne to spen' it, but I had a dream, en dc dream tole me to give it to a nigger name' Balum—Balum's Ass dey call him for short, he's one er dem chuckle-heads, you know. But he's lucky, dey say, en I see I warn't lucky. De dream say let Balum inves' de ten cents en he'd make a raise for me. Well, Balum he tuck de money, en when he wuz in church he hear de preacher say dat whoever give to de po' len' to de Lord, en boun' to git his money back a hund'd times. So Balum he tuck en give de ten cents to de po', en laid low to see what wuz gwyne to come of it.'

'Well, what did come of it, Jim?'

'Nuffn' never come of it. I couldn' manage to k'leck dat money no way; en Balum he couldn'. I ain't gwyne to len' no mo' money 'dout I see de security. Boun' to git yo' money back a hund'd times, de preacher says! Ef I could git de ten *cents* back, I'd call it squah, en be glad er de chanst.'

'Well, it's all right, anyway, Jim, long as you're going to be rich again some time or other.'

'Yes—en I's rich now, come to look at it. I owns mysef, en I's wuth eight hund'd dollars. I wisht I had de money, I wouldn' want no mo'.'

## *Chapter 9*

### THE CAVE—THE FLOATING HOUSE—A GOOD HAUL

I WANTED to go and look at a place right about the middle of the island, that I'd found when I was exploring; so we started, and soon got to it, because the island was only three miles long and a quarter of a mile wide.

This place was a tolerable long steep hill or ridge, about forty foot high. We had a rough time getting to the top, the sides was so steep and the bushes so thick. We tramped and clumb around all over it, and by-and-by found a good big cavern in the rock, most up to the top on the side towards Illinois. The cavern was as big as two or three rooms bunched together, and Jim could stand up straight in it. It was cool in there. Jim was for putting our traps in there, right away, but I said we didn't want to be climbing up and down there all the time.

Jim said if we had the canoe hid in a good place, and had all the traps in the cavern, we could rush there if anybody was to come to the island, and they would never find us without dogs. And besides, he said them little birds had said it was going to rain, and did I want the things to get wet?

So we went back and got the canoe and paddled up abreast the cavern, and lugged all the traps up there. Then we hunted up a place close by to hide the canoe in, amongst the thick willows. We took some fish off of the lines and set them again, and begun to get ready for dinner.

The door of the cavern was big enough to roll a hogshead in, and on one side of the door the floor stuck out a little bit and was flat and a good place to build a fire on. So we built it there and cooked dinner.

We spread the blankets inside for a carpet, and eat our dinner in there. We put all the other things handy at the back of the cavern. Pretty soon it darkened up and begun to thunder and lighten; so the birds was right about it. Directly it begun to rain, and it rained like all fury, too, and I never see the wind blow so. It was one of these regular summer storms. It would get so dark that it looked all blue-black outside, and lovely; and the rain would thrash along by so thick that the trees off a little ways looked dim and spider-webby; and here would come a blast of wind that would bend the trees down and turn up the pale underside of the leaves; and then a perfect ripper of a gust would follow along and set the branches to tossing their arms as if they was just wild; and next, when it was just about the bluest and blackest—*fst*! it was as bright as glory and you'd have a little glimpse of tree-tops a-plunging about, away off yonder in the storm, hundreds of yards further than you could see before; dark as sin again in a second, and now you'd hear the thunder let go with an awful crash and then go rumbling, grumbling, tumbling down the sky towards the underside of the world, like rolling empty barrels downstairs, where it's long stairs and they bounce a good deal, you know.

'Jim, this is nice,' I says. 'I wouldn't want to be nowhere else but here. Pass me along another hunk of fish and some hot corn-bread.'

'Well, you wouldn't a ben here, 'f it hadn't a ben for Jim. You'd a ben down dah in de woods widout any dinner, en gittin' mos' drownded, too, dat you would, honey. Chickens knows when it's gwyne to rain, en so do de birds, chile.'

The river went on raising and raising for ten or twelve days, till at last it was over the banks. The water was three or four foot deep on the island in the low places and on the Illinois bottom. On that side it was a good many miles wide; but on the Missouri side it was the same old distance across—a half a mile—because the Missouri shore was just a wall of high bluffs.

Daytimes we paddled all over the island in the canoe. It was mighty cool and shady in the deep woods even if the sun was blazing outside. We went winding in and out amongst the trees; and sometimes the vines hung so thick we had to back away and go some other way. Well, on every old broken-down tree you could see rabbits, and snakes, and such things; and when the island had been overflowed a day or two, they got so tame, on account of being hungry, that you could paddle right up and put your hand on them if you wanted to; but not the snakes and turtles—they would slide off in the water. The ridge our cavern was in was full of them. We could a had pets enough if we'd wanted them.

One night we catched a little section of a lumber raft—nice pine planks. It was twelve foot wide and about fifteen or sixteen foot long, and the top stood above-water six or seven inches, a solid level floor. We could see saw-logs go by in the daylight, sometimes, but we let them go; we didn't show ourselves in daylight.

Another night, when we was up at the head of the island, just before daylight, here comes a frame house down, on the west side. She was a two-story, and tilted over, considerable. We paddled out and got aboard—clumb in at an upstairs window. But it was too dark to see yet, so we made the canoe fast and set in her to wait for daylight.

The light begun to come before we got to the foot of the island. Then we looked in at the window. We could make out a bed, and a table, and two old chairs, and lots of things around about on the floor; and there was clothes hanging against the wall. There was something laying on the floor in the far corner that looked like a man. So Jim says:

'Hello, you!'

But it didn't budge. So I hollered again, and then Jim says:

'De man ain't asleep—he 's dead. You hold still—I'll go en see.'

He went and bent down and looked, and says:

'It's a dead man. Yes, indeedy; naked, too. He 's ben shot in de back. I reck'n he 's ben dead two er three days. Come in, Huck, but doan' look at his face—it 's too gashly.'

I didn't look at him at all. Jim throwed some old rags over him, but he needn't done it; I didn't want to see him. There was heaps of old greasy cards scattered around over the floor, and old whisky bottles, and a couple of masks made out of black cloth; and all over the walls was the ignorantest kind of words and pictures, made with charcoal. There was two old dirty calico dresses, and a sun-bonnet, and some women's under-clothes, hanging against the wall, and some men's clothing, too. We put the lot into the canoe; it might come good. There was a boy's old speckled straw hat on the floor; I took that too. And there was a bottle that had had milk in it; and it had a rag stopper for a baby to suck. We would a took the bottle, but it was broke. There was a seedy old chest, and an old hair trunk with the hinges broke. They stood open, but there warn't nothing left in them that was any account. The way things was scattered about, we reckoned the people left in a hurry and warn't fixed so as to carry off most of their stuff.

We got an old tin lantern, and a butcher knife without any handle, and a bran-new Barlow knife worth two bits in any store, and a lot of tallow candles, and a tin candlestick, and a gourd, and a tin cup, and a ratty old bed-quilt off the bed, and a reticule with needles and pins and beeswax and buttons and thread and all such truck in it, and a hatchet and some nails, and a fish-line as thick as my little finger, with some monstrous hooks on it, and a roll of buckskin, and a leather dog-collar, and horse-shoe, and some vials of medicine that didn't have no label on them; and just as we was leaving I found a tolerable good curry-comb, and Jim he found a ratty old fiddle-bow, and a wooden leg. The straps was broke off of it, but barring that, it was a good enough leg, though it was too long for me and not long enough for Jim, and we couldn't find the other one, though we hunted all around.

And so, take it all around, we made a good haul. When we was ready to shove off, we was a quarter of a mile below the island, and it was pretty broad day; so I made Jim lay down in the canoe and cover up with the quilt, because if he set up, people could tell he was a nigger a good ways off. I paddled over to the Illinois shore, and drifted down most a half a mile doing it. I crept up the dead water under the bank, and hadn't no accidents and didn't see nobody. We got home all safe.

## *Chapter 10*

### THE FIND—OLD HANK BUNKER—IN DISGUISE

AFTER breakfast I wanted to talk about the dead man and guess out how he come to be killed, but Jim didn't want to. He said it would fetch bad luck; and besides, he said, he might come and ha'nt us; he said a man that warn't buried was more likely to go a-ha'nting around than one that was planted and comfortable. That sounded pretty reasonable, so I didn't say no more; but I couldn't keep from studying over it and wishing I knowed who shot the man, and what they done it for.

We rummaged the clothes we'd got, and found eight dollars in silver sewed up in the lining of an old blanket overcoat. Jim said he reckoned the people in that house stole the coat, because if they'd a knowed the money was there they wouldn't a left it. I said I reckoned they killed him, too; but Jim didn't want to talk about that. I says:

'Now you think it's bad luck; but what did you say when I fetched in the snake-skin that I found on the top of the ridge day before yesterday? You said it was the worst bad luck in the world to touch a snake-skin with my hands. Well, here's your bad luck! We've raked in all this truck and eight dollars besides. I wish we could have some bad luck like this every day, Jim.'

'Never you mind, honey, never you mind. Don't you git too peart. It's a-comin'. Mind I tell you, it's a-comin'.'

It did come, too. It was a Tuesday that we had that talk. Well, after dinner Friday, we was laying around in the grass at the upper end of the ridge, and got out of tobacco. I went to the cavern to get some, and found a rattlesnake in there. I killed him, and curled him up on the foot of Jim's blanket, ever so natural, thinking there'd be some fun when Jim found him there. Well, by night I forgot all about the snake, and when Jim flung himself down on the blanket while I struck a light, the snake's mate was there, and bit him.

He jumped up yelling, and the first thing the light showed was the varmint curled up and ready for another spring. I laid him out in a second with a stick, and Jim grabbed pap's whisky jug and begun to pour it down.

He was barefooted, and the snake bit him right on the heel. That all comes of my being such a fool as to not remember that wherever you leave a dead snake its mate always comes there and curls around it. Jim told me to chop off the snake's head and throw it away, and then skin the body and roast a piece of it. I done it, and he eat it and said it would help cure him. He made me take off the rattles and tie them around his wrist, too. He said that that would help. Then I slid out quiet and throwed the snakes clear away amongst the bushes; for I warn't going to let Jim find out it was all my fault, not if I could help it.

Jim sucked and sucked at the jug, and now and then he got out of his head and pitched around and yelled; but every time he come to himself he went to sucking at the jug again. His foot swelled up pretty big, and so did his leg; but by-and-by the drunk begun to come, and so I judged he was all right; but I'd druther been bit with a snake than pap's whisky.

Jim was laid up for four days and nights. Then the swelling was all gone and he was around again. I made up my mind I wouldn't ever take aholt of a snake-skin again with my hands, now that I see what had come of it. Jim said he reckoned I would believe him next time. And he said that handling a snake-skin was such awful bad luck that maybe we hadn't got to the end of it yet. He said he druther see the new moon over his left shoulder as much as a thousand times than take up a snake-skin in his hand. Well, I was getting to feel that way myself, though I've always reckoned that looking at the new moon over your left shoulder is one of the carelessest and foolishest things a body can do. Old Hank Bunker done it once, and bragged about it; and in less than two years he got drunk and fell off of the shot-tower and spread himself out so that he was just a kind of a layer, as you may say; and they slid him edgeways between two barn doors for a coffin, and buried him so, so they say, but I didn't see it. Pap told me. But anyway, it all come of looking at the moon that way, like a fool.

Well, the days went along, and the river went down between its banks again; and about the first thing we done was to bait one of the big hooks with a skinned rabbit and set it and catch a cat-fish that was as big as a man, being six foot two inches long, and weighed over two hundred pounds. We couldn't handle him, of course; he would a flung us into Illinois. We just set there and watched him rip and tear around till he drownded. We found a brass button in his stomach, and a round ball, and lots of rubbage. We split the ball open with the hatchet, and there was a spool in it. Jim said he'd had it there a long time, to coat it over so and make a ball of it. It was as big a fish as was ever catched in the Mississippi, I reckon. Jim said he h adn't ever seen a bigger one. He would a been worth a good deal over at the village. They peddle out such a fish as that by the pound in the market house there; everybody buys some of him; his meat 's as white as snow and makes a good fry.

Next morning I said it was getting slow and dull, and I wanted to get a stirring up, some way. I said I reckoned I would slip over the river and find out what was going on. Jim liked that notion; but he said I must go in the dark and look sharp. Then he studied it over and said, Couldn't I put on some of them old things and dress up like a girl? That was a good notion, too. Se we shortened up one of the calico gowns and I turned up my trowser-legs to my knees and got into it. Jim hitched it behind with the hooks, and it was a fair fit. I put on the sun-bonnet and tied it under my chin, and then for a body to look in and see my face was like looking down a joint of stove-pipe. Jim said nobody would know me, even in the daytime, hardly. I practised around all day to get the hang of the things, and by-and-by I could do pretty well in them, only Jim said I didn't walk like a girl; and he said I must quit pulling up my gown to get at my britches pocket. I took notice, and done better.

I started up the Illinois shore in the canoe just after dark.

I started across to the town from a little below the ferry landing, and the drift of the current fetched me in at the bottom of the town. I tied up and started along the bank. There was a light burning in a little shanty that hadn't been lived in for a long time, and I wondered who had took up quarters there. I slipped up and peeped in at the window. There was a woman about forty year old in there, knitting by a candle that was on a pine table. I didn't know her face; she was a stranger, for you couldn't start a face in that town that I didn't know. Now this was lucky, because I was weakening; I was getting afraid I had come; people might know my voice and find me out. But if this woman had been in such a little town two days she could tell me all I wanted to know; so I knocked at the door, and made up my mind I wouldn't forget I was a girl.

## *Chapter 11*

### HUCK AND THE WOMAN—THE SEARCH—PREVARICATION—GOING TO GOSHEN—'THEY'RE AFTER US!'

'Come in,' says the woman, and I did. She says: 'Take a cheer.'

I done it. She looked me all over with her little shiny eyes, and says:

'What might your name be?'

'Sarah Williams.'

'Where 'bouts do you live? In this neighbourhood?'

'No'm. In Hookerville, seven mile below. I've walked all the way, and I'm all tired out.'

'Hungry, too, I reckon. I'll find you something.'

'No'm, I ain't hungry. I was so hungry I had to stop two mile below here at a farm; so I ain't hungry no more. It's what makes me so late. My mother's down sick, and out of money and everything, and I come to tell my uncle, Abner Moore. He lives at the upper end of the town, she says. I hain't ever been here before. Do you know him?'

'No; but I don't know everybody yet. I haven't lived here quite two weeks. It's a considerable ways to the upper end of the town. You better stay here all night. Take off your bonnet.'

'No,' I says, 'I'll rest awhile, I reckon, and go on. I ain't afeard of the dark.'

She said she wouldn't let me go by myself, but her husband would be in by-and-by, maybe in a hour and a half, and she'd send him along with me. Then she got to talking about her husband, and about her relations up the river, and her relations down the river, and about how much better off they used to was, and how they didn't know but they'd made a mistake coming to our town, instead of letting well alone—and so on and so on, till I was afeard *I* had made a mistake coming to her to find out what was going on in the town; but by-and-by she dropped on to pap and the murder, and then I was pretty willing to let her clatter right along. She told about me and Tom Sawyer finding the six thousand dollars (only she got it ten) and all about pap and what a hard lot he was, and what a hard lot I was, and at last she got down to where I was murdered. I says:

'Who done it? We've heard considerable about these goings on, down in Hookerville, but we don't know who 'twas that killed Huck Finn.'

'Well, I reckon there's a right smart chance of people *here* that'd like to know who killed him. Some thinks old Finn done it himself.'

'No—is that so?'

'Most everybody thought it at first. He'll never know how nigh he come to getting lynched. But before night they changed around and judged it was done by a runaway nigger named Jim.'

'Why *he*——'

I stopped. I reckoned I better keep still. She run on, and never noticed I had put in at all.

'The nigger run off the very night Huck Finn was killed. So there's a reward out for him—three hundred dollars. And there's a reward out for old Finn too—two hundred dollars. You see, he come to town the morning after the murder, and told about it, and was out with 'em on the ferry-boat hunt, and right away after he up and left. Before night they wanted to lynch him, but he was gone, you see. Well, next day they found out the nigger was gone; they found out he hadn't ben seen sence ten o'clock the night the murder was done. So then they put it on him, you see, and while they was full of it, next day back comes old Finn and went boo-hooing to Judge Thatcher to get money to hunt for the nigger all over Illinois with. The judge give him some, and that evening he got drunk and was around till after midnight with a couple of mighty hard-looking strangers, and then went off with them. Well, he hain't come back sence, and they ain't looking for him back till this thing blows over a little, for people thinks now that he killed his boy and fixed things so folks would think robbers done it, and then he'd get Huck's money without having to bother a long time with a lawsuit. People do say he warn't any too good to do it. Oh, he's sly, I reckon. If he don't come back for a year, he'll be all right. You can't prove anything on him, you know; everything will be quieted down then, and he'll walk into Huck's money as easy as nothing.'

'Yes, I reckon so, 'm. I don't see nothing in the way of it. Has everybody quit thinking the nigger done it?'

'Oh, no, not everybody. A good many thinks he done it. But they'll get the nigger pretty soon, now, and maybe they can scare it out of him.'

'Why, are they after him yet?'

'Well, you're innocent, ain't you! Does three hundred dollars lay round every day for people to pick up? Some folks thinks the nigger ain't far from here. I'm one of them—but I hain't talked it around. A few days ago I was talking with an old couple that lives next door in the log shanty, and they happened to say hardly anybody ever goes to that island over yonder that they call Jackson's Island. Don't anybody live there? says I. No, nobody, says they. I didn't say any more, but I done some thinking. I was pretty near certain I'd seen smoke over there, about the head of the island, a day or two before that, so I says to myself, like as not that nigger's hiding over there; anyway, says I, it's worth the trouble to give the place a hunt. I hain't seen any smoke sence, so I reckon maybe he's gone, if it was him; but husband's going over to see—him and another man. He was gone up the river; but he got back to-day and I told him as soon as he got here two hours ago.'

I had got so uneasy I couldn't set still. I had to do something with my hands; so I took up a needle off of the table and went to threading it. My hands shook, and I was making a bad job of it. When the woman stopped talking, I looked up, and she was looking at me pretty curious, and smiling a little. I put down the needle and thread and let on to be interested—and I was, too—and says:

'Three hundred dollars is a power of money. I wish my mother could get it. Is your husband going over there to-night?'

'Oh, yes. He went up-town with the man I was telling you of, to get a boat and see if they could borrow another gun. They'll go over after midnight.'

'Couldn't they see better if they was to wait till day-time?'

'Yes. And couldn't the nigger see better, too? After midnight he'll likely be asleep, and they can slip around through the woods and hunt up his camp-fire all the better for the dark, if he's got one.'

'I didn't think of that.'

The woman kept looking at me pretty curious, and I didn't feel a bit comfortable. Pretty soon she says:

'What did you say your name was, honey?'

'M—Mary Williams.'

Somehow it didn't seem to me that I said it was Mary before, so I didn't look up; seemed to me I said it was Sarah; so I felt sort of cornered, and was afeard maybe I was looking it too. I wished the woman would say something more; the longer she set still, the uneasier I was. But now she says:

'Honey, I thought you said it was Sarah when you first come in?'

'Oh, yes'm, I did. Sarah Mary Williams. Sarah's my first name. Some calls me Sarah, some calls me Mary.'

'Oh, that's the way of it?'

'Yes'm.'

I was feeling better, then, but I wished I was out of there, anyway. I couldn't look up yet.

Well, the woman fell to talking about how hard times was, and how poor they had to live, and how the rats was as free as if they owned the place, and so forth, and so on, and then I got easy again. She was right about the rats. You'd see one stick his nose out of a hole in the corner every little while. She said she had to have things handy to throw at them when she was alone, or they wouldn't give her no peace. She showed me a bar of lead, twisted up into a knot, and said she was a good shot with it generly, but she'd wrenched her arm a day or two ago, and didn't know whether she could throw true, now. But she watched for a chance, and directly she banged away at a rat, but she missed him wide, and said 'Ouch!' it hurt her arm so. Then she told me to try for the next one. I wanted to be getting away before the old man got back, but of course I didn't let on. I got the thing, and the first rat that showed his nose I let drive, and if he'd a stayed where he was he'd a been a tolerable sick rat. She said that that was first-rate, and she reckoned I would hive the next one. She went and got the lump of lead and fetched it back and brought along a hank of yarn, which she wanted me to help her with. I held up my two hands and she put the hank over them and went on talking about her and her husband's matters. But she broke off to say:

'Keep your eye on the rats. You better have the lead in your lap, handy.'

So she dropped the lump into my lap, just at that moment, and I clapped my legs together on it and she went on talking. But only about a minute. Then she took off the hank and looked me straight in the face, but very pleasant, and says:

'Come, now—what's your real name?'

'Wh-what, mum?'

'What's your real name? Is it Bill, or Tom, or Bob?—or what is it?'

I reckon I shook like a leaf, and I didn't know hardly what to do. But I says:

'Please to don't poke fun at a poor girl like me, mum. If I'm in the way, here, I'll——'

'No, you won't. Set down and stay where you are. I ain't going to hurt you, and I ain't going to tell on you, nuther. You just tell me your secret, and trust me. I'll keep it; and what's more, I'll help you.

So'll my old man, if you want him to. You see, you're a runaway 'prentice—that's all. It ain't anything. There ain't any harm in it. You've been treated bad, and you made up your mind to cut. Bless you, child, I wouldn't tell on you. Tell me all about it, now—that's a good boy.'

So I said it wouldn't be no use to try to play it any longer, and I would just make a clean breast and tell her everything, but she mustn't go back on her promise. Then I told her my father and mother was dead, and the law had bound me out to a mean old farmer in the country thirty mile back from the river, and he treated me so bad I couldn't stand it no longer; he went away to be gone a couple of days, and so I took my chance and stole some of his daughter's old clothes, and cleared out, and I had been three nights coming the thirty miles; I travelled nights, and hid daytimes and slept, and the bag of bread and meat I carried from home lasted me all the way and I had a plenty. I said I believed my uncle, Abner Moore, would take care of me, and so that was why I struck out for this town of Goshen.

'Goshen, child? This ain't Goshen. This is St. Petersburg. Goshen's ten mile further up the river. Who told you this was Goshen?'

'Why, a man I met at daybreak this morning, just as I was going to turn into the woods for my regular sleep. He told me when the roads forked I must take the right hand, and five mile would fetch me to Goshen.'

'He was drunk, I reckon. He told you just exactly wrong.'

'Well, he did act like he was drunk, but it ain't no matter now. I got to be moving along. I'll fetch Goshen before daylight.'

'Hold on a minute. I'll put you up a snack to eat. You might want it.'

So she put me up a snack, and says:

'Say—when a cow's laying down, which end of her gets up first? Answer up prompt, now—don't stop to study over it. Which end gets up first?'

'The hind end, mum.'

'Well, then, a horse?'

'The for'rard end, mum.'

'Which side of a tree does the most moss grow on?'

'North side.'

'If fifteen cows is browsing on a hill-side, how many of them eats with their heads pointing the same direction?'

'The whole fifteen, mum.'

'Well, I reckon you *have* lived in the country. I thought maybe you was trying to hocus me again. What's your real name, now?'

'George Peters, mum.'

'Well, try to remember it, George. Don't forget and tell me it's Elexander before you go, and then get out by saying it's George-Elexander when I catch you. And don't go about women in that old calico. You do a girl tolerable poor, but you might fool men, maybe. Bless you, child, when you set out to thread a needle, don't hold the thread still and fetch the needle up to it; hold the needle still and poke the thread at it—that's the way a woman most always does; but a man always does t'other way. And when you throw at a rat or anything, hitch yourself up a tip-toe, and fetch your hand up over your head as awkard as you can, and miss your rat about six or seven foot. Throw stiff-armed from the shoulder, like there was a pivot there for it to turn on—like a girl; not from the wrist and elbow, with your arm out to one side, like a boy. And mind you, when a girl tries to catch anything in her lap, she throws her knees apart; she don't clap them together, the way you did when you catched the lump of lead. Why, I spotted you for a boy when you was threading the needle; and I contrived the other things just to make certain. Now trot along to your uncle, Sarah Mary Williams George Elexander Peters, and if you get into trouble you send word to Mrs. Judith Loftus, which is me, and I'll do what I can to get you out of it. Keep the river road, all the way, and next time you tramp, take shoes and socks with you. The river road's a rocky one, and your feet'll be in a condition when you get to Goshen, I reckon.'

I went up the bank about fifty yards, and then I doubled on my tracks and slipped back to where my canoe was, a good piece below the house. I jumped in and was off in a hurry. I went up-stream far enough to make the head of the island, and then started across. I took off the sun-bonnet, for I didn't want no blinders on, then. When I was about the middle, I hear the clock begin to strike; so I stops and listens; the sound come faint over the water, but clear—eleven. When I struck the head of the island I never waited to blow, though I was most winded, but I shoved right into the timber where my old camp used to be, and started a good fire there on a high-and-dry spot. Then I jumped in the canoe and dug out for our place a mile and a half below, as hard as I could go. I landed, and slopped through the timber and up the ridge and into the cavern. There Jim laid, sound asleep on the ground. I roused him out and says:

'Git up and hump yourself, Jim! There ain't a minute to lose. They're after us!'

Jim never asked no questions, he never said a word; but the way he worked for the next half an hour showed about how he was scared. By that time everything we had in the world was on our raft and she was ready to be shoved out from the willow cove where she was hid. We put out the camp-fire at the cavern the first thing, and didn't show a candle outside after that.

I took the canoe out from shore a little piece and took a look, but if there was a boat around I couldn't see it, for stars and shadows ain't good to see by. Then we got out the raft and slipped along down in the shade, past the foot of the island, dead still, never saying a word.

## *Chapter 12*

### SLOW NAVIGATION—BORROWING THINGS—BOARDING THE WRECK—THE PLOTTERS—'IT AIN'T GOOD MORALS'—HUNTING FOR THE BOAT

IT must a been close on to one o'clock when we got below the island at last, and the raft did seem to go mighty slow. If a boat was to come along, we was going to take to the canoe and break for the Illinois shore; and it was well a boat didn't come, for we hadn't ever thought to put the gun into the canoe, or a fishing-line or anything to eat. We was in ruther too much of a sweat to think of so many things. It warn't good judgment to put *everything* on the raft.

If the men went to the island, I just expect they found the camp-fire I built, and watched it all night for Jim to come. Anyways, they stayed away from us, and if my building the fire never fooled them it warn't no fault of mine. I played it as low-down on them as I could.

When the first streak of day begun to show, we tied up to a tow-head in a big bend on the Illinois side, and hacked off cotton-wood branches with the hatchet and covered up the raft with them so she looked like there had been a cave-in in the bank there. A tow-head is a sand-bar that has cotton-woods on it as thick as harrow-teeth.

We had mountains on the Missouri shore and heavy timber on the Illinois side, and the channel was down the Missouri shore at that place, so we warn't afraid of anybody running across us. We laid there all day and watched the rafts and steamboats spin down the Missouri shore, and up-bound steamboats fight the big river in the middle. I told Jim all about the time I had jabbering with that woman; and Jim said she was a smart one, and if she was to start after us herself *she* wouldn't set down and watch a camp-fire—no, sir, she'd fetch a dog. Well, then, I said, why couldn't she tell her husband to fetch a dog? Jim said he bet she did think of it by the time the men was ready to start, and he believed they must a gone up-town to get a dog, and so they lost all that time, or else we wouldn't be here on a tow-head sixteen or seventeen mile below the village—no, indeedy, we would be in that same old town again. So I said I didn't care what was the reason they didn't get us, as long as they didn't.

When it was beginning to come on dark, we poked our heads out of the cotton-wood thicket and looked up, and down, and across; nothing in sight; so Jim took up some of the top planks of the raft and built a snug wigwam to get under in blazing weather and rainy, and to keep the things dry. Jim made a floor for the wigwam, and raised it a foot or more above the level of the raft, so now the blankets and all the traps was out of the reach of steamboat waves. Right in the middle of the wigwam we made a layer of dirt about five or six inches deep with a frame around it for to hold it to its place; this was to build a fire on in sloppy weather or chilly; the wigwam would keep it from being seen. We made an extra steering oar, too, because one of the others might get broke, on a snag or something. We fixed up a short forked stick to hang the old lantern on; because we must always light the lantern whenever we see a steamboat coming downstream, to keep from getting run over; but we wouldn't have to light it for up-stream boats unless we see we was in what they call a 'crossing'; for the river was pretty high yet, very low banks being still a little under-water; so up-bound boats didn't always run the channel, but hunted easy water.

This second night we run between seven and eight hours, with a current that was making over four mile an hour. We catched fish, and talked, and we took a swim now and then to keep off sleepiness. It was kind of solemn, drifting down the big still river, laying on our backs looking up at the stars, and we didn't ever feel like talking loud, and it warn't often that we laughed, only a little kind of a low chuckle. We had mighty good weather, as a general thing, and nothing ever happened to us at all, that night, nor the next, nor the next.

Every night we passed towns, some of them away up on black hill-sides, nothing but just a shiny bed of lights, not a house could you see. The fifth night we passed St. Louis, and it was like the whole world lit up. In St. Petersburg they used to say there was twenty or thirty thousand people in St. Louis, but I never believed it till I see that wonderful spread of lights at two o'clock that still night. There warn't a sound there; everybody was asleep.

Every night, now, I used to slip ashore, towards ten o'clock, at some little village, and buy ten or fifteen cents' worth of meal or bacon or other stuff to eat; and sometimes I lifted a chicken that warn't roosting comfortable, and took him along. Pap always said, take a chicken when you get a chance, because if you don't want him yourself you can easy find somebody that does, and a good deed ain't ever forgot. I never see pap when he didn't want the chicken himself, but that is what he used to say, anyway.

Mornings, before daylight, I slipped into corn-fields and borrowed a watermelon, or a mushmelon, or a punkin, or some new corn, or things of that kind. Pap always said it warn't no harm to borrow things, if you was meaning to pay them back, sometime; but the widow said it warn't anything but a soft name for stealing, and no decent body would do it. Jim said he reckoned the widow was partly right and pap was partly right; so the best way would be for us to pick out two or three things from the list and say we wouldn't borrow them any more—then he reckoned it wouldn't be no harm to borrow the others. So we talked it over all one night, drifting along down the river, trying to make up our minds whether to drop the watermelons, or the cantelopes, or the mushmelons, or what. But towards daylight we got it all settled satisfactory, and concluded to drop crab-apples and p'simmons. We warn't feeling just right before that, but it was all comfortable now. I was glad the way it came out, too, because crab-apples ain't ever good, and the p'simmons wouldn't be ripe for two or three months yet.

We shot a water-fowl, now and then, that got up too early in the morning or didn't go to bed early enough in the evening. Take it all around, we lived pretty high.

The fifth night below St. Louis we had a big storm after midnight, with a power of thunder and lightning, and the rain poured down in a solid sheet. We stayed in the wigwam and let the raft take care of itself. When the lightning glared out we could see a big straight river ahead, and high rocky bluffs on both sides. By-and-by says I, 'Hel-*lo*, Jim, looky yonder!' It was a steamboat that had killed herself on a rock. We was drifting straight down for her. The lightning showed her very distinct. She was leaning over, with part of her upper deck above-water, and you could see every little chimbly-guy clean and clear, and a chair by the big bell, with an old slouch hat hanging on the back of it when the flashes come.

Well, it being away in the night, and stormy, and all so mysterious-like, I felt just the way any other boy would a felt when I see that wreck laying there so mournful and lonesome in the middle of the river. I wanted to get aboard of her and slink around a little, and see what there was there. So I says:

'Le's land on her, Jim.'

But Jim was dead against it, at first. He says:

'I doan' want to go fool'n 'long er no wrack. We's doin' blame' well, en we better let blame' well alone, as de good book says. Like as not dey's a watchman on dat wrack.'

'Watchman your grandmother!' I says; 'there ain't nothing to watch but the texas and the pilot-house; and do you reckon anybody's going to resk his life for a texas and a pilot-house such a night as this, when it's likely to break up and wash off down the river any minute?' Jim couldn't say nothing to that, so he didn't try. 'And besides,' I says, 'we might borrow something worth having, out of the captain's state-room. Seegars, *I* bet you—and cost five cents apiece, solid cash. Steamboat captains is always rich, and gets sixty dollars a month, and *they* don't care a cent what a thing costs, you know, long as they want it. Stick a candle in your pocket; I can't rest, Jim, till we give her a rummaging. Do you reckon Tom Sawyer would ever go by this thing? Not for pie, he wouldn't. He'd call it an adventure—that's what he'd call it; and he'd land on that wreck if it was his last act. And wouldn't he throw style into it?—wouldn't he spread himself, nor nothing? Why, you'd think it was Christopher C'lumbus discovering Kingdom-Come. I wish Tom Sawyer *was* here.'

Jim he grumbled a little, but give in. He said we mustn't talk any more than we could help, and then talk mighty low. The lightning showed us the wreck again, just in time, and we fetched the stabboard derrick, and made fast there.

The deck was high out, here. We went sneaking down the slope of it to labboard, in the dark, towards the texas, feeling our way slow with our feet, and spreading our hands out to fend off the guys, for it was so dark we couldn't see no sign of them. Pretty soon we struck the forward end of the sky-light, and clumb on to it; and the next step fetched us in front of the captain's door, which was open, and by Jimminy, away down through the texas hall we see a light! and all in the same second we seemed to hear low voices in yonder!

Jim whispered and said he was feeling powerful sick, and told me to come along. I says, all right; and was going to start for the raft; but just then I heard a voice wail out and say:

'Oh, please don't, boys: I swear I won't ever tell!'

Another voice said, pretty loud:

'It's a lie, Jim Turner. You've acted this way before. You always want more'n your share of the truck, and you've always got it, too, because you've swore 't if you didn't you'd tell. But this time you've said it jest one time too many. You're the meanest, treacherousest hound in this country.'

By this time Jim was gone for the raft. I was just a-biling with curiosity; and I says to myself, Tom Sawyer wouldn't back out now, and so I won't either; I'm agoing to see what's going on here. So I dropped on my hands and knees, in the little passage, and crept aft in the dark, till there warn't but about one stateroom betwixt me and the cross-hall of the texas. Then, in there I see a man stretched on the floor and tied hand and foot, and two men standing over him, and one of them had a dim lantern in his hand, and the other one had a pistol. This one kept pointing the pistol at the man's head on the floor and saying:

'I'd *like* to! And I orter, too, a mean skunk!'

The man on the floor would shrivel up, and say: 'Oh, please don't, Bill—I hain't ever goin' to tell.'

And every time he said that, the man with the lantern would laugh, and say:

' 'Deed you *ain't*! You never said no truer thing'n that, you bet you.' And once he said: 'Hear him beg! and yit if we hadn't got the best of him and tied him, he'd a killed us both. And what *for*? Jist for noth'n. Jist because we stood on our *rights*—that's what for. But I lay you ain't agoin' to threaten nobody any more, Jim Turner. Put *up* that pistol, Bill.'

Bill says:

'I don't want to, Jake Packard. I'm for killin' him—and didn't he kill old Hatfield jist the same way—and don't he deserve it?'

'But I don't *want* him killed, and I've got my reasons for it.'

'Bless yo' heart for them words, Jake Packard! I'll never forgit you, long 's I live!' says the man on the floor, sort of blubbering.

Packard didn't take no notice of that, but hung up his lantern on a nail, and started towards where I was, there in the dark, and motioned Bill to come. I crawfished as fast as I could, about two yards, but the boat slanted so that I couldn't make very good time; so to keep from getting run over and catched I crawled into a stateroom on the upper side. The man come a-pawing along in the dark, and when Packard got to my stateroom, he says:

'Here—come in here.'

And in he came, and Bill after him. But before they got in, I was up in the upper berth, cornered, and sorry I come. Then they stood there, with their hands on the ledge of the berth, and talked. I couldn't see them, but I could tell where they was, by the whisky they'd been having. I was glad I didn't drink whisky; but it wouldn't made much difference, anyway, because most of the time they couldn't a treed me because I didn't breathe. I was too scared. And besides, a body *couldn't* breathe, and hear such talk. They talked low and earnest. Bill wanted to kill Turner. He says:

'He 's said he'll tell, and he will. If we was to give both our shares to him *now*, it wouldn't make no difference after the row, and the way we've served him. Shore 's you're born, he'll turn State's evidence; now you hear *me*. I'm for putting him out of his troubles.'

'So'm I,' says Packard, very quiet.

'Blame it, I'd sorter begun to think you wasn't. Well, then, that 's all right. Le 's go and do it.'

'Hold on a minute; I ain't had my say yit. You listen to me. Shooting 's good, but there 's quieter ways if the thing 's *got* to be done. But what *I* say, is this; it ain't good sense to go court'n around after a halter, if you can git at what you're up to in some way that 's jist as good and at the same time don't bring you into no resks. Ain't that so?'

'You bet it is. But how you goin' to manage it this time?'

'Well, my idea is this; we'll rustle around and gether up whatever pickins we've overlooked in the staterooms, and shove for shore and hide the truck. Then we'll wait. Now I say it ain't agoin' to be more'n two hours befo' this wrack breaks up and washes off down the river. See? He'll be drownded, and won't have nobody to blame for it but his own self. I reckon that 's a considerable sight better'n killin' of him. I'm unfavourable to killin' a man as long as you can git around it; it ain't good sense, it ain't good morals. Ain't I right?'

'Yes—I reck'n you are. But s'pose she *don't* break up and wash off?'

'Well, we can wait the two hours, anyway, and see, can't we?'

'All right, then; come along.'

So they started, and I lit out, all in a cold sweat, and scrambled forward. It was dark as pitch there; but I said in a kind of coarse whisper, 'Jim!' and he answered up, right at my elbow, with a sort of moan, and I says:

'Quick, Jim, it ain't no time for fooling around and moaning; there 's a gang of murderers in yonder, and if we don't hunt up their boat and set her drifting down the river so these fellows can't get away from the wreck, there's one of 'em going to be in a bad fix. But if we find their boat we can put *all* of 'em in a bad fix—for the Sheriff'll get 'em. Quick—hurry! I'll hunt the labboard side, you hunt the stabboard. You start at the raft, and——'

'Oh! my lordy, lordy! *Raf'*? Dey ain' no raf' no mo', she done broke loose en gone!—en here we is!'

## Chapter 13

ESCAPING FROM THE WRECK—THE WATCHMAN—SINKING—A DEAD SLEEP

WELL, I catched my breath and most fainted. Shut up on a wreck with such a gang as that! But it warn't no time to be sentimentering. We'd *got* to find that boat, now—had to have it for ourselves. So we went a-quaking and shaking down the stabboard side, and slow work it was, too—seemed a week before we got to the stern. No sign of a boat. Jim said he didn't believe he could go any further—so scared he hadn't hardly any strength left, he said. But I said come on, if we get left on this wreck, we are in a fix, sure. So on we prowled, again. We struck for the stern of the texas, and found it, and then scrabbled along forwards on the sky-light, hanging on from shutter to shutter, for the edge of the sky-light was in the water. When we got pretty close to the cross-hall door, there was the skiff, sure enough! I could just barely see her. I felt ever so thankful. In another second I would a been aboard of her; but just then the door opened. One of the men stuck his head out, only about a couple of foot from me, and I thought I was gone; but he jerked it in again, and says:

'Heave that blame lantern out o' sight, Bill!'

He flung a bag of something into the boat, and then got in himself, and set down. It was Packard. Then Bill *he* come out and got in. Packard says, in a low voice:

'All ready—shove off!'

I couldn't hardly hang on to the shutters, I was so weak. But Bill says:

'Hold on—'d you go through him?'

'No. Didn't you?'

'No. So he's got his share o' the cash, yet.'

'Well, then, come along—no use to take truck and leave money.'

'Say—won't he suspicion what we're up to?'

'Maybe he won't. But we got to have it anyway. Come along.'

So they got out and went in.

The door slammed to, because it was on the careened side; and in a half-second I was in the boat, and Jim come a-tumbling after me. I out with my knife and cut the rope, and away we went!

We didn't touch an oar, and we didn't speak nor whisper, nor hardly even breathe. We went gliding swift along, dead silent, past the tip of the paddle-box, and past the stern; then in a second or two more we was a hundred yards below the wreck, and the darkness soaked her up, every last sign of her, and we was safe, and knowed it.

When we was three or four hundred yards down-stream, we see the lantern show like a little spark at the texas door, for a second, and we knowed by that the rascals had missed their boat, and was beginning to understand that they was in just as much trouble, now, as Jim Turner was.

Then Jim manned the oars, and we took out after our raft. Now was the first time that I begun to worry about the men—I reckon I hadn't had time to before. I begun to think how dreadful it was, even for murderers, to be in such a fix. I says to myself, there ain't no telling but I might come to be a murderer myself, yet, and then how would *I* like it? So says I to Jim:

'The first light we see, we'll land a hundred yards below it or above it, in a place where it's a good hiding-place for you and the skiff, and then I'll go and fix up some kind of a yarn, and get somebody to go for that gang and get them out of their scrape, so they can be hung when their time comes.'

But that idea was a failure; for pretty soon it begun to storm again, and this time worse than ever. The rain poured down, and never a light showed; everybody in bed, I reckon. We boomed along down the river, watching for lights and watching for our raft. After a long time the rain let up, but the clouds staid, and the lightning kept whimpering, and by-and-by a flash showed us a black thing ahead, floating, and we made for it.

It was the raft, and mighty glad was we to get aboard of it again. We seen a light, now, away down to the right, on shore. So I said I would go for it. The skiff was half full of plunder which that gang had stole, there on the wreck. We hustled it on to the raft in a pile, and I told Jim to float along down, and show a light when he judged he had gone about two mile, and keep it burning till I come; then I manned my oars and shoved for the light. As I got down towards it, three or four more showed—up on a hill-side. It was a village. I closed in above the shore-light, and laid on my oars and floated. As I went by, I see it was a lantern hanging on the jackstaff of a double-hull ferry-boat. I skimmed around for the watchman, a-wondering whereabouts he slept; and by-and-by I found him roosting on the bitts, forward, with his head down between his knees. I give his shoulder two or three little shoves, and begun to cry.

He stirred up, in a kind of startlish way; but when he see it was only me, he took a good gap and stretch, and then he says:

'Hello, what's up? Don't cry, bub. What's the trouble?'

I says:

'Pap, and mam, and sis, and——'

Then I broke down. He says:

'Oh, dang it, now, *don't* take on so, we all has to have our troubles, and this'n'll come out all right. What's the matter with 'em?'

'They're—they're—are you the watchman of the boat?'

'Yes,' he says, kind of pretty-well-satisfied like. 'I'm the captain and the owner, and the mate, and the pilot, and watchman, and head deck-hand: and sometimes I'm the freight and passengers. I ain't as rich as old Jim Hornback, and I can't be so blame' generous and good to Tom, Dick, and Harry as what he is, and slam around money the way he does; but I've told him a many a time 't I wouldn't trade places with him; for, says I, a sailor's life's the life for me, and I'm derned if *I'd* live two mile out o' town, where there ain't nothing ever goin' on, not for all his spondulicks and as much more on top of it. Says I——'

I broke in and says:

'They're in an awful peck of trouble, and——'

'*Who* is?'

'Why, pap, and mam, and sis, and Miss Hooker; and if you'd take your ferry-boat and go up there—'

'Up where? Where are they?'

'On the wreck.'

'What wreck?'

'Why, there ain't but one.'

'What, you don't mean the *Walter Scott*?'

'Yes.'

'Good land! what are they doin' *there*, for gracious sakes?'

'Well, they didn't go there a-purpose.'

'I bet they didn't! Why, great goodness, there ain't no chance for 'em if they don't get off mighty quick! Why, how in the nation did they ever git into such a scrape?'

'Easy enough. Miss Hooker was a-visiting, up there to the town——'

'Yes, Booth's Landing—go on.'

'She was a-visiting, there at Booth's Landing, and just in the edge of the evening she started over with her nigger woman in the horse-ferry, to stay all night at her friend's house, Miss What-you-may-call-her, I disremember her name, and they lost their steering-oar, and swung around and went a-floating down, stern-first, about two mile, and saddle-baggsed on the wreck, and the ferry-man and the nigger woman and the horses was all lost, but Miss Hooker she made a grab and got aboard the wreck. Well, about an hour after dark, we come along down in our trading-scow, and it was so dark we didn't notice the wreck till we was right on it; and so *we* saddle-baggsed; but all of us was saved but Bill Whipple—and oh, he *was* the best cretur!—I most wish't it had been me, I do.'

'My George! It's the beatenest thing I ever struck. And *then* what did you all do?'

'Well, we hollered and took on, but it's so wide there, we couldn't make anybody hear. So pap said somebody got to get ashore and get help somehow. I was the only one that could swim, so I made a dash for it, and Miss Hooker she said if I didn't strike help sooner, come here and hunt up her uncle, and he'd fix the thing. I made the land about a mile below, and been fooling along ever since, trying to get people to do something, but they said, "What, in such a night and such a current? there ain't no sense to it; go for the steam-ferry." Now if you'll go, and——'

'By Jackson, I'd *like* to, and blame it I don't know but I will; but who in the 'dingnations agoin' to *pay* for it? Do you reckon your pap——'

'Why *that's* all right. Miss Hooker she told me, *particular*, that her Uncle Hornback——'

'Great guns! is *he* her uncle? Looky here, you break for that light over yonder-way, and turn out west when you git there, and about a quarter of a mile out you'll come to the tavern; tell 'em to dart you out to Jim Hornback's and he'll foot the bill. And don't you fool around any, because he'll want to know the news. Tell him I'll have his niece all safe before he can get to town. Hump yourself, now; I'm agoing up around the corner here, to roust out my engineer.'

I struck for the light, but as soon as he turned the corner I went back and got into my skiff and baled her out and then pulled up-shore in the easy water about six hundred yards, and tucked myself in among some woodboats; for I couldn't rest easy till I could see the ferry-boat start. But take it all around, I was feeling ruther comfortable on accounts of taking all this trouble for that gang, for not many would a done it. I wished the widow knowed about it. I judged she would be proud of me for helping these rapscallions, because rapscallions and dead-beats is the kind the widow and good people takes the most interest in.

Well, before long, here comes the wreck, dim and dusky, sliding along down! A kind of cold shiver went through me, and then I struck out for her. She was very deep, and I see in a minute there warn't much chance for anybody being alive in her. I pulled all around her and hollered a little, but there wasn't any answer; all dead still. I felt a little bit heavy-hearted about the gang, but not much, for I reckoned if they could stand it, I could.

Then here comes the ferry-boat; so I shoved for the middle of the river on a long down-stream slant; and when I judged I was out of eye-reach, I laid on my oars, and looked back and see her go and smell around the wreck for Miss Hooker's remainders, because the captain would know her Uncle Hornback would want them; and then pretty soon the ferry-boat give it up and went for shore, and I laid into my work and went a-booming down the river.

It did seem a powerful long time before Jim's light showed up; and when it did show, it looked like it was a thousand mile off. By the time I got there the sky was beginning to get a little grey in the east; so we struck for an island, and hid the raft, and sunk the skiff, and turned in and slept like dead people.

## *Chapter 14*

### A GENERAL GOOD TIME—THE HAREM—FRENCH

BY-AND-BY, when we got up, we turned over the truck the gang had stole off of the wreck, and found boots, and blankets, and clothes, and all sorts of other things, and a lot of books, and a spy-glass, and three boxes of seegars. We hadn't ever been this rich before, in neither of our lives. The seegars was prime. We laid off all the afternoon in the woods talking, and me reading the books, and having a general good time. I told Jim all about what happened inside the wreck, and at the ferry-boat; and I said these kinds of things was adventures; but he said he didn't want no more adventures. He said that when I went in the texas, and he crawled back to get on the raft and found her gone, he nearly died; because he judged it was all up with *him*, anyway it could be fixed; for if he didn't get saved he would get drownded; and if he did get saved, whoever saved him would send him back home so as to get the reward, and then Miss Watson would sell him South, sure. Well, he was right; he was most always right; he had an uncommon level head, for a nigger.

I read considerable to Jim about kings, and dukes, and earls, and such, and how gaudy they dressed, and how much style they put on, and called each other your majesty, and your grace, and your lordship, and so on, 'stead of mister; and Jim's eyes bugged out, and he was interested. He says:

'I didn't know dey was so many un um. I hain't hearn 'bout none un um, skasely, but ole King Sollermun, onless you counts dem kings dat's in a pack er k'yards. How much do a king git?'

'Get?' I says; 'why, they get a thousand dollars a month if they want it; they can have just as much as they want; everything belongs to them.'

'*Ain't* dat gay? En what dey got to do, Huck?'

'*They* don't do nothing! Why, how you talk. They just set around.'

'No—is dat so?'

'Of course it is. They just set around. Except maybe when there's a war; then they go to the war. But other times they just lazy around; or go hawking—just hawking and sp—— Sh!—d'you hear a noise?'

We skipped out and looked; but it warn't nothing but the flutter of a steamboat's wheel, away down coming around the point; so we come back.

'Yes,' says I, 'and other times, when things is dull, they fuss with the parlyment; and if everybody don't go just so he whacks their heads off. But mostly they hang round the harem.'

'Roun' de which?'

'Harem.'

'What's de harem?'

'The place where he keep his wives. Don't you know about the harem? Solomon had one; he had about a million wives.'

'Why, yes, dat's so; I—I'd done forgot it. A harem's a bo'd'n-house, I reck'n. Mos' likely dey has rackety times in de nussery. En I reck'n de wives quarrels considable; en dat 'crease de racket. Yit dey say Sollermun de wises' man dat ever live'. I doan' take no stock in dat. Bekase why: would a wise man want to live in de mids' er sich a blimblammin' all de time? No—'deed he wouldn't. A wise man 'ud take en buil' a biler-factry; en den he could shet *down* de biler-factry when he want to res'.'

'Well, but he *was* the wisest man, anyway; because the widow she told me so, her own self.'

'I doan' k'yer what de widder say, he *warn't* no wise man, nuther. He had some er de dad-fetchedes' ways I ever see. Does you know 'bout dat chile dat he 'uz gwyne to chop in two?'

'Yes, the widow told me all about it.'

'*Well*, den! Warn' dat de beatenes' notion in de worl'? You jes' take en look at it a minute. Dah's de stump, dah—dat's one er de women; heah's you—dat's de yuther one; I's Sollermun; en dish-yer dollar bill's de chile. Bofe un you claims it. What does I do? Does I shin aroun' mongs' de neighbours en fine out which un you de bill *do* b'long to, en han' it over to de right one, all safe en soun', de way dat anybody dat had any gumption would? No—I take en whack de bill in *two*, en give half un it to you, en de yuther half to de yuther woman. Dat's de way Sollermun was gwyne to do wid de chile. Now I want to ast you: what's de use er dat half a bill?—can't buy noth'n wid it. En what use is a half a chile? I wouldn' give a dern for a million un um.'

'But hang it, Jim, you've clean missed the point—blame it, you've missed it a thousand mile.'

'Who? Me? Go 'long. Doan' talk to *me* 'bout yo' pints. I reck'n I knows sense when I sees it; en dey ain' no sense in sich doin's as dat. De 'spute warn't 'bout a half a chile, de 'spute was 'bout a whole chile; en de man dat think he kin settle a 'spute 'bout a whole chile wid a half a chile, doan' know enough to come in out'n de rain. Doan' talk to me 'bout Sollermun, Huck. I knows him by de back.'

'But I tell you you don't get the point.'

'Blame de pint! I reck'n I knows what I knows. En mine you, de *real* point is down furder—it's down deeper. It lays in de way Sollermun was raised. You take a man dat's got on'y one er two chillen; is dat man gwyne to be waseful o' chillen? No, he ain't; he can't 'ford it. *He* knows how to value 'em. But you take a man dat's got 'bout five million chillen runnin' roun' de house, en it's diffunt. *He* as soon chop a chile in two as a cat. Dey's plenty mo'. A chile er two, mo' er less, warn't no consekens to Sollermun, dad fetch him!'

I never see such a nigger. If he got a notion in his head once, there warn't no getting it out again. He was the most down on Solomon of any nigger I ever see. So I went to talking about other kings, and let Solomon slide. I told about Louis Sixteenth that got his head cut off in France long time ago; and about his little boy the dolphin, that would a been a king, but they took and shut him up in jail, and some say he died there.

'Po' little chap.'

'But some says he got out and got away, and come to America.'

'Dat's good! But he'll be pooty lonesome—dey ain' no kings here, is dey, Huck?'

'No.'

'Den he cain't git no situation. What he gwyne to do?'

'Well, I don't know. Some of them gets on the police, and some of them learns people how to talk French.'

'Why, Huck, doan' de French people talk de same way we does?'

'*No*, Jim; you couldn't understand a word they said—not a single word.'

'Well, now, I be ding-busted! How do dat come?'

'*I* don't know; but it's so. I got some of their jabber out of a book. S'pose a man was to come to you and say *Polly-voo-franzy*—what would you think?'

'I wouldn' think nuff'n; I'd take en bust him over de head. Dat is, if he warn't white. I wouldn' 'low no nigger to call me dat.'

'Shucks, it ain't calling you anything. It's only saying do you know how to talk French.'

'Well, den, why couldn't he *say* it?'

'Why, he *is* a-saying it. That's a Frenchman's *way* of saying it.'

'Well, it's a blame' ridicklous way, en I doan' want to hear no mo' 'bout it. Dey ain' no sense in it.'

'Looky here, Jim; does a cat talk like we do?'

'No, a cat don't.'

'Well, does a cow?'

'No, a cow don't, nuther.'

'Does a cat talk like a cow, or a cow talk like a cat?'

'No, dey don't.'

'It's natural and right for 'em to talk different from each other, ain't it?'

''Course.'

'And ain't it natural and right for a cat and a cow to talk different from *us*?'

'Why, mos' sholy it is.'

'Well, then, why ain't it natural and right for a *Frenchman* to talk different from us? You answer me that.'

'Is a cat a man, Huck?'

'No.'

'Well, den, dey ain't no sense in a cat talkin' like a man. Is a cow a man?—er is a cow a cat?'

'No, she ain't either of them.'

'Well, den, she ain't got no business to talk like either one er the yuther of 'em. Is a Frenchman a man?'

'Yes.'

'*Well*, den! Dad blame it, why doan' he *talk* like a man? You answer me *dat*!'

I see it warn't no use wasting words—you can't learn a nigger to argue. So I quit.

## *Chapter 15*

### HUCK LOSES THE RAFT—IN THE FOG—ASLEEP ON THE RAFT—HUCK FINDS THE RAFT—TRASH

WE judged that three nights more would fetch us to Cairo, at the bottom of Illinois, where the Ohio River comes in, and that was what we was after. We would sell the raft and get on a steamboat and go way up the Ohio amongst the free States, and then be out of trouble.

Well, the second night a fog begun to come on, and we made for a tow-head to tie to, for it wouldn't do to try to run in fog; but when I paddled ahead in the canoe, with the line, to make fast, there warn't anything but little saplings to tie to. I passed the line around one of them right on the edge of the cut bank, but there was a stiff current, and the raft come booming down so lively she tore it out by the roots and away she went. I see the fog closing down, and it made me so sick and scared I couldn't budge for most a half a minute it seemed to me —and then there warn't no raft in sight; you couldn't see twenty yards. I jumped into the canoe and run back to the stern and grabbed the paddle and set her back a stroke. But she didn't come. I was in such a hurry I hadn't untied her. I got up and tried to untie her, but I was so excited my hands shook so I couldn't hardly do anything with them.

As soon as I got started I took out after the raft, hot and heavy, right down the tow-head. That was all right as far as it went, but the tow-head warn't sixty yards long, and the minute I flew by the foot of it I shot out into the solid white fog, and hadn't no more idea which way I was going than a dead man.

Thinks I, it won't do to paddle; first I know I'll run into the bank or a tow-head or something; I got to set still and float, and yet it's mighty fidgety business to have to hold your hands still at such a time. I whooped and listened. Away down there, somewheres, I hears a small whoop, and up comes my spirits. I went tearing after it, listening sharp to hear it again. The next time it come, I see I warn't heading for it but heading away to the right of it. And the next time, I was heading away to the left of it—and not gaining on it much, either, for I was flying around, this way and that and t'other, but it was going straight ahead all the time.

I did wish the fool would think to beat a tin pan, and beat it all the time, but he never did, and it was the still places between the whoops that was making the trouble for me. Well, I fought along, and directly I hears the whoop *behind* me. I was tangled good, now. That was somebody else's whoop, or else I was turned around.

I throwed the paddle down. I heard the whoop again; it was behind me yet, but in a different place; it kept coming, and kept changing its place, and I kept answering, till by-and-by it was in front of me again and I knowed the current had swung the canoe's head down-stream and I was all right, if that was Jim and not some other raftsman hollering. I couldn't tell nothing about voices in a fog, for nothing don't look natural nor sound natural in a fog.

The whooping went on, and in about a minute I come a booming down on a cut bank with smoky ghosts of big trees on it, and the current throwed me off to the left and shot by, amongst a lot of snags that fairly roared, the current was tearing by them so swift.

In another second or two it was solid white and still again. I set perfectly still, then, listening to my heart thump, and I reckon I didn't draw a breath while it thumped a hundred.

I just give up, then. I knowed what the matter was. That cut bank was an island, and Jim had gone down t'other side of it. It warn't no tow-head, that you could float by in ten minutes. It had the big timber of a regular island; it might be five or six mile long and more than a half mile wide.

I kept quiet, with my ears cocked, about fifteen minutes, I reckon. I was floating along, of course, four or five mile an hour; but you don't ever think of that. No, you *feel* like you are laying dead still on the water; and if a little glimpse of a snag slips by, you don't think to yourself how fast *you're* going, but you catch your breath and think, my! how that snag's tearing along. If you think it ain't dismal and lonesome out in a fog that way, by yourself, in the night, you try it once—you'll see.

Next, for about a half an hour, I whoops now and then; at last I hears the answer a long ways off, and tries to follow it, but I couldn't do it, and directly I judged I'd got into a nest of tow-heads, for I had little dim glimpses of them on both sides of me, sometimes just a narrow channel between; and some that I couldn't see, I knowed was there, because I'd hear the wash of the current against the old dead brush and trash that hung over the banks. Well, I warn't long losing the whoops, down amongst the tow-heads; and I only tried to chase them a little while, anyway, because it was worse than chasing a Jack-o-lantern. You never knowed a sound dodge around so, and swap places so quick and so much.

I had to claw away from the bank pretty lively, four or five times, to keep from knocking the islands out of the river; and so I judged the raft must be butting into the bank every now and then, or else it would get further ahead and clear out of hearing—it was floating a little faster than what I was.

Well, I seemed to be in the open river again, by-and-by, but I couldn't hear no sign of a whoop nowheres. I reckoned Jim had fetched up on a snag, maybe, and it was all up with him. I was good and tired, so I laid down in the canoe and said I wouldn't bother no more. I didn't want to go to sleep, of course; but I was so sleepy I couldn't help it; so I thought I would take just one little cat-nap.

But I reckon it was more than a cat-nap, for when I waked up the stars was shining bright, the fog was all gone, and I was spinning down a big bend stern first. First I didn't know where I was; I thought I was dreaming; and when things begun to come back to me, they seemed to come up dim out of last week.

It was a monstrous big river here, with the tallest and the thickest kind of timber on both banks; just a solid wall, as well as I could see, by the stars. I looked away down-stream, and seen a black speck on the water. I took out after it; but when I got to it it warn't nothing bu a couple of saw-logs made fast together. Then I see another speck, and chased that; then another, and this time I was right. It was the raft.

When I got to it Jim was sitting there with his head down between his knees, asleep, with his right arm hanging over the steering-oar. The other oar was smashed off, and the raft was littered up with leaves and branches and dirt. So she'd had a rough time.

I made fast and laid down under Jim's nose on the raft, and begun to gap, and stretch my fists out against Jim, and says:

'Hello, Jim, have I been asleep? Why didn't you stir me up?'

'Goodness gracious, is dat you, Huck? En you ain' dead—you ain' drownded—you's back agin? It's too good for true, honey, it's too good for true. Lemme look at you, chile, lemme feel o' you. No, you ain' dead! you's back agin', live en soun', jis de same ole Huck—de same ole Huck, thanks to goodness!'

'What's the matter with you, Jim? You been a-drinking?'

'Drinkin'? Has I ben a-drinkin'? Has I had a chance to be a-drinkin'?'

'Well, then, what makes you talk so wild?'

'How does I talk wild?'

'*How*? Why, hain't you been talking about my coming back, and all that stuff, as if I'd been gone away?'

'Huck—Huck Finn, you look me in de eye, look me in de eye. *Hain't* you ben gone away?'

'Gone away? Why, what in the nation do you mean? I hain't been gone anywheres. Where would I go to?'

'Well, looky here, boss, dey's sumf'n wrong, dey is. Is I *me*, or who *is* I? Is I heah, or whah *is* I? Now dat's what I wants to know?'

'Well, I think you're here, plain enough, but I think you're a tangle-headed old fool, Jim.'

'I is, is I? Well you answer me dis. Didn't you tote out de line in de canoe, fer to make fas' to de tow-head?'

'No, I didn't. What tow-head? I hain't seen no tow-head.'

'You hain't seen no tow-head? Looky here—didn't de line pull loose en de raf' go a-hummin' down de river, en leave you en de canoe behine in de fog?'

'What fog?'

'Why *de* fog. De fog dat's ben aroun' all night. En didn't you whoop, en didn't I whoop, tell we got mix' up in de islands en one un us got los' en t'other one was jis' as good as los', 'kase he didn' know whah he wuz? En didn't I bust up agin a lot er dem islands en have a turrible time en mos' git drownded? Now ain' dat so, boss—ain't it so? You answer me dat.'

'Well, this is too many for me, Jim. I hain't seen no fog, nor no islands, nor no troubles, nor nothing. I been setting here talking with you all night till you went to sleep about ten minutes ago, and I reckon I done the same. You couldn't a got drunk in that time, so of course you've been dreaming.'

'Dad fetch it, how is I gwyne to dream all dat in ten minutes?'

'Well, hang it all, you did dream it, because there didn't any of it happen.'

'But Huck, it's all jis' as plain to me as——'

'It don't make no difference how plain it is, there ain't nothing in it. I know, because I've been here all the time.'

Jim didn't say nothing for about five minutes, but set there studying over it. Then he says:

'Well, den, I reck'n I did dream it, Huck; but dog my cats ef it ain't de powerfullest dream I ever see. En I hain't ever had no dream b'fo' dat's tired me like dis one.'

'Oh, well, that's all right, because a dream does tire a body like everything, sometimes. But this one was a staving dream—tell me all about it, Jim.'

So Jim went to work and told me the whole thing right through, just as it happened, only he painted it up considerable. Then he said he must start in and ''terpret' it, because it was sent for a warning. He said the first tow-head stood for a man that would try to do us some good, but the current was another man that would get us away from him. The whoops was warnings that would come to us every now and then, and if we didn't try hard to make out to understand them they'd just take us into bad luck, 'stead of keeping us out of it. The lot of tow-heads was troubles we was going to get into with quarrelsome people and all kinds of mean folks, but if we minded our business and didn't talk back and aggravate them, we would pull through and get out of the fog and into the big clear river, which was the free States, and wouldn't have no more trouble.

It had clouded up pretty dark just after I got on to the raft, but it was clearing up again, now.

'Oh, well, that's all interpreted well enough, as far as it goes, Jim,' I says; 'but what does *these* things stand for?'

It was the leaves and rubbish on the raft, and the smashed oar. You could see them first-rate, now.

Jim looked at the trash, and then looked at me, and back at the trash again. He had got the dream fixed so strong in his head that he couldn't seem to shake it loose and get the facts back into its place again, right away. But when he did get the thing straightened around, he looked at me steady, without ever smiling, and says:

'What do dey stan' for? I's gwyne to tell you. When I got all wore out wid work, en wid de callin' for you, en went to sleep, my heart wuz mos' broke bekase you wuz los', en I didn' k'yer no mo' what become er me en de raf'. En when I wake up en fine you back agin', all safe en soun', de tears come en I could a got down on my knees en kiss' yo' foot I's so thankful. En all you wuz thinkin' 'bout wuz how you could make a fool uv ole Jim wid a lie. Dat truck dah is *trash*; en trash is what people is dat puts dirt on de head er dey fren's en makes 'em ashamed.'

Then he got up slow, and walked to the wigwam, and went in there, without saying anything but that. But that was enough. It made me feel so mean I could almost kissed *his* foot to get him to take it back.

It was fifteen minutes before I could work myself up to go and humble myself to a nigger—but I done it, and I warn't ever sorry for it afterwards, neither. I didn't do him no more mean tricks, and I wouldn't done that one if I'd a knowed it would make him feel that way.

## *Chapter 16*

EXPECTATION—'GOOD OLE CAIRO'—A WHITE LIE—FLOATING CURRENCY—RUNNING BY CAIRO—SWIMMING ASHORE

WE slept most all day, and started out at night, a little ways behind a monstrous long raft that was as long going by as a procession. She had four long sweeps at each end, so we judged she carried as many as thirty men, likely. She had five big wigwams aboard, wide apart, and an open camp-fire in the middle, and a tall flag-pole at each end.

There was a power of style about her. It *amounted* to something being a raftsman on such a craft as that.

We went drifting down into a big bend, and the night clouded up and got hot. The river was very wide, and was walled with solid timber on both sides; you couldn't see a break in it hardly ever, or a light. We talked about Cairo, and wondered whether we would know it when we got to it. I said likely we wouldn't, because I had heard say there warn't but about a dozen houses there, and if they didn't happen to have them lit up, how was we going to know we was passing a town? Jim said if the two big rivers joined together there, that would show. But I said maybe we might think we was passing the foot of an island and coming into the same old river again. That disturbed Jim—and me too. So the question was, what to do? I said, paddle ashore the first time a light showed, and tell them pap was behind, coming along with a trading-scow, and was a green hand at the business, and wanted to know how far it was to Cairo. Jim thought it was a good idea, so we took a smoke on it and waited.

There warn't nothing to do, now, but to look out sharp for the town, and not pass it without seeing it. He said he'd be mighty sure to see it, because he'd be a free man the minute he seen it, but if he missed it he'd be in the slave country again and no more show for freedom. Every little while he jumps up and says:

'Dah she is!'

But it warn't. It was Jack-o-lanterns, or lightning-bugs; so he set down again, and went to watching, same as before. Jim said it made him all over trembly and feverish to be so close to freedom. Well, I can tell you it made me all over trembly and feverish, too, to hear him, because I begun to get it through my head that he *was* most free—and who was to blame for it? Why, *me.* I couldn't get that out of my conscience, no how nor no way. It got to troubling me so I couldn't rest; I couldn't stay still in one place. It hadn't ever come home to me before, what this thing was that I was doing. But now it did; and it staid with me, and scorched me more and more. I tried to make out to myself that *I* warn't to blame, because *I* didn't run Jim off from his rightful owner; but it warn't no use, conscience up and says, every time, 'But you knowed he was running for his freedom, and you could a paddled ashore and told somebody.' That was so—I couldn't get around that, no way. That was where it pinched. Conscience says to me, 'What had poor Miss Watson done to you, that you could see her nigger go off right under your eyes and never say one single word? What did that poor old woman do to you, that you could treat her so mean? Why, she tried to learn you your book, she tried to learn you your manners, she tried to be good to you every way she knowed how. *That's* what she done.'

I got to feeling so mean and so miserable I most wished I was dead. I fidgeted up and down the raft, abusing myself to myself, and Jim was fidgeting up and down past me. We neither of us could keep still. Every time he danced around and says, 'Dah's Cairo!' it went through me like a shot, and I thought if it *was* Cairo I reckoned I would die of miserableness.

Jim talked out loud all the time while I was talking to myself. He was saying how the first thing he would do when he got to a free State he would go to saving up money and never spend a single cent, and when he got enough he would buy his wife, which was owned on a farm close to where Miss Watson lived; and then they would both work to buy the two children, and if their master wouldn't sell them, they'd get an Ab'litionist to go and steal them.

It most froze me to hear such talk. He wouldn't ever dared to talk such talk in his life before. Just see what a difference it made in him the minute he judged he was about free. It was according to the old saying, 'Give a nigger an inch and he'll take an ell.' Thinks I, this is what comes of my not thinking. Here was this nigger which I had as good as helped to run away, coming right out flat-footed and saying he would steal his children—children that belonged to a man I didn't even know; a man that hadn't ever done me no harm.

I was sorry to hear Jim say that, it was such a lowering of him. My conscience got to stirring me up hotter than ever, until at last I says to it, 'Let up on me—it ain't too late, yet—I'll paddle ashore at the first light, and tell.' I felt easy, and happy, and light as a feather, right off. All my troubles was gone. I went to looking out sharp for a light, and sort of singing to myself. By-and-by one showed. Jim sings out:

'We's safe, Huck, we's safe! Jump up and crack yo' heels, dat's de good ole Cairo at las', I jis knows it!'

I says:

'I'll take the canoe and go see, Jim. It mightn't be, you know.'

He jumped and got the canoe ready, and put his old coat in the bottom for me to set on, and give me the paddle; and as I shoved off, he says:

'Pooty soon I'll be a-shout'n for joy, en I'll say, it's all on accounts o' Huck; I's a free man, en I couldn't ever ben free ef it hadn' been for Huck; Huck done it. Jim won't ever forgit you, Huck; you's de bes' fren' Jim's ever had; en you's de *only* fren' ole Jim's got now.'

I was paddling off, all in a sweat to tell on him; but when he says this, it seemed to kind of take the tuck all out of me. I went along slow then, and I warn't right down certain whether I was glad I started or whether I warn't. When I was fifty yards off, Jim says:

'Dah you goes, de ole true Huck; de on'y white genlman dat ever kep' his promise to ole Jim.'

Well, I just felt sick. But I says, I *got* to do it—I can't get *out* of it. Right then, along comes a skiff with two men in it, with guns, and they stopped and I stopped. One of them says:

'What's that, yonder?'

'A piece of a raft,' I says.

'Do you belong on it?'

'Yes, sir.'

'Any men on it?'

'Only one, sir.'

'Well, there's five niggers run off to-night, up yonder above the head of the bend. Is your man white or black?'

I didn't answer up prompt. I tried to, but the words wouldn't come. I tried, for a second or two, to brace up and out with it, but I warn't man enough—hadn't the spunk of a rabbit. I see I was weakening; so I just give up trying, and up and says:

'He's white.'

'I reckon we'll go and see for ourselves.'

'I wish you would,' says I, 'because it's pap that's there, and maybe you'd help me tow the raft ashore where the light is. He's sick—and so is mam and Mary Ann.'

'Oh, the devil! we're in a hurry, boy. But I s'pose we've got to. Come—buckle to your paddle, and let's get along.'

I buckled to my paddle and they laid to their oars. When we had made a stroke or two, I says:

'Pap'll be mighty much obleeged to you, I can tell you. Everybody goes away when I want them to help me tow the raft ashore, and I can't do it by myself.'

'Well, that's infernal mean. Odd, too. Say, boy, what's the matter with your father?'

'It's the—a—the—well, it ain't anything much.'

They stopped pulling. It warn't but a mighty ways to the raft, now. One says:

'Boy, that's a lie. What *is* the matter with your pap? Answer up square, now, and it'll be the better for you.'

'I will, sir, I will, honest—but don't leave us, please. It's the—the —gentlemen, if you'll only pull ahead, and let me heave you the head-line, you won't have to come a-near the raft—please do.'

'Set her back, John, set her back!' says one. They backed water. 'Keep away, boy—keep to looard. Confound it, I just expect the wind has blowed it to us. Your pap's got the smallpox, and you know it precious well. Why didn't you come out and say so? Do you want to spread it all over?'

'Well,' says I, a-blubbering, 'I've told everybody before, and then they just went away and left us.'

'Poor devil, there's something in that. We are right down sorry for you, but we—well, hang it, we don't want the smallpox, you see. Look here, I'll tell you what to do. Don't you try to land by yourself, or you'll smash everything to pieces. You float along down about twenty miles and you'll come to a town on the left-hand side of the river. It will be long after sun-up, then, and when you ask for help, you tell them your folks are all down with chills and fever. Don't be a fool again, and let people guess what is the matter. Now we're trying to do you a kindness; so you just put twenty miles between us, that's a good boy. It wouldn't do any good to land yonder where the light is—it's only a wood-yard. Say—I reckon your father's poor, and I'm bound to say he's in pretty hard luck. Here—I'll put a twenty-dollar gold piece on this board, and you get it when it floats by. I feel mighty mean to leave you, but my kingdom! it won't do to fool with smallpox, don't you see?'

'Hold on, Parker,' says the other man, 'here's a twenty to put on the board for me. Good-bye, boy, you do as Mr. Parker told you, and you'll be all right.'

'That's so, my boy—good-bye, good-bye. If you see any runaway niggers, you get help and nab them, and you can make some money by it.'

'Good-bye, sir,' says I, 'I won't let no runaway niggers get by me if I can help it.'

They went off and I got aboard the raft, feeling bad and low, because I knowed very well I had done wrong, and I see it warn't no use for me to try to learn to do right; a body that don't get *started* right when he's little, ain't got no show—when the pinch comes there ain't nothing to back him up and keep him to his work, and so he gets beat. Then I thought a minute, and says to myself, hold on,—s'pose you'd a done right and give Jim up; would you felt better than what you do now? No, says I, I'd feel bad—I'd feel just the same way I do now. Well, then, says I, what's the use you learning to do right, when it's troublesome to do right and ain't no trouble to do wrong, and the wages is just the same? I was stuck. I couldn't answer that. So I reckoned I wouldn't bother no more about it, but after this always do whichever come handiest at the time.

I went into the wigwam; Jim warn't there. I looked all around; he warn't anywhere. I says:

'Jim!'

'Here I is, Huck. Is dey out o' sight yit? Don't talk loud.'

He was in the river, under the stern oar, with just his nose out. I told him they was out of sight, so he come aboard. He says:

'I was a-listening' to all de talk, en I slips into de river en was gwyne to shove for sho' if dey come aboard. Den I was gwyne to swim to de raf' agin when dey was gone. But lawsy, how you did fool 'em, Huck! Dat *wuz* de smartes' dodge! I tell you, chile, I 'speck it save' ole Jim—ole Jim ain't gwyne to forgit you for dat, honey.'

Then we talked about the money. It was a pretty good raise, twenty dollars apiece. Jim said we could take deck passage on a steamboat now, and the money would last us as far as we wanted to go in the free States. He said twenty mile more warn't far for the raft to go, but he wished we was already there.

Towards daybreak we tied up, and Jim was mighty particular about hiding the raft good. Then he worked all day fixing things in bundles, and getting all ready to quit rafting.

That night about ten we hove in sight of the lights of a town away down in a left-hand bend.

I went off in the canoe, to ask about it. Pretty soon I found a man out in the river with a skiff, setting a trot-line. I ranged up and says: 'Mister, is that town Cairo?'

'Cairo? no. You must be a blame' fool.'

'What town is it, mister?'

'If you want to know, go and find out. If you stay here botherin' around me for about half a minute longer, you'll get something you won't want.'

I paddled to the raft. Jim was awful disappointed, but I said never mind, Cairo would be the next place, I reckoned.

We passed another town before daylight, and I was going out again; but it was high ground, so I didn't go. No high ground about Cairo, Jim said. I had forgot it. We laid up for the day, on a tow-head tolerably close to the left-hand bank. I begun to suspicion something. So did Jim. I says:

'Maybe we went by Cairo in the fog that night.'

He says:

'Doan' less' talk about it, Huck. Po' niggers can't have no luck. I awluz 'spected dat rattlesnake skin warn't done wid its work.'

'I wish I'd never seen that snake-skin, Jim—I do wish I'd never laid eyes on it.'

'It ain't yo' fault, Huck; you didn't know. Don't you blame yo'self 'bout it.'

When it was daylight, here was the clear Ohio water in shore, sure enough, and outside was the old regular Muddy! So it was all up with Cairo.

We talked it all over. It wouldn't do to take to the shore; we couldn't take the raft up the stream, of course. There warn't no way but to wait for dark, and start back in the canoe and take the chances. So we slept all day amongst the cotton-wood thicket, so as to be fresh for the work, and when we went back to the raft about dark the canoe was gone!

We didn't say a word for a good while. There warn't anything to say. We both knowed well enough it was some more work of the rattle-snake skin; so what was the use to talk about it? It would only look like we was finding fault, and that would be bound to fetch more bad luck—and keep on fetching it, too, till we knowed enough to keep still.

By-and-by we talked about what we better do, and found there warn't no way but just to go along down with the raft till we got a chance to buy a canoe to go back in. We warn't going to borrow it when there warn't anybody around, the way pap would do, for that might set people after us.

So we shoved out, after dark, on the raft.

Anybody that don't believe yet, that it's foolishness to handle a snake-skin, after all that that snake-skin done for us, will believe it now, if they read on and see what more it done for us.

The place to buy canoes is off of rafts laying up at shore. But we didn't see no rafts laying up; so we went along during three hours and more. Well, the night got grey, and ruther thick, which is the next meanest thing to fog. You can't tell the shape of the river, and you can't see no distance. It got to be very late and still, and then along comes a steamboat up the river. We lit the lantern, and judged she would see it. Up-stream boats didn't generly come close to us; they go out and follow the bars and hunt for easy water under the reefs; but nights like this they bull right up the channel against the whole river.

We could hear her pounding along, but we didn't see her good till she was close. She aimed right for us. Often they do that and try to see how close they can come without touching; sometimes the wheel bites off a sweep, and then the pilot sticks his head out and laughs, and thinks he's mighty smart. Well, here she comes, and we said she was going to try to shave us; but she didn't seem to be sheering off a bit. She was a big one, and she was coming in a hurry, too, looking like a black cloud with rows of glow-worms around it; but all of a sudden she bulged out, big and scary, with a long row of wide-open furnace doors shining like red-hot teeth, and her monstrous bows and guards hanging right over us. There was a yell at us, and a jingling of bells to stop the engines, a pow-wow of cussing, and whistling of steam—and as Jim went overboard on one side and I on the other, she come smashing straight through the raft.

I dived—and I aimed to find the bottom, too, for a thirty-foot wheel had got to go over me, and I wanted it to have plenty of room. I could always stay under-water a minute; this time I reckon I staid under-water a minute and a half. Then I bounced for the top in a hurry, for I was nearly busting. I popped out to my arm-pits and blowed the water out of my nose, and puffed a bit. Of course there was a booming current; and of course that boat started her engines again ten seconds after she stopped them, for they never cared much for raftsmen; so now she was churning along up the river, out of sight in the thick weather, though I could hear her.

I sung out for Jim about a dozen times, but I didn't get any answer; so I grabbed a plank that touched me while I was 'treading water,' and struck out for shore, shoving it ahead of me. But I made out to see that the drift of the current was towards the left-hand shore, which meant that I was in a crossing; so I changed off and went that way.

It was one of these long, slanting, two-mile crossings; so I was a good long time in getting over. I made a safe landing, and clumb up the bank. I couldn't see but a little ways, but I went poking along over rough ground for a quarter of a mile or more, and then I run across a big old-fashioned double log house before I noticed it. I was going to rush by and get away, but a lot of dogs jumped out and went to howling and barking at me, and I knowed better than to move another peg.

## *Chapter 17*

AN EVENING CALL—THE FARM IN ARKANSAW—INTERIOR DECORATIONS—STEPHEN DOWLING BOTS—POETICAL EFFUSIONS —A TIN PAN PIANO

IN about half a minute somebody spoke out of a window, without putting his head out, and says:

'Be done, boys! Who's there?'

I says:

'It's me.'

'Who's me?'

'George Jackson, sir.'

'What do you want?'

'I don't want nothing, sir. I only want to go along by, but the dogs won't let me.'

'What are you prowling around here this time of night for—hey?'

'I warn't prowling around, sir; I fell overboard off of the steamboat.'

'Oh, you did, did you? Strike a light there, somebody. What did you say your name was?'

'George Jackson, sir. I'm only a boy.'

'Look here; if you're telling the truth, you needn't be afraid—nobody'll hurt you. But don't try to budge; stand right where you are. Rouse out Bob and Tom, some of you, and fetch the guns. George Jackson, is there anybody with you?'

'No, sir, nobody.'

I heard the people stirring around in the house, now, and see a light. The man sung out:

'Snatch that light away, Betsy, you old fool—ain't you got any sense? Put it on the floor behind the front door. Bob, if you and Tom are ready, take your places.'

'All ready.'

'Now, George Jackson, do you know the Shepherdsons?'

'No, sir—I never heard of them.'

'Well, that may be so, and it mayn't. Now, all ready. Step forward, George Jackson. And mind, don't you hurry—come mighty slow. If there's anybody with you, let him keep back—if he shows himself he'll be shot. Come along, now. Come slow; push the door open, yourself—just enough to squeeze in, d'you hear?'

I didn't hurry, I couldn't if I'd a wanted to. I took one slow step at a time, and there warn't a sound, only I thought I could hear my heart. The dogs were as still as the humans, but they followed a little behind me. When I got to the three log door-steps, I heard them unlocking and unbarring and unbolting. I put my hand on the door and pushed it a little and a little more, till somebody said, 'There, that's enough—put your head in.' I done it, but I judged they would take it off.

The candle was on the floor, and there they all was, looking at me, and me at them, for about a quarter of a minute. Three big men with guns pointed at me, which made me wince, I tell you; the oldest, grey and about sixty, the other two thirty or more—all of them fine and handsome—and the sweetest old grey-headed lady, and back of her two young women which I couldn't see right well. The old gentleman says:

'There—I reckon it's all right. Come in.'

As soon as I was in, the old gentleman he locked the door and barred it and bolted it, and told the young men to come in with their guns, and they all went in a big parlour that had a new rag carpet on the floor, and got together in a corner that was out of range of the front windows—there warn't none on the side. They held the candle, and took a good look at me, and all said, 'Why, *he* ain't a Shepherdson—no, there ain't any Shepherdson about him.' Then the old man said he hoped I wouldn't mind being searched for arms, because he didn't mean no harm by it—it was only to make sure. So he didn't pry into my pockets, but only felt outside with his hands, and said it was all right. He told me to make myself easy and at home, and tell all about myself; but the old lady says:

'Why bless you, Saul, the poor thing's as wet as he can be; and don't you reckon it may be he's hungry?'

'True for you, Rachel—I forgot.'

So the old lady says:

'Betsy' (this was a nigger woman), 'you fly around and get him something to eat, as quick as you can, poor thing; and one of you girls go and wake up Buck and tell him——Oh, here he is himself. Buck, take this little stranger and get the wet clothes off from him and dress him up in some of yours that's dry.'

Buck looked about as old as me—thirteen or fourteen or along there, though he was a little bigger than me. He hadn't on anything but a shirt, and he was very frowsy-headed. He come in gaping and digging one fist into his eyes, and he was dragging a gun along with the other one. He says:

'Ain't they no Shepherdsons around?'

They said, no, 'twas a false alarm.

'Well,' he says, 'if they'd a ben some, I reckon I'd a got one.'

They all laughed, and Bob says:

'Why, Buck, they might have scalped us all, you've been so slow in coming.'

'Well, nobody come after me, and it ain't right. I'm always kep' down; I don't get no show.'

'Never mind, Buck, my boy,' says the old man, 'you'll have show enough, all in good time, don't you fret about that. Go 'long with you now, and do as your mother told you.'

When we got upstairs to his room, he got me a coarse shirt and a roundabout and pants of his, and I put them on. While I was at it he asked me what my name was, but before I could tell him, he started to telling me about a blue jay and a young rabbit he had catched in the woods day before yesterday, and he asked me where Moses was when the candle went out. I said I didn't know; I hadn't heard about it before, no way.

'Well, guess,' he says.

'How'm I going to guess,' says I, 'when I never heard tell about it before?'

'But you can guess, can't you? It's just as easy.'

'*Which* candle?' I says.

'Why, any candle,' he says.

'I don't know where he was,' says I; 'where was he?'

'Why, he was in the *dark*! That's where he was!'

'Well, if you knowed where he was, what did you ask me for?'

'Why, blame it, it's a riddle, don't you see? Say, how long are you going to stay here? You got to stay always. We can just have booming times—they don't have no school now. Do you own a dog? I've got a dog—and he'll go in the river and bring out chips that you throw in. Do you like to comb up, Sundays, and all that kind of foolishness? You bet I don't, but ma she makes me. Confound these old britches, I reckon I'd better put 'em on, but I'd ruther not, it's so warm. Are you all ready? All right—come along, old hoss.'

Cold corn-pone, cold corn-beef, butter and butter-milk—that is what they had for me down there, and there ain't nothing better that ever I've come across yet. Buck and his ma and all of them smoked cob pipes, except the nigger woman, which was gone, and the two young women. They all smoked and talked, and I eat and talked. The young women had quilts around them, and their hair down their backs. They all asked me questions, and I told them how pap and me and all the family was living on a little farm down at the bottom of Arkansaw, and my sister Mary Ann run off and got married and never was heard of no more, and Bill went to hunt them and he warn't heard of no more, and Tom and Mort died, and then there warn't nobody but just me and pap left, and he was just trimmed down to nothing, on account of his troubles; so when he died I took what there was left, because the farm didn't belong to us, and started up the river, deck passage, and fell overboard; and that was how I come to be here. So they said I could have a home there as long as I wanted it. Then it was most daylight, and everybody went to bed, and I went to bed with Buck, and when I waked up in the morning, drat it all, I had forgot what my name was. So I laid there about an hour trying to think, and when Buck waked up, I says:

'Can you spell, Buck?'

'Yes,' he says.

'I bet you can't spell my name,' says I.

'I bet you what you dare I can,' says he.

'All right,' says I, 'go ahead.'

'G-o-r-g-e J-a-x-o-n—there now,' he says.

'Well,' says I, 'you done it, but I didn't think you could. It ain't no slouch of a name to spell—right off without studying.'

I set it down, private, because somebody might want *me* to spell it, next, and so I wanted to be handy with it and rattle it off like I was used to it.

It was a mighty nice family, and a mighty nice house, too. I hadn't seen no house out in the country before that was so nice and had so much style. It didn't have an iron latch on the front door, nor a wooden one with a buckskin string, but a brass knob to turn, the same as houses in a town. There warn't no bed in the parlour, not a sign of a bed; but heaps of parlours in towns has beds in them. There was a big fireplace that was bricked on the bottom, and the bricks was kept clean and red by pouring water on them and scrubbing them with another brick; sometimes they washed them over with red water-paint that they call Spanish-brown, same as they do in town. They had big brass dog-irons that could hold up a saw-log. There was a clock on the middle of the mantelpiece, with a picture of a town painted on the bottom half of the glass front, and a round place in the middle of it for the sun, and you could see the pendulum swing behind it. It was beautiful to hear that clock tick; and sometimes when one of these peddlers had been along and scoured her up and got her in good shape, she would start in and strike a hundred and fifty before she got tuckered out. They wouldn't took any money for her.

Well, there was a big outlandish parrot on each side of the clock, made out of something like chalk, and painted up gaudy. By one of the parrots was a cat made of crockery, and a crockery dog by the other; and when you pressed down on them they squeaked, but didn't open their mouths nor look different nor interested. They squeaked through underneath. There was a couple of big wild-turkey-wing fans spread out behind those things. On a table in the middle of the room was a kind of a lovely crockery basket that had apples and oranges and peaches and grapes piled up in it, which was much redder and yellower and prettier than real ones is, but they warn't real because you could see where pieces had got chipped off and showed the white chalk, or whatever it was, underneath.

This table had a cover made out of beautiful oil-cloth, with a red and blue spread-eagle painted on it, and a painted border all around. It come all the way from Philadelphia, they said. There was some books, too, piled up perfectly exact, on each corner of the table. One was a big family Bible, full of pictures. One was *Pilgrim's Progress*, about a man that left his family it didn't say why. I read considerable in it now and then. The statements was interesting, but tough. Another was *Friendship's Offering*, full of beautiful stuff and poetry; but I didn't read the poetry. Another was Henry Clay's Speeches, and another was Dr. Gunn's Family Medicine, which told you all about what to do if a body was sick or dead. There was a Hymn Book, and a lot of other books. And there was nice split-bottom chairs, and perfectly sound, too—not bagged down in the middle and busted, like an old basket.

They had pictures hung on the walls—mainly Washingtons and Lafayettes, and battles, and Highland Marys, and one called 'Signing the Declaration.' There was some that they called crayons, which one of the daughters which was dead made her own self when she was only fifteen years old. They was different from any pictures I ever see before; blacker, mostly, than is common. One was a woman in a slim black dress, belted small under the arm-pits, with bulges like a cabbage in the middle of the sleeves, and a large black scoop-shovel bonnet with a black veil, and white slim ankles crossed about with black tape, and very wee black slippers, like a chisel, and she was leaning pensive on a tombstone on her right elbow, under a weeping willow, and her other hand hanging down her side holding a white handkerchief and a reticule, and underneath the picture it said, 'Shall I Never See Thee More Alas?' Another one was a young lady with her hair all combed up straight to the top of her head, and knotted there in front of a comb like a chair-back, and she was crying into a handkerchief and had a dead bird laying on its back in her other hand with its heels up, and underneath the picture it said, 'I Shall Never Hear Thy Sweet Chirrup More Alas!' There was one where a young lady was at a window looking up at the moon, and tears running down her cheeks; and she had an open letter in one hand with black sealing-wax showing on one edge of it, and she was mashing a locket with a chain to it against her mouth, and underneath the picture it said, 'And Art Thou Gone Yes Thou Art Gone Alas!' These was all nice pictures, I reckon, but I didn't somehow seem to take to them, because if ever I was down a little, they always give me the fan-tods. Everybody was sorry she died, because she had laid out a lot more of these pictures to do, and a body could see by what she had done what they had lost. But I reckoned, that with her disposition, she was having a better time in the graveyard. She was at work on what they said was her greatest picture when she took sick, and every day and every night it was her prayer to be allowed to live till she got it done, but she never got the chance. It was a picture of a young woman in a long white gown, standing on the rail of a bridge all ready to jump off, with her hair all down her back, and looking up to the moon, with the tears running down her face, and she had two arms folded across her breast, and two arms stretched out in front, and two more reaching up towards the moon—and the idea was, to see which pair would look best and then scratch out all the other arms; but, as I was saying, she died before she got her mind made up, and now they kept this picture over the head of the bed in her room, and every time her birthday come they hung flowers on it. Other times it was hid with a little curtain. The young woman in the picture had a kind of a nice sweet face, but there was so many arms it made her look too spidery, seemed to me.

This young girl kept a scrap-book when she was alive, and used to paste obituaries and accidents and cases of patient suffering in it out of the *Presbyterian Observer*, and write poetry after them out of her own head. It was very good poetry. This is what she wrote about a boy by the name of Stephen Dowling Bots that fell down a well and was drowned:

ODE TO STEPHEN DOWLING BOTS, DEC'D.

And did young Stephen sicken,
And did young Stephen die?
And did the sad hearts thicken,
And did the mourners cry?

No; such was not the fate of
Young Stephen Dowling Bots;
Though sad hearts round him thickened,
'Twas not from sickness' shots.

No whooping-cough did rack his frame,
Nor measles drear, with spots:
Not these impaired the sacred name
Of Stephen Dowling Bots.

Despised love struck not with woe
That head of curly knots,
Nor stomach troubles laid him low,
Young Stephen Dowling Bots.

Oh no. Then list with tearful eye,
Whilst I his fate do tell.
His soul did from this cold world fly,
By falling down a well.

They got him out and emptied him;
Alas, it was too late;
His spirit was gone for to sport aloft
In the realms of the good and great.

If Emmeline Grangerford could make poetry like that before she was fourteen, there ain't no telling what she could a done by-and-by. Buck said she could rattle off poetry like nothing. She didn't ever have to stop to think. He said she would slap down a line, and if she couldn't find anything to rhyme with it she would just scratch it out and slap down another one, and go ahead. She warn't particular, she could write about anything you choose to give her to write about, just so it was sadful. Every time a man died, or a woman died, or a child died, she would be on hand with her 'tribute' before he was cold. She called them tributes. The neighbours said it was the doctor first, then Emmeline, then the undertaker—the undertaker never got in ahead of Emmeline but once, and then she hung fire on a rhyme for the dead person's name, which was Whistler. She warn't ever the same, after that; she never complained, but she kind of pined away and did not live long. Poor thing, many 's the time I made myself go up to the little room that used to be hers and get out her poor old scrap-book and read in it when her pictures had been aggravating me and I had soured on her a little. I liked all that family, dead ones and all, and warn't going to let anything come between us. Poor Emmeline made poetry about all the dead people when she was alive, and it didn't seem right that there warn't nobody to make some about her, now she was gone; so I tried to sweat out a verse or two myself, but I couldn't seem to make it go, somehow. They kept Emmeline's room trim and nice and all the things fixed in it just the way she liked to have them when she was alive, and nobody ever slept there. The old lady took care of the room herself, though there was plenty of niggers, and she sewed there a good deal and read her Bible there, mostly.

Well, as I was saying about the parlour, there was beautiful curtains on the windows: white, with pictures painted on them, of castles with vines all down the walls, and cattle coming down to drink. There was a little old piano, too, that had tin pans in it, I reckon, and nothing was ever so lovely as to hear the young ladies sing 'The Last Link is Broken' and play 'The Battle of Prague' on it. The walls of all the rooms was plastered, and most had carpets on the floors, and the whole house was whitewashed on the outside.

It was a double house, and the big open place betwixt them was roofed and floored, and sometimes the table was set there in the middle of the day, and it was a cool, comfortable place. Nothing couldn't be better. And warn't the cooking good, and just bushels of it too!

## *Chapter 18*

COL. GRANGERFORD—ARISTOCRACY—FEUDS—THE TESTAMENT—'WATER-MOCCASINS!'—RECOVERING THE RAFT—THE WOOD PILE—PORK AND CABBAGE—'IS DAT YOU, HONEY?'

COL. GRANGERFORD was a gentleman, you see. He was a gentleman all over; and so was his family. He was well born, as the saying is, and that's worth as much in a man as it is in a horse, so the Widow Douglas said, and nobody ever denied that she was of the first aristocracy in our town; and pap he always said it, too, though he warn't no more quality than a mud-cat, himself. Col. Grangerford was very tall and very slim, and had a darkish-paly complexion, not a sign of red in it anywheres; he was clean-shaved every morning, all over his thin face, and he had the thinnest kind of lips, and the thinnest kind of nostrils, and a high nose, and heavy eyebrows, and the blackest kind of eyes, sunk so deep back that they seemed like they was looking out of caverns at you, as you may say. His forehead was high, and his hair was black and straight, and hung to his shoulders. His hands was long and thin, and every day of his life he put on a clean shirt and a full suit from head to foot made out of linen so white it hurt your eyes to look at it; and on Sundays he wore a blue tail-coat with brass buttons on it. He carried a mahogany cane with a silver head to it. There warn't no frivolishness about him, not a bit, and he warn't ever loud. He was as kind as he could be—you could feel that, you know, and so you had confidence. Sometimes he smiled, and it was good to see; but when he straightened himself up like a liberty-pole, and the lightning begun to flicker out from under his eyebrows, you wanted to climb a tree first, and find out what the matter was afterwards. He didn't ever have to tell anybody to mind their manners—everybody was always good-mannered where he was. Everybody loved to have him around, too; he was sunshine most always—I mean he made it seem like good weather. When he turned into a cloud-bank it was awful dark for a half a minute, and that was enough; there wouldn't nothing go wrong again for a week.

When him and the old lady come down in the morning, all the family got up out of their chairs and give them good-day, and didn't set down again till they had set down. Then Tom and Bob went to the sideboard where the decanters was, and mixed a glass of bitters and handed it to him, and he held it in his hand and waited till Tom's and Bob's was mixed, and then they bowed and said, 'Our duty to you, sir, and madam'; and *they* bowed the least bit in the world and said thank you, and so they drank, all three, and Bob and Tom poured a spoonful of water on the sugar and the mite of whisky or apple brandy in the bottom of their tumblers, and give it to me and Buck, and we drank to the old people too.

Bob was the oldest, and Tom next. Tall, beautiful men with very broad shoulders and brown faces, and long black hair and black eyes. They dressed in white linen from head to foot, like the old gentleman, and wore broad Panama hats.

Then there was Miss Charlotte, she was twenty-five, and tall and proud and grand, but as good as she could be, when she warn't stirred up; but when she was, she had a look that would make you wilt in your tracks, like her father. She was beautiful.

So was her sister, Miss Sophia, but it was a different kind. She was gentle and sweet, like a dove, and she was only twenty.

Each person had their own nigger to wait on them—Buck, too. My nigger had a monstrous easy time, because I warn't used to having anybody do anything for me, but Buck's was on the jump most of the time.

This was all there was of the family, now; but there used to be more—three sons; they got killed; and Emmeline that died.

The old gentleman owned a lot of farms, and over a hundred niggers. Sometimes a stack of people would come there, horseback, from ten or fifteen mile around, and stay five or six days, and have such junketings round about and on the river, and dances and picnics in the woods, day-times, and balls at the house, nights. These people was mostly kin-folks of the family. The men brought their guns with them. It was a handsome lot of quality, I tell you.

There was another clan of aristocracy around there—five or six families—mostly of the name of Shepherdson. They was as high-toned, and well born, and rich and grand, as the tribe of Grangerfords. The Shepherdsons and the Grangerfords used the same steamboat landing, which was about two mile above our house; so sometimes when I went up there with a lot of our folks I used to see a lot of the Shepherdsons there, on their fine horses.

One day Buck and me was away out in the woods, hunting, and heard a horse coming. We was crossing the road. Buck says:

'Quick! Jump for the woods!'

We done it, and then peeped down the woods through the leaves. Pretty soon a splendid young man come galloping down the road, setting his horse easy and looking like a soldier. He had his gun across his pommel. I had seen him before. It was young Harney Shepherdson. I heard Buck's gun go off at my ear, and Harney's hat tumbled off from his head. He grabbed his gun and rode straight to the place where we was hid. But we didn't wait. We started through the woods on a run. The woods warn't thick, so I looked over my shoulder, to dodge the bullet, and twice I seen Harney cover Buck with his gun; and then he rode away the way he come—to get his hat, I reckon, but I couldn't see. We never stopped running till we got home. The old gentleman's eyes blazed a minute—'twas pleasure, mainly, I judged—then his face sort of smoothed down, and he says, kind of gentle:

'I don't like that shooting from behind a bush. Why didn't you step into the road, my boy?'

'The Shepherdsons don't, father. They always take advantage.'

Miss Charlotte she held her head up like a queen while Buck was telling his tale, and her nostrils spread and her eyes snapped. The two young men looked dark, but never said nothing. Miss Sophia she turned pale, but the colour come back when she found the man warn't hurt.

Soon as I could get Buck down by the corn-cribs under the trees by ourselves, I says:

'Did you want to kill him, Buck?'

'Well, I bet I did.'

'What did he do to you?'

'Him? He never done nothing to me.'

'Well, then, what did you want to kill him for?'

'Why, nothing—only it's on account of the feud.'

'What's a feud?'

'Why, where was you raised? Don't you know what a feud is?'

'Never heard of it before—tell me about it.'

'Well,' says Buck, 'a feud is this way. A man has a quarrel with another man, and kills him; then that other man's brother kills *him*; then the other brothers, on both sides, goes for one another; then the *cousins* chip in—and by-and-by everybody's killed off, and there ain't no more feud. But it's kind of slow, and takes a long time.'

'Has this one been going on long, Buck?'

'Well, I should *reckon*! it started thirty year ago, or som'ers along there. There was trouble 'bout something and then a lawsuit to settle it; and the suit went agin one of the men, and so he up and shot the man that won the suit—which he would naturally do, of course. Anybody would.'

'What was the trouble about, Buck?—land?'

'I reckon maybe—I don't know.'

'Well, who done the shooting?—was it a Grangerford or a Shepherdson?'

'Laws, how do *I* know? it was so long ago.'

'Don't anybody know?'

'Oh, yes, pa knows, I reckon, and some of the other old folks; but they don't know now what the row was about in the first place.'

'Has there been many killed, Buck?'

'Yes—right smart chance of funerals. But they don't always kill. Pa's got a few buck-shot in him; but he don't mind it 'cuz he don't weigh much anyway. Bob's been carved up some with a bowie, and Tom's been hurt once or twice.'

'Has anybody been killed this year, Buck?'

'Yes, we got one and they got one. 'Bout three months ago, my cousin Bud, fourteen year old, was riding through the woods, on t'other side of the river, and didn't have no weapon with him, which was blame' foolishness, and in a lonesome place he hears a horse a-coming behind him, and sees old Baldy Shepherdson a-linkin' after him with his gun in his hand and his white hair a-flying in the wind; and 'stead of jumping off and taking to the brush, Bud 'lowed he could outrun him; so they had it, nip and tuck, for five mile or more, the old man a-gaining all the time; so at last Bud seen it warn't any use, so he stopped and faced around so as to have the bullet-holes in front, you know, and the old man he rode up and shot him down. But he didn't git much chance to enjoy his luck, for inside of a week our folks laid *him* out.'

'I reckon that old man was a coward, Buck.'

'I reckon he *warn't* a coward. Not by a blame' sight. There ain't a coward amongst them Shepherdsons—not a one. And there ain't no cowards amongst the Grangerfords, either. Why, that old man kep' up his end in a fight one day, for a half an hour, against three Grangerfords, and come out winner. They was all a-horseback; he lit off of his horse and got behind a little wood-pile, and kep' his horse before him to stop the bullets; but the Grangerfords staid on their horses and capered around the old man, and peppered away at him, and he peppered away at them. Him and his horse both went home pretty leaky and crippled, but the Grangerfords had to be *fetched* home—and one of 'em was dead, and another died the next day. No, sir, if a body 's out hunting for cowards, he don't want to fool away any time amongst them Shepherdsons, becuz they don't breed any of that *kind*.'

Next Sunday we all went to church, about three mile, everybody a-horseback. The men took their guns along, so did Buck, and kept them between their knees or stood them handy against the wall. The Shepherdsons done the same. It was pretty ornery preaching—all about brotherly love, and such-like tiresomeness; but everybody said it was a good sermon, and they all talked it over going home, and had such a powerful lot to say about faith, and good works, and free grace, and prefore-ordestination, and I don't know what all, that it did seem to me to be one of the roughest Sundays I had run across yet.

About an hour after dinner everybody was dozing around, some in their chairs and some in their rooms, and it got to be pretty dull. Buck and a dog was stretched out on the grass in the sun, sound asleep. I went up to our room, and judged I would take a nap myself. I found that sweet Miss Sophia standing in her door, which was next to ours, and she took me in her room and shut the door very soft, and asked me if I liked her, and I said I did; and she asked me if I would do something for her and not tell anybody, and I said I would. Then she said she'd forgot her Testament, and left it in the seat at church, between two other books, and would I slip out quiet and go there and fetch it to her, and not say nothing to nobody. I said I would. So I slid out and slipped off up the road, and there warn't anybody at the church, except maybe a hog or two, for there warn't any lock on the door, and hogs likes a puncheon floor in summer-time because it's cool. If you notice, most folks don't go to church only when they've got to; but a hog is different.

Says I to myself something 's up—it ain't natural for a girl to be in such a sweat about a Testament; so I give it a shake, and out drops a little piece of paper with '*Half-past-two*' wrote on it with a pencil. I ransacked it, but couldn't find anything else. I couldn't make anything out of that, so I put the paper in the book again, and when I got home and upstairs, there was Miss Sophia in her door waiting for me. She pulled me in and shut the door; then she looked in the Testament till she found the paper, and as soon as she read it she looked glad; and before a body could think, she grabbed me and give me a squeeze, and said I was the best boy in the world, and not to tell anybody. She was mighty red in the face, for a minute, and her eyes lighted up, and it made her powerful pretty. I was a good deal astonished, but when I got my breath I asked her what the paper was about, and she asked me if I had read it, and I said 'no', and she asked me if I could read writing, and I told her, 'No, only coarse-hand,' and then she said the paper warn't anything but a book-mark to keep her place, and I might go and play now.

I went off down to the river, studying over this thing, and pretty soon I noticed that my nigger was following along behind. When we was out of sight of the house, he looked back and around a second, and then comes a-running, and says:

'Mars Jawge, if you'll come down into de swamp, I'll show you a whole stack o' water-moccasins.'

Thinks I, that 's mighty curious; he said that yesterday. He oughter know a body don't love water-moccasins enough to go around hunting for them. What is he up to anyway? So I says:

'All right, trot ahead.'

I followed a half a mile, then he struck out over the swamp and waded ankle deep as much as another half-mile. We come to a little flat piece of land which was dry and very thick with trees and bushes and vines, and he says:

'You shove right in dah, jist a few steps, Mars Jawge, dah 's whah dey is. I 's seed 'm befo', I don't k'yer to see'm no mo'.

Then he slopped right along and went away, and pretty soon the trees hid him. I poked into the place a-ways, and come to a little open patch as big as a bedroom, all hung around with vines, and found a man laying there asleep—and by jings it was my old Jim!

I waked him up, and I reckoned it was going to be a grand surprise to him to see me again, but it warn't. He nearly cried, he was so glad, but he warn't surprised. Said he swum along behind me, that night, and heard me yell every time, but dasn't answer, because he didn't want nobody to pick *him* up, and take him into slavery again. Says he:

'I got hurt a little, en couldn't swim fas', so I wuz a considable ways behine you, towards de las'; when you landed I reck'ned I could ketch up wid you on de lan' 'doubt havin' to shout at you, but when I see dat house I begin to go slow. I 'uz off too fur to hear what dey say to you—I wuz 'fraid o' de dogs—but when it 'uz all quiet agin, I knowed you 's in de house, so I struck out for de woods to wait for day. Early in de mawnin' some er de niggers come along, gwyne to de fields, en dey tuck me en showed me dis place, whah de dogs can't track me on accounts o' de water, en dey brings me truck to eat every night, en tells me how you 's a-gitt'n along.'

'Why didn't you tell my Jack to fetch me here sooner, Jim?'

'Well, 'twarn't no use to 'sturb you, Huck, tell we could do sumfn—

but we's all right, now. I ben a-buyin' pots en pans en vittles, as I got a chanst, en a-patchin' up de raf', nights, when——'

'*What* raft, Jim?'

'Our ole raf'.'

'You mean to say our old raft warn't smashed all to flinders?'

'No, she warn't. She was tore up a good deal—one en' of her was—but dey warn't no great harm done, on'y our traps was mos' all los'. Ef we hadn' dive' so deep en swum so fur under-water, en de night hadn' ben so dark, en we warn't so sk'yerd, en ben sich punkin-heads, as de sayin' is, we'd a seed de raf'. But it's jis' as well we didn't, 'kase now she's all fixed up agin mos' as good as new, en we's got a new lot o' stuff, too, in de place o' what 'uz los'.'

'Why, how did you get hold of the raft again, Jim—did you catch her?'

'How I gwyne to ketch her, en I out in de woods? No, some er de niggers foun' her ketched on a snag, along heah in de ben', en dey hid her in a crick, 'mongst de willows, en dey wuz so much jawin' 'bout which un 'um she b'long to de mos', dat I come to heah 'bout it pooty soon, so I ups en settles de trouble by tellin' 'um she don't b'long to none uv um, but to you en me; en I ast 'm if dey gwyne to grab a young white genlman's propaty, en git a hid'n for it? Den I gin 'm ten cents apiece, en dey 'uz mighty well satisfied, en wisht some mo' raf's 'ud come along en make 'm rich agin. Dey's mighty good to me, dese niggers is, en whatever I wants 'm to do fur me, I doan' have to ast 'm twice, honey. Dat Jack's a good nigger, en pooty smart.'

'Yes, he is. He ain't ever told me you was here; told me to come, and he'd show me a lot of water-moccasins. If anything happens, *he* ain't mixed up in it. He can say he never seen us together, and it'll be the truth.'

I don't want to talk much about the next day. I reckon I'll cut it pretty short. I waked up about dawn, and was agoing to turn over and go to sleep again, when I noticed how still it was—didn't seem to be anybody stirring. That warn't usual. Next I noticed that Buck was up and gone. Well, I gets up, a-wondering, and goes downstairs—nobody around; everything as still as a mouse. Just the same outside; thinks I, what does it mean? Down by the wood-pile I comes across my Jack, and says:

'What's it all about?'

Says he:

'Don't you know, Mars Jawge?'

'No,' says I, 'I don't.'

'Well, den, Miss Sophia's run off! 'deed she has. She run off in de night, sometime—nobody don't know jis' when—run off to git married to dat young Harney Shepherdson, you know—leastways, so dey 'spec. De fambly foun' it out, 'bout half an hour ago—maybe a little mo'—en' I *tell* you dey warn't no time los'. Sich another hurryin' up guns en hosses *you* never see! De women folks has gone for to stir up de relations, en ole Mars Saul en de boys tuck dey guns en rode up de river road for to try to ketch dat young man en kill him 'fo' he kin git acrost de river wid Miss Sophia. I reck'n dey 's gwyne to be mighty rough times.'

'Buck went off 'thout waking me up.'

'Well, I reck'n he *did*! Dey warn't gwyne to mix you up in it. Mars Buck he loaded up his gun en 'lowed he 's gwyne to fetch home a Shepherdson or bust. Well, dey'll be plenty un 'm dah, I reck'n, en you bet you he'll fetch one ef he gits a chanst.'

I took up the river road as hard as I could put. By-and-by I begin to hear guns a good ways off. When I come in sight of the log-store and the wood-pile where the steamboats land, I worked along under the trees and brush till I got to a good place, and then I clumb up into the forks of a cotton-wood that was out of reach, and watched. There was a wood-rank four foot high, a little ways in front of the tree, and first I was going to hide behind that; but maybe it was luckier I didn't.

There was four or five men cavorting around on their horses in the open place before the log-store, cussing and yelling, and trying to get at a couple of young chaps that was behind the wood-rank alongside of the steamboat landing—but they couldn't come in. Every time one of them showed himself on the river side of the wood-pile he got shot at. The two boys was squatting back to back behind the pile, so they could watch both ways.

By-and-by the men stopped cavorting around and yelling. They started riding towards the store; then up gets one of the boys, draws a steady bead over the wood-rank, and drops one of them out of his saddle. All the men jumped off of their horses and grabbed the hurt one and started to carry him to the store; and that minute the two boys started on the run. They got half-way to the tree I was in before the men noticed. Then the men see them, and jumped on their horses and took out after them. They gained on the boys, but it didn't do no good, the boys had too good a start; they got to the wood-pile that was in front of my tree, and slipped in behind it, and so they had the bulge on the men again. One of the boys was Buck, and the other was a slim young chap about nineteen years old.

The men ripped around awhile, and then rode away. As soon as they was out of sight, I sung out to Buck and told him. He didn't know what to make of my voice coming out of the tree, at first. He was awful surprised. He told me to watch out sharp and let him know when the men came in sight again; said they was up to some devilment or other—wouldn't be gone long. I wished I was out of that tree, but I dasn't come down. Buck began to cry and rip, and 'lowed that him and his cousin Joe (that was the other young chap) would make up for this day, yet. He said his father and his two brothers was killed, and two or three of the enemy. Said the Shepherdsons laid for them, in ambush. Buck said his father and brothers ought to waited for their relations—the

Shepherdsons was too strong for them. I asked him what was become of young Harney and Miss Sophia. He said they'd got across the river and was safe. I was glad of that; but the way Buck did take on because he didn't manage to kill Harney that day he shot at him—I hain't ever heard anything like it.

All of a sudden, bang! bang! bang! goes three or four guns—the men had slipped around through the woods and come in from behind without their horses! The boys jumped for the river—both of them hurt—and as they swum down the current the men run along the bank shooting at them and singing out, 'Kill them, kill them!' It made me so sick I most fell out of the tree. I ain't agoing to tell *all* that happened—it would make me sick again if I was to do that. I wished I hadn't ever come ashore that night, to see such things. I ain't ever going to get shut of them—lots of times I dream about them.

I staid in the tree till it begun to get dark, afraid to come down. Sometimes I heard guns away off in the woods; and twice I seen little gangs of men gallop past the log-store with guns; so I reckoned the trouble was still agoing on. I was mighty down-hearted; so I made up my mind I wouldn't ever go a-near that house again, because I reckoned I was to blame, somehow. I judged that that piece of paper meant that Miss Sophia was to meet Harney somewheres at half-past two and run off; and I judged I ought to told her father about that paper and the curious way she acted, and then maybe he would a locked her up and this awful mess wouldn't ever happened.

When I got down out of the tree, I crept along down the river bank a piece, and found the two bodies laying in the edge of the water, and tugged at them till I got them ashore; then I covered up their faces, and got away as quick as I could. I cried a little when I was covering up Buck's face, for he was mighty good to me.

It was just dark, now. I never went near the house, but struck through the woods and made for the swamp. Jim warn't on his island, so I tramped off in a hurry for the crick, and crowded through the willows, red-hot to jump aboard and get out of that awful country—the raft was gone! My souls, but I was scared! I couldn't get my breath for most a minute. Then I raised a yell. A voice not twenty-five foot from me, says:

'Good lan'! is dat you, honey? Doan' make no noise.'

It was Jim's voice—nothing ever sounded so good before. I run along the bank a piece and got aboard, and Jim he grabbed me and hugged me, he was so glad to see me. He says:

'Laws bless you, chile, I 'uz right down sho' you 's dead agin. Jack's been heah, he say he reck'n you 's ben shot, kase you didn' come home no mo'; so I 's jes' dis minute astartin' de raf' down towards de mouf er de crick, so's to be all ready for to shove out en leave soon as Jack comes agin en tells me for certain you *is* dead. Lawsy, I 's mighty glad to git you back agin, honey.'

I says:

'All right—that's mighty good; they won't find me, and they'll think I've been killed, and floated down the river—there's something up there that'll help them to think so—so don't you lose no time, Jim, but just shove off for the big water as fast as ever you can.'

I never felt easy till the raft was two mile below there and out in the middle of the Mississippi. Then we hung up our signal lantern, and judged that we was free and safe once more. I hadn't had a bite to eat since yesterday; so Jim he got out some corn-dodgers and butter-milk, and pork and cabbage, and greens—there ain't nothing in the world so good, when it's cooked right—and whilst I eat my supper we talked, and had a good time. I was powerful glad to get away from the feuds, and so was Jim to get away from the swamp. We said there warn't no home like a raft, after all. Other places do seem so cramped up and smothery, but a raft don't. You feel mighty free and easy and comfortable on a raft.

## *Chapter 19*

TYING UP DAY-TIMES—AN ASTRONOMICAL THEORY—'DOGS A-COMING'—RUNNING A TEMPERANCE REVIVAL—THE DUKE OF BRIDGEWATER—THE TROUBLES OF ROYALTY

TWO or three days and nights went by; I reckon I might say they swum by, they slid along so quiet and smooth and lovely. Here is the way we put in the time. It was a monstrous big river down there—sometimes a mile and a half wide; we run nights, and laid up and hid day-times; soon as night was most gone, we stopped navigating and tied up—nearly always in the dead water under a tow-head; and then cut young cotton-woods and willows and hid the raft with them. Then we set out the lines. Next we slid into the river and had a swim, so as to freshen up and cool off; then we set down on the sandy bottom where the water was about knee-deep, and watched the daylight come. Not a sound anywheres—perfectly still—just like the whole world was asleep, only sometimes the bull-frogs a-clattering, maybe. The first thing to see, looking away over the water, was a kind of dull line—that was the woods on t'other side—you couldn't make nothing else out; then a pale place in the sky; then more paleness, spreading around; then the river softened up, away off, and warn't black any more, but grey; you could see little dark spots drifting along, ever so far away—trading-scows, and such things; and long black streaks—rafts; sometimes you could hear a sweep screaking; or jumbled-up voices, it was so still, and sounds come so far; and by-and-by you could see a streak on the water which you know by the look of the streak that there's a snag there in a swift current which breaks on it and makes that streak look that way; and you see the mist curl up off of the water, and the east reddens up, and the river, and you make out a log cabin in the edge of the woods, away on the bank on t'other side of the river, being a wood-yard, likely, and piled by them cheats so you can throw a dog through it anywheres; then the nice breeze springs up, and comes fanning you from over there, so cool and fresh, and sweet to smell, on account of the woods and the flowers; but sometimes not that way, because they've left dead fish laying around, gars, and such, and they do get pretty rank; and next you've got the full day, and everything smiling in the sun, and the song-birds just going it!

A little smoke couldn't be noticed, now, so we would take some fish off of the lines and cook up a hot breakfast. And afterwards we would watch the lonesomeness of the river, and kind of lazy along, and by-and-by lazy off to sleep. Wake up, by-and-by, and look to see what done it, and maybe see a steamboat, coughing along up-stream, so far off towards the other side you couldn't tell nothing about her only whether she was stern-wheel or side-wheel; then for about an hour there wouldn't be nothing to hear nor nothing to see—just solid lonesomeness. Next you'd see a raft sliding by, away off yonder, and maybe a galoot on it chopping, because they're most always doing it on a raft; you'd see the axe flash, and come down—you don't hear nothing; you see that axe go up again, and by the time it's above the man's head, then you hear the *k'chunk*!—it had took all that time to come over the water. So we would put in the day, lazying around, listening to the stillness. Once there was a thick fog, and the rafts and things that went by was beating tin pans so the steamboats wouldn't run over them. A scow or a raft went by so close we could hear them talking and cussing and laughing—heard them plain; but we couldn't see no sign of them; it made you feel crawly, it was like spirits carrying on that way in the air. Jim said he believed it was spirits; but I says:

'No, spirits wouldn't say, "dern the dern fog." '

Soon as it was night, out we shoved; when we got her out to about the middle, we let her alone, and let her float wherever the current wanted her to; then we lit the pipes, and dangled our legs in the water and talked about all kinds of things—we was always naked, day and night, whenever the mosquitoes would let us—the new clothes Buck's folks made for me was too good to be comfortable, and besides, I didn't go much on clothes, nohow.

Sometimes we'd have that whole river all to ourselves for the longest time. Yonder was the banks and the islands, across the water; and maybe a spark—which was a candle in a cabin window—and sometimes on the water you could see a spark or two—on a raft or a scow, you know; and maybe you could hear a fiddle or a song coming over from one of them crafts. It's lovely to live on a raft. We had the sky, up there, all speckled with stars, and we used to lay on our backs and look up at them, and discuss about whether they was made, or only just happened—Jim he allowed they was made, but I allowed they happened; I judged it would have took too long to *make* so many. Jim said the moon could a *laid* them; well, that looked kind of reasonable, so I didn't say nothing against it, because I've seen a frog lay most as many, so of course it could be done. We used to watch the stars that fell, too, and see them streak down. Jim allowed they'd got spoiled and was hove out of the nest.

Once or twice of a night we would see a steamboat slipping along in the dark, and now and then she would belch a whole world of sparks up out of her chimbleys, and they would rain down in the river and look awful pretty; then she would turn a corner and her lights would wink out and her pow-wow shut off and leave the river still again; and by-and-by her waves would get to us, a long time after she was gone, and joggle the raft a bit, and after that you wouldn't hear nothing for you couldn't tell how long, except maybe frogs or something.

After midnight the people on shore went to bed, and then for two or three hours the shores was black—no more sparks in the cabin windows. These sparks was our clock—the first one that showed again meant morning was coming, so we hunted a place to hide and tie up, right away.

One morning about daybreak, I found a canoe and crossed over a chute to the main shore—it was only two hundred yards—and paddled about a mile up a crick amongst the cypress woods, to see if I couldn't get some berries. Just as I was passing a place where a kind of cow-path crossed the crick, here comes a couple of men tearing up the path as tight as they could foot it. I thought I was a goner, for whenever anybody was after anybody I judged it was *me*—or maybe Jim. I was about to dig out from there in a hurry, but they was pretty close to me then, and sung out and begged me to save their lives—said they hadn't been doing nothing, and was being chased for it—said there was men and dogs a-coming. They wanted to jump right in, but I says:

'Don't you do it. I don't hear the dogs and horses yet; you've got time to crowd through the brush and get up the crick a little ways; then you take to the water and wade down to me and get in—that'll throw the dogs off the scent.'

They done it, and soon as they was aboard I lit out for our tow-head, and in about five or ten minutes we heard the dogs and the men away off, shouting. We heard them come along towards the crick, but couldn't see them; they seemed to stop and fool around awhile; then, as we got further and further away all the time, we couldn't hardly hear them at all; by the time we had left a mile of woods behind us and struck the river, everything was quiet, and we paddled over to the tow-head and hid in the cotton-woods and was safe.

One of these fellows was about seventy, or upwards, and had a bald head and very grey whiskers. He had an old battered-up slouch hat on, and a greasy blue woollen shirt, and ragged old blue jeans britches stuffed into his boot-tops, and home-knit galluses—no, he only had one. He had an old long-tailed blue jeans coat with slick brass buttons, flung over his arm, and both of them had big, fat, ratty-looking carpet-bags.

The other fellow was about thirty and dressed about as ornery. After breakfast we all laid off and talked, and the first thing that come out was that these chaps didn't know one another.

'What got you into trouble?' says the baldhead to t'other chap.

'Well, I'd been selling an article to take the tartar off the teeth—and it does take it off, too, and generly the enamel along with it—but I staid about one night longer than I ought to, and was just in the act of sliding out when I ran across you on the trail this side of town, and you told me they were coming, and begged me to help you to get off. So I told you I was expecting trouble myself and would scatter out *with* you. That's the whole yarn—what's yourn?'

"Well, I'd ben a-runnin' a little temperance revival thar, 'bout a week, and was the pet of the women-folks, big and little, for I was makin' it mighty warm for the rummies, I *tell* you, and takin' as much as five or six dollars a night—ten cents a head, children and niggers free—and business a-growin' all the time; when somehow or another a little report got around, last night, that I had a way of puttin' in my time with a private jug, on the sly. A nigger rousted me out this mornin', and told me the people was getherin' on the quiet, with their dogs and horses, and they'd be along pretty soon and give me 'bout half an hour's start, and then run me down, if they could; and if they got me they'd tar and feather me and ride me on a rail, sure. I didn't wait for no breakfast—I warn't hungry.'

'Old man,' says the young one, 'I reckon we might double-team it together. What do you think?'

'I ain't undisposed. What's your line—mainly?'

'Jour printer, by trade; do a little in patent medicines; theatre-actor—tragedy, you know; take a turn at mesmerism and phrenology when there's a chance; teach singing geography school for a change; sling a lecture, sometimes—oh, I do lots of things—most anything that comes handy, so it ain't work. What's your lay?'

'I've done considerble in the doctoring way in my time. Layin' on o' hands is my best holt—for cancer, and paralysis, and sich things; and I k'n tell a fortune pretty good, when I've got somebody along to find out the facts for me. Preachin's my line, too; and workin' camp-meetin's; and missionaryin' around.'

Nobody never said anything for awhile; then the young man hove a sigh and says:

'Alas!'

'What're you alassin' about?' says the baldhead.

'To think I should have lived to be leading such a life, and be degraded down into such company.' And he begun to wipe the corner of his eye with a rag.

'Dern your skin, ain't the company good enough for you?' says the baldhead, pretty pert and uppish.

'Yes, it *is* good enough for me; it's as good as I deserve; for who fetched me so low, when I was so high? *I* did myself. I don't blame *you*, gentlemen—far from it; I don't blame anybody. I deserve it all. Let the cold world do its worst; one thing I know—there's a grave somewhere for me. The world may go on just as it's always done, and take everything from me—loved ones, property, everything—but it can't take that. Some day I'll lie down in it and forget it all, and my poor broken heart will be at rest.' He went on a-wiping.

'Drot your pore broken heart,' says the baldhead. 'What are you heaving your pore broken heart at *us* f'r? *We* hain't done nothing.'

'No, I know you haven't. I ain't blaming you, gentlemen. I brought myself down—yes, I did it myself. It's right I should suffer—perfectly right—I don't make any moan.'

'Brought you down from whar? Whar was you brought down from?'

'Ah, you would not believe me; the world never believes—let it pass—'tis no matter. The secret of my birth——'

'The secret of your birth? Do you mean to say——'

'Gentlemen,' says the young man, very solemn, 'I will reveal it to you, for I feel I may have confidence in you. By rights I am a duke!'

Jim's eyes bugged out when he heard that; and I reckon mine did, too. Then the baldhead says: 'No! you can't mean it?'

'Yes. My great-grandfather, eldest son of the Duke of Bridgewater, fled to this country about the end of the last century, to breathe the pure air of freedom; married here, and died, leaving a son, his own father dying about the same time. The second son of the late duke seized the title and estates—the infant real duke was ignored. I am the lineal descendant of that infant—I am the rightful Duke of Bridgewater; and here am I, forlorn, torn from my high estate, hunted of men, despised by the cold world, ragged, worn, heart-broken, and degraded to the companionship of felons on a raft!'

Jim pitied him ever so much, and so did I. We tried to comfort him, but he said it warn't much use, he couldn't be much comforted; said if we was a mind to acknowledge him, that would do him more good than most anything else; so we said we would, if he would tell us how. He said we ought to bow, when we spoke to him, and say 'Your Grace,' or 'My Lord,' or 'Your Lordship'—and he wouldn't mind it if we called him plain 'Bridgewater,' which he said was a title, anyway, and not a name; and one of us ought to wait on him at dinner, and do any little thing for him he wanted done.

Well, that was all easy, so we done it. All through dinner Jim stood around and waited on him, and says, 'Will yo' Grace have some o' dis, or some o' dat?' and so on, and a body could see it was mighty pleasing to him.

But the old man got pretty silent, by-and-by—didn't have much to say, and didn't look pretty comfortable over all that petting that was going on around that duke. He seemed to have something on his mind. So, along in the afternoon, he says:

'Looky here, Bilgewater,' he says, 'I'm nation sorry for you, but you ain't the only person that's had troubles like that.'

'No?'

'No, you ain't. You ain't the only person that's ben snaked down wrongfully out'n a high place.'

'Alas!'

'No, you ain't the only person that's had a secret of his birth.' And by jings, *he* begins to cry.

'Hold! What do you mean?'

'Bilgewater, kin I trust you?' says the old man, still sort of sobbing.

'To the bitter death!' He took the old man by the hand and squeezed it, and says, 'The secret of your being: speak!'

'Bilgewater, I am the late Dauphin!'

You bet you Jim and me stared, this time. Then the duke says:

'You are what?'

'Yes, my friend, it is too true—your eyes is lookin' at this very moment on the pore disappeared Dauphin, Looy the Seventeen, son of Looy the Sixteen and Marry Antonette.'

'You! At your age! No! You mean you're the late Charlemagne; you must be six or seven hundred years old, at the very least.'

'Trouble has done it, Bilgewater, trouble has done it; trouble has brung these grey hairs and this premature balditude. Yes, gentlemen, you see before you, in blue jeans and misery, the wanderin', exiled, trampled-on, and sufferin' rightful King of France.'

Well, he cried and took on so, that me and Jim didn't know hardly what to do, we was so sorry—and so glad and proud we'd got him with us, too. So we set in, like we done before with the duke, and tried to comfort *him*. But he said it warn't no use, nothing but to be dead and done with it all could do him any good; though he said it often made him feel easier and better for awhile if people treated him according to his rights, and got down on one knee to speak to him, and always called him 'Your Majesty,' and waited on him first at meals, and didn't set down in his presence till he asked them. So Jim and me set to majestying him, and doing this and that and t'other for him, and standing up till he told us we might set down. This done him heaps of good, and so he got cheerful and comfortable. But the duke kind of soured on him, and didn't look a bit satisfied with the way things was going; still, the king acted real friendly towards him, and said the duke's great-grandfather and all the other Dukes of Bilgewater was a good deal thought of by *his* father, and was allowed to come to the palace considerable; but the duke staid huffy a good while, till by-and-by the king says:

'Like as not we got to be together a blamed long time, on this h-yer raft, Bilgewater, and so what's the use o' your bein' sour? It'll only make things oncomfortable. It ain't my fault I warn't born a duke, it ain't your fault you warn't born a king—so what's the use to worry? Make the best o' things the way you find 'em, says I—that's my motto. This ain't no bad thing that we've struck here—plenty grub and an easy life—come, give us your hand, Duke, and less all be friends.'

The duke done it, and Jim and me was pretty glad to see it. It took away all the uncomfortableness, and we felt mighty good over it, because it would a been a miserable business to have any unfriendliness on the raft; for what you want, above all things, on a raft, is for everybody to be satisfied, and feel right and kind towards the others.

It didn't take me long to make up my mind that these liars warn't no kings nor dukes at all, but just low-down humbugs and frauds. But I never said nothing, never let on; kept it to myself; it's the best way; then you don't have no quarrels, and don't get into no trouble. If they wanted us to call them kings and dukes, I hadn't no objections, 'long as it would keep peace in the family; and it warn't no use to tell Jim, so I didn't tell him. If I never learnt nothing else out of pap, I learnt that the best way to get along with his kind of people is to let them have their own way.

## *Chapter 20*

HUCK EXPLAINS—LAYING OUT A CAMPAIGN—WORKING THE CAMP-MEETING—SLY COURTING—A PIRATE AT THE CAMP-MEETING—THE DUKE AS A PRINTER—JIM WANTED

THEY asked us considerable many questions; wanted to know what we covered up the raft that way for, and laid by in the day-time instead of running—was Jim a runaway nigger? Says I:

'Goodness sakes, would a runaway nigger run *south*?'

No, they allowed he wouldn't. I had to account for things some way, so I says:

'My folks was living in Pike Country, in Missouri, where I was born, and they all died off but me and pa and my brother Ike. Pa, he 'lowed he'd break up and go down and live with Uncle Ben, who's got a little one-horse place on the river, forty-four mile below Orleans. Pa was pretty poor, and had some debts; so when he'd squared up there warn't nothing left but sixteen dollars and our nigger, Jim. That warn't enough to take us fourteen hundred mile, deck passage nor no other way. Well, when the river rose, pa had a streak of luck one day —he ketched this piece of a raft; so we reckoned we'd go down to Orleans on it. Pa's luck didn't hold out; a steamboat run over the forrard corner of the raft, one night, and we all went overboard and dove under the wheel; Jim and me come up all right, but pa was drunk, and Ike was only four years old, so they never come up no more. Well, for the next day or two we had considerable trouble, because people was always coming out in skiffs and trying to take Jim away from me, saying they believed he was a runaway nigger. We don't run day-times no more, now; nights they don't bother us.'

The duke says:

'Leave me alone to cipher out a way so we can run in the day-time if we want to. I'll think the thing over—I'll invent a plan that'll fix it. We'll let it alone for to-day, because, of course, we don't want to go by that town yonder in daylight—it mightn't be healthy.'

Towards night it begun to darken up and look like rain: the heat lightning was squirting around, low down in the sky, and the leaves was beginning to shiver—it was going to be pretty ugly, it was easy to see that. So the duke and the king went to overhauling our wigwam, to see what the beds was like. My bed was a straw tick—better than Jim's, which was a corn-shuck tick; there's always cobs around about in a shuck tick, and they poke into you and hurt; and when you roll over, the dry shucks sound like you was rolling over in a pile of dead leaves; it makes such a rustling that you wake up. Well, the duke allowed he would take my bed; but the king allowed he wouldn't. He says:

'I should a reckoned the difference in rank would a sejested to you that a corn-shuck bed warn't just fitten for me to sleep on. Your Grace'll take the shuck bed yourself.'

Jim and me was in a sweat again, for a minute, being afraid there was going to be some more trouble amongst them; so we was pretty glad when the duke says:

''Tis my fate to be always ground into the mire under the iron heel of oppression. Misfortune has broken my once haughty spirit; I yield, I submit; 'tis my fate. I am alone in the world—let me suffer; I can bear it.'

We got away as soon as it was good and dark. The king told us to stand well out towards the middle of the river, and not show a light till we got a long ways below the town. We come in sight of the little bunch of lights by-and-by—that was the town, you know—and slid by, about a half a mile out, all right. When we was three-quarters of a mile below, we hoisted up our signal lantern; and about ten o'clock it come on to rain and blow and thunder and lighten like everything; so the king told us to both stay on watch till the weather got better; then him and the duke crawled into the wigwam and turned in for the night. It was my watch below, till twelve, but I wouldn't a turned in, anyway, if I'd had a bed; because a body don't see such a storm as that every day in the week, not by a long sight. My souls, how the wind did scream along! And every second or two there'd come a glare that lit up the white-caps for half a mile around, and you'd see the islands looking dusty through the rain, and the trees thrashing around in the wind; then comes a *h-wack*!—bum! bum! bumble-umble-um-bum-bum-bum-bum—and the thunder would go rumbling and grumbling away, and quit—and then *rip* comes another flash and another sockdolager. The waves most washed me off the raft, sometimes, but I hadn't any clothes on, and didn't mind. We didn't have no trouble about snags; the lightning was glaring and flittering around so constant that we could see them plenty soon enough to throw her head this way or that and miss them.

I had the middle watch, you know, but I was pretty sleepy by that time, so Jim he said he would stand the first half of it for me; he was always mighty good that way, Jim was. I crawled into the wigwam, but the king and the duke had their legs sprawled around so there warn't no show for me; so I laid outside—I didn't mind the rain, because it was warm, and the waves warn't running so high, now. About two they come up again, though, and Jim was going to call me, but he changed his mind because he reckoned they warn't high enough yet to do any harm; but he was mistaken about that, for pretty soon all of a sudden along comes a regular ripper, and washed me overboard. It most killed Jim a-laughing. He was the easiest nigger to laugh that ever was, anyway.

I took the watch, and Jim he laid down and snored away; and by-and-by the storm let up for good and all; and the first cabin-light that showed, I rousted him out and we slid the raft into hiding-quarters for the day.

The king got out an old ratty deck of cards, after breakfast, and him and the duke played seven-up awhile, five cents a game. Then they got tired of it, and allowed they would 'lay out a campaign', as they called it. The duke went down into his carpet-bag and fetched up a lot of little printed bills, and read them out loud. One bill said 'The celebrated Dr. Armand de Montalban, of Paris', would 'lecture on the Science of Phrenology' at such and such a place, on the blank day of blank, at ten cents admission, and 'furnish charts of character at twenty-five cents apiece.' The duke said that was *him*. In another bill he was the 'world-renowned Shaksperean tragedian, Garrick the Younger, of Drury Lane, London.' In other bills he had a lot of other names and done other wonderful things, like finding water and gold with a 'divining-rod,' 'dissipating witch-spells,' and so on. By-and-by he says:

'But the histrionic muse is the darling. Have you ever trod the boards, Royalty?'

'No,' says the king.

'You shall, then, before you're three days older, Fallen Grandeur,' says the duke. 'The first good town we come to, we'll hire a hall and do the sword-fight in *Richard III* and the balcony scene in *Romeo and Juliet*. How does that strike you?'

'I'm in, up to the hub, for anything that will pay, Bilgewater, but you see I don't know nothing about play-actn', and hain't ever seen much of it. I was too small when pap used to have 'em at the palace. Do you reckon you can learn me?'

'Easy!'

'All right. I'm jist a-freezn' for something fresh, anyway. Less commence, right away.'

So the duke he told him all about who Romeo was, and who Juliet was, and said he was used to being Romeo, so the king could be Juliet.

'But if Juliet's such a young gal, duke, my peeled head and my white whiskers is goin' to look oncommon odd on her, maybe.'

'No, don't you worry—these country jakes won't ever think of that. Besides, you know, you'll be in costume, and that makes all the difference in the world; Juliet's in a balcony, enjoying the moonlight before she goes to bed, and she's got on her night-gown and her ruffled night-cap. Here are the costumes for the parts.'

He got out two or three curtain-calico suits, which he said was meedyevil armour for Richard III and t'other chap, and a long white cotton night-shirt and a ruffled night-cap to match. The king was satisfied; so the duke got out his book and read the parts over in the most splendid spread-eagle way, prancing around and acting at the same time, to show how it had got to be done; then he give the book to the king and told him to get his part by heart.

There was a little one-horse town about three mile down the bend, and after dinner the duke said he had ciphered out his idea about how to run in daylight without it being dangersome for Jim; so he allowed he would go down to the town and fix that thing. The king allowed he would go too, and see if he couldn't strike something. We was out of coffee, so Jim said I better go along with them in the canoe and get some.

When we got there, there warn't nobody stirring; streets empty, and perfectly dead and still, like Sunday. We found a sick nigger sunning himself in a back-yard, and he said everybody that warn't too young or too sick or too old was gone to camp-meeting, about two mile back in the woods. The king got the directions, and allowed he'd go and work that camp-meeting for all it was worth, and I might go too.

The duke said what he was after was a printing office. We found it; a little bit of a concern, up over a carpenter shop—carpenters and printers all gone to the meeting, and no doors locked. It was a dirty, littered-up place, and had ink-marks, and handbills with pictures of horses and runaway niggers on them, all over the walls. The duke shed his coat and said he was all right now. So me and the king lit out for the camp-meeting.

We got there in about a half an hour, fairly dripping, for it was a most awful hot day. There was as much as a thousand people there, from twenty mile around. The woods was full of teams and wagons, hitched everywheres, feeding out of the wagon troughs and stomping to keep off the flies. There was sheds made out of poles and roofed over with branches, where they had lemonade and gingerbread to sell, and piles of water-melons and green corn and such-like truck.

The preaching was going on under the same kinds of sheds, only they was bigger and held crowds of people. The benches was made out of outside slabs of logs, with holes bored in the round side to drive sticks into for legs. They didn't have no backs. The preachers had high platforms to stand on, at one end of the sheds. The women had on sun-bonnets; and some had linsey-woolsey frocks, some gingham ones, and a few of the young ones had on calico. Some of the young men was barefooted, and some of the children didn't have on any clothes but just a tow-linen shirt. Some of the old women was knitting, and some of the young folks was courting on the sly.

The first shed we come to, the preacher was lining out a hymn. He lined out two lines, everybody sung it, and it was kind of grand to hear it, there was so many of them and they done it in such a rousing way; then he lined out two more for them to sing—and so on. The people woke up more and more, and sung louder and louder; and towards the end some begun to groan, and some begun to shout. Then the preacher begun to preach; and begun in earnest, too; and went weaving first to one side of the platform and then the other, and then a-leaning down over the front of it, with his arms and his body going all the time, and shouting his words out with all his might; and every now and then he would hold up his Bible and spread it open, and kind of pass it around this way and that, shouting, 'It's the brazen serpent in the wilderness! Look upon it and live!' And people would shout out, 'Glory!—A-a-*men!*' And so he went on, and the people groaning and crying and saying amen:

'Oh, come to the mourners' bench! come, black with sin! (*amen!*) come, sick and sore! (*amen!*) come, lame and halt, and blind! (*amen!*) come, pore and needy, sunk in shame! (*a-a-men!*) come all that's worn, and soiled, and suffering!—come with a broken spirit! come with a contrite heart! come in your rags and sin and dirt! the waters that cleanse is free, the door of heaven stands open—oh, enter in and be at rest!' (*a-a-men! glory, glory hallelujah!*)

And so on. You couldn't make out what the preacher said, any more, on account of the shouting and crying. Folks got up, everywheres in the crowd, and worked their way, just by main strength, to the mourners' bench, with the tears running down their faces; and when all the mourners had got up there to the front benches in a crowd, they sung, and shouted, and flung themselves down on the straw, just crazy and wild.

Well, the first I knowed, the king got agoing; and you could hear him over everybody; and next he went a-charging up on to the platform and the preacher he begged him to speak to the people, and he done it. He told them he was a pirate—been a pirate for thirty years, out in the Indian Ocean, and his crew was thinned out considerable, last spring, in a fight, and he was home now, to take out some fresh men, and thanks to goodness he'd been robbed last night, and put ashore off of a steamboat without a cent, and he was glad of it, it was the blessedest thing that ever happened to him, because he was a changed man now, and happy for the first time in his life; and poor as he was, he was going to start right off and work his way back to the Indian Ocean and put in the rest of his life trying to turn the pirates into the true path: for he could do it better than anybody else, being acquainted with all the pirate crews in that ocean; and though it would take him a long time to get there without money, he would get there anyway, and every time he convinced a pirate he would say to him, 'Don't you thank me, don't you give me no credit, it all belongs to them dear people in Pokeville camp-meeting, natural brothers and benefactors of the race—and that dear preacher there, the truest friend a pirate ever had!'

And then he busted into tears, and so did everybody. Then somebody sings out, 'Take up a collection for him, take up a collection!' Well, a half a dozen made a jump to do it, but somebody sings out, 'Let *him* pass the hat around!' Then everybody said it, the preacher too.

So the king went all through the crowd with his hat, swabbing his eyes, and blessing the people and praising them and thanking them for being so good to the poor pirates away off there; and every little while the prettiest kind of girls, with the tears running down their cheeks, would up and ask him would he let them kiss him, for to remember him by; and he always done it; and some of them he hugged and kissed as many as five or six times—and he was invited to stay a week; and everybody wanted him to live in their houses, and said they'd think it was an honour; but he said as this was the last day of the camp-meeting he couldn't do no good, and besides, he was in a sweat to get to the Indian Ocean right off and go to work on the pirates.

When we got back to the raft and he come to count up, he found he had collected eighty-seven dollars and seventy-five cents. And then he had fetched away a three-gallon jug of whisky, too, that he found under a wagon when we was starting home through the woods. The king said, take it all around, it laid over any day he'd ever put in in the missionarying line. He said it warn't no use talking, heathens don't amount to shucks, alongside of pirates, to work a camp-meeting with.

The duke was thinking *he'd* been doing pretty well, till the king come to show up, but after that he didn't think so so much. He had set up and printed off two little jobs for farmers, in that printing office —horse bills—and took the money, four dollars. And he had got in ten dollars' worth of advertisements for the paper, which he said he would put in for four dollars if they would pay in advance—so they done it. The price of the paper was two dollars a year, but he took in three subscriptions for half a dollar apiece on condition of them paying him in advance; they were going to pay in cord-wood and onions, as usual, but he said he had just bought the concern and knocked down the price as low as he could afford it, and was going to run it for cash. He set up a little piece of poetry, which he made, himself, out of his own head—three verses—kind of sweet and saddish—the name of it was, 'Yes, crush, cold world, this breaking heart'—and he left that all set up and ready to print in the paper and didn't charge nothing for it. Well, he took in nine dollars and a half, and said he'd done a pretty square day's work for it.

Then he showed us another little job he'd printed and hadn't charged for, because it was for us. It had a picture of a runaway nigger, with a bundle on a stick over his shoulder, and '$200 reward' under it. The reading was all about Jim, and just described him to a dot. It said he run away from St. Jacques' plantation, forty mile below New Orleans, last winter, and likely went north, and whoever would catch him and send him back, he could have the reward and expenses.

'Now,' says the duke, 'after to-night we can run in the day-time if we want to. Whenever we see anybody coming, we can tie Jim hand and foot with a rope, and lay him in the wigwam and show this hand-bill and say we captured him up the river, and were too poor to travel on a steamboat, so we got this little raft on credit from our friends and are going down to get the reward. Handcuffs and chains would look still better on Jim, but it wouldn't go well with the story of us being so poor. Too much like jewellery. Ropes are the correct thing—we must preserve the unities, as we say on the boards.'

We all said the duke was pretty smart, and there couldn't be no trouble about running day-times. We judged we could make miles enough that night to get out of the reach of the pow-wow we reckoned the duke's work in the printing office was going to make in that little town—then we could boom right along, if we wanted to.

We laid low and kept still, and never shoved out till nearly ten o'clock; then we slid by, pretty wide away from the town, and didn't hoist our lantern till we was clear out of sight of it.

When Jim called me to take the watch at four in the morning, he says:

'Huck, does you reck'n we gwyne to run across any mo' kings on dis trip?'

'No,' I says, 'I reckon not.'

'Well,' says he, 'dat's all right, den. I doan' mine one er two kings, but dat's enough. Dis one's powerful drunk, en de duke ain' much better.'

I found Jim had been trying to get him to talk French, so he could hear what it was like; but he said he had been in this country so long, and had so much trouble, he'd forgot it.

## *Chapter 21*

SWORD EXERCISE—HAMLET'S SOLILOQUY—THEY LOAFED AROUND TOWN—A LAZY TOWN—OLD BOGGS—DEATH OF BOGGS

IT was after sun-up, now, but we went right on, and didn't tie up. The king and the duke turned out, by-and-by, looking pretty rusty; but after they'd jumped overboard and took a swim, it chippered them up a good deal. After breakfast the king he took a seat on a corner of the raft, and pulled off his boots and rolled up his britches, and let his legs dangle in the water, so as to be comfortable, and lit his pipe, and went to getting his *Romeo and Juliet* by heart. When he had got it pretty good, him and the duke begun to practise it together. The duke had to learn him over and over again, how to say every speech; and he made him sigh, and put his hand on his heart, and after awhile he said he done it pretty well; 'only,' he says, 'you mustn't bellow out *Romeo!* that way, like a bull—you must say it soft, and sick, and languishy, so—R-o-o-meo! that is the idea; for Juliet's a dear, sweet, mere child of a girl, you know, and she don't bray like a jackass.'

Well, next they got out a couple of long swords that the duke made out of oak laths, and begun to practise the sword-fight—the duke called himself Richard III; and the way they laid on and pranced around the raft was grand to see. But by-and-by the king tripped and fell overboard, and after that they took a rest, and had a talk about all kinds of adventures they'd had in other times along the river.

After dinner, the duke says:

'Well, Capet, we'll want to make this a first-class show, you know, so I guess we'll add a little more to it. We want a little something to answer encores with, anyway.'

'What's onkores, Bilgewater?'

The duke told him, and then says:

'I'll answer by doing the Highland fling or the sailor's hornpipe; and you—well, let me see—oh, I've got it—you can do Hamlet's soliloquy.'

'Hamlet's which?'

'Hamlet's soliloquy, you know; the most celebrated thing in Shakespeare. Ah, it's sublime, sublime! Always fetches the house. I haven't got it in the book—I've only got one volume—but I reckon I can piece it out from memory. I'll just walk up and down a minute, and see if I can call it back from recollection's vaults.'

So he went to marching up and down, thinking, and frowning horrible every now and then; then he would hoist up his eyebrows; next he would squeeze his hand on his forehead and stagger back and kind of moan; next he would sigh, and next he'd let on to drop a tear. It was beautiful to see him. By-and-by he got it. He told us to give attention. Then he strikes a most noble attitude, with one leg shoved forwards, and his arms stretched away up, and his head tilted back, looking up at the sky; and then he begins to rip and rave and grit his teeth; and after that, all through his speech he howled, and spread around, and swelled up his chest, and just knocked the spots out of any acting ever *I* see before. This is the speech—I learned it, easy enough, while he was learning it to the king:

To be, or not to be; that is the bare bodkin
That makes calamity of so long life;
For who would fardels bear, till Birnam Wood do come to Dunsinane.
But that the fear of something after death
Murders the innocent sleep,
Great nature's second course,
And makes us rather sling the arrows of outrageous fortune
Than fly to others that we know not of.
There's the respect must give us pause:
Wake Duncan with thy knocking! I would thou couldst;
For who would bear the whips and scorns of time,
The oppressor's wrong, the proud man's contumely,
The law's delay, and the quietus which his pangs might take,
In the dead waste and middle of the night, when churchyards yawn
In customary suits of solemn black,
But that the undiscovered country from whose bourne no traveller returns,
Breathes forth contagion on the world,
And thus the native hue of resolution, like the poor cat i' the adage,
Is sicklied o'er with care,
And all the clouds that lowered o'er our housetops,
With this regard their currents turn awry,
And lose the name of action.
'Tis a consummation devoutly to be wished. But soft you, the fair Ophelia:
Ope not thy ponderous and marble jaws,
But get thee to a nunnery—go!

Well, the old man he liked that speech, and he mighty soon got it so he could do it first-rate. It seemed like he was just born for it; and when he had his hand in and was excited, it was perfectly lovely the way he would rip and tear and rair up behind when he was getting it off.

The first chance we got, the duke he had some show-bills printed; and after that, for two or three days as we floated along, the raft was a most uncommon lively place, for there warn't nothing but sword-fighting and rehearsing—as the duke called it—going on all the time. One morning, when we was pretty well down the State of Arkansaw, we come in sight of a little one-horse town in a big bend; so we tied up about three-quarters of a mile above it, in the mouth of a crick which was shut in like a tunnel by the cypress trees, and all of us but Jim took the canoe and went down there to see if there was any chance in that place for our show.

We struck it mighty lucky; there was going to be a circus there that afternoon, and the country people was already beginning to come in, in all kinds of old shackly wagons, and on horses. The circus would leave before night, so our show would have a pretty good chance. The duke he hired the court-house, and we went around and stuck up our bills. They read like this:

Shaksperean Revival ! ! !

Wonderful Attraction!

For One Night Only!

The world-renowned tragedians,

David Garrick the younger, of Drury Lane Theatre, London,

and

Edmund Kean the elder, of the Royal Haymarket Theatre, Whitechapel, Pudding Lane, Piccadilly, London, and the Royal Continental Theatres, in their sublime Shaksperean Spectacle entitled

The Balcony Scene

in

Romeo and Juliet ! ! !

Romeo........................................................Mr. Garrick

Juliet..........................................................Mr. Kean

Assisted by the whole strength of the company!

New costumes, new scenery, new appointments!

Also:

The thrilling, masterly, and blood-curdling

Broad-sword conflict

In Richard III ! ! !

Richard III..................................................Mr. Garrick

Richmond...................................................Mr. Kean

also:

(by special request,)

Hamlet's Immortal Soliloquy ! !

By the Illustrious Kean!

Done by him 300 consecutive nights in Paris!

For One Night Only,

On account of imperative European engagements!

Admission 25 cents, children and servants, 10 cents.

Then we went loafing around the town. The stores and houses was most all old shackly dried-up frame concerns that hadn't ever been painted; they was set up three or four foot above-ground on stilts, so as to be out of reach of the water when the river was overflowed. The houses had little gardens around them, but they didn't seem to raise hardly anything in them but jimpson weeds, and sunflowers, and ash-piles, and old curled-up boots and shoes, and pieces of bottles, and rags, and played-out tinware. The fences was made of different kinds of boards, nailed on at different times; and they leaned every which-way, and had gates that didn't generly have but one hinge—a leather one. Some of the fences had been whitewashed, some time or another but the duke said it was in C'lumbus's time, like enough. There was generly hogs in the garden, and people driving them out.

All the stores was along one street. They had white-domestic awnings in front, and the country people hitched their horses to the awning-posts. There was empty dry-goods boxes under the awnings, and loafers roosting on them all day long, whittling them with their Barlow knives; and chawing tobacco, and gaping and yawning and stretching—a mighty ornery lot. They generly had on yellow straw hats most as wide as an umbrella, but didn't wear no coats nor waist-coats; they called one another Bill, and Buck, and Hank, and Joe, and Andy, and talked lazy and drawly, and used considerable many cuss-words. There was as many as one loafer leaning up against every awning-post, and he most always had his hands in his britches pockets, except when he fetched them out to lend a chaw of tobacco or scratch. What a body was hearing amongst them all the time was:

'Gimme a chaw 'v tobacker, Hank.'

'Cain't—I hain't got but one chaw left. Ask Bill.'

Maybe Bill he gives him a chaw; maybe he lies and says he ain't got none. Some of them kinds of loafers never has a cent in the world, nor a chaw of tobacco of their own. They get all their chawing by borrowing—they say to a fellow, 'I wisht you'd len' me a chaw, Jack, I jist this minute give Ben Thompson the last chaw I had'—which is a lie, pretty much every time; it don't fool nobody but a stranger; but Jack ain't no stranger, so he says:

'*You* give him a chaw, did you? so did your sister's cat's grand-mother. You pay me back the chaws you've awready borry'd off'n me, Lafe Buckner, then I'll loan you one or two ton of it, and won't charge you no back intrust nuther.'

'Well, I *did* pay you back some of it wunst.'

'Yes, you did—'bout six chaws. You borry'd store tobacker and paid back nigger-head.'

Store tobacco is flat black plug, but these fellows mostly chaws the natural leaf twisted. When they borrow a chaw, they don't generly cut it off with a knife, but they set the plug in between their teeth, and gnaw with their teeth and tug at the plug with their hands till they get it in two—then sometimes the one that owns the tobacco looks mournful at it when it's handed back, and says, sarcastic:

'Here, gimme the *chaw*, and you take the *plug*.'

All the streets and lanes was just mud, they warn't nothing else *but* mud—mud as black as tar, and nigh about a foot deep in some places; and two or three inches deep in *all* the places. The hogs loafed and grunted around, everywheres. You'd see a muddy sow and a litter of pigs come lazying along the street and whollop herself right down in the way, where folks had to walk around her, and she'd stretch out, and shut her eyes, and wave her ears, whilst the pigs was milking her, and look as happy as if she was on salary. And pretty soon you'd hear a loafer sing out, 'Hi! *so* boy! sick him, Tige!' and away the sow would go, squealing most horrible, with a dog or two swinging to each ear, and three or four dozen more a-coming; and then you would see all the loafers get up and watch the thing out of sight, and laugh at the fun and look grateful for the noise. Then they'd settle back again till there was a dog-fight. There couldn't anything wake them up all over, and make them happy all over, like a dog-fight—unless it might be putting turpentine on a stray dog and setting fire to him, or tying a tin pan to his tail and see him run himself to death.

On the river front some of the houses was sticking out over the bank, and they was bowed and bent, and about ready to tumble in. The people had moved out of them. The bank was caved away under one corner of some others, and that corner was hanging over. People lived in them yet, but it was dangersome, because sometimes a strip of land as wide as a house caves in at a time. Sometimes a belt of land a quarter of a mile deep will start in and cave along and cave along till it all caves into the river in one summer. Such a town as that has to be always moving back, and back, and back, because the river's always gnawing at it.

The nearer it got to noon that day, the thicker and thicker was the wagons and horses in the streets, and more coming all the time. Families fetched their dinners with them, from the country, and eat them in the wagons. There was considerable whisky-drinking going on, and I seen three fights. By-and-by somebody sings out:

'Here comes old Boggs!—in from the country for his little old monthly drunk—here he comes, boys!'

All the loafers looked glad—I reckoned they was used to having fun out of Boggs. One of them says:

'Wonder who he's a-gwyne to chaw up this time. If he'd a chawed up all the men he's ben a-gwyne to chaw up in the last twenty year, he'd have considerble ruputation, now.'

Another one says, 'I wisht old Boggs'd threaten me, 'cuz then I'd know I warn't gwyne to die for a thousan' year.'

Boggs comes a-tearing along on his horse, whooping and yelling like an Injun, and singing out:

'Cler the track, thar. I'm on the waw-path, and the price uv coffins is a-gwyne to raise.'

He was drunk, and weaving about in his saddle; he was over fifty year old, and had a very red face. Everybody yelled at him, and laughed at him, and sassed him, and he sassed back, and said he'd attend to them and lay them out in their regular turns, but he couldn't wait now, because he'd come to town to kill old Colonel Sherburn, and his motto was, 'Meat first, and spoon vittles to top off on.'

He see me, and rode up and says:

'Whar'd you come f'm, boy? You prepared to die?'

Then he rode on. I was scared; but a man says:

'He don't mean nothing; he's always a-carryin' on like that, when he's drunk. He's the best-naturedest old fool in Arkansaw—never hurt nobody, drunk nor sober.'

Boggs rode up before the biggest store in town and bent his head down so he could see under the curtain of the awning, and yells:

'Come out here, Sherburn! Come out and meet the man you've swindled. You're the houn' I'm after, and I'm a-gwyne to have you, too!'

And so he went on, calling Sherburn everything he could lay his tongue to, and the whole street packed with people listening and laughing and going on. By-and-by a proud-looking man about fifty-five—and he was a heap the best-dressed man in that town, too—steps out of the store, and the crowd drops back on each side to let him come. He says to Boggs, mighty calm and slow—he says:

'I'm tired of this; but I'll endurc it till one o'clock. Till one o'clock, mind—no longer. If you open your mouth against me only once, after that time, you can't travel so far but I will find you.'

Then he turns and goes in. The crowd looked mighty sober; nobody stirred, and there warn't no more laughing. Boggs rode off blackguarding Sherburn as loud as he could yell, all down the street; and pretty soon back he comes and stops before the store, still keeping it up. Some men crowded around him and tried to get him to shut up, but he wouldn't; they told him it would be one o'clock in about fifteen minutes, and so he *must* go home—he must go right away. But it didn't do no good. He cussed away, with all his might, and throwed his hat down in the mud and rode over it, and pretty soon away he went a-raging down the street again, with his grey hair a-flying. Everybody that could get a chance at him tried their best to coax him off of his horse so they could lock him up and get him sober; but it warn't no use—up the street he would tear again, and give Sherburn another cussing. By-and-by somebody says:

'Go for his daughter!—quick, go for his daughter; sometimes he'll listen to her. If anybody can persuade him, she can.'

So somebody started on a run. I walked down-street a ways, and stopped. In about five or ten minutes, here comes Boggs again—but not on his horse. He was a-reeling across the street towards me, bareheaded, with a friend on both sides of him aholt of his arms and hurrying him along. He was quiet, and looked uneasy; and he warn't hanging back any, but was doing some of the hurrying himself. Somebody sings out:

'Boggs!'

I looked over there to see who said it, and it was that Colonel Sherburn. He was standing perfectly still in the street, and had a pistol raised in his right hand—not aiming it, but holding it out with the barrel tilted up towards the sky. The same second I see a young girl coming on the run, and two men with her. Boggs and the men turned round, to see who called him, and when they see the pistol the men jumped to one side, and the pistol barrel come down slow and steady to a level—both barrels cocked. Boggs throws up both of his hands, and says, 'O Lord, don't shoot!' Bang! goes the first shot, and he staggers back clawing at the air—bang! goes the second one, and he tumbles backwards on to the ground, heavy and solid, with his arms spread out. That young girl screamed out, and comes rushing, and down she throws herself on her father, crying, and saying, 'Oh, he's killed him, he's killed him!' The crowd closed up around them, and shouldered and jammed one another, with their necks stretched, trying to see, and people on the inside trying to shove them back, and shouting, 'Back, back! give him air, give him air!'

Colonel Sherburn he tossed his pistol on to the ground, and turned around on his heels and walked off.

They took Boggs to a little drug-store, the crowd pressing around, just the same, and the whole town following, and I rushed and got a good place at the window, where I was close to him and could see in. They laid him on the floor, and put one large Bible under his head, and opened another one and spread it on his breast—but they tore open his shirt first, and I seen where one of the bullets went in. He made about a dozen long gasps, his breast lifting the Bible up when he drawed in his breath, and letting it down again when he breathed it out—and after that he laid still; he was dead. Then they pulled his daughter away from him, screaming and crying, and took her off. She was about sixteen, and very sweet and gentle-looking, but awful pale and scared.

Well, pretty soon the whole town was there, squirming and scrouging and pushing and shoving to get at the window and have a look, but people that had the places wouldn't give them up, and folks behind them was saying all the time, 'Say, now, you've looked enough, you fellows; 'tain't right and 'tain't fair, for you to stay thar all the time, and never give nobody a chance; other folks has their rights as well as you.'

There was considerable jawing back, so I slid out, thinking maybe there was going to be trouble. The streets was full, and everybody was excited. Everybody that seen the shooting was telling how it happened, and there was a big crowd packed around each one of these fellows, stretching their necks and listening. One long, lanky man, with long hair and a big white fur stove-pipe hat on the back of his head, and a crooked-handled cane, marked out the places on the ground where Boggs stood, and where Sherburn stood, and the people following him around from one place to t'other and watching everything he done, and bobbing their heads to show they understood, and stooping a little, and resting their hands on their thighs to watch him mark the places on the ground with his cane; and then he stood up straight and stiff where Sherburn had stood, frowning and having his hat-brim down over his eyes, and sung out, 'Boggs!' and then fetched his cane down slow to a dead level, and says 'Bang!' staggered backwards, says 'Bang!' again, and fell down flat on his back. The people that had seen the thing said he done it perfect; said it was just exactly the way it all happened. Then as much as a dozen people got out their bottles and treated him.

Well, by-and-by somebody said Sherburn ought to be lynched. In about a minute everybody was saying it; so away they went, mad and yelling, and snatching down every clothes-line they come to, to do the hanging with.

## *Chapter 22*

SHERBURN—ATTENDING THE CIRCUS—INTOXICATION IN THE RING—THE THRILLING TRAGEDY

THEY swarmed up the street towards Sherburn's house, a-whooping and yelling and raging like Injuns, and everything had to clear the way or get run over and tromped to mush, and it was awful to see. Children was heeling it ahead of the mob, screaming and trying to get out of the way; and every window along the road was full of women's heads, and there was nigger boys in every tree, and bucks and wenches looking over every fence; and as soon as the mob would get nearly to them they would break and skaddle back out of reach. Lots of the women and girls was crying and taking on, scared most to death.

They swarmed up in front of Sherburn's palings as thick as they could jam together, and you couldn't hear yourself think for the noise. It was a little twenty-foot yard. Some sung out, 'Tear down the fence! tear down the fence!' Then there was a racket of ripping and tearing and smashing, and down she goes, and the front wall of the crowd begins to roll in like a wave.

Just then Sherburn steps out on to the roof of his little front porch, with a double-barrel gun in his hand, and takes his stand perfectly calm and deliberate, not saying a word. The racket stopped, and the wave sucked back.

Sherburn never said a word—just stood there, looking down. The stillness was awful creepy and uncomfortable. Sherburn run his eye slow along the crowd; and wherever it struck, the people tried a little to outgaze him, but they couldn't; they dropped their eyes and looked sneaky. Then pretty soon Sherburn sort of laughed; not the pleasant kind, but the kind that makes you feel like when you are eating bread that's got sand in it.

Then he says, slow and scornful:

'The idea of *you* lynching anybody! It's amusing. The idea of you thinking you had pluck enough to lynch a *man*! Because you're brave enough to tar and feather poor friendless cast-out women that come along here, did that make you think you had grit enough to lay your hands on a *man*? Why, a *man's* safe in the hands of ten thousand of your kind—as long as it's day-time and you're not behind him.

'Do I know you? I know you clear through. I was born and raised in the South, and I've lived in the North; so I know the average all around. The average man's a coward. In the North he lets anybody walk over him that wants to, and goes home and prays for a humble spirit to bear it. In the South one man, all by himself, has stopped a stage full of men, in the day-time, and robbed the lot. Your newspapers call you a brave people so much that you think you *are* braver than any other people—whereas you're just *as* brave, and no braver. Why don't your juries hang murderers? Because they're afraid the man's friends will shoot them in the back, in the dark—and it's just what they *would* do.

'So they always acquit; and then a *man* goes in the night, with a hundred masked cowards at his back, and lynches the rascal. Your mistake is, that you didn't bring a man with you; that's one mistake, and the other is that you didn't come in the dark, and fetch your masks. You brought *part* of a man—Buck Harkness, there—and if you hadn't had him to start you, you'd a taken it out in blowing.

'You didn't want to come. The average man don't like trouble and danger. *You* don't like trouble and danger. But if only *half* a man—like Buck Harkness, there—shouts "Lynch him, lynch him!" you're afraid to back down—afraid you'll be found out to be what you are—*cowards*—and so you raise a yell, and hang yourselves on to that half-a-man's coat-tail and come raging up here, swearing what big things you're going to do. The pitifullest thing out is a mob; that's what an army is—a mob; they don't fight with courage that's born in them, but with courage that's borrowed from their mass, and from their officers. But a mob without any *man* at the head of it, is *beneath* pitifulness. Now the thing for *you* to do, is to droop your tails and go home and crawl in a hole. If any real lynching's going to be done, it will be done in the dark, Southern fashion; and when they come they'll bring their masks, and fetch a *man* along. Now *leave*—and take your half-a-man with you'—tossing his gun up across his left arm and cocking it, when he says this.

The crowd washed back sudden, and then broke all apart and went tearing off every which way, and Buck Harkness he heeled it after them, looking tolerable cheap. I could a staid, if I'd a wanted to, but I didn't want to.

I went to the circus, and loafed around the back side till the watchman went by, and then dived in under the tent. I had my twenty-dollar gold piece and some other money, but I reckoned I better save it, because there ain't no telling how soon you are going to need it, away from home and amongst strangers, that way. You can't be too careful. I ain't opposed to spending money on circuses, when there ain't no other way, but there ain't no use in *wasting* it on them.

It was a real bully circus. It was the splendidest sight that ever was, when they all come riding in, two and two, a gentleman and lady, side by side, the men just in their drawers and under-shirts, and no shoes nor stirrups, and resting their hands on their thighs, easy and comfortable—there must a been twenty of them—and every lady with a lovely complexion, and perfectly beautiful, and looking just like a gang of real sure-enough queens, and dressed in clothes that cost millions of dollars, and just littered with diamonds. It was a powerful fine sight; I never see anything so lovely. And then one by one they got up and stood, and went a-weaving around the ring so gentle and wavy and graceful, the men looking ever so tall and airy and straight, with their heads bobbing and skimming along, away up there under the tent-roof, and every lady's rose-leafy dress flapping soft and silky around her hips, and she looking like the most loveliest parasol.

And then faster and faster they went, all of them dancing, first one foot stuck out in the air and then the other, the horses leaning more and more, and the ring-master going round and round the centre-pole, cracking his whip and shouting 'Hi!—hi!' and the clown cracking jokes behind him; and by-and-by all hands dropped the reins, and every lady put her knuckles on her hips and every gentleman folded his arms, and then how the horses did lean over and hump themselves! And so, one after the other they all skipped off into the ring, and made the sweetest bow I ever see, and then scampered out, and everybody clapped their hands and went just about wild.

Well, all through the circus they done the most astonishing things; and all the time that clown carried on so it most killed the people. The ring-master couldn't ever say a word to him but he was back at him quick as a wink with the funniest things a body ever said; and how he ever *could* think of so many of them, and so sudden and so pat, was what I couldn't noway understand. Why, I couldn't a thought of them in a year. And by-and-by a drunk man tried to get into the ring—said he wanted to ride; said he could ride as well as anybody that ever was. They argued and tried to keep him out, but he wouldn't listen, and the whole show come to a standstill. Then the people begun to holler at him and make fun of him, and that made him mad, and he begun to rip and tear; so that stirred up the people, and a lot of men begun to pile down off of the benches and swarm towards the ring, saying, 'Knock him down! throw him out!' and one or two women begun to scream. So, then, the ring-master he made a little speech, and said he hoped there wouldn't be no disturbance, and if the man would promise he wouldn't make no more trouble, he would let him ride, if he thought he could stay on the horse. So everybody laughed and said all right, and the man got on. The minute he was on, the horse begun to rip and tear and jump and cavort around, with two circus men hanging on to his bridle trying to hold him, and the drunk man hanging on to his neck and his heels flying in the air every jump, and the whole crowd of people standing up shouting and laughing till the tears rolled down. And at last, sure enough, all the circus men could do, the horse broke loose, and away he went like the very nation, round and round the ring, with that sot laying down on him and hanging to his neck, with first one leg hanging most to the ground on one side, and then t'other one on t'other side, and the people just crazy. It warn't funny to me, though; I was all of a tremble to see his danger. But pretty soon he struggled up astraddle and grabbed the bridle, a-reeling this way and that; and the next minute he sprung up and dropped the bridle and stood! and the horse agoing like a house afire too. He just stood up there, a-sailing around as easy and comfortable as if he warn't ever drunk in his life—and then he begun to pull off his clothes and sling them. He shed them so thick they kind of clogged up the air, and altogether he shed seventeen suits. And then, there he was, slim and handsome, and dressed the gaudiest and prettiest you ever saw, and he lit into that horse with his whip and made him fairly hum—and finally skipped off, and made his bow and danced off to the dressing-room, and everybody just a-howling with pleasure and astonishment.

Then the ring-master he see how he had been fooled, and he *was* the sickest ring-master you ever see, I reckon. Why, it was one of his own men! He had got up that joke all out of his own head, and never let on to nobody. Well, I felt sheepish enough, to be took in so, but I wouldn't a been in that ring-master's place, not for a thousand dollars. I don't know; there may be bullier circuses than what that one was, but I never struck them yet. Anyways, it was plenty good enough for *me*; and wherever I run across it, it can have all of *my* custom, every time.

Well, that night we had *our* show; but there warn't only about twelve people there; just enough to pay expenses. And they laughed all the time, and that made the duke mad; and everybody left, anyway, before the show was over, but one boy which was asleep. So the duke said these Arkansaw lunkheads couldn't come up to Shakespeare; what they wanted was low comedy—and maybe something ruther worse than low comedy, he reckoned. He said he could size their style. So next morning he got some big sheets of wrapping-paper and some black paint, and drawed off some handbills and stuck them up all over the village. The bills said:

AT THE COURT HOUSE!
FOR 3 NIGHTS ONLY!
*The World-Renowned Tragedians*
DAVID GARRICK THE YOUNGER!
AND
EDMUND KEAN THE ELDER!
*Of the London and Continental Theatres,*
In their Thrilling Tragedy of
THE KING'S CAMELOPARD
OR
THE ROYAL NONESUCH ! ! !
*Admission 50 cents.*

Then at the bottom was the biggest line of all—which said:

LADIES AND CHILDREN NOT ADMITTED

'There,' says he, 'if that line don't fetch them, I don't know Arkansaw!'

## *Chapter 23*

### SOLD—ROYAL COMPARISONS—JIM GETS HOME-SICK

WELL, all day him and the king was hard at it, rigging up a stage, and a curtain, and a row of candles for foot-lights; and that night the house was jam full of men in no time. When the place couldn't hold no more, the duke he quit tending door and went around the back way and come on to the stage and stood up before the curtain, and made a little speech, and praised up this tragedy, and said it was the most thrillingest one that ever was; and so he went on a-bragging about the tragedy, and about Edmund Kean the Elder, which was to play the main principal part in it; and at last when he'd got everybody's expectations up high enough, he rolled up the curtain, and the next minute the king come a-prancing out on all fours, naked; and he was painted all over, ring-streaked-and-striped, all sorts of colours, as splendid as a rainbow. And —but never mind the rest of his outfit, it was just wild, but it was awful funny. The people most killed themselves laughing; and when the king got done capering, and capered off behind the scenes, they roared and clapped and stormed and haw-hawed till he come back and done it over again; and after that, they made him do it another time.

Well, it would a made a cow laugh to see the shines that old idiot cut.

Then the duke he lets the curtain down, and bows to the people, and says the great tragedy will be performed only two nights more, on accounts of pressing London engagements, where the seats is all sold aready for it in Drury Lane; and then he makes them another bow, and says if he has succeeded in pleasing them and instructing them, he will be deply obleeged if they will mention it to their friends and get them to come and see it.

Twenty people sings out:

'What, is it over? Is that *all*?'

The duke says 'yes.' Then there was a fine time. Everybody sings out 'sold,' and rose up mad, and was agoing for that stage and them tragedians. But a big, fine-looking man jumps up on a bench, and shouts:

'Hold on! Just a word, gentlemen.' They stopped to listen. 'We are sold—mighty badly sold. But we don't want to be the laughing-stock of this whole town, I reckon, and never hear the last of this thing as long as we live. *No*. What we want, is to go out of here quiet, and talk this show up, and sell the *rest* of the town! Then we'll all be in the same boat. Ain't that sensible?' ('You bet it is!—the jedge is right!' everybody sings out.) 'All right, then—not a word about any sell. Go along home, and advise everybody to come and see the tragedy.'

Next day you couldn't hear nothing around that town but how splendid that show was. House was jammed again, that night, and we sold this crowd the same way. When me and the king and the duke got home to the raft, we all had a supper; and by-and-by, about midnight, they made Jim and me back her out and float her down the middle of the river and fetch her in and hide her about two mile below-town.

The third night the house was crammed again—and they warn't new-comers, this time, but people that was at the show the other two nights. I stood by the duke at the door, and I see that every man that went in had his pockets bulging, or something muffled up under his coat—and I see it warn't no perfumery neither, not by a long sight. I smelt sickly eggs by the barrel, and rotten cabbages, and such things; and if I know the signs of a dead cat being around, and I bet I do, there was sixty-four of them went in. I shoved in there for a minute, but it was too various for me, I couldn't stand it. Well, when the place couldn't hold no more people, the duke he give a fellow a quarter and told him to tend door for him a minute, and then he started around for the stage door, I after him; but the minute we turned the corner and was in the dark, he says:

'Walk fast, now, till you get away from the houses, and then shin for the raft like the dickens was after you!'

I done it, and he done the same. We struck the raft at the same time, and in less than two seconds we was gliding down-stream, all dark and still, and edging towards the middle of the river, nobody saying a word. I reckoned the poor king was in for a gaudy time of it with the audience; but nothing of the sort; pretty soon he crawls out from under the wigwam, and says:

'Well, how'd the old thing pan out this time, Duke?'

He hadn't been up-town at all.

We never showed a light till we was about ten mile below that village. Then we lit up and had a supper, and the king and the duke fairly laughed their bones loose over the way they'd served them people. The duke says:

'Greenhorns, flatheads! *I* knew the first house would keep mum and let the rest of the town get roped in; and I knew they'd lay for us the third night, and consider it was *their* turn now. Well, it *is* their turn, and I'd give something to know how much they take for it. I *would* just like to know how they're putting in their opportunity. They can turn it into a picnic if they want to—they brought plenty provisions.'

Them rapscallions took in four hundred and sixty-five dollars in that three nights. I never see money hauled in by the wagon-load like that, before.

By-and-by, when they was asleep and snoring, Jim says:

'Don't it s'prise you, de way dem kings carries on, Huck?'

'No,' I says, 'it don't.'

'Why don't it, Huck?'

'Well, it don't, because it's in the breed. I reckon they're all alike.'

'But, Huck, dese kings o' ourn is reglar rapscallions; dat's jist what dey is; dey's reglar rapscallions.'

'Well, that's what I'm a-saying; all kings is mostly rapscallions, as fur as I can make out.

'Is dat so?'

'You read about them once—you'll see. Look at Henry the Eight; this'n's a Sunday-school Superintendent to *him*. And look at Charles Second, and Louis Fourteen, and Louis Fifteen, and James Second, and Edward Second, and Richard Third, and forty more; besides all them Saxon heptarchies that used to rip around so in old times and raise Cain. My, you ought to seen old Henry the Eight when he was in bloom. He *was* a blossom. He used to marry a new wife every day, and chop off her head next morning. And he would do it just as indifferent as if he was ordering up eggs. "Fetch up Nell Gwynn," he says. They fetch her up. Next morning, "Chop off her head!" And they chop it off. "Fetch up Jane Shore," he says; and up she comes. Next morning, "Chop off her head"—and they chop it off. "Ring up Fair Rosamun." Fair Rosamun answers the bell. Next morning, "Chop off her head." And he made every one of them tell him a tale every night; and he kept that up till he had hogged a thousand and one tales that way, and then he put them all in a book, and called it Domesday Book—which was a good name and stated the case. You don't know kings, Jim, but I know them; and this old rip of ourn is one of the cleanest I've struck in history. Well, Henry he takes a notion he wants to get up some trouble with this country. How does he go at it?—give notice?—give the country a show? No. All of a sudden he heaves all the tea in Boston Harbour overboard, and whacks out a declaration of independence, and dares them to come on. That was *his* style—he never give anybody a chance. He had suspicions of his father, the Duke of Wellington. Well, what did he do?—ask him to show up? No—drownded him in a butt of mamsey, like a cat. S'pose people left money laying around where he was—what did he do? He collared it. S'pose he contracted to do a thing; and you paid him, and didn't set down there and see that he done it—what did he do? He always done the other thing. S'pose he opened his mouth—what then? If he didn't shut it up powerful quick, he'd lose a lie, every time. That's the kind of a bug Henry was; and if we'd a had him along 'stead of our kings, he'd a fooled that town a heap worse than ourn done. I don't say that ourn is lambs, because they ain't, when you come right down to the cold facts; but they ain't nothing to *that* old ram, anyway. All I say is, kings is kings, and you got to make allowances. Take them all around, they're a mighty ornery lot. It's the way they're raised.'

'But dis one do *smell* so like de nation, Huck.'

'Well, they all do, Jim. *We* can't help the way a king smells; history don't tell no way.'

'Now de duke, he's a tolerble likely man, in some ways.'

'Yes, a duke's different. But not very different. This one's a middling hard lot for a duke. When he's drunk, there ain't no near-sighted man could tell him from a king.'

'Well, anyways, I doan' hanker for no mo' un um, Huck. Dese is all I kin stan'.'

'It's the way I feel too, Jim. But we've got them on our hands, and we got to remember what they are, and make allowances. Sometimes I wish we could hear of a country that's out of kings.'

What was the use to tell Jim these warn't real kings and dukes? It wouldn't a done no good; and besides, it was just as I said; you couldn't tell them from the real kind.

I went to sleep, and Jim didn't call me when it was my turn. He often done that. When I waked up, just at daybreak, he was setting there with his head down betwixt his knees, moaning and mourning to himself. I didn't take notice, nor let on. I knowed what it was about. He was thinking about his wife and his children, away up yonder, and he was low and home-sick; because he hadn't ever been away from home before in his life; and I do believe he cared just as much for his people as white folks does for ther'n. It don't seem natural, but I reckon it's so. He was often moaning and mourning that way, nights, when he judged I was asleep, and saying, 'Po' little 'Lizabeth! po' little Johnny! it's mighty hard; I spec' I ain't ever gwyne to see you no mo', no mo'!' He was a mighty good nigger, Jim was.

But this time I somehow got to talking to him about his wife and young ones; and by-and-by he says:

'What makes me feel so bad dis time, 'uz bekase I hear sumpn over yonder on de bank like a whack, er a slam, while ago, en it mine me er de time I treat my little 'Lizabeth so ornery. She warn't on'y 'bout fo' year ole, en she tuck de sk'yarlet-fever, en had a powful rough spell; but she got well, en one day she was a-stannin' aroun' en I says to her, I says:

' "Shet de do'."

'She never done it; jis' stood dah, kiner smilin' up at me. It make me mad; en I says agin, mighty loud, I says:

' "Doan' you hear me?—shet de do'!"

'She jis' stood de same way, kiner smilin' up. I was a-bilin'! I says:

' "I lay I *make* you mine!"

'En wid dat I fetch' her a slap side de head dat sont her a-sprawlin'. Den I went into de yuther room, en 'uz gone 'bout ten minutes; en when I come back, dah was dat do' a-stannin' open *yit*, en dat chile stannin' mos' right in it, a-lookin' down and mournin', en de tears runnin' down. My, but I *wuz* mad, I was a-gwyne for de chile, but jis' den—it was a do' dat open innerds—jis' den, 'long come de wind en slam it to, behine de chile, ker-*blam*!—en my lan', de chile never move'! My breff mos' hop outer me; en I feel so—so—I doan' know *how* I feel. I crope out, all a-tremblin', en crope aroun' en open de do' easy en slow, en poke my head in behine de chile, sof' en still, en all uv a sudden, I says *pow!* jis' as loud as I could yell. *She never budge!* Oh, Huck, I bust out a-cryin' en grab her up in my arms, en say, "Oh, de po' little thing! de Lord God Amighty fogive po' ole Jim, kaze he never gwyne to fogive hisself as long's he live!" Oh, she was plumb deef en dumb, Huck, plumb deef en dumb—en I'd ben a-treat'n her so!'

## *Chapter 24*

JIM IN ROYAL ROBES—THEY TAKE A PASSENGER—GETTING INFORMATION—FAMILY GRIEF

NEXT day, towards night, we laid up under a little willow tow-head out in the middle, where there was a village on each side of the river, and the duke and the king begun to lay out a plan for working them towns. Jim he spoke to the duke, and said he hoped it wouldn't take but a few hours, because it got mighty heavy and tiresome to him when he had to lay all day in the wigwam tied with the rope. You see, when we left him all alone we had to tie him, because if anybody happened on him all by himself and not tied, it wouldn't look much like he was a runaway nigger, you know. So the duke said it *was* kind of hard to have to lay roped all day, and he'd cipher out some way to get around it.

He was uncommon bright, the duke was, and he soon struck it. He dressed Jim up in King Lear's outfit—it was a long curtain-calico gown, and a white horse-hair wig and whiskers; and then he took his theatre-paint and painted Jim's face and hands and ears and neck all over a dead dull solid blue, like a man that 's been drownded nine days. Blamed if he warn't the horriblest-looking outrage I ever see. Then the duke took and wrote out a sign on a shingle so—

*Sick Arab—but harmless when not out of his head.*

And he nailed that shingle to a lath, and stood the lath up four or five foot in front of the wigwam. Jim was satisfied. He said it was a sight better than laying tied a couple of years every day and trembling all over every time there was a sound. The duke told him to make himself free and easy, and if anybody ever come meddling around, he must hop out of the wigwam, and carry on a little, and fetch a howl or two like a wild beast, and he reckoned they would light out and leave him alone. Which was sound enough judgment; but you take the average man, and he wouldn't wait for him to howl. Why, he didn't only look like he was dead, he looked considerable more than that.

These rapscallions wanted to try the Nonesuch again, because there was so much money in it, but they judged it wouldn't be safe, because maybe the news might a worked along down by this time. They couldn't hit no project that suited, exactly; so at last the duke said he reckoned he'd lay off and work his brains an hour or two and see if he couldn't put up something on the Arkansaw village; and the king he allowed he would drop over to t'other village, without any plan, but just trust in Providence to lead him the profitable way—meaning the devil, I reckon. We had all bought store clothes where we stopped last; and now the king put his'n on, and he told me to put mine on. I done it, of course. The king's duds was all black, and he did look real swell and starchy. I never knowed how clothes could change a body before. Why, before, he looked like the orneriest old rip that ever was; but now, when he'd take off his new white beaver and make a bow and do a smile, he looked that grand and good and pious that you'd say he had walked right out of the ark, and maybe was old Leviticus himself. Jim cleaned up the canoe, and I got my paddle ready. There was a big steamboat laying at the shore away up under the point, about three mile above-town—been there a couple of hours, taking on freight. Says the king:

'Seein' how I'm dressed, I reckon maybe I better arrive down from St. Louis or Cincinnati, or some other big place. Go for the steamboat, Huckleberry; we'll come down to the village on her.'

I didn't have to be ordered twice, to go and take a steamboat ride. I fetched the shore a half a mile above the village, and then went scooting along the bluff bank in the easy water. Pretty soon we come to a nice innocent-looking young country jake setting on a log swabbing the sweat off of his face, for it was powerful warm weather; and he had a couple of big carpet-bags by him.

'Run her nose in-shore,' says the king. I done it. 'Wher' you bound for, young man?'

'For the steamboat; going to Orleans.'

'Git aboard,' says the king. 'Hold on a minute, my servant'll he'p you with them bags. Jump out and he'p the gentleman, Adolphus'—meaning me, I see.

I done so, and then we all three started on again. The young chap was mighty thankful; said it was tough work toting his baggage such weather. He asked the king where he was going, and the king told him he'd come down the river and landed at the other village this morning, and now he was going up a few mile to see an old friend on a farm up there. The young fellow says:

'When I first see you, I says to myself, "It's Mr. Wilks, sure, and he come mighty near getting here in time." But then I says again, "No, I reckon it ain't him, or else he wouldn't be paddling up the river." You *ain't* him, are you?'

'No, my name 's Blodgett—Elexander Blodgett—*Reverend* Elexander Blodgett, I s'pose I must say, as I'm one o' the Lord's poor servants. But still I'm jist as able to be sorry for Mr. Wilks for not arriving in time, all the same, if he's missed anything by it—which I hope he hasn't.'

'Well, he don't miss any property by it, because he'll get that all right; but he's missed seeing his brother Peter die—which he mayn't mind, nobody can tell as to that—but his brother would a give anything in this world to see *him* before he died; never talked about nothing else all these three weeks; hadn't seen him since they was boys together—and hadn't ever seen his brother William at all—that 's the deef and dumb one—William ain't more than thirty or thirty-five. Peter and George was the only ones that come out here; George was the married brother; him and his wife both died last year. Harvey and William's the only ones that 's left now; and, as I was saying, they haven't got here in time.'

'Did anybody send 'em word?'

'Oh, yes; a month or two ago, when Peter was first took; because Peter said then that he sorter felt like he warn't going to get well this time. You see, he was pretty old, and George's g'yirls was too young to be much company for him, except Mary Jane, the red-headed one; and so he was kinder lonesome after George and his wife died, and didn't seem to care much to live. He most desperately wanted to see Harvey—and William too, for that matter—because he was one of them kind that can't bear to make a will. He left a letter behind for Harvey, and said he'd told in it where his money was hid, and how he wanted the rest of the property divided up so George's g'yirls would be all right—for George didn't leave nothing. And that letter was all they could get him to put a pen to.'

'Why do you reckon Harvey don't come? Wher' does he live?'

'Oh, he lives in England—Sheffield—preaches there—hasn't ever been in this country. He hasn't had any too much time—and besides, he mightn't a got the letter at all, you know.'

'Too bad, too bad he couldn't a lived to see his brothers, poor soul. You going to Orleans, you say?'

'Yes, but that ain't only a part of it. I'm going in a ship, next Wednesday, for Ryo Janeero, where my uncle lives.'

'It's a pretty long journey. But it'll be lovely; I wisht I was agoing. Is Mary Jane the eldest? How old is the others?'

'Mary Jane's nineteen, Susan's fifteen, and Joanna's about fourteen—that's the one that gives herself to good works and has a hare-lip.'

'Poor things! to be left alone in the cold world so.'

'Well, they could be worse off. Old Peter had friends, and they ain't going to let them come to no harm. There's Hobson, the Babtis' preacher; and Deacon Lot Hovey, and Ben Rucker, and Abner Shackleford, and Levi Bell, the lawyer; and Dr. Robinson, and their wives, and the widow Bartley, and—well, there's a lot of them; but these are the ones that Peter was thickest with, and used to write about sometimes, when he wrote home; so Harvey'll know where to look for friends when he gets here.'

Well, the old man he went on asking questions till he just fairly emptied that young fellow. Blamed if he didn't inquire about everybody and everything in that blessed town, and all about all the Wilkses; and about Peter's business—which was a tanner; and about George's—which was a carpenter; and about Harvey's—which was a dissentering minister; and so on, and so on. Then he says:

'What did you want to walk all the way up to the steamboat for?'

'Because she's a big Orleans boat, and I was afeard she mightn't stop there. When they're deep they won't stop for a hail. A Cincinnati boat will, but this is a St. Louis one.'

'Was Peter Wilks well off?'

'Oh, yes, pretty well off. He had houses and land, and it's reckoned he left three or four thousand in cash hid up som'ers.'

'When did you say he died?'

'I didn't say, but it was last night.'

'Funeral to-morrow, likely?'

'Yes, 'bout the middle of the day.'

'Well, it's all terrible sad; but we've all got to go, one time or another. So what we want to do is to be prepared; then we're all right.'

'Yes, sir, it's the best way. Ma used to always say that.'

When we struck the boat, she was about done loading, and pretty soon she got off. The king never said nothing about going aboard, so I lost my ride, after all. When the boat was gone, the king made me paddle up another mile to a lonesome place, then he got ashore, and says:

'Now hustle back, right off, and fetch the duke up here, and the new carpet-bags. And if he's gone over to t'other side, go over there and git him. And tell him to git himself up regardless. Shove along, now.'

I see what *he* was up to; but I never said nothing, of course. When I got back with the duke, we hid the canoe and then they set down on a log, and the king told him everything, just like the young fellow had said it—every last word of it. And all the time he was a-doing it, he tried to talk like an Englishman; and he done it pretty well too, for a slouch. I can't imitate him, and so I ain't agoing to try to; but he really done it pretty good. Then he says:

'How are you on the deef and dumb, Bilgewater?'

The duke said, leave him alone for that; said he had played a deef and dumb person on the histrionic boards. So then they waited for a steamboat.

About the middle of the afternoon a couple of little boats come along, but they didn't come from high enough up the river; but at last there was a big one, and they hailed her. She sent out her yawl, and we went aboard, and she was from Cincinnati; and when they found we only wanted to go four or five mile, they was booming mad, and give us a cussing, and said they wouldn't land us. But the king was calm. He says:

'If gentlemen kin afford to pay a dollar a mile apiece, to be took on and put off in a yawl, a steamboat kin afford to carry 'em, can't it?'

So they softened down and said it was all right; and when we got to the village, they yawled us ashore. About two dozen men flocked down, when they see the yawl a-coming; and when the king says:

'Kin any of you gentlemen tell me wher Mr. Peter Wilks lives?' they give a glance at one another, and nodded their heads, as much as to say, 'What d' I tell you?' Then one of them says, kind of soft and gentle:

'I'm sorry, sir, but the best we can do is to tell you where he *did* live yesterday evening.'

Sudden as winking, the ornery old cretur went all to smash, and fell up against the man, and put his chin on his shoulder, and cried down his back, and says:

'Alas, alas! our poor brother—gone, and we never got to see him; oh, it's too, *too* hard!'

Then he turns around, blubbering, and makes a lot of idiotic signs to the duke on his hands, and blamed if *he* didn't drop a carpet-bag and bust out a-crying. If they warn't the beatenest lot, them two frauds, that ever I struck.

Well, the men gethered around, and sympathized with them, and said all sorts of kind things to them, and carried their carpet-bags up the hill for them, and let them lean on them and cry, and told the king all about his brother's last moments, and the king he told it all over again on his hands to the duke, and both of them took on about that dead tanner like they'd lost the twelve disciples. Well, if ever I struck anything like it, I'm a nigger. It was enough to make a body ashamed of the human race.

## *Chapter 25*

IS IT THEM?—SINGING THE 'DOXOLOJER'—WE CAN SPARE IT—AWFUL SQUARE—FUNERAL ORGIES—A BAD INVESTMENT

THE news was all over town in two minutes, and you could see the people tearing down on the run, from every which way, some of them putting on their coats as they come. Pretty soon we was in the middle of a crowd, and the noise of the tramping was like a soldier-march. The windows and door-yards was full; and every minute somebody would say, over a fence:

'Is it *them*?'

And somebody trotting along with the gang would answer back and say:

'You bet it is.'

When we got to the house, the street in front of it was packed, and the three girls was standing in the door. Mary Jane *was* red-headed, but that don't make no difference, she was most awful beautiful, and her face and her eyes was all lit up like glory, she was so glad her uncles was come. The king he spread his arms, and Mary Jane she jumped for them, and the hare-lip jumped for the duke, and there they *had* it! Everybody most, leastways women, cried for joy to see them meet again at last and have such good times.

Then the king he hunched the duke, private—I see him do it—and then he looked around and see the coffin, over in the corner on two chairs; so then, him and the duke, with a hand across each other's shoulder, and t'other hand to their eyes, walked slow and solemn over there, everybody dropping back to give them room, and all the talk and noise stopping, people saying 'Sh!' and all the men taking their hats off and drooping their heads, so you could hear a pin fall. And when they got there, they bent over and looked in the coffin, and took one sight, and then they burst out a-crying so you could a heard them to Orleans, most; and then they put their arms around each other's necks, and hung their chins over each other's shoulders; and then for three minutes, or maybe four, I never see two men leak the way they done. And mind you, everybody was doing the same; and the place was that damp I never see anything like it. Then one of them got on one side of the coffin, and t'other on t'other side, and they kneeled down and rested their foreheads on the coffin, and let on to pray all to theirselves. Well, when it come to that, it worked the crowd like you never see anything like it, and so everybody broke down and went to sobbing right out loud—the poor girls too; and every woman, nearly, went up to the girls, without saying a word, and kissed them, solemn, on the forehead, and then put their hand on their head, and looked up towards the sky, with the tears running down, and then busted out and went off sobbing and swabbing, and give the next woman a show. I never see anything so disgusting.

Well, by-and-by the king he gets up and comes forward a little, and works himself up and slobbers out a speech, all full of tears and flap-doodle about its being a sore trial for him and his poor brother to lose the diseased, and to miss seeing diseased alive, after the long journey of four thousand mile, but it's a trial that's sweetened and sanctified to us by this dear sympathy and these holy tears, and so he thanks them out of his heart and out of his brother's heart, because out of their mouths they can't, words being too weak and cold, and all that kind of rot and slush, till it was just sickening; and then he blubbers out a pious goody-goody Amen, and turns himself loose and goes to crying fit to bust.

And the minute the words was out of his mouth somebody over in the crowd struck up the doxolojer, and everybody joined it with all their might, and it just warmed you up and made you feel as good as church letting out. Music *is* a good thing; and after all that soul-butter and hogwash, I never see it freshen up things so, and sound so honest and bully.

Then the king begins to work his jaw again, and says how him and his nieces would be glad if a few of the main principal friends of the family would take supper here with them this evening, and help set up with the ashes of the diseased; and says if his poor brother laying yonder could speak, he knows who he would name, for they was names that was very dear to him, and mentioned often in his letters; and so he will name the same, to wit, as follows, viz.:—Rev. Mr. Hobson, and Deacon Lot Hovey, and Mr. Ben Rucker, and Abner Shackleford, and Levi Bell, and Dr. Robinson, and their wives, and the widow Bartley.

Rev. Hobson and Dr. Robinson was down to the end of the town, a-hunting together; that is, I mean the doctor was shipping a sick man to t'other world, and the preacher was pinting him right. Lawyer Bell was away up to Louisville on some business. But the rest was on hand, and so they all come and shook hands with the king and thanked him and talked to him; and then they shook hands with the duke, and didn't say nothing but just kept a-smiling and bobbing their heads like a passel of sapheads whilst he made all sorts of signs with his hands and said 'Goo-goo—goo-goo-goo,' all the time, like a baby that can't talk.

So the king he blatted along, and managed to inquire about pretty much everybody and dog in town, by his name, and mentioned all sorts of little things that happened one time or another in the town, or to George's family, or to Peter; and he always let on that Peter wrote him the things, but that was a lie, he got every blessed one of them out of that young flathead that we canoed up to the steamboat.

Then Mary Jane she fetched the letter her father left behind, and the king he read it out loud and cried over it. It give the dwelling-house and three thousand dollars, gold, to the girls; and it give the tanyard (which was doing a good business), along with some other houses and land (worth about seven thousand), and three thousand dollars in gold, to Harvey and William, and told where the six thousand cash was hid, down cellar. So these two frauds said they'd go and fetch it up, and have everything square and above-board; and told me to come with a candle. We shut the cellar door behind us, and when they found the bag they spilt it out on the floor, and it was a lovely sight, all them yaller-boys. My, the way the king's eyes did shine! He slaps the duke on the shoulder, and says:

'Oh, *this* ain't bully, nor noth'n! Oh, no, I reckon not! Why, Biljy, it beats the Nonesuch, *don't* it?'

The duke allowed it did. They pawed the yaller-boys, and sifted them through their fingers and let them jingle down on the floor, and the king says:

'It ain't no use talkin'; bein' brothers to a rich dead man, and representatives of furrin heirs that's got left, is the line for you and me, Bilge. This h-yer comes of trust'n to Providence. It's the best way, in the long run. I've tried 'em all, and ther' ain't no better way.'

Most everybody would a been satisfied with the pile, and took it on trust; but no, they must count it. So they counts it, and it comes out four hundred and fifteen dollars short. Says the king:

'Dern him, I wonder what he done with that four hundred and fifteen dollars?'

They worried over that awhile, and ransacked all around for it. Then the duke says:

'Well, he was a pretty sick man, and likely he made a mistake—I reckon that's the way of it. The best way's to let it go, and keep still about it. We can spare it.'

'Oh, shucks, yes, we can *spare* it. I don't k'yer noth'n 'bout that—it's the *count* I'm thinkin' about. We want to be awful square and open and above-board, here, you know. We want to lug this h-yer money upstairs and count it before everybody—then ther' ain't noth'n suspicious. But when the dead man says ther's six thous'n dollars, you know, we don't want to——'

'Hold on,' says the duke. 'Less make up the deffisit'—and he begun to haul out yaller-boys out of his pocket.

'It's a most amaz'n good idea, duke—you *have* got a rattlin' clever head on you,' says the king. 'Blest if the old Nonesuch ain't a-heppin' us out agin'—and *he* begun to haul out yaller-jackets and stack them up.

It most busted them, but they made up the six thousand clean and clear.

'Say,' says the duke, 'I got another idea. Le's go upstairs and count this money, and then take and *give it to the girls*.'

'Good land, duke, lemme hug you! It's the most dazzling idea 'at ever a man struck. You have cert'nly got the most astonishin' head I ever see. Oh, this is the boss dodge, ther' ain't no mistake 'bout it. Let 'em fetch along their suspicions now, if they want to—this'll lay 'em out.'

When we got upstairs, everybody gethered around the table, and the king he counted it and stacked it up, three hundred dollars in a pile—twenty elegant little piles. Everybody looked hungry at it, and licked their chops. Then they raked it into the bag again, and I see the king begin to swell himself up for another speech. He says:

'Friends all, my poor brother that lays yonder has done generous by them that's left behind in the vale of sorrers. He has done generous by these-yer poor little lambs that he loved and sheltered, and that's left fatherless and motherless. Yes, and we that knowed him, knows that he would a done *more* generous by 'em if he hadn't ben afeard o' woundin' his dear William and me. Now, *wouldn't* he? Ther' ain't no question 'bout it, in *my* mind. Well, then—what kind o' brothers would it be, that'd stand in his way at sech a time? And what kind o' uncles would it be that'd rob—yes, *rob*—sech poor sweet lambs as these 'at he loved so, at sech a time? If I know William—and I *think* I do—he—well, I'll jest ask him.' He turns around and begins to make a lot of signs to the duke with his hands; and the duke he looks at him stupid and leather-headed awhile, then all of a sudden he seems to catch his meaning, and jumps for the king, goo-gooing with all his might for joy, and hugs him about fifteen times before he lets up. Then the king says, 'I knowed it; I reckon *that* 'll convince anybody the way *he* feels about it. Here, Mary Jane, Susan, Joanner, take the money—take it *all*. It's the gift of him that lays yonder, cold but joyful.'

Mary Jane she went for him, Susan and the hare-lip went for the duke, and then such another hugging and kissing I never see yet. And everybody crowded up with the tears in their eyes, and most shook the hands off of them frauds, saying all the time:

'You *dear* good souls!—how *lovely*!—how *could* you!'

Well, then, pretty soon all hands got to talking about the diseased again, and how good he was, and what a loss he was, and all that; and before long a big iron-jawed man worked himself in there from outside, and stood a-listening and looking, and not saying anything; and nobody saying anything to him either, because the king was talking and they was all busy listening. The king was saying—in the middle of something he'd started in on:

'—they bein' partickler friends o' the diseased. That's why they're invited here this evenin'; but to-morrow we want *all* to come—everybody; for he respected everybody, he liked everybody, and so it's fitten that his funeral orgies sh'd be public.'

And so he went a-mooning on and on, liking to hear himself talk, and every little while he fetched in his funeral orgies again, till the duke he couldn't stand it no more; so he writes on a little scrap of paper, '*obsequies*, you old fool,' and folds it up and goes to goo-gooing and reaching it over people's heads to him. The king he reads it, and puts it in his pocket, and says:

'Poor William, afflicted as he is, his *heart's* aluz right. Asks me to invite everybody to come to the funeral—wants me to make 'em all welcome. But he needn't a worried—it was jest what I was at.'

Then he weaves along again, perfectly calm, and goes to dropping in his funeral orgies again every now and then, just like he done before. And when he done it the third time, he says:

'I say orgies, not because it's the common term, because it ain't—obsequies bein' the common term—but because orgies is the right term. Obsequies ain't used in England no more, now—it's gone out. We say orgies now, in England. Orgies is better, because it means the thing you're after, more exact. It's a word that's made up out'n the Greek *orgo*, outside, open, abroad; and the Hebrew *jeesum*, to plant, cover up; hence in*ter*. So, you see, funeral orgies is an open er public funeral.'

He was the *worst* I ever struck. Well, the iron-jawed man he laughed right in his face. Everybody was shocked. Everybody says, 'Why, *doctor*!' and Abner Shackleford says:

'Why, Robinson, hain't you heard the news? This is Harvey Wilks.'

The king he smiled eager, and shoved out his flapper, and says:

'*Is* it my poor brother's dear good friend and physician? I——'

'Keep your hands off of me!' says the doctor. '*You* talk like an Englishman—*don't* you? It's the worst imitation I ever heard. *You* Peter Wilks' brother. You're a fraud, that's what you are!'

Well, how they all took on! They crowded around the doctor, and tried to quiet him down, and tried to explain to him, and tell him how Harvey'd showed in forty ways that he *was* Harvey, and knowed everybody by name, and the names of the very dogs, and begged and *begged* him not to hurt Harvey's feelings and the poor girls' feelings, and all that; but it warn't no use, he stormed right along, and said any man that pretended to be an Englishman and couldn't imitate the lingo no better than what he did, was a fraud and a liar. The poor girls was hanging to the king and crying; and all of a sudden the doctor ups and turns on *them*. He says:

'I was your father's friend, and I'm your friend; and I warn you *as* a friend, and an honest one, that wants to protect you and keep you out of harm and trouble, to turn your backs on that scoundrel, and have nothing to do with him, the ignorant tramp, with his idiotic Greek and Hebrew as he calls it. He is the thinnest kind of an imposter—has come here with a lot of empty names and facts which he has picked up somewheres, and you take them for *proofs*, and are helped to fool yourselves by these foolish friends here, who ought to know better. Mary Jane Wilks, you know me for your friend, and for your unselfish friend, too. Now listen to me; turn this pitiful rascal out—I *beg* you to do it. Will you?'

Mary Jane straightened herself up, and my, but she was handsome! She says:

'*Here* is my answer.' She hove up the bag of money and put it in the king's hands, and says, 'Take this six thousand dollars, and invest for me and my sisters any way you want to, and don't give us no receipt for it.'

Then she put her arm around the king on one side, and Susan and the hare-lip done the same on the other. Everybody clapped their hands and stomped on the floor like a perfect storm, whilst the king held up his head and smiled proud. The doctor says:

'All right, I wash *my* hands of the matter. But I warn you all that a time's coming when you're going to feel sick whenever you think of this day'—and away he went.

'All right, doctor,' says the king, kinder mocking him, 'we'll try and get 'em to send for you'—which made them all laugh, and they said it was a prime good hit.

## *Chapter 26*

### A PIOUS KING—THE KING'S CLERGY—SHE ASKED HIS PARDON—HIDING IN THE ROOM—HUCK TAKES THE MONEY

WELL, when they was all gone, the king he asks Mary Jane how they was off for spare rooms, and she said she had one spare room, which would do for Uncle William, and she'd give her own room to Uncle Harvey, which was a little bigger, and she would turn into the room with her sisters and sleep on a cot; and up garret was a little cubby, with a pallet in it. The king said the cubby would do for his valley—meaning me.

So Mary Jane took us up, and she showed them their rooms, which was plain but nice. She said she'd have her frocks and a lot of other traps took out of her room if they was in Uncle Harvey's way, but he said they warn't. The frocks was hung along the wall, and before them was a curtain made out of calico that hung down to the floor. There was an old hair trunk in one corner, and a guitar-box in another, and all sorts of little knick-knacks and jimcracks around, like girls brisken up a room with. The king said it was all the more homely and more pleasanter for these fixings, and so don't disturb them. The duke's room was pretty small, but plenty good enough, and so was my cubby.

That night they had a big supper, and all them men and women was there, and I stood behind the king and the duke's chairs and waited on them, and the niggers waited on the rest. Mary Jane she set at the head of the table, with Susan alongside of her, and said how bad the biscuits was, and how mean the preserves was, and how ornery and tough the fried chickens was—and all that kind of rot, the way women always do for to force out compliments; and the people all knowed everything was tip-top, and said so—said, 'How *do* you get biscuits to brown so nice?' and, 'Where, for the land's sake, *did* you get these amaz'n pickles?' and all that kind of humbug talky-talk, just the way people always does at a supper, you know.

And when it was all done, me and the hare-lip had supper in the kitchen off of the leavings, whilst the others was helping the niggers clean up the things. The hare-lip she got to pumping me about England, and blest if I didn't think the ice was getting mighty thin, sometimes. She says:

'Did you ever see the king?'

'Who? William Fourth? Well, I bet I have—he goes to our church.' I knowed he was dead years ago, but I never let on. So when I says he goes to our church, she says:

'What—regular?'

'Yes—regular. His pew's right over opposite ourn—on t'other side the pulpit.'

'I thought he lived in London?'

'Well, he does. Where *would* he live?'

'But I thought *you* lived in Sheffield?'

I see I was up a stump. I had to let on to get choked with a chicken-bone, so as to get time to think how to get down again. Then I says:

'I mean he goes to our church regular when he's in Sheffield. That's only in the summer-time, when he comes there to take the sea baths.'

'Why, how you talk—Sheffield ain't on the sea.'

'Well, who said it was?'

'Why, you did.'

'I *didn't*, nuther.'

'You did!'

'I didn't.'

'You did.'

'I never said nothing of the kind.'

'Well, what *did* you say, then?'

'Said he come to take the sea *baths*—that's what I said.'

'Well, then! how's he going to take the sea baths if it ain't on the sea?'

'Looky here,' I says; 'did you ever see any Congress water?'

'Yes.'

'Well, did you have to go to Congress to get it?'

'Why, no.'

'Well, neither does William Fourth have to go to the sea to get a sea bath.'

'How does he get it, then?'

'Gets it the way people down here gets Congress water—in barrels. There in the palace at Sheffield they've got furnaces, and he want his water hot. They can't bile that amount of water away off there at the sea. They haven't got no conveniences for it.'

'Oh, I see, now. You might a said that in the first place and saved time.'

When she said that, I see I was out of the woods again, and so I was comfortable and glad. Next, she says:

'Do you go to church, too?'

'Yes—regular.'

'Where do you set?'

'Why, in our pew.'

'*Whose* pew?'

'Why, *ourn*—your Uncle Harvey's.'

'His'n? What does *he* want with a pew?'

'Wants it to set in. What did you *reckon* he wanted with it?'

'Why, I thought he'd be in the pulpit.'

Rot him, I forgot he was a preacher. I see I was up a stump again, so I played another chicken-bone and got another think. Then I says:

'Blame it, do you suppose there ain't but one preacher to a church?'

'Why, what do they want with more?'

'What!—to preach before a king! I never see such a girl as you. They don't have no less than seventeen.'

'Seventeen! My land! Why, I wouldn't set out such a string as that, not if I *never* got to glory. It must take 'em a week.'

'Shucks, they don't *all* of 'em preach the same day—only *one* of 'em.'

'Well, then, what does the rest of 'em do?'

'Oh, nothing much. Loll around, pass the plate—and one thing or another. But mainly they don't do nothing.'

'Well, then, what are they *for*?'

'Why, they're for *style*. Don't you know nothing?'

'Well, I don't *want* to know no such foolishness as that. How is servants treated in England? Do they treat 'em better'n we treat our niggers?'

'*No!* A servant ain't nobody there. They treat them worse than dogs.'

'Don't they give 'em holidays, the way we do, Christmas and New Year's week, and Fourth of July?'

'Oh, just listen! A body could tell *you* hain't ever been to England by that. Why, Hare-l—why, Joanna, they never see a holiday from year's end to year's end; never go to the circus, nor theatre, nor nigger shows, nor nowheres.'

'Nor church?'

'Nor church.'

'But *you* always went to church?'

Well, I was gone up again. I forgot I was the old man's servant. But next minute I whirled in on a kind of an explanation how a valley was different from a common servant, and *had* to go to church whether he wanted to or not, and set with the family, on account of its being the law. But I didn't do it pretty good, and when I got done I see she warn't satisfied. She says:

'Honest Injun, now, hain't you been telling me a lot of lies?'

'Honest Injun,' says I.

'None of it at all?'

'None of it at all. Not a lie in it,' says I.

'Lay your hand on this book and say it.'

I see it warn't nothing but a dictionary, so I laid my hand on it and said it. So then she looked a little better satisfied, and says:

'Well, then, I'll believe some of it; but I hope to gracious if I'll believe the rest.'

'What is it you won't believe, Joe?' says Mary Jane, stepping in with Susan behind her. 'It ain't right nor kind for you to talk so to him, and him a stranger and so far from his people. How would you like to be treated so?'

'That's always your way, Maim—always sailing in to help somebody before they're hurt. I hain't done nothing to him. He's told some stretchers, I reckon; and I said I wouldn't swallow it all; and that's every bit and grain I *did* say. I reckon he can stand a little thing like that, can't he?'

'I don't care whether 'twas little or whether 'twas big, he's here in our house and a stranger, and it wasn't good of you to say it. If you was in his place, it would make you feel ashamed; and so you oughtn't to say a thing to another person that will make *them* feel ashamed.'

'Why, Maim, he said——'

'It don't make no difference what he *said*—that ain't the thing. The thing is for you to treat him *kind*, and not be saying things to make him remember he ain't in his own country and amongst his own folks.'

I says to myself, *this* is a girl that I'm letting that ole reptle rob her of her money!

Then Susan *she* waltzed in; and if you'll believe me, she did give Hare-lip hark from the tomb!

Says I to myself, And this is *another* one that I'm letting him rob her of her money!

Then Mary Jane she took another inning, and went in sweet and lovely again—which was her way—but when she got done there warn't hardly anything left o' poor Hare-lip. So she hollered.

'All right, then,' says the other girls, 'you just ask his pardon.'

She done it, too. And she done it beautiful. She done it so beautiful it was good to hear; and I wished I could tell her a thousand lies, so she could do it again.

I says to myself, this is *another* one that I'm letting him rob her of her money. And when she got through, they all jest laid themselves out to make me feel at home and know I was amongst friends. I felt so ornery and low-down and mean, that I says to myself, My mind's made up; I'll hive that money for them or bust.

So then I lit out—for bed, I said, meaning some time or another. When I got by myself, I went to thinking the thing over. I says to myself, Shall I go to that doctor, private, and blow on these frauds? No—that won't do. He might tell who told him; then the king and the duke would make it warm for me. Shall I go, private, and tell Mary Jane? No—I dasn't do it. Her face would give them a hint, sure; they've got the money, and they'd slide right out and get away with it. If she was to fetch in help, I'd get mixed up in the business, before it was done with, I judge. No, there ain't no good way but one. I got to steal that money, somehow; and I got to steal it some way that they won't suspicion that I done it. They've got a good thing, here; and they ain't agoing to leave till they've played this family and this town for all they're worth, so I'll find a chance time enough. I'll steal it, and hide it; and by-and-by, when I'm away down the river, I'll write a letter and tell Mary Jane where it's hid. But I'd better hive it to-night, if I can, because the doctor maybe hasn't let up as much as he lets on he has; he might scare them out of here, yet.

So, thinks I, I'll go and search them rooms. Upstairs the hall was dark, but I found the duke's room, and started to paw around it with my hands; but I recollected it wouldn't be much like the king to let anybody else take care of that money but his own self; so then I went to his room and begun to paw around there. But I see I couldn't do nothing without a candle, and I dasn't light one, of course. So I judged I'd got to do the other thing—lay for them, and eavesdrop. About that time, I hears their footsteps coming, and was going to skip under the bed; I reached for it, but it wasn't where I thought it would be; but I touched the curtain that hid Mary Jane's frocks, so I jumped in behind that and snuggled in amongst the gowns, and stood there perfectly still.

They come in and shut the door; and the first thing the duke done was to get down and look under the bed. Then I was glad I hadn't found the bed when I wanted it. And yet, you know, it's kind of natural to hide under the bed when you are up to anything private. They sets down, then, and the king says:

'Well, what is it? and cut it middlin' short, because it's better for us to be down there a whoopin'-up the mournin', than up here givin' 'em a chance to talk us over.'

'Well, this is it, Capet. I ain't easy; I ain't comfortable. That doctor lays on my mind. I wanted to know your plans. I've got a notion, and I think it's a sound one.'

'What is it, Duke?'

'That we better glide out of this, before three in the morning, and clip it down the river with what we've got. Specially, seeing we got it so easy—*given* back to us, flung at our heads, as you may say, when of course we allowed to have to steal it back. I'm for knocking off and lighting out.'

That made me feel pretty bad. About an hour or two ago, it would a been a little different, but now it made me feel bad and disappointed. The king rips out and says:

'What! And not sell out the rest o' the property? March off like a passel o' fools and leave eight or nine thous'n' dollars' worth o' property layin' around jest sufferin' to be scooped in?—and all good saleable stuff, too.'

The duke he grumbled; said the bag of gold was enough, and he didn't want to go no deeper—didn't want to rob a lot of orphans of *everything* they had.

'Why, how you talk!' says the king. 'We shan't rob 'em of nothing at all but jest this money. The people that *buys* the property is the suff'rers; because as soon's it's found out 'at we didn't own it—which won't be long after we've slid—the sale won't be valid, and it'll all go back to the estate. These-yer orphans'll git their house back agin, and that's enough for *them*; they're young and spry, and k'n easy earn a livin'. *They* ain't agoing to suffer. Why, jest think—there's thous'n's and thous'n's that ain't nigh so well off. Bless you, *they* ain't got noth'n to complain of.'

Well, the king he talked him blind; so at last he give in, and said all right, but said he believed it was blame foolishness to stay, and that doctor hanging over them. But the king says:

'Cuss the doctor! What do we k'yer for *him*? Hain't we got all the fools in town on our side? and ain't that a big enough majority in any town?'

So they got ready to go downstairs again. The duke says:

'I don't think we put that money in a good place.'

That cheered me up. I'd begun to think I warn't going to get a hint of no kind to help me. The king says:

'Why?'

'Because Mary Jane'll be in mourning from this out; and first you know the nigger that does up the rooms will get an order to box these duds up and put 'em away; and do you reckon a nigger can run across money and not borrow some of it?'

'Your head's level agin, Duke,' says the king; and he come a-fumbling under the curtain two or three foot from where I was. I stuck tight to the wall, and kept mighty still, though quivery; and I wondered what them fellows would say to me if they catched me; and I tried to think what I'd better do if they did catch me. But the king he got the bag before I could think more than about a half a thought, and he never suspicioned I was around. They took and shoved the bag through a rip in the straw tick that was under the feather bed, and crammed it in a foot or two amongst the straw and said it was all right, now, because a nigger only makes up the feather bed, and don't turn over the straw tick only about twice a year, and so it warn't in no danger of getting stole, now.

But I knowed better. I had it out of there before they was half-way downstairs. I groped along up to my cubby, and hid it there till I could get a chance to do better. I judged I better hide it outside of the house somewheres, because if they missed it they would give the house a good ransacking. I knowed that very well. Then I turned in, with my clothes all on; but I couldn't a gone to sleep, if I'd a wanted to, I was in such a sweat to get through with the business. By-and-by I heard the king and the duke come up; so I rolled off of my pallet and laid with my chin at the top of my ladder and waited to see if anything was going to happen. But nothing did.

So I held on till all the late sounds had quit and the early ones hadn't begun, yet; and then I slipped down the ladder.

## *Chapter 27*

THE FUNERAL—THE UNDERTAKER—SATISFYING CURIOSITY—SUSPICIOUS OF HUCK—QUICK SALES AND SMALL PROFITS

I CREPT to their doors and listened; they was snoring, so I tip-toed along, and got downstairs all right. There warn't a sound anywheres. I peeped through a crack of the dining-room door, and see the men that was watching the corpse all sound asleep on their chairs. The door was open into the parlour, where the corpse was laying, and there was a candle in both rooms. I passed along, and the parlour door was open; but I see there warn't nobody in there but the remainders of Peter; so I shoved on by; but the front door was locked, and the key wasn't there. Just then I heard somebody coming down the stairs, back behind me. I run in the parlour, and took a swift look around, and the only place I see to hide the bag was in the coffin. The lid was shoved along about a foot, showing the dead man's face down in there, with a wet cloth over it, and his shroud on. I tucked the money-bag in under the lid, just down beyond where his hands was crossed, which made me creep, they was so cold, and then I run back across the room and in behind the door.

The person coming was Mary Jane. She went to the coffin, very soft, and kneeled down and looked in; then she put up her handkerchief and I see she begun to cry, though I couldn't hear her, and her back was to me. I slid out, and as I passed the dining-room I thought I'd make sure them watchers hadn't seen me; so I looked through the crack and everything was all right. They hadn't stirred.

I slipped up to bed, feeling ruther blue, on accounts of the thing playing out that way after I had took so much trouble and run so much resk about it. Says I, if it could stay where it is, all right; because when we get down the river a hundred mile or two, I could write back to Mary Jane, and she could dig him up again and get it; but that ain't the thing that's going to happen; the thing that's going to happen is, the money'll be found when they come to screw on the lid. Then the king'll get it again, and it'll be a long day before he gives anybody another chance to smouch it from him. Of course, I *wanted* to slide down and get it out of there, but I dasn't try it. Every minute it was getting earlier, now, and pretty soon some of them watchers would begin to stir, and I might get catched—catched with six thousand dollars in my hands that nobody hadn't hired me to take care of. I don't wish to be mixed up in no such business as that, I says to myself.

When I got downstairs in the morning the parlour was shut up, and the watchers was gone. There warn't nobody around but the family and the widow Bartley and our tribe. I watched their faces to see if anything had been happening, but I couldn't tell.

Towards the middle of the day the undertaker come, with his man, and they set the coffin in the middle of the room on a couple of chairs, and then set all our chairs in rows, and borrowed more from the neighbours till the hall and the parlour and the dining-room was full. I see the coffin lid was the way it was before, but I dasn't go to look in under it, with folks around.

Then the people begun to flock in, and the beats and the girls took seats in the front row at the head of the coffin, and for a half an hour the people filed around slow, in single rank, and looked down at the dead man's face a minute, and some dropped in a tear, and it was all very still and solemn, only the girls and the beats holding handkerchiefs to their eyes and keeping their heads bent, and sobbing a little. There warn't no other sound but the scraping of the feet on the floor, and blowing noses—because people always blows them more at a funeral than they do at other places except church.

When the place was packed full, the undertaker he slid around in his black gloves with his softy soothering ways, putting on the last touches, and getting people and things all shipshape and comfortable, and making no more sound than a cat. He never spoke; he moved people around, he squeezed in late ones, he opened up passage-ways, and done it all with nods and signs with his hands. Then he took his place over against the wall. He was the softest, glidingest, stealthiest man I ever see; and there warn't no more smile to him than there is to a ham.

They had borrowed a melodeum—a sick one; and when everything was ready, a young woman set down and worked it, and it was pretty skreeky and colicky, and everybody joined in and sung, and Peter was the only one that had a good thing, according to my notion. Then the Reverend Hobson opened up, slow and solemn, and begun to talk; and straight off the most outrageous row busted out in the cellar a body ever heard; it was only one dog, but he made a most powerful racket, and he kept it up, right along; the parson he had to stand there, over the coffin, and wait—you couldn't hear yourself think. It was right down awkward, and nobody didn't seem to know what to do. But pretty soon they see that long-legged undertaker make a sign to the preacher as much as to say, 'Don't you worry—just depend on me.' Then he stooped down and begun to glide along the wall, just his shoulders showing over the people's heads. So he glided along, and the pow-wow and racket getting more and more outrageous all the time; and at last, when he had gone around two sides of the room, he disappears down cellar. Then, in about two seconds we heard a whack, and the dog he finished up with a most amazing howl or two, and then everything was dead still, and the parson begun his solemn talk where he left off. In a minute or two here comes this undertaker's back and shoulders gliding along the wall again; and so he glided, and glided, around three sides of the room, and then rose up, and shaded his mouth with his hands, and stretched his neck out towards the preacher, over the people's heads, and says, in a kind of a coarse whisper, '*He had a rat!*' Then he drooped down and glided along the wall again to his place. You could see it was a great satisfaction to the people, because naturally they wanted to know. A little thing like that don't cost nothing, and it's just the little things that makes a man to be looked up to and liked. There warn't no more popular man in town than what that undertaker was.

Well, the funeral sermon was very good, but pison long and tiresome; and then the king he shoved in and got off some of his usual rubbage, and at last the job was through, and the undertaker begun to sneak up on the coffin with his screwdriver. I was in a sweat then, and watched him pretty keen. But he never meddled at all; just slid the lid along, as soft as mush, and screwed it down tight and fast. So there I was! I didn't know whether the money was in there, or not. So, says I, s'pose somebody has hogged that bag on the sly?—now how do *I* know whether to write to Mary Jane or not? S'pose she dug him up and didn't find nothing—what would she think of me? Blame it, I says, I might get hunted up and jailed; I'd better lay low and keep dark, and not write at all; the thing's awful mixed, now; trying to better it, I've worsened it a hundred times, and I wish to goodness I'd just let it alone, dad fetch the whole business!

They buried him, and we come back home, and I went to watching faces again—I couldn't help it, and I couldn't rest easy. But nothing come of it; the faces didn't tell me nothing.

The king he visited around, in the evening, and sweetened everybody up, and made himself ever so friendly; and he give out the idea that his congregation over in England would be in a sweat about him, so he must hurry and settle up the estate right away, and leave for home. He was very sorry he was so pushed, and so was everybody; they wished he could stay longer, but they said they could see it couldn't be done. And he said of course him and William would take the girls home with them; and that pleased everybody too, because then the girls would be well fixed, and amongst their own relations; and it pleased the girls too —tickled them so they clean forgot they ever had a trouble in the world; and told him to sell out as quick as he wanted to, they would be ready. Them poor things was that glad and happy it made my heart ache to see them getting fooled and lied to so, but I didn't see no safe way for me to chip in and change the general tune.

Well, blamed if the king didn't bill the house and the niggers and all the property for auction straight off—sale two days after the funeral; but anybody could buy private beforehand if they wanted to.

So the next day after the funeral, along about noontime, the girls' joy got the first jolt; a couple of nigger traders come along, and the king sold them the niggers reasonable, for three-day drafts, as they called it, and away they went, the two sons up the river to Memphis, and their mother down the river to Orleans. I thought them poor girls and them niggers would break their hearts for grief; they cried around each other, and took on so it most made me down sick to see it. The girls said they hadn't ever dreamed of seeing the family separated or sold away from the town. I can't ever get it out of my memory, the sight of them poor miserable girls and niggers hanging around each other's necks and crying; and I reckon I couldn't a stood it all but would a had to bust out and tell on our gang if I hadn't knowed the sale warn't no account and the niggers would be back home in a week or two.

The thing made a big stir in the town, too, and a good many come out flat-footed and said it was scandalous to separate the mother and the children that way. It injured the frauds some; but the old fool he bulled right along, spite of all the duke could say or do, and I tell you the duke was powerful uneasy.

Next day was auction day. About broad-day in the morning, the king and the duke come up in the garret and woke me up, and I see by their look that there was trouble. The king says:

'Was you in my room night before last?'

'No, your majesty'—which was the way I always called him when nobody but our gang warn't around.

'Was you in there yisterday er last night?'

'No, your majesty.'

'Honour bright, now—no lies.'

'Honour bright, your majesty, I'm telling you the truth. I hain't been a-near your room since Miss Mary Jane took you and the duke and showed it to you.'

The duke says:

'Have you seen anybody else go in there?'

'No, your grace, not as I remember, I believe.'

'Stop and think.'

I studied awhile, and see my chance, then I says:

'Well, I see the niggers go in there several times.'

Both of them give a little jump; and looked like they hadn't ever expected it, and then like they *had*. Then the duke says:

'What, *all* of them?'

'No—leastways not all at once. That is, I don't think I ever see them all come *out* at once but just one time.'

'Hello—when was that?'

'It was the day we had the funeral. In the morning. It warn't early, because I overslept. I was just starting down the ladder, and I see them.'

'Well, go on, *go* on—what did they do? How'd they act?'

'They didn't do nothing. And they didn't act anyway, much, as fur as I see. They tip-toed away; so I seen, easy enough, that they'd shoved in there to do up your majesty's room, or something, s'posing you was up; and found you *warn't* up, and so they was hoping to slide out of the way of trouble without waking you up, if they hadn't already waked you up.'

'Great guns, *this* is a go!' says the king; and both of them looked pretty sick and tolerable silly. They stood there a-thinking and scratching their heads a minute, and then the duke he bust into a kind of a little raspy chuckle, and says:

'It does beat all, how neat the niggers played their hand. They let on to be *sorry* they was going out of this region! and I believed they *was* sorry. And so did you, and so did everybody. Don't ever tell *me* any more that a nigger ain't got any histrionic talent. Why, the way they played that thing, it would fool *anybody*. In my opinion there's a fortune in 'em. If I had capital and a theatre, I wouldn't want a better lay out than that—and here we've gone and sold 'em for a song. Yes, and ain't privileged to sing the song, yet. Say, where *is* that song?—that draft?'

'In the bank for to be collected. Where *would* it be?'

'Well, *that's* all right then, thank goodness.'

Says I, kind of timid-like:

'Is something gone wrong?'

The king whirls on me and rips out:

'None o' your business! You keep your head shet, and mind y'r own affairs—if you got any. Long as you're in this town, don't you forgit *that*, you hear?' Then he says to the duke: 'We got to jest swaller it, and say noth'n: mum's the word for *us*.'

As they was starting down the ladder, the duke he chuckles again, and says:

'Quick sales *and* small profits! It's a good business—yes.'

The king snarls around on him and says:

'I was trying to do for the best, in sellin' 'm out so quick. If the profits has turned out to be none, lackin' considable, and none to carry, is it my fault any more'n it's yourn?'

'Well, *they'd* be in this house yet, and we *wouldn't* if I could a got my advice listened to.'

The king sassed back, as much as was safe for him, and then swapped around and lit into *me* again. He give me down the banks for not coming and *telling* him I see the niggers come out of his room acting that way—said any fool would a *knowed* something was up. And then waltzed in and cussed *himself* awhile; and said it all come of him not laying late and taking his natural rest that morning, and he'd be blamed if he'd ever do it again. So they went off a-jawing; and I felt dreadful glad I'd worked it all off on to the niggers, and yet hadn't done the niggers no harm by it.

## *Chapter 28*

THE TRIP TO ENGLAND—'THE BRUTE!'—ROYAL NONESUCH—MARY JANE DECIDES TO LEAVE—HUCK PARTING WITH MARY JANE—MUMPS—THE OPPOSITION LINE

BY-AND-BY it was getting-up time; so I come down the ladder and started for downstairs, but as I come to the girls' room, the door was open, and I see Mary Jane setting by her old hair trunk, which was open, and she'd been packing things in it—getting ready to go to England. But she had stopped now, with a folded gown in her lap, and had her face in her hands, crying. I felt awful bad to see it; of course, anybody would. I went in there, and says:

'Miss Mary Jane, you can't abear to see people in trouble, and *I* can't—most always. Tell me about it.'

So she done it. And it was the niggers—I just expected it. She said the beautiful trip to England was most about spoiled for her; she didn't know *how* she was ever going to be happy there, knowing the mother and the children warn't ever going to see each other no more—and then busted out bitterer than ever, and flung up her hands, and says:

'Oh, dear, dear, to think they ain't *ever* going to see each other any more!'

'But they *will*—and inside of two weeks—and I *know* it!' says I.

Laws it was out before I could think!—and before I could budge, she throws her arms around my neck, and told me to say it *again*, say it *again*, say it *again*!

I see I had spoke too sudden, and said too much, and was in a close place. I asked her to let me think a minute; and she set there, very impatient and excited, and handsome, but looking kind of happy and eased-up, like a person that's had a tooth pulled out. So I went to studying it out. I says to myself, I reckon a body that ups and tells the truth when he is in a tight place, is taking considerable many resks, though I ain't had no experience, and can't say for certain; but it looks so to me, anyway; and yet here's a case where I'm blest if it don't look to me like the truth is better, and actually *safer*, than a lie. I must lay it by in my mind, and think it over some time or other, it's so kind of strange and unregular. I never see nothing like it. Well, I says to myself at last, I'm agoing to chance it; I'll up and tell the truth this time, though it does seem most like setting down on a kag of powder and touching it off just to see where you'll go to. Then I says:

'Miss Mary Jane, is there any place out of town a little ways, where you could go and stay three or four days?'

'Yes—Mr. Lothrop's. Why?'

'Never mind why, yet. If I'll tell you how I know the niggers will see each other again—inside of two weeks—here in this house—and *prove* how I know it—will you go to Mr. Lothrop's and stay four days?'

'Four days!' she says. 'I'll stay a year!'

'All right,' I says, 'I don't want nothing more out of *you* than just your word—I druther have it than another man's kiss-the-Bible.' She smiled, and reddened up very sweet, and I says, 'If you don't mind it, I'll shut the door—and bolt it.'

Then I come back and set down again, and says:

'Don't you holler. Just set still, and take it like a man. I got to tell the truth, and you want to brace up, Miss Mary, because it's a bad kind, and going to be hard to take, but there ain't no help for it. These uncles of yourn ain't no uncles at all—they're a couple of frauds—regular dead-beats. There, now we're over the worst of it—you can stand the rest middling easy.'

It jolted her up like everything, of course; but I was over the shoal-water now, so I went right along, her eyes a-blazing higher and higher all the time, and told her every blame thing, from where we first struck that young fool going up to the steamboat, clear through to where she flung herself on to the king's breast at the front door, and he kissed her sixteen or seventeen times—and then up she jumps, with her face afire like sunset, and says:

'The brute! Come—don't waste a minute—not a *second*—we'll have them tarred and feathered, and flung in the river!'

Says I:

'Cert'nly. But do you mean, *before* you go to Mr. Lothrop's, or——'

'Oh,' she says, 'what am I *thinking* about!' she says, and set right down again. 'Don't mind what I said—please don't—you *won't*, now, *will* you?' Laying her silky hand on mine in that kind of a way that I said I would die first. 'I never thought, I was so stirred up,' she says; 'now go on, and I won't do so any more. You tell me what to do, and whatever you say, I'll do it.'

'Well,' I says, 'it's a rough gang, them two frauds, and I'm fixed so I got to travel with them a while longer, whether I want to or not—I druther not tell you why—and if you was to blow on them this town would get me out of their claws, and *I'd* be all right, but there'd be another person that you don't know about who'd be in big trouble. Well, we got to save *him*, hain't we? Of course. Well, then, we won't blow on them.'

Saying them words put a good idea in my head. I see how maybe I could get me and Jim rid of the frauds; get them jailed here, and then leave. But I didn't want to run the raft in day-time, without anybody aboard to answer questions but me; so I didn't want the plan to begin working till pretty late to-night. I says:

'Miss Mary Jane, I'll tell you what we'll do—and you won't have to stay at Mr. Lothrop's so long, nuther. How fur is it?'

'A little short of four miles—right out in the country, back here.'

'Well, that'll answer. No you go along out there, and lay low till nine or half-past, to-night, and then get them to fetch you home again—tell them you've thought of something. If you get here before eleven, put a candle in this window, and if I don't turn up, wait *till* eleven, and *then* if I don't turn up it means I'm gone, and out of the way, and safe. Then you come out and spread the news around, and get these beats jailed.'

'Good,' she says. 'I'll do it.'

'And if it just happens so that I don't get away, but get took up along with them, you must up and say I told you the whole thing beforehand, and you must stand by me all you can.'

'Stand by you, indeed I will. They shan't touch a hair of your head!' she says, and I see her nostrils spread and her eyes snap when she said it, too.

'If I get away, I shan't be here,' I says, 'to prove these rapscallions ain't your uncles, and I couldn't do it if I *was* here. I could swear they was beats and bummers, that's all; though that's worth something. Well, there's others can do that better than what I can—and they're people that ain't going to be doubted as quick as I'd be. I'll tell you how to find them. Gimme a pencil and a piece of paper. There—"*Royal Nonesuch, Bricksville.*" Put it away, and don't lose it. When the court wants to find out something about these two, let them send up to Bricksville and say they've got the men that played the Royal Nonesuch, and ask for some witnesses—why, you'll have that entire town down here before you can hardly wink, Miss Mary. And they'll come a-biling, too.'

I judged we had got everything fixed about right, now. So I says:

'Just let the auction go right along, and don't worry. Nobody don't have to pay for the things they buy till a whole day after the auction, on accounts of the short notice, and they ain't going out of this till they get that money—and the way we've fixed it the sale ain't going to count, and they ain't going to *get* no money. It's just like the way it was with the niggers—it warn't no sale, and the niggers will be back before long. Why, they can't collect the money for the *niggers*, yet—they're in the worst kind of a fix, Miss Mary.'

'Well,' she says, 'I'll run down to breakfast now, and then I'll start straight for Mr. Lothrop's.'

''Deed, *that* ain't the ticket, Miss Mary Jane,' I says, 'by no manner of means; go *before* breakfast.'

'Why?'

'What did you reckon I wanted you to go at all for, Miss Mary?'

'Well, I never thought—and come to think, I don't know. What was it?'

'Why, it's because you ain't one of these leather-face people. I don't want no better book than what your face is. A body can set down and read it off like coarse print. Do you reckon you can go and face your uncles, when they come to kiss you good morning, and never——'

'There, there, don't! Yes, I'll go before breakfast—I'll be glad to. And leave my sisters with them?'

'Yes—never mind about them. They've got to stand it yet awhile. They might suspicion something if all of you was to go. I don't want you to see them, nor your sisters, nor nobody in this town—if a neighbour was to ask how is your uncles this morning, your face would tell something. No, you go right along, Miss Mary Jane, and I'll fix it with all of them. I'll tell Miss Susan to give your love to your uncles and say you've went away for a few hours for to get a little rest and change, or to see a friend, and you'll be back to-night or early in the morning.'

'Gone to see a friend is all right, but I won't have my love given to them.'

'Well, then, it shan't be.' It was well enough to tell *her* so—no harm in it. It was only a little thing to do, and no trouble; and it's the little things that smoothes people's roads the most, down here below; it would make Mary Jane comfortable, and it wouldn't cost nothing. Then I says: 'There's one more thing—that bag of money.'

'Well, they've got that; and it makes me feel pretty silly to think *how* they got it.'

'No, you're out, there. They hain't got it.'

'Why, who's got it?'

'I wish I knowed, but I don't. I *had* it, because I stole it from them: and I stole it to give to you; and I know where I hid it, but I'm afraid it ain't there no more. I'm awful sorry, Miss Mary Jane, I'm just as sorry as I can be; but I done the best I could; I did, honest. I come nigh getting caught, and I had to shove it into the first place I come to, and run—and it warn't a good place.'

'Oh, stop blaming yourself—it's too bad to do it, and I won't allow it—you couldn't help it; it wasn't your fault. Where did you hide it?'

I didn't want to set her to thinking about her troubles again; and I couldn't seem to get my mouth to tell her what would make her see that corpse laying in the coffin with that bag of money on his stomach. So for a minute I didn't say nothing—then I says:

'I'd ruther not *tell* you where I put it, Miss Mary Jane, if you don't mind letting me off; but I'll write it for you on a piece of paper, and you can read it along the road to Mr. Lothrop's, if you want to. Do you reckon that'll do?'

'Oh, yes.'

So I wrote: 'I put it in the coffin. It was in there when you was crying there, away in the night. I was behind the door, and I was mighty sorry for you, Miss Mary Jane.'

It made my eyes water a little, to remember her crying there all by herself in the night, and them devils laying there right under her own roof, shaming her and robbing her; and when I folded it up and give it to her, I see the water come into her eyes too; and she shook me by the hand, hard, and says:

'*Good*-bye—I'm going to do everything just as you've told me; and if I don't ever see you again I shan't ever forget you, and I'll think of you a many and a many a time, and I'll *pray* for you too!'—and she was gone.

Pray for me! I reckoned if she knowed me she'd take a job that was more nearer her size. But I bet she done it, just the same—she was just that kind. She had the grit to pray for Judus if she took the notion—there warn't no backdown to her, I judge. You may say what you want to, but in my opinion she had more sand in her than any girl I ever see; in my opinion she was just full of sand. It sounds like flattery, but it ain't no flattery. And when it comes to beauty—and goodness too—she lays over them all. I hain't ever seen her since that time that I see her go out of that door; no, I hain't ever seen her since, but I reckon I've thought of her a many and a many a million times, and of her saying she would pray for me; and if ever I'd a thought it would do any good for me to pray for *her*, blamed if I wouldn't a done it or bust.

Well, Mary Jane she lit out the back way, I reckon; because nobody see her go. When I struck Susan and the hare-lip, I says:

'What's the name of them people over on t'other side of the river that you all goes to see sometimes?'

They says:

'There's several; but it's the Proctors, mainly.'

'That's the name,' I says; 'I most forgot it. Well, Miss Mary Jane she told me to tell you she's gone over there in a dreadful hurry—one of them's sick.'

'Which one?'

'I don't know; leastways I kinder forget; but I think it's——'

'Sakes alive, I hope it ain't *Hanner*?'

'I'm sorry to say it,' I says, 'but Hanner's the very one.'

'My goodness—and she so well only last week! Is she took bad?'

'It ain't no name for it. They set up with her all night, Miss Mary Jane said, and they don't think she'll last many hours.'

'Only think of that, now! What's the matter with her?'

I couldn't think of anything reasonable, right off that way, so I says:

'Mumps.'

'Mumps your granny! They don't set up with people that's got the mumps.'

'They don't, don't they? You better bet they do with *these* mumps. These mumps is different. It's a new kind, Miss Mary Jane said.'

'How's it a new kind?'

'Because it's mixed up with other things.'

'What other things?'

'Well, measles, and whooping-cough, and erysipelas, and consumption, and yaller janders, and brain-fever, and I don't know what all.'

'My land! And they call it the *mumps*?'

'That's what Miss Mary Jane said.'

'Well, what in the nation do they call it the *mumps* for?'

'Why, because it *is* the mumps. That's what it starts with.'

'Well, ther' ain't no sense in it. A body might stump his toe, and take pison, and fall down the well, and break his neck, and bust his brains out, and somebody come along and ask what killed him, and some mumskull up and say, "Why, he stumped his *toe*." Would ther' be any sense in that? *No*. And ther' ain't no sense in *this*, nuther. Is it ketching?'

'Is it *ketching*? Why, how you talk. Is a *harrow* catching?—in the dark? If you don't hitch on to one tooth, you're bound to on another, ain't you? And you can't get away with that tooth without fetching the whole harrow along, can you? Well, these kind of mumps is a kind of a harrow, as you may say—and it ain't no slouch of a harrow, nuther, you come to get it hitched on good.'

'Well, it's awful, *I* think,' says the hare-lip. 'I'll go to Uncle Harvey and——'

'Oh, yes,' I says, 'I *would*. Of *course* I would. I wouldn't lose no time.'

'Well, why wouldn't you?'

'Just look at it a minute, and maybe you can see. Hain't your uncles obleeged to get along home to England as fast as they can? And do you reckon they'd be mean enough to go off and leave you to go all that journey by yourselves? *You* know they'll wait for you. So fur, so good. Your Uncle Harvey's a preacher, ain't he? Very well, then; is a *preacher* going to deceive a steamboat clerk? is he going to deceive a *ship-clerk*?—so as to get them to let Miss Mary Jane go aboard? Now *you* know he ain't. What *will* he do, then? Why, he'll say, "It's a great pity, but my church matters has got to get along the best way they can; for my niece has been exposed to the dreadful pluribus-unum mumps, and so it's my bounden duty to set down here and wait the three months it takes to show on her if she's got it." But never mind, if you think it's best to tell your Uncle Harvey——'

'Shucks, and stay fooling around here when we could all be having good times in England whilst we was waiting to find out whether Mary Jane's got it or not? Why, you talk like a muggins.'

'Well, anyway, maybe you better tell some of the neighbours.'

'Listen at that, now. You do beat all, for natural stupidness. Can't you *see* that *they'd* go and tell? Ther' ain't no way but just to not tell anybody at *all*.'

'Well, maybe you're right—yes, I judge you *are* right.'

'But I reckon we ought to tell Uncle Harvey she's gone out awhile, anyway, so he won't be uneasy about her?'

'Yes, Miss Mary Jane she wanted you to do that. She says, "Tell them to give Uncle Harvey and William my love and a kiss, and say I've run over the river to see Mr.—Mr.—what *is* the name of that rich family your Uncle Peter used to think so much of?—I mean the one that——'

'Why, you must mean the Apthorps, ain't it?'

'Of course; bother them kind of names, a body can't ever seem to remember them, half the time, somehow. Yes, she said, say she has run over for to ask the Apthorps to be sure and come to the auction and buy this house, because she allowed her Uncle Peter would ruther they had it than anybody else; and she's going to stick to them till they say they'll come, and then, if she ain't too tired, she's coming home; and if she is, she'll be home in the morning, anyway. She said, don't say nothing about the Proctors, but only about the Apthorps—which'll be perfectly true, because she *is* going there to speak about their buying the house; I know it, because she told me so, herself.'

'All right,' they said, and cleared out to lay for their uncles, and give them the love and the kisses, and tell them the message.

Everything was all right now. The girls wouldn't say nothing because they wanted to go to England; and the king and the duke would ruther Mary Jane was off working for the auction than around in reach of Doctor Robinson. I felt very good; I judged I had done it pretty neat—I reckoned Tom Sawyer couldn't a done it no neater himself. Of course, he would a throwed more style into it, but I can't do that very handy, not being brung up to it.

Well, they held the auction in the public square, along towards the end of the afternoon, and it strung along and strung along, and the old man he was on hand and looking his level pisonest, up there 'longside of the auctioneer, and chipping in a little Scripture, now and then, or a little goody-goody saying, of some kind, and the duke he was around goo-gooing for sympathy all he knowed how, and just spreading himself generly.

But by-and-by the thing dragged through, and everything was sold. Everything but a little old trifling lot in the graveyard. So they'd got to work *that* off—I never see such a girafft as the king was for wanting to swallow *everything*. Well, whilst they was at it, a steamboat landed, and in about two minutes up comes a crowd a-whooping and yelling and laughing and carrying on, and singing out:

'*Here's* your opposition line! here's your two sets o' heirs to old Peter Wilks—and you pays your money and you takes your choice!'

## *Chapter 29*

CONTESTED RELATIONSHIP—THE KING EXPLAINS THE LOSS—A QUESTION OF HANDWRITING—TATTOOING—DIGGING UP THE CORPSE—HUCK ESCAPES

THEY was fetching a very nice-looking old gentleman along, and a nice-looking younger one, with his right arm in a sling. And my souls, how the people yelled, and laughed, and kept it up. But I didn't see no joke about it, and I judged it would strain the duke and the king some to see any. I reckoned they'd turn pale. But no, nary a pale did *they* turn. The duke he never let on he suspicioned what was up, but just went a goo-gooing around, happy and satisfied, like a jug that's googling out buttermilk; and as for the king, he just gazed and gazed down sorrowful on them new-comers like it give him the stomach-ache in his very heart to think there could be such frauds and rascals in the world. Oh, he done it admirable. Lots of the principal people gethered around the king, to let him see they was on his side. That old gentleman that had just come looked all puzzled to death. Pretty soon he begun to speak, and I see, straight off, he pronounced *like* an Englishman, not the king's way, though the king's *was* pretty good, for an imitation. I can't give the old gent's words, nor I can't imitate him; but he turned around to the crowd, and says, about like this:

'This is a surprise to me which I wasn't looking for; and I'll acknowledge, candid and frank, I ain't very well fixed to meet it and answer it; for my brother and me has had misfortunes, he's broke his arm, and our baggage got put off at a town above here, last night in the night by a mistake. I am Peter Wilks's brother Harvey, and this is his brother William, which can't hear nor speak—and can't even make signs to amount to much, now 't he's only got one hand to work them with. We are who we say we are; and in a day or two, when I get the baggage, I can prove it. But, up till then, I won't say nothing more, but go to the hotel and wait.'

So him and the new dummy started off; and the king he laughs, and blethers out:

'Broke his arm—*very* likely, *ain't* it?—and very convenient, too, for a fraud that's got to make signs, and hain't learnt how. Lost their baggage! That's *mighty* good!—and mighty ingenious—under the *circumstances*!'

So he laughed again; and so did everybody else, except three or four, or maybe half a dozen. One of these was that doctor; another one was a sharp-looking gentleman, with a carpet-bag of the old-fashioned kind made out of carpet-stuff, that had just come off of the steamboat and was talking to him in a low voice, and glancing towards the king now and then and nodding their heads—it was Levi Bell, the lawyer that was gone up to Louisville; and another one was a big rough husky that come along and listened to all the old gentleman said, and was listening to the king now. And when the king got done, this husky up and says:

'Say, looky here; if you are Harvey Wilks, when'd you come to this town?'

'The day before the funeral, friend,' says the king.

'But what time o' day?'

'In the evenin'—'bout an hour er two before sundown.'

'*How'd* you come?'

'I come down on the *Susan Powell*, from Cincinnati.'

'Well, then, how'd you come to be up at the Pint in the *mornin'*—in a canoe?'

'I warn't up at the Pint in the mornin'.'

'It's a lie.'

Several of them jumped for him and begged him not to talk that way to an old man and a preacher.

'Preacher be hanged, he's a fraud and a liar. He was up at the Pint that mornin'. I live up there, don't I? Well, I was up there, and he was up there. I *see* him there. He come in a canoe, along with Tim Collins and a boy.'

The doctor he up and says:

'Would you know the boy again if you was to see him, Hines?'

'I reckon I would, but I don't know. Why, yonder he is, now. I know him perfectly easy.'

It was me he pointed at. The doctor says:

'Neighbours, I don't know whether the new couple is frauds or not; but if *these* two ain't frauds, I am an idiot, that's all. I think it's our duty to see that they don't get away from here till we've looked into this thing. Come along, Hines; come along, the rest of you. We'll take these fellows to the tavern and affront them with t'other couple, and I reckon we'll find out *something* before we get through.'

It was nuts for the crowd, though maybe not for the king's friends; so we all started. It was about sundown. The doctor he led me along by the hand, and was plenty kind enough, but he never let *go* my hand.

We all got in a big room in the hotel, and lit up some candles, and fetched in the new couple. First, the doctor says:

'I don't wish to be too hard on these two men, but *I* think they're frauds, and they may have 'complices that we don't know nothing about. If they have, won't the 'complices get away with that bag of gold Peter Wilks left? It ain't unlikely. If these men ain't frauds, they won't object to sending for that money and letting us keep it till they prove they're all right—ain't that so?'

Everybody agreed to that. So I judged they had our gang in a pretty tight place, right at the outstart. But the king he only looked sorrowful, and says:

'Gentlemen, I wish the money was there, for I ain't got no disposition to throw anything in the way of a fair, open, out-and-out investigation o' this misable business; but, alas! the money ain't there; you k'n send and see, if you want to.'

'Where is it, then?'

'Well, when my niece give it to me to keep for her, I took and hid it inside o' the straw tick o' my bed, not wishin' to bank it for the few days we'd be here, and considerin' the bed a safe place, we not bein' used to niggers, and suppos'n' 'em honest, like servants in England. The niggers stole it the very next mornin' after I had went downstairs; and when I sold 'em I hadn't missed the money yit, so they got clean away with it. My servant here k'n tell you 'bout it, gentlemen.'

The doctor and several said 'Shucks!' and I see nobody didn't altogether believe him. One man asked me if I see the niggers steal it. I said 'no,' but I see them sneaking out of the room and hustling away, and I never thought nothing, only I reckoned they was afraid they had waked up my master and was trying to get away before he made trouble with them. That was all they asked me. Then the doctor whirls on me and says:

'Are *you* English too?'

I says 'yes'; and him and some others laughed, and said, 'Stuff!'

Well, then they sailed in on the general investigation, and there we had it, up and down, hour in, hour out, and nobody never said a word about supper, nor ever seemed to think about it—and so they kept it up, and kept it up; and it *was* the worst mixed-up thing you ever see. They made the king tell his yarn, and they made the old gentleman tell his'n; and anybody but a lot of prejudiced chuckleheads would a *seen* that the old gentleman was spinning truth and t'other one lies. And by-and-by they had me up to tell what I knowed. The king he give me a left-handed look out of the corner of his eye, and so I knowed enough to talk on the right side. I begun to tell about Sheffield, and how we lived there, and all about the English Wilkses, and so on; but I didn't get pretty fur till the doctor begun to laugh; and Levi Bell, the lawyer, says:

'Set down, my boy, I wouldn't strain myself, if I was you. I reckon you ain't used to lying, it don't seem to come handy; what you want is practice. You do it pretty awkward.'

I didn't care nothing for the compliment, but I was glad to be let off, anyway.

The doctor he started to say something, and turns and says:

'If you'd been in town at first, Levi Bell——'

The king broke in and reached out his hand, and says:

'Why, is this my poor dead brother's old friend that he's wrote so often about?'

The lawyer and him shook hands, and the lawyer smiled and looked pleased, and they talked right along awhile, and then got to one side and talked low; and at last the lawyer speaks up and says:

'That'll fix it. I'll take the order and send it, along with your brother's, and then they'll know it's all right.'

So they got some paper and a pen, and the king he set down and twisted his head to one side, and chawed his tongue, and scrawled off something; and then they give the pen to the duke—and then for the first time the duke looked sick. But he took the pen and wrote. So then the lawyer turns to the new old gentleman and says:

'You and your brother please write a line or two and sign your names.'

The old gentleman wrote, but nobody couldn't read it. The lawyer looked powerful astonished, and says:

'Well, it beats *me*'—and snaked a lot of old letters out of his pocket, and examined them, and then examined the old man's writing, and then *them* again; and then says: 'These old letters is from Harvey Wilks; and here's *these* two's handwritings, and anybody can see *they* didn't write them' (the king and the duke looked sold and foolish, I tell you, to see how the lawyer had took them in), 'and here's *this* old gentleman's handwriting, and anybody can tell, easy enough, *he* didn't write them—fact is, the scratches he makes ain't properly *writing* at all. Now here's some letters from——'

The new old gentleman says:

'If you please, let me explain. Nobody can read my hand but my brother there—so he copies for me. It's *his* hand you've got there, not mine.'

'*Well!*' says the lawyer, 'this *is* a state of things. I've got some of William's letters too; so if you'll get him to write a line or so we can com——'

'He *can't* write with his left hand,' says the old gentleman. 'If he could use his right hand, you would see that he wrote his own letters and mine too. Look at both, please—they're by the same hand.'

The lawyer done it, and says:

'I believe it's so—and if it ain't so, there's a heap stronger resemblance than I'd noticed before, anyway. Well, well, well! I thought we was right on the track of a slution, but it's gone to grass, partly. But anyway, *one* thing is proved—*these* two ain't either of 'em Wilkses'—and he wagged his head towards the king and the duke.

Well, what do you think?—that muleheaded old fool wouldn't give in *then*! Indeed he wouldn't. Said it warn't no fair test. Said his brother William was the cussedest joker in the world, and hadn't *tried* to write—*he* see William was going to play one of his jokes the minute he put the pen to paper. And so he warmed up and went warbling and warbling right along, till he was actually beginning to believe what he was saying, *himself*—but pretty soon the new old gentleman broke in, and says:

'I've thought of something. Is there anybody here that helped to lay out my br—helped to lay out the late Peter Wilks for burying?'

'Yes,' says somebody, 'me and Ab Turner done it. We're both here.'

Then the old man turns towards the king, and says:

'Per'aps this gentleman can tell me what was tattooed on his breast?'

Blamed if the king didn't have to brace up mighty quick, or he'd a squshed down like a bluff bank that the river has cut under, it took him so sudden—and mind you, it was a thing that was calculated to make most *anybody* sqush to get fetched such a solid one as that without any notice—because how was *he* going to know what was tattooed on the man? He whitened a little; he couldn't help it; and it was mighty still in there, and everybody bending a little forwards and gazing at him. Says I to myself, *Now* he'll throw up the sponge—there ain't no more use. Well, did he? A body can't hardly believe it, but he didn't. I reckon he thought he'd keep the thing up till he tired them people out, so they'd thin out, and him and the duke could break loose and get away. Anyway, he set there, and pretty soon he begun to smile, and says:

'Mf! It's a *very* tough question, *ain't* it! *Yes*, sir, I k'n tell you what's tattooed on his breast. It's jest a small, thin, blue arrow—that's what it is; and if you don't look clost, you can't see it. *Now* what do you say—hey?'

Well, *I* never see anything like that old blister for clean out-and-out cheek.

The new old gentleman turns brisk towards Ab Turner and his pard, and his eye lights up like he judged he had got the king *this* time, and says:

'There—you've heard what he said! Was there any such mark on Peter Wilks's breast?'

Both of them spoke up and says:

'We didn't see no such mark.'

'Good!' says the old gentleman. 'Now, what you *did* see on his breast was a small dim P, and a B (which is an initial he dropped when he was young), and a W, with dashes between them, so: P—B—W'—and he marked them that way on a piece of paper. 'Come—ain't that what you saw?'

Both of them spoke up again, and says:

'No, we *didn't*. We never seen any marks at all.'

Well, everybody *was* in a state of mind now; and they sings out:

'The whole *bilin*' of'm 's frauds! Le's duck 'em! le's drown 'em! le's ride 'em on a rail!' and everybody was whooping at once, and there was a rattling pow-wow. But the lawyer he jumps on the table and yells, and says:

'Gentlemen—gentle*men*! Hear me just a word—just a *single* word—if you PLEASE! There 's one way yet—let 's go and dig up the corpse and look.'

That took them.

'Hooray!' they all shouted, and was starting right off; but the lawyer and the doctor sung out:

'Hold on, hold on! Collar all these four men and the boy, and fetch *them* along, too!'

'We'll do it!' they all shouted; 'and if we don't find them marks we'll lynch the whole gang!'

I *was* scared, now, I tell you. But there warn't no getting away, you know. They gripped us all, and marched us right along, straight for the graveyard, which was a mile and a half down the river, and the whole town at our heels, for we made noise enough, and it was only nine in the evening.

As we went by our house I wished I hadn't sent Mary Jane out of town; because now if I could tip her the wink, she'd light out and save me, and blow on our dead-beats.

Well, we swarmed along down the river road, just carrying on like wild-cats; and to make it more scary, the sky was darking up, and the lightning beginning to wink and flitter, and the wind to shiver amongst the leaves. This was the most awful trouble and most dangersome I ever was in; and I was kinder stunned; everything was going so different from what I had allowed for; 'stead of being fixed so I could take my own time, if I wanted to, and see all the fun, and have Mary Jane at my back to save me and set me free when the close-fit come, here was nothing in the world betwixt me and sudden death but just them tattoo-marks. If they didn't find them——

I couldn't bear to think about it; and yet, somehow, I couldn't think about nothing else. It got darker and darker, and it was a beautiful time to give the crowd the slip; but that big husky had me by the wrist—Hines—and a body might as well try to give Goliar the slip. He dragged me right along, he was so excited; and I had to run to keep up.

When they got there they swarmed into the graveyard and washed over it like an overflow. And when they got to the grave, they found they had about a hundred times as many shovels as they wanted, but nobody hadn't thought to fetch a lantern. But they sailed into digging, anyway, by the flicker of the lightning, and sent a man to the nearest house a half a mile off, to borrow one.

So they dug and dug, like everything; and it got awful dark, and the rain started, and the wind swished and swushed along, and the lightning come brisker and brisker, and the thunder boomed; but them people never took no notice of it, they was so full of this business; and one minute you could see everything and every face in that big crowd, and the shovelfuls of dirt sailing up out of the grave, and the next second the dark wiped it all out, and you couldn't see nothing at all.

At last they got out the coffin, and begun to unscrew the lid, and then such another crowding, and shouldering, and shoving as there was, to scrouge in and get a sight, you never see; and in the dark, that way, it was awful. Hines he hurt my wrist dreadful, pulling and tugging so, and I reckon he clean forgot I was in the world, he was so excited and panting.

All of a sudden the lightning let go a perfect sluice of white glare, and somebody sings out:

'By the living jingo, here's the bag of gold on his breast!'

Hines let out a whoop, like everybody else, and dropped my wrist and give a big surge to bust his way in and get a look, and the way I lit out and shinned for the road in the dark, there ain't nobody can tell.

I had the road all to myself, and I fairly flew—leastways I had it all to myself except the solid dark, and the now-and-then glares, and the buzzing of the rain, and the thrashing of the wind, and the splitting of the thunder; and sure as you are born I did clip it along!

When I struck the town, I see there warn't nobody out in the storm, so I never hunted for no back streets, but humped it straight through the main one; and when I begun to get towards our house I aimed my eye and set it. No light there; the house all dark—which made me feel sorry and disappointed, I didn't know why. But at last, just as I was sailing by, *flash* comes the light in Mary Jane's window! and my heart swelled up sudden, like to bust; and the same second the house and all was behind me in the dark, and wasn't ever going to be before me no more in this world. She *was* the best girl I ever see, and had the most sand.

The minute I was far enough above the town to see I could make the tow-head, I begun to look sharp for a boat to borrow; and the first time the lightning showed me one that wasn't chained, I snatched it and shoved. It was a canoe, and warn't fastened with nothing but a rope. The tow-head was a rattling big distance off, away out there in the middle of the river, but I didn't lose no time; and when I struck the raft at last, I was so fagged I would a just laid down to blow and gasp if I could afforded it. But I didn't. As I sprung aboard I sung out:

'Out with you, Jim, and set her loose! Glory be to goodness, we're shut of them.'

Jim lit out, and was a-coming for me with both arms spread, he was so full of joy; but when I glimpsed him in the lightning, my heart shot up in my mouth, and I went overboard backwards; for I forgot he was old King Lear and a drownded A-rab all in one, and it most scared the livers and lights out of me. But Jim fished me out, and was going to hug me and bless me, and so on, he was so glad I was back and we was shut of the king and the duke, but I says:

'Not now—have it for breakfast, have it for breakfast. Cut loose and let her slide!'

So, in two seconds, away we went, a-sliding down the river, and it *did* seem so good to be free again and all by ourselves on the big river and nobody to bother us. I had to skip around a bit, and jump up and crack my heels a few times, I couldn't help it; but about the third crack I noticed a sound that I knowed mighty well—and held my breath and listened and waited—and sure enough, when the next flash busted out over the water, here they come!—and just a-laying to their oars and making their skiff hum! It was the king and the duke.

So I wilted right down on to the planks, then, and give up; and it was all I could do to keep from crying.

## *Chapter 30*

THE KING WENT FOR HIM—A ROYAL ROW—POWERFUL MELLOW

WHEN they got aboard, the king went for me, and shook me by the collar, and says:

'Tryin' to give us the slip, was ye, you pup! Tired of our company—hey?'

I says:

'No, your majesty, we warn't—*please* don't, your majesty!'

'Quick, then, and tell us what *was* your idea, or I'll shake the insides out o' you!'

'Honest, I'll tell you everything, just as it happened, your majesty. The man that had aholt of me was very good to me, and kept saying he had a boy about as big as me that died last year, and he was sorry to see a boy in such a dangerous fix; and when they was all took by surprise by finding the gold, and made a rush for the coffin, he lets go of me and whispers, "Heel it, now, or they'll hang ye, sure!" and I lit out. It didn't seem no good for *me* to stay—*I* couldn't do nothing, and I didn't want to be hung if I could get away. So I never stopped running till I found the canoe; and when I got here I told Jim to hurry, or they'd catch me and hang me yet, and said I was afeard you and the duke wasn't alive, now, and I was awful sorry, and so was Jim, and was awful glad when we see you coming, you may ask Jim if I didn't.'

Jim said it was so; and the king told him to shut up, and said, 'Oh, yes, it's *mighty* likely!' and shook me up again, and said he reckoned he'd drownd me. But the duke says:

'Leggo the boy, you old idiot! Would *you* a done any different? Did you inquire around for *him*, when you got loose? *I* don't remember it.'

So the king let go of me, and begun to cuss that town and everybody in it. But the duke says:

'You better a blame' sight give *yourself* a good cussing, for you're the one that's entitled to it most. You hain't done a thing, from the start, that had any sense in it, except coming out so cool and cheeky with that imaginary blue-arrow mark. That *was* bright—it was right down bully; and it was the thing that saved us. For if it hadn't been for that, they'd a jailed us till them Englishmen's baggage come—and then—the penitentiary, you bet! But that trick took 'em to the graveyard, and the gold done us a still bigger kindness; for if the excited fools hadn't let go all holts and made that rush to get a look, we'd a slept in our cravats to-night—cravats warranted to *wear*, too—longer than *we'd* need 'em.'

They was still a minute—thinking—then the king says, kind of absent-minded like:

'Mf! And we reckoned the *niggers* stole it!'

That made me squirm!

'Yes,' says the duke, kinder slow, and deliberate, and sarcastic, '*We* did.'

After about a half a minute, the king drawls out:

'Leastways—*I* did.'

The duke says, the same way:

'On the contrary—*I* did.'

The king kind of ruffles up, and says:

'Looky here, Bilgewater, what'r you referrin' to?'

The duke says, pretty brisk:

'When it comes to that, maybe you'll let me ask, what was *you* referring to?'

'Shucks!' says the king, very sarcastic; 'but *I* don't know—maybe you was asleep, and didn't know what you was about.'

The duke bristles right up now, and says:

'Oh, let *up* on this cussed nonsense—do you take me for a blame' fool? Don't you reckon *I* know who hid that money in that coffin?'

'*Yes*, sir! I know you *do* know—because you done it yourself!'

'It's a lie!'—and the duke went for him. The king sings out:

'Take y'r hands off!—leggo my throat!—I take it all back!'

The duke says:

'Well, you just own up, first, that you *did* hide that money there, intending to give me the slip one of these days, and come back and dig it up, and have it all to yourself.'

'Wait jest a minute, duke—answer me this one question, honest and fair; if you didn't put the money there, say it, and I'll b'lieve you, and take back everything I said.'

'You old scoundrel, I didn't, and you know I didn't. There, now!'

'Well, then, I b'lieve you. But answer me only jest this one more—now *don't* git mad; didn't you have it in your *mind* to hook the money and hide it?'

The duke never said nothing for a little bit; then he says:

'Well—I don't care if I *did*, I didn't *do* it, anyway. But you not only had it in mind to do it, but you *done* it.'

'I wisht I may never die if I done it, duke, and that's honest. I won't say I warn't *goin'* to do it, because I *was*; but you—I mean somebody—got in ahead o' me.'

'It's a lie! You done it, and you got to *say* you done it, or——'

The king begun to gurgle, and then he gasps out:

''Nough!—*I own up!*'

I was very glad to hear him say that, it made me feel much more easier than what I was feeling before. So the duke took his hands off, and says:

'If you ever deny it again I'll drown you. It's *well* for you to set there and blubber like a baby—it's fitten for you, after the way you've acted. I never see such an old ostrich for wanting to gobble everything—and I a-trusting you all the time, like you was my own father. You ought to been ashamed of yourself to stand by and hear it saddled on to a lot of poor niggers and you never say a word for 'em. It makes me feel ridiculous to think I was soft enough to *believe* that rubbage. Cuss you, I can see, now, why you was so anxious to make up the deffersit—you wanted to get what money I'd got out of the Nonesuch, and one thing or another, and scoop it *all*!'

The king says, timid, and still a-snuffling:

'Why, duke, it was you that said make up the deffersit, it warn't me.'

'Dry up! I don't want to hear no more *out* of you!' says the duke. 'And *now* you see what you *got* by it. They've got all their own money back, and all of *ourn* but a shekel or two, *besides*. G'long to bed—and don't you deffersit *me* no more deffersits, long 's *you* live!'

So the king sneaked into the wigwam, and took to his bottle for comfort; and before long the duke tackled *his* bottle; and so in about a half an hour they was as thick as thieves again, and the tighter they got, the lovinger they got; and went off a-snoring in each other's arms. They both got powerful mellow, but I noticed the king didn't get mellow enough to forget to remember to not deny about hiding the money-bag again. That made me feel easy and satisfied. Of course, when they got to snoring, we had a long gabble, and I told Jim everything.

## *Chapter 31*

OMINOUS PLANS—JIM GONE!—NEWS FROM JIM—OLD RECOLLECTIONS—A SHEEP STORY—VALUABLE INFORMATION—THE BACK COUNTRY

WE dasn't stop again at any town, for days and days; kept right along down the river. We was down south in the warm weather, now, and a mighty long ways from home. We begun to come to trees with Spanish moss on them, hanging down from the limbs like long grey beards. It was the first I ever see it growing, and it made the woods look solemn and dismal. So now the frauds reckoned they was out of danger, and they begun to work the villages again.

First they done a lecture on temperance; but they didn't make enough for them both to get drunk on. Then in another village they started a dancing school; but they didn't know no more how to dance than a kangaroo does; so the first prance they made, the general public jumped in and pranced them out of town. Another time they tried a go at yellocution; but they didn't yellocute long till the audience got up and give them a solid good cussing and made them skip out. They tackled missionarying, and mesmerizering, and doctoring, and telling fortunes, and a little of everything; but they couldn't seem to have no luck. So at last they got just about dead broke, and laid around the raft, as she floated along, thinking, and thinking, and never saying nothing, by the half a day at a time, and dreadful blue and desperate.

And at last they took a change, and begun to lay their heads together in the wigwam and talk low and confidential two or three hours at a time. Jim and me got uneasy. We didn't like the look of it. We judged they was studying up some kind of worse deviltry than ever. We turned it over and over, and at last we made up our minds they was going to break into somebody's house or store, or was going into the counterfeit-money business, or something. So then we was pretty scared, and made up an agreement that we wouldn't have nothing in the world to do with such actions, and if we ever got the least show we would give them the cold shake, and clear out and leave them behind. Well, early one morning we hid the raft in a good safe place about two mile below a little bit of a shabby village, named Pikesville, and the king he went ashore, and told us all to stay hid whilst he went up to town and smelt around to see if anybody had got any wind of the Royal Nonesuch there yet. ('House to rob, you *mean*,' says I to myself; 'and when you get through robbing it you'll come back here and wonder what's become of me and Jim and the raft—and you'll have to take it out in wondering.') And he said if he warn't back by midday, the duke and me would know it was all right, and we was to come along.

So we staid where we was. The duke he fretted and sweated around, and was in a mighty sour way. He scolded us for everything, and we couldn't seem to do nothing right; he found fault with every little thing. Something was a-brewing, sure. I was good and glad when midday come and no king; we could have a change, anyway—and maybe a chance for *the* change, on top of it. So me and the duke went up to the village, and hunted around there for the king, and by-and-by we found him in the back room of a little low doggery, very tight, and a lot of loafers bullragging him for sport, and he a-cussing and threatening with all his might, and so tight he couldn't walk, and couldn't do nothing to them. The duke he begun to abuse him for an old fool, and the king begun to sass back; and the minute they was fairly at it, I lit out, and shook the reefs out of my hind legs, and spun down the river road like a deer—for I see our chance; and I made up my mind that it would be a long day before they ever see me and Jim again. I got down there all out of breath but loaded up with joy, and sung out:

'Set her loose, Jim, we're all right, now!'

But there warn't no answer, and nobody come out of the wigwam. Jim was gone! I set up a shout—and then another—and then another one; and run this way and that in the woods, whooping and screeching; but it warn't no use—old Jim was gone. Then I set down and cried; I couldn't help it. But I couldn't set long. Pretty soon I went out on the road, trying to think what I better do, and I run across a boy walking, and asked him if he'd seen a strange nigger, dressed so and so, and he says:

'Yes.'

'Whereabouts?' says I.

'Down to Silas Phelps' place, two mile below here. He's a runaway nigger, and they've got him. Was you looking for him?'

'You bet I ain't. I run across him in the woods about an hour or two ago, and he said if I hollered he'd cut my livers out—and told me to lay down and stay where I was; and I done it. Been there ever since; afeared to come out.'

'Well,' he says, 'you needn't be afeared no more, becuz they've got him. He run off f'm down South, som'ers.'

'It's a good job they got him.'

'Well, I *reckon*! There's two hundred dollars reward on him. It's like picking money out'n the road.'

'Yes, it is—and *I* could a had it if I'd been big enough; I see him *first*. Who nailed him?'

'It was an old fellow—a stranger—and he sold out his chance in him for forty dollars, becuz he's got to go up the river and can't wait. Think o' that, now! You bet *I'd* wait, if it was seven year.'

'That's me, every time,' says I. 'But maybe his chance ain't worth no more than that, if he'll sell it so cheap. Maybe there's something ain't straight about it.'

'But it *is*, though—straight as a string. I see the handbill myself. It tells all about him, to a dot—paints him like a picture, and tells the plantation he's frum below New*rleans*. No-sirree-*bob*, they ain't no trouble 'bout *that* speculation, you bet you. Say, gimme a chaw tobacker, won't ye?'

I didn't have none, so he left. I went to the raft, and set down in the wigwam to think. But I couldn't come to nothing. I thought till I wore my head sore, but I couldn't see no way out of the trouble. After all this long journey, and after all we'd done for them scoundrels, here was it all come to nothing, everything all busted up and ruined, because they could have the heart to serve Jim such a trick as that, and make him a slave again all his life, and amongst strangers, too, for forty dirty dollars.

Once I said to myself it would be a thousand times better for Jim to be a slave at home where his family was, as long as he'd *got* to be a slave, and so I'd better write a letter to Tom Sawyer, and tell him to tell Miss Watson where he was. But I soon give up that notion, for two things: she'd be mad and disgusted at his rascality and ungratefulness for leaving her, and so she'd sell him straight down the river again; and if she didn't, everybody naturally despises an ungrateful nigger, and they'd make Jim feel it all the time, and so he'd feel ornery and disgraced. And then think of *me*! It would get all around that Huck Finn helped a nigger to get his freedom; and if I was to ever see anybody from that town again, I'd be ready to get down and lick his boots for shame. That's just the way; a person does a low-down thing, and then he don't want to take no consequences of it. Thinks as long as he can hide it, it ain't no disgrace. That was my fix exactly. The more I studied about this, the more my conscience went to grinding me, and the more wicked and low-down and ornery I got to feeling. And at last, when it hit me all of a sudden that here was the plain hand of Providence slapping me in the face and letting me know my wickedness was being watched all the time from up there in heaven, whilst I was stealing a poor old woman's nigger that hadn't ever done me no harm, and now was showing me there's One that's always on the look-out, and ain't agoing to allow no such miserable doings to go only just so fur and no further, I most dropped in my tracks I was so scared. Well, I tried the best I could to kinder soften it up somehow for myself, by saying I was brung up wicked, and so I warn't so much to blame; but something inside of me kept saying, 'There was the Sunday-school, you could a gone to it; and if you'd a done it they'd a learnt you, there, that people that acts as I'd been acting about that nigger goes to everlasting fire.'

It made me shiver. And I about made up my mind to pray; and see if I couldn't try to quit being the kind of boy I was, and be better. So I kneeled down. But the words wouldn't come. Why wouldn't they? It warn't no use to try and hide it from Him. Nor from *me*, neither. I knowed very well why they wouldn't come. It was because my heart warn't right; it was because I warn't square; it was because I was playing double. I was letting *on* to give up sin, but away inside of me I was holding on to the biggest one of all. I was trying to make my mouth *say* I would do the right thing and the clean thing, and go and write to that nigger's owner and tell where he was; but deep down in me I knowed it was a lie—and He knowed it. You can't pray a lie—I found that out.

So I was full of trouble, full as I could be; and didn't know what to do. At last I had an idea; and I says, I'll go and write the letter—and *then* see if I can pray. Why, it was astonishing, the way I felt as light as a feather, right straight off, and my troubles all gone. So I got a piece of paper and a pencil, all glad and excited, and set down and wrote:

> Miss Watson your runaway nigger Jim is down here two mile below Pikesville and Mr. Phelps has got him and he will give him up for the reward if you send. HUCK FINN.

I felt good and all washed clean of sin for the first time I had ever felt so in my life, and I knowed I could pray now. But I didn't do it straight off, but laid the paper down and set there thinking—thinking how good it was all this happened so, and how near I come to being lost and going to hell. And went on thinking. And got to thinking over our trip down the river; and I see Jim before me, all the time, in the day, and in the night-time, sometimes moonlight, sometimes storms, and we a-floating along, talking, and singing, and laughing. But somehow I couldn't seem to strike no places to harden me against him, but only the other kind. I'd see him standing my watch on top of his'n, 'stead of calling me, so I could go on sleeping; and see him how glad he was when I come back out of the fog; and when I come to him again in the swamp, up there where the feud was; and such-like times; and would always call me honey, and pet me, and do everything he could think of for me, and how good he always was; and at last I struck the time I saved him by telling the men we had smallpox aboard, and he was so grateful, and said I was the best friend old Jim ever had in the world, and the *only* one he's got now; and then I happened to look around, and see that paper.

It was a close place. I took it up, and held it in my hand. I was a-trembling, because I'd got to decide, for ever, betwixt two things, and I knowed it. I studied a minute sort of holding my breath, and then says to myself:

'All right, then, I'll *go* to hell'—and tore it up.

It was awful thoughts, and awful words, but they was said. And I let them stay said; and never thought no more about reforming. I shoved the whole thing out of my head; and said I would take up wickedness again, which was in my line, being brung up to it, and the other warn't. And for a starter, I would go to work and steal Jim out of slavery again; and if I could think up anything worse, I would do that too; because as long as I was in, and in for good, I might as well go the whole hog.

Then I set to thinking over how to get at it, and turned over considerable many ways in my mind; and at last fixed up a plan that suited me. So then I took the bearings of a woody island that was down the river a piece, and as soon as it was fairly dark I crept out with my raft and went for it, and hid it there, and then turned in. I slept the night through, and got up before it was light, and had my breakfast, and put on my store clothes, and tied up some others and one thing or another in a bundle, and took the canoe and cleared for shore. I landed below where I judged was Phelps' place, and hid my bundle in the woods, and then filled up the canoe with water, and loaded rocks into her and sunk her where I could find her again when I wanted her, about a quarter of a mile below a little steam sawmill that was on the bank.

Then I struck up the road, and when I passed the mill I see a sign on it, 'Phelps' Sawmill,' and when I come to the farm-houses, two or three hundred yards further along, I kept my eyes peeled, but didn't see nobody around, though it was good daylight, now. But I didn't mind, because I didn't want to see nobody just yet—I only wanted to get the lay of the land. According to my plan, I was going to turn up there from the village, not from below. So I just took a look, and shoved along, straight for town. Well, the very first man I see, when I got there, was the duke. He was sticking up a bill for the Royal Nonesuch—three-night performance—like that other time. *They* had the cheek, them frauds! I was right on him, before I could shirk. He looked astonished, and says:

'Hel-*lo*! Wher'd *you* come from?' Then he says, kind of glad and eager, 'Where's the raft?—got her in a good place?'

I says:

'Why, that's just what I was agoing to ask your grace.'

Then he didn't look so joyful—and says:

'What was your idea for asking *me*?' he says.

'Well,' I says, 'when I see the king in that doggery yesterday, I says to myself, we can't get him home for hours, till he's soberer; so I went a-loafing around town to put in the time, and wait. A man up and offered me ten cents to help him pull a skiff over the river and back to fetch a sheep, and so I went along; but when we was dragging him to the boat, and the man left me aholt of the rope and went behind him to shove him along, he was too strong for me, and jerked loose and run, and we after him. We didn't have no dog, and so we had to chase him all over the country till we tired him out. We never got him till dark, then we fetched him over, and I started down for the raft. When I got there and see it was gone, I says to myself, "They've got into trouble and had to leave; and they've took my nigger, which is the only nigger I've got in the world, and now I'm in a strange country, and ain't got no property no more, nor nothing, and no way to make my living"; so I set down and cried. I slept in the woods all night. But what *did* become of the raft then?—and Jim, poor Jim!'

'Blamed if *I* know—that is, what's become of the raft. That old fool had made a trade and got forty dollars, and when we found him in the doggery the loafers had matched half-dollars with him and got every cent but what he'd spent for whisky; and when I got him home late last night and found the raft gone, we said, "That little rascal has stole our raft and shook us, and run off down the river."'

'I wouldn't shake my *nigger*, would I?—the only nigger I had in the world, and the only property.'

'We never thought of that. Fact is, I reckon we'd come to consider him *our* nigger; yes, we did consider him so—goodness knows we had trouble enough for him. So when we see the raft was gone, and we flat broke, there warn't anything for it but to try the Royal Nonesuch another shake. And I've pegged along ever since, dry as a powder-horn. Where's that ten cents? Give it here.'

I had considerable money, so I give him ten cents, but begged him to spend it for something to eat, and give me some, because it was all the money I had, and I hadn't had nothing to eat since yesterday. He never said nothing. The next minute he whirls on me and says:

'Do you reckon that nigger would blow on us? We'd skin him if he done that!'

'How can he blow? Hain't he run off?'

'No! That old fool sold him, and never divided with me, and the money's gone.'

'*Sold* him?' I says, and begun to cry; 'why, he was *my* nigger, and that was my money. Where is he?—I want my nigger.'

'Well, you can't *get* your nigger, that's all—so dry up your blubbering. Looky here—do you think *you'd* venture to blow on us? Blamed if I think I'd trust you. Why, if you *was* to blow on us——'

He stopped, but I never see the duke look so ugly out of his eyes before. I went on a-whimpering, and says:

'I don't want to blow on nobody; and I ain't got no time to blow, nohow. I got to turn out and find my nigger.'

He looked kinder bothered, and stood there with his bills fluttering on his arm, thinking, and wrinkling up his forehead. At last he says:

'I'll tell you something. We got to be here three days. If you'll promise you won't blow, and won't let the nigger blow, I'll tell you where to find him.'

So I promised, and he says:

'A farmer by the name of Silas Ph——' and then he stopped. You see he started to tell me the truth; but when he stopped, that way, and begun to study and think again, I reckoned he was changing his mind. And so he was. He wouldn't trust me; he wanted to make sure of having me out of the way the whole three days. So pretty soon he says: 'The man that bought him is named Abram Foster—Abram G. Foster—and he lives forty mile back here in the country, on the road to Lafayette.'

'All right,' I says, 'I can walk it in three days. And I'll start this very afternoon.'

'No you won't, you'll start *now*; and don't you lose any time about it, neither, nor do any gabbling by the way. Just keep a tight tongue in your head and move right along, and then you won't get into trouble with *us*, d'ye hear?'

That was the order I wanted, and that was the one I played for. I wanted to be left free to work my plans.

'So clear out,' he says; 'and you can tell Mr. Foster whatever you want to. Maybe you can get him to believe that Jim *is* your nigger—some idiots don't require documents—leastways I've heard there's such down South here. And when you tell him the handbill and the reward's bogus, maybe he'll believe you when you explain to him what the idea was for getting 'em out. Go 'long, now, and tell him anything you want to; but mind you don't work your jaw any *between* here and there.'

So I left, and struck for the back country. I didn't look around, but I kinder felt like he was watching me. But I knowed I could tire him out at that. I went straight out in the country as much as a mile, before I stopped; then I doubled back through the woods towards Phelps'. I reckoned I better start in on my plan straight off, without fooling around, because I wanted to stop Jim's mouth till these fellows could get away. I didn't want no trouble with their kind. I'd seen all I wanted to of them, and wanted to get entirely shut of them.

## *Chapter 32*

STILL AND SUNDAY-LIKE—MISTAKEN IDENTITY—UP A STUMP—IN A DILEMMA

WHEN I got there it was all still and Sunday-like, and hot and sunshiny—the hands was gone to the fields; and there was them kind of faint dronings of bugs and flies in the air that makes it seem so lonesome and like everybody's dead and gone; and if a breeze fans along and quivers the leaves, it makes you feel mournful, because you feel like it's spirits whispering—spirits that's been dead ever so many years—and you always think they're talking about *you*. As a general thing it makes a body wish *he* was dead too, and done with it all.

Phelps' was one of these little one-horse cotton plantations; and they all look alike. A rail fence round a two-acre yard; a stile, made out of logs sawed off and up-ended, in steps, like barrels of a different length, to climb over the fence with, and for the women to stand on when they are going to jump on to a horse; some sickly grass-patches in the big yard, but mostly it was bare and smooth, like an old hat with the nap rubbed off; big double log house for the white folks—hewed logs, with the chinks stopped up with mud or mortar, and these mud-stripes been whitewashed some time or another; round-log kitchen, with a big, broad, open but roofed passage joining it to the house; log smoke-house back of the kitchen; three little log nigger-cabins in a row t'other side the smoke-house; one little hut all by itself away down against the back fence, and some outbuildings down a piece the other side; ash-hopper, and big kettle to bile soap in, by the little hut; bench by the kitchen door, with bucket of water and a gourd; hound asleep there, in the sun; more hounds asleep, round about; about three shade-trees away off in a corner; some currant bushes and gooseberry bushes in one place by the fence; outside of the fence a garden and a water-melon patch; then the cotton-fields begins; and after the fields, the woods.

I went around and clumb over the back stile by the ash-hopper, and started for the kitchen. When I got a little ways, I heard the dim hum of a spinning-wheel wailing along up and sinking along down again; and then I knowed for certain I wished I was dead—for that *is* the lonesomest sound in the whole world.

I went right along, not fixing up any particular plan, but just trusting to Providence to put the right words in my mouth when the time come; for I'd noticed that Providence always did put the right words in my mouth, if I left it alone.

When I got half-way, first one hound and then another got up and went for me, and of course I stopped and faced them, and kept still. And such another pow-wow as they made! In a quarter of a minute I was a kind of a hub of a wheel, as you may say—spokes made out of dogs—circle of fifteen of them packed together around me, with their necks and noses stretched up towards me, a-barking and howling; and more a-coming; you could see them sailing over fences and around corners from everywheres.

A nigger woman come tearing out of the kichen with a rolling-pin in her hand, singing out, 'Begone! *you* Tige! you Spot! begone, sah!' and she fetched first one and then another of them a clip and sent him howling, and then the rest followed; and the next second, half of them come back, wagging their tails around me and making friends with me. There ain't no harm in a hound, nohow.

And behind the woman comes a little nigger girl and two little nigger boys, without anything on but tow-linen shirts, and they hung on to their mother's gown, and peeped out from behind her at me, bashful, the way they always do. And here comes the white woman running from the house, about forty-five or fifty year old, bareheaded, and her spinning-stick in her hand; and behind her comes her little white children, acting the same way the little niggers was doing. She was smiling all over so she could hardly stand—and says:

'It's *you*, at last!—*ain't* it?'

I out with a 'Yes'm,' before I thought.

She grabbed me and hugged me tight; and then gripped me by both hands and shook and shook; and the tears come in her eyes, and run down over; and she couldn't seem to hug and shake enough, and kept saying, 'You don't look as much like your mother as I reckoned you would, but law sakes, I don't care for that, I'm *so* glad to see you! Dear, dear, it does seem like I could eat you up! Childern, it's your Cousin Tom!—tell him howdy.'

But they ducked their heads, and put their fingers in their mouths, and hid behind her. So she run on:

'Lize, hurry up and get him a hot breakfast, right away—or did you get your breakfast on the boat?'

I said I had got it on the boat. So then she started for the house, leading me by the hand, and the children tagging after. When we got there, she set me down in a split-bottomed chair, and set herself down on a little low stool in front of me, holding both of my hands, and says:

'Now I can have a *good* look at you; and laws-a-me, I've been hungry for it a many and a many a time, all these long years, and it's come at last! We been expecting you a couple of days and more. What's kep' you?—boat get aground?'

'Yes'm—she——'

'Don't say yes'm—say Aunt Sally. Where'd she get aground?'

I didn't rightly know what to say, because I didn't know whether the boat would be coming up the river or down. But I go a good deal on instinct; and my instinct said she would be coming up—from down towards Orleans. That didn't help me much, though; for I didn't know the names of bars down that way. I see I'd got to invent a bar, or forget the name of the one we got aground on—or—— Now I struck an idea, and fetched it out:

'It warn't the grounding—that didn't keep us back but a little. We blowed out a cylinder-head.'

'Good gracious! anybody hurt?'

'No'm. Killed a nigger.'

'Well, it's lucky; because sometimes people do get hurt. Two years ago last Christmas, your Uncle Silas was coming up from Newrleans on the old *Lally Rook*, and she blowed out a cylinder-head and crippled a man. And I think he died afterwards. He was a Babtist. Your Uncle Silas knowed a family in Baton Rouge that knowed his people very well. Yes, I remember, now he *did* die. Mortification set in, and they had to amputate him. But it didn't save him. Yes, it was mortification—that was it. He turned blue all over, and died in the hope of a glorious resurrection. They say he was a sight to look at. Your uncle's been up to the town every day to fetch you. And he's gone again, not more'n hour ago; he'll be back any minute, now. You must a met him on the road, didn't you?—oldish man, with a——'

'No, I didn't see nobody, Aunt Sally. The boat landed just at daylight, and I left my baggage on the wharf-boat and went looking around the town and out a piece in the country, to put in the time and not get here too soon; and so I come down the back way.'

'Who'd you give the baggage to?'

'Nobody.'

'Why, child, it'll be stole!'

'Not where *I* hid it I reckon it won't,' I says.

'How'd you get your breakfast so early on the boat?'

It was kinder thin ice, but I says:

'The captain see me standing around, and told me I better have something to eat before I went ashore; so he took me in the texas to the officers' lunch, and give me all I wanted.'

I was getting so uneasy I couldn't listen good. I had my mind on the children all the time; I wanted to get them out to one side, and pump them a little, and find out who I was. But I couldn't get no show, Mrs. Phelps kept it up and run on so. Pretty soon she made the cold chills streak all down my back, because she says:

'But here we're a-running on this way, and you hain't told me a word about Sis, nor any of them. Now I'll rest my works a little, and you start up yourn; just tell me *everything*—tell me all about 'm all—every one of 'm; and how they are, and what they're doing, and what they told you to tell me; and every last thing you can think of.'

Well, I see I was up a stump—and up it good. Providence had stood by me this fur, all right, but I was hard and tight aground, now. I see it warn't a bit of use to try to go ahead—I'd *got* to throw up my hand. So I says to myself, here's another place where I got to resk the truth. I opened my mouth to begin; but she grabbed me and hustled me in behind the bed, and says:

'Here he comes! stick your head down lower—there, that'll do; you can't be seen, now. Don't you let on you're here. I'll play a joke on him. Childern, don't you say a word.'

I see I was in a fix, now. But it warn't no use to worry; there warn't nothing to do but just hold still, and try and be ready to stand from under when the lightning struck.

I had just one little glimpse of the old gentleman when he come in, then the bed hid him. Mrs. Phelps she jumps for him and says:

'Has he come?'

'No,' says her husband.

'Good-*ness* gracious!' she says, 'what in the world *can* have become of him?'

'I can't imagine,' says the old gentleman; 'and I must say, it makes me dreadful uneasy.'

'Uneasy!' she says, 'I'm ready to go distracted! He *must* a come; and you've missed him along the road. I *know* it's so—something *tells* me so.'

'Why, Sally, I *couldn't* miss him along the road—*you* know that.'

'But oh, dear, dear, what *will* Sis say! He must a come! You must a missed him. He——'

'Oh, don't distress me any more'n I'm already distressed. I don't know what in the world to make of it. I'm at my wits' end, and I don't mind acknowledging 't I'm right down scared. But there's no hope that he's come! for he *couldn't* come and me miss him. Sally, it's terrible—just terrible—something's happened to the boat, sure!'

'Why, Silas! Look yonder!—up the road!—ain't that somebody coming?'

He sprung to the window at the head of the bed, and that give Mrs.

Phelps the chance she wanted. She stooped down quick, at the foot of the bed, and give me a pull, and out I come; and when he turned back from the window, there she stood, a-beaming and a-smiling like a house afire, and I standing pretty meek and sweaty alongside. The old gentleman stared, and says:

'Why, who 's that?'

'Who do you reckon 't is?'

'I hain't no idea. Who *is* it?'

'It's *Tom Sawyer*!'

By jings, I most slumped through the floor. But there warn't no time to swap knives; the old man grabbed me by the hand and shook, and kept on shaking; and all the time, how the woman did dance around and laugh and cry; and then how they both did fire off questions about Sid, and Mary, and the rest of the tribe.

But if they was joyful, it warn't nothing to what I was; for it was like being born again, I was so glad to find out who I was. Well, they froze to me for two hours; and at last when my chin was so tired it couldn't hardly go, any more, I had told them more about my family—I mean the Sawyer family—than ever happened to any six Sawyer families. And I explained all about how we blowed out a cylinder-head at the mouth of White River and it took us three days to fix it. Which was all right, and worked first-rate; because *they* didn't know but what it would take three days to fix it. If I'd a called it a bolt-head it would a done just as well.

Now I was feeling pretty comfortable all down one side, and pretty uncomfortable all up the other. Being Tom Sawyer was easy and comfortable; and it stayed easy and comfortable till by-and-by I hear a steamboat coughing along down the river—then I says to myself, s'pose Tom Sawyer come down on that boat?—and s'pose he steps in here, any minute, and sings out my name before I can throw him a wink to keep quiet? Well, I couldn't *have* it that way—it wouldn't do at all. I must go up the road and waylay him. So I told the folks I reckoned I would go up to the town and fetch down my baggage. The old gentleman was for going along with me, but I said no, I could drive the horse myself, and I druther he wouldn't take no trouble about me.

## *Chapter 33*

### A NIGGER STEALER—SOUTHERN HOSPITALITY—'YOU IMPUDENT YOUNG RASCAL'—A PRETTY LONG BLESSING—TAR AND FEATHERS

So I started for town, in the wagon, and when I was half-way I see a wagon coming, and sure enough it was Tom Sawyer, and I stopped and waited till he come along. I says, 'Hold on!' and it stopped alongside, and his mouth opened like a trunk, and staid so; and he swallowed two or three times like a person that's got a dry throat, and then says:

'I hain't ever done you no harm. You know that. So, then, what you want to come back and ha'nt *me* for?'

I says:

'I hain't come back—I hain't been *gone*.'

When he heard my voice, it righted him up some, but he warn't quite satisfied yet. He says:

'Don't you play nothing on me, because I wouldn't on you. Honest injun, now, you ain't a ghost?'

'Honest injun, I ain't,' I says.

'Well—I—I—well, that ought to settle it, of course; but I can't somehow seem to understand it, no way. Looky here, warn't you ever murdered *at all*?'

'No. I warn't ever murdered at all—I played it on them. You come in here and feel of me if you don't believe me.'

So he done it, and it satisfied him; and he was that glad to see me again, he didn't know what to do. And he wanted to know all about it right off; because it was a grand adventure, and mysterious, and so it hit him where he lived. But I said, leave it alone till by-and-by; and told his driver to wait, and we drove off a little piece, and I told him the kind of a fix I was in, and what did he reckon we better do? He said, let him alone a minute, and don't disturb him. So he thought and thought, and pretty soon he says:

'It's all right, I've got it. Take my trunk in your wagon, and let on it's yourn; and you turn back and fool along slow, so as to get to the house about the time you ought to; and I'll go towards town a piece, and take a fresh start, and get there a quarter or a half an hour after you; and you needn't let on to know me, at first.'

I says:

'All right; but wait a minute. There's one more thing—a thing that *nobody* don't know but me. And that is, there's a nigger here that I'm a-trying to steal out of slavery—and his name is *Jim*—old Miss Watson's Jim.'

He says:

'What! Why, Jim is——'

He stopped, and went to studying. I says:

'*I* know what you'll say. You'll say it's dirty, low-down business; but what if it is?—*I'm* low-down; and I'm agoing to steal him, and I want you to keep mum and not let on. Will you?'

His eye lit up, and he says:

'I'll *help* you steal him!'

Well, I let go all holts then, like I was shot. It was the most astonishing speech I ever heard—and I'm bound to say Tom Sawyer fell, considerable, in my estimation. Only I couldn't believe it. Tom Sawyer a *nigger stealer*!

'Oh, shucks,' I says, 'you're joking.'

'I ain't joking, either.'

'Well, then,' I says, 'joking or no joking, if you hear anything said about a runaway nigger, don't forget to remember that *you* don't know nothing about him, and *I* don't know nothing about him.'

Then we took the trunk and put it in my wagon, and he drove off his way, and I drove mine. But of course I forgot all about driving slow, on accounts of being glad and full of thinking; so I got home a heap too quick for that length of a trip. The old gentleman was at the door, and he says:

'Why, this is wonderful. Whoever would have thought it was in that mare to do it. I wish we'd a timed her. And she hain't sweated a hair—not a hair. It's wonderful. Why, I wouldn't take a hunderd dollars for that horse now; I wouldn't, honest; and yet I'd a sold her for fifteen before, and thought 'twas all she was worth.'

That's all he said. He was the innocentest, best old soul I ever see. But it warn't surprising; because he warn't only just a farmer, he was a preacher too, and had a little one-horse log church down back of the plantation, which he built himself at his own expense, for a church and school-house, and never charged nothing for his preaching, and it was worth it too. There was plenty other farm-preachers like that, and done the same way, down South.

In about half an hour Tom's wagon drove up to the front stile, and Aunt Sally she see it through the window because it was only about fifty yards, and says:

'Why, there's somebody come! I wonder who 'tis? Why, I do believe it's a stranger. Jimmy' (that's one of the children), 'run and tell Lize to put on another plate for dinner.'

Everybody made a rush for the front door, because, of course, a stranger don't come *every* year, and so he lays over the yaller fever, for interest, when he does come. Tom was over the stile and starting for the house; the wagon was spinning up the road for the village, and we was all bunched in the front door. Tom had his store clothes on, and an audience—and that was always nuts for Tom Sawyer. In them circumstances it warn't no trouble to him to throw in an amount of style that was suitable. He warn't a boy to meeky along up that yard like a sheep; no, he come calm and important, like the ram. When he got afront of us, he lifts his hat ever so gracious and dainty, like it was the lid of a box that had butterflies asleep in it, and he didn't want to disturb them, and says:

'Mr. Archibald Nichols, I presume?'

'No, my boy,' says the old gentleman, 'I'm sorry to say 't your driver has deceived you; Nichols's place is down a matter of three mile more. Come in, come in.'

Tom he took a look back over his shoulder, and says, 'Too late—he's out of sight.'

'Yes, he 's gone, my son, and you must come in and eat your dinner with us; and then we'll hitch up and take you down to Nichols's.'

'Oh, I *can't* make you so much trouble, I couldn't think of it. I'll walk—I don't mind the distance.'

'But we won't *let* you walk—it wouldn't be Southern hospitality to do it. Come right in.'

'Oh, *do*,' says Aunt Sally; 'it ain't a bit of trouble to us, not a bit in the world. You *must* stay. It's a long, dusty three mile, and we *can't* let you walk. And besides, I've already told 'em to put on another plate, when I see you coming; so you mustn't disappoint us. Come right in, and make yourself at home.'

So Tom he thanked them very hearty and handsome, and let himself be persuaded, and come in; and when he was in, he said he was a stranger from Hicksville, Ohio, and his name was William Thompson—and he made another bow.

Well, he run on, and on, and on, making up stuff about Hicksville and everybody in it he could invent, and I getting a little nervious, and wondering how this was going to help me out of my scrape; and at last, still talking along, he reached over and kissed Aunt Sally right on the mouth, and then settled back again in his chair, comfortable, and was going on talking; but she jumped up and wiped it off with the back of her hand, and says:

'You owdacious puppy!'

He looked kind of hurt, and says:

'I'm surprised at you, m'am.'

'You're s'rp—— Why, what do you reckon *I* am? I've a good notion to take and—say, what do you mean by kissing me?'

He looked kind of humble, and says:

'I didn't mean nothing, m'am. I didn't mean no harm. I—I—thought you'd like it.'

'Why, you born fool!' She took up the spinning-stick, and it looked like it was all she could do to keep from giving him a crack with it. 'What made you think I'd like it?'

'Well, I don't know. Only, they—they—told me you would.'

'*They* told you I would. Whoever told you 's *another* lunatic. I never heard the beat of it. Who's *they*?'

'Why—everybody. They all said so, m'am.'

It was all she could do to hold in; and her eyes snapped, and her fingers worked like she wanted to scratch him; and she says:

'Who's "everbody"? Out with their names—or ther'll be an idiot short.'

He got up and looked distressed, and fumbled his hat, and says:

'I'm sorry, and I warn't expecting it. They told me to. They all told me to. They all said kiss her; and said she'll like it. They all said it—every one of them. But I'm sorry, m'am, and I won't do it no more—I won't, honest.'

'You won't, won't you? Well, I sh'd *reckon* you won't!'

'No'm, I'm honest about it; I won't ever do it again. Till you ask me.'

'Till I *ask* you! Well, I never see the beat of it in my born days! I lay you'll be the Methusalem-numskull of creation before ever *I* ask you—or the likes of you.'

'Well,' he says, 'it does surprise me so. I can't make it out, somehow. They said you would, and I thought you would. But——' He stopped and looked around slow, like he wished he could run across a friendly eye, somewhere's; and fetched up on the old gentleman's, and says, 'Didn't *you* think she'd like me to kiss her, sir?'

'Why, no, I—I—well, no, I b'lieve I didn't.'

Then he looks on around, the same way, to me—and says:

'Tom, didn't *you* think Aunt Sally 'd open out her arms and say, "Sid Sawyer——" '

'My land!' she says, breaking in and jumping for him, 'you impudent young rascal, to fool a body so——' and was going to hug him, but he fended her off, and says:

'No, not till you've asked me, first.'

So she didn't lose no time, but asked him; and hugged him and kissed him, over and over again, and then turned him over to the old man, and he took what was left. And after they got a little quiet again, she says:

'Why, dear me, I never see such a surprise. We warn't looking for *you*, at all, but only Tom. Sis never wrote to me about anybody coming but him.'

'It's because it warn't *intended* for any of us to come but Tom,' he says; 'but I begged and begged, and at the last minute she let me come too; so, coming down the river, me and Tom thought it would be a first-rate surprise for him to come here to the house first, and for me to by-and-by tag along and drop in and let on to be a stranger. But it was a mistake, Aunt Sally. This ain't no healthy place for a stranger to come.'

'No—not impudent whelps, Sid. You ought to had your jaws boxed; I hain't been so put out since I don't know when. But I don't care, I don't mind the terms—I'd be willing to stand a thousand such jokes to have you here. Well, to think of that performance! I don't deny it, I was most putrified with astonishment when you give me that smack.'

We had dinner out in that broad, open passage betwixt the house and the kitchen; and there was things enough on that table for seven families—and all hot too; none of your flabby tough meat that's laid in a cupboard in a damp cellar all night and tastes like a hunk of old cold cannibal in the morning. Uncle Silas he asked a pretty long blessing over it, but it was worth it; and it didn't cool it a bit, neither, the way I've seen them kind of interruptions do, lots of times.

There was a considerable good deal of talk, all the afternoon, and me and Tom was on the look-out all the time, but it warn't no use, they didn't happen to say nothing about any runaway nigger, and we was afraid to try to work up to it. But at supper, at night, one of the little boys says:

'Pa, mayn't Tom and Sid and me go to the show?'

'No,' says the old man, 'I reckon there ain't going to be any; and you couldn't go if there was; because the runaway nigger told Burton and me all about that scandalous show, and Burton said he would tell the people; so I reckon they've drove the owdacious loafers out of town before this time.'

So there it was!—but *I* couldn't help it. Tom and me was to sleep in the same room and bed; so, being tired, we bid good night and went up to bed, right after supper, and clumb out of the window and down the lightning-rod, and shoved for the town; for I didn't believe anybody was going to give the king and the duke a hint, and so, if I didn't hurry up and give them one they'd get into trouble, sure.

On the road Tom he told me all about how it was reckoned I was murdered, and how pap disappeared, pretty soon, and didn't come back no more, and what a stir there was when Jim run away; and I told Tom all about our Royal Nonesuch rapscallions, and as much of the raft-voyage as I had time to; and as we struck into the town and up through the middle of it—it was as much as half-after eight, then—here comes a raging rush of people, with torches, and an awful whooping and yelling, and banging tin pans and blowing horns; and we jumped to one side to let them go by; and as they went by, I see they had the king and the duke astraddle of a rail—that is, I knowed it *was* the king and the duke, though they was all over tar and feathers, and didn't look like nothing in the world that was human—just looked like a couple of monstrous big soldier-plumes. Well, it made me sick to see it; and I was sorry for them poor pitiful rascals, it seemed like I couldn't ever feel any hardness against them any more in the world. It was a dreadful thing to see. Human beings *can* be awful cruel to one another.

We see we was too late—couldn't do no good. We asked some stragglers about it, and they said everybody went to the show looking very innocent; and laid low and kept dark till the poor old king was in the middle of his cavortings on the stage; then somebody give a signal, and the house rose up and went for them.

So we poked along back home, and I warn't feeling so brash as I was before, but kind of ornery, and humble, and to blame, somehow—though *I* hadn't done nothing. But that's always the way; it don't make no difference whether you do right or wrong, a person's conscience ain't got no sense, and just goes for him *anyway*. If I had a yaller dog that didn't know no more than a person's conscience does, I would pison him. It takes up more room than all the rest of a person's insides, and yet ain't no good, nohow. Tom Sawyer he says the same.

## Chapter 34

THE HUT BY THE ASH-HOPPER—OUTRAGEOUS—A SIMPLE JOB—CLIMBING THE LIGHTNING-ROD—TROUBLED WITH WITCHES

We stopped talking, and got to thinking. By-and-by Tom says:

'Looky here, Huck, what fools we are, to not think of it before! I bet I know where Jim is.'

'No! Where?'

'In that hut down by the ash-hopper. Why, looky here. When we was at dinner, didn't you see a nigger man go in there with some vittles?'

'Yes.'

'What did you think the vittles was for?'

'For a dog.'

'So'd I. Well, it wasn't for a dog.'

'Why?'

'Because part of it was watermelon."

'So it was—I noticed it. Well, it does beat all, that I never thought about a dog not eating watermelon. It shows how a body can see and don't see at the same time.'

'Well, the nigger unlocked the padlock when he went in, and he locked it again when he come out. He fetched uncle a key, about the time we got up from table—same key, I bet. Watermelon shows man, lock shows prisoner; and it ain't likely there's two prisoners on such a little plantation, and where the people's all so kind and good. Jim's the prisoner. All right—I'm glad we found it out detective fashion; I wouldn't give shucks for any other way. Now you work your mind and study out a plan to steal Jim, and I will study out one too; and we'll take the one we like the best.'

What a head for just a boy to have! If I had Tom Sawyer's head, I wouldn't trade it off to be a duke, nor mate of a steamboat, nor clown in a circus, nor nothing I can think of. I went to thinking out a plan, but only just to be doing something; I knowed very well where the right plan was going to come from. Pretty soon, Tom says:

'Ready?'

'Yes,' I says.

'All right—bring it out.'

'My plan is this,' I says. 'We can easy find out if it's Jim in there. Then get up my canoe to-morrow night, and fetch my raft over from the island. Then the first dark night that comes, steal the key out of the old man's britches, after he goes to bed, and shove off down the river on the raft, with Jim, hiding day-times and running nights, the way me and Jim used to do before. Wouldn't that plan work?'

'*Work?* Why cert'nly, it would work, like rats a-fighting. But it's too blame' simple; there ain't nothing *to* it. What's the good of a plan that ain't no more trouble than that? It's as mild as goose-milk. Why,

Huck, it wouldn't make no more talk than breaking into a soap factory.'

I never said nothing, because I warn't expecting nothing different; but I knowed mighty well that whenever he got *his* plan ready it wouldn't have none of them objections to it.

And it didn't. He told me what it was, and I see in a minute it was worth fifteen of mine, for style, and would make Jim just as free a man as mine would, and maybe get us all killed besides. So I was satisfied, and said we would waltz in on it. I needn't tell what it was, here, because I knowed it wouldn't stay the way it was. I knowed he would be changing it around, every which way, as we went along, and heaving in new bullinesses wherever he got a chance. And that is what he done.

Well, one thing was dead sure; and that was, that Tom Sawyer was in earnest and was actually going to help steal that nigger out of slavery. That was the thing that was too many for me. Here was a boy that was respectable, and well brung up; and had a character to lose; and folks at home that had characters; and he was bright and not leather-headed; and knowing and not ignorant; and not mean, but kind; and yet here he was, without any more pride, or rightness, or feeling, than to stoop to this business, and make himself a shame, and his family a shame, before everybody. I *couldn't* understand it, no way at all. It was outrageous, and I knowed I ought to just up and tell him so; and so be his true friend, and let him quit the thing right where he was, and save himself. And I *did* start to tell him; but he shut me up, and says:

'Don't you reckon I know what I'm about? Don't I generly know what I'm about?'

'Yes.'

'Didn't I *say* I was going to help steal the nigger?'

'Yes.'

'*Well*, then.'

That's all he said, and that's all I said. It warn't no use to say any more; because when he said he'd do a thing, he always done it. But *I* couldn't make out how he was willing to go into this thing; so I just let it go, and never bothered no more about it. If he was bound to have it so, *I* couldn't help it.

When we got home, the house was all dark and still; so we went on down to the hut by the ash-hopper, for to examine it. We went through the yard, so as to see what the hounds would do. They knowed us, and didn't make no more noise than country dogs is always doing when anything comes by in the night. When we got to the cabin, we took a look at the front and the two sides; and on the side I warn't acquainted with—which was the north side—we found a square window-hole, up tolerable high, with just one stout board nailed across it. I says:

'Here's the ticket. This hole's big enough for Jim to get through, if we wrench off the board.'

Tom says:

'It's as simple as tit-tat-toe, three-in-a-row, and as easy as playing hooky. I should *hope* we can find a way that's a little more complicated than *that*, Huck Finn.'

'Well, then,' I says, 'how'll it do to saw him out, the way I done before I was murdered, that time?'

'That's more *like*,' he says. 'It's real mysterious and troublesome, and good,' he says; 'but I bet we can find a way that's twice as long. There ain't no hurry; le's keep on looking around.'

Betwixt the hut and the fence, on the back side, was a lean-to, that joined the hut at the eaves, and was made out of plank. It was as long as the hut, but narrow—only about six foot wide. The door to it was at the south end, and was padlocked. Tom he went to the soap-kettle, and searched around and fetched back the iron thing they lift the lid with; so he took it and prized out one of the staples. The chain fell down, and we opened the door and went in, and shut it, and struck a match, and see the shed was only built against the cabin and hadn't no connection with it; and there warn't no floor to the shed, nor nothing in it but some old rusty played-out hoes, and spades, and picks, and a crippled plow. The match went out, and so did we, and shoved in the staple again, and the door was locked as good as ever. Tom was joyful. He says:

'Now we're all right. We'll *dig* him out. It'll take about a week!'

Then we started for the house, and I went in the back door—you only have to pull a buckskin latch-string, they don't fasten the doors—but that warn't romantical enough for Tom Sawyer: no way would do him but he must climb up the lightning-rod. But after he got up half-way about three times, and missed fire and fell every time, and the last time most busted his brains out, he thought he'd got to give it up; but after he was rested, he allowed he would give her one more turn for luck, and this time he made the trip.

In the morning we was up at break of day, and down to the nigger cabins to pet the dogs and make friends with the nigger that fed Jim—if it *was* Jim that was being fed. The niggers was just getting through breakfast and starting for the fields; and Jim's nigger was piling up a tin pan with bread and meat and things; and whilst the others was leaving, the key come from the house.

This nigger had a good-natured, chuckle-headed face, and his wool was all tied up in little bunches with thread. That was to keep witches off. He said the witches was pestering him awful, these nights, and making him see all kinds of strange things, and hear all kinds of strange words and noises, and he didn't believe he was ever witched so long, before, in his life. He got so worked up, and got to running on so about his troubles, he forgot all about what he'd been agoing to do. So Tom says:

'What's the vittles for? Going to feed the dogs?'

The nigger kind of smiled around graduly over his face, like when you heave a brickbat in a mud-puddle, and he says:

'Yes, Mars Sid, *a* dog. Cur'us dog, too. Does you want to go en look at 'im?'

'Yes.'

I hunched Tom, and whispers:

'You going, right here in the daybreak? *That* warn't the plan.'

'No, it warn't—but it's the plan *now*.'

So, drat him, we went along, but I didn't like it much. When we got in, we couldn't hardly see anything, it was so dark; but Jim was there, sure enough, and could see us; and he sings out:

'Why *Huck*! En good *lan*'! ain' dat Misto Tom?'

I just knowed how it would be; I just expected it. *I* didn't know nothing to do; and if I had, I couldn't a done it; because that nigger busted in and says:

'Why, de gracious sakes! do he know you genlmen?'

We could see pretty well, now. Tom he looked at the nigger, steady and kind of wondering, and says:

'Does *who* know us?'

'Why, dish-yer runaway nigger.'

'I don't reckon he does; but what put that into your head?'

'What *put* it dar? Didn' he jis' dis minute sing out like he knowed you?'

Tom says, in a puzzled-up kind of way:

'Well, that's mighty curious. *Who* sung out? *When* did he sing out? *What* did he sing out?' And turns to me, perfectly calm, and says, 'Did *you* hear anybody sing out?'

Of course there warn't nothing to be said but the one thing; so I says:

'No; *I* ain't heard nobody say nothing.'

Then he turns to Jim, and looks him over like he never see him before; and says:

'Did you sing out?'

'No, sah,' says Jim; '*I* hain't said nothing, sah.'

'Not a word?'

'No, sah, I hain't said a word.'

'Did you ever see us before?'

'No, sah; not as *I* knows on.'

So Tom turns to the nigger, which was looking wild and distressed, and says, kind of severe:

'What do you reckon's the matter with you, anyway? What made you think somebody sung out?'

'Oh, it's de dad-blame' witches, sah, en I wisht I was dead, I do. Dey's awluz at it, sah, en dey do mos' kill me, dey sk'yers me so. Please to don't tell nobody 'bout it, sah, er ole Mars Silas he'll scole me; 'kase he says dey *ain't* no witches. I jis' wish to goodness he was heah now—*den* what would he say! I jis' bet he couldn' fine no way to git aroun' it *dis* time. But it's awluz jis' so; people dat's *sot*, stays sot; dey won't look into noth'n en fine it out f'r deyselves, en when *you* fine it out en tell um 'bout it, dey doan' b'lieve you.'

Tom give him a dime, and said we wouldn't tell nobody; and told him to buy some more thread to tie up his wool with; and then looks at Jim, and says:

'I wonder if Uncle Silas is going to hang this nigger. If I was to catch a nigger that was ungrateful enough to run away, *I* wouldn't give him up, I'd hang him.' And whilst the nigger stepped to the door to look at the dime and bite it to see if it was good, he whispers to Jim, and says:

'Don't ever let on to know us. And if you hear any digging going on nights, it's us: we're going to set you free.'

Jim had only time to grab us by the hand and squeeze it, then the nigger come back, and we said we'd come again some time if the nigger wanted us to; and he said he would, more particular if it was dark, because the witches went for him mostly in the dark, and it was good to have folks around then.

## *Chapter 35*

### ESCAPING PROPERLY—DARK SCHEMES—DISCRIMINATION IN STEALING—A DEEP HOLE

It would be most an hour, yet, till breakfast, so we left, and struck down into the woods; because Tom said we got to have *some* light to see how to dig by, and a lantern makes too much, and might get us into trouble; what we must have was a lot of them rotten chunks that's called fox-fire and just makes a soft kind of a glow when you lay them in a dark place. We fetched an armful and hid it in the weeds, and set down to rest, and Tom says, kind of dissatisfied:

'Blame it, this whole thing is just as easy and awkard as it can be. And so it makes it so rotten difficult to get up a difficult plan. There ain't no watchman to be drugged—now there *ought* to be a watchman. There ain't even a dog to give a sleeping-mixture to. And there's Jim chained by one leg, with a ten-foot chain, to the leg of his bed: why, all you got to do is to lift up the bedstead and slip off the chain. And Uncle Silas he trusts everybody; sends the key to the punkin-headed nigger, and don't send nobody to watch the nigger. Jim could a got out of that window-hole before this, only there wouldn't be no use trying to travel with a ten-foot chain on his leg. Why, drat it, Huck, it's the stupidest arrangement I ever see. You got to invent *all* the difficulties. Well, we can't help it, we got to do the best we can with the materials we've got. Anyhow, there's one thing—there's more honour in getting him out through a lot of difficulties and dangers, where there warn't one of them furnished to you by the people who it was their duty to furnish them, and you had to contrive them all out of your own head. Now look at just that one thing of the lantern. When you come down to the cold facts, we simply got to *let on* that a lantern's resky. Why, we could work with a torchlight procession if we wanted to, *I* believe. Now, whilst I think of it, we got to hunt up something to make a saw out of, the first chance we get.'

'What do we want of a saw?'

'What do we *want* of it? Hain't we got to saw the leg of Jim's bed off, so as to get the chain loose?'

'Why, you just said a body could lift up the bedstead and slip the chain off.'

'Well, if that ain't just like you, Huck Finn. You *can* get up the infant-schooliest ways of going at a thing. Why, hain't you ever read any books at all?—Baron Trenck, nor Casanova, nor Benvenuto Chelleeny, nor Henri IV, nor none of them heroes? Whoever heard of getting a prisoner loose in such an old-maidy way as that? No; the way all the best authorities does, is to saw the bed-leg in two, and leave it just so, and swallow the sawdust, so it can't be found, and put some dirt and grease around the sawed place so the very keenest seneskal can't see no sign of its being sawed, and thinks the bed-leg is perfectly sound. Then, the night you're ready, fetch the leg a kick, down she goes; slip off your chain, and there you are. Nothing to do but hitch your rope-ladder to the battlements, shin down it, break your leg in the moat—because a rope-ladder is nineteen foot too short, you know—and there's your horses and your trusty vassles, and they scoop you up and fling you across a saddle and away you go, to your native Langudoc, or Navarre, or wherever it is. It's gaudy, Huck. I wish there was a moat to this cabin. If we get time, the night of the escape, we'll dig one.'

I says:

'What do we want of a moat, when we're going to snake him out from under the cabin?'

But he never heard me. He had forgot me and everything else. He had his chin in his hand, thinking. Pretty soon, he sighs, and shakes his head; then sighs again, and says:

'No, it wouldn't do—there ain't necessity enough for it.'

'For what?' I says.

'Why, to saw Jim's leg off.' he says.

'Good land!' I says, 'why, there ain't *no* necessity for it. And what would you want to saw his leg off for, anyway?'

'Well, some of the best authorities has done it. They couldn't get the chain off, so they just cut their hand off, and shoved. And a leg would be better still. But we got to let that go. There ain't necessity enough in this case; and besides, Jim's a nigger and wouldn't understand the reasons for it, and how it's the custom in Europe; so we'll let it go. But there's one thing—he can have a rope-ladder; we can tear up our sheets and make him a rope-ladder easy enough. And we can send it to him in a pie; it's mostly done that way. And I've et worse pies.'

'Why, Tom Sawyer, how you talk,' I says; 'Jim ain't got no use for a rope-ladder.'

'He *has* got use for it. How *you* talk; you better say you don't know nothing about it. He's *got* to have a rope-ladder; they all do.'

'What in the nation can he *do* with it?'

'*Do* with it? He can hide it in his bed, can't he? That's what they all do; and *he's* got to, too. Huck, you don't ever seem to want to do anything that's regular; you want to be starting something fresh all the time. S'pose he *don't* do nothing with it? ain't it there in his bed, for a clew, after he's gone? and don't you reckon they'll want clews? Of course they will. And you wouldn't leave them any? That would be a *pretty* howdy-do, *wouldn't* it? I never heard of such a thing.'

'Well,' I says, 'if it's in the regulations, and he's got to have it, all right, let him have it; because I don't wish to go back on no regulations; but there's one thing, Tom Sawyer—if we go to tearing up our sheets to make Jim a rope-ladder, we're going to get into trouble with Aunt Sally, just as sure as you're born. Now, the way I look at it, a hickry-bark ladder don't cost nothing, and don't waste nothing, and is just as good to load up a pie with, and hide in a straw tick, as any rag-ladder you can start; and as for Jim, he ain't had no experience, and so *he* don't care what kind of a——'

'Oh, shucks, Huck Finn, if I was as ignorant as you, I'd keep still—that's what *I'd* do. Whoever heard of a State prisoner escaping by a hickry-bark ladder? Why, it's perfectly ridiculous.'

'Well, all right, Tom, fix it your own way; but if you'll take my advice, you'll let me borrow a sheet off of the clothes-line.'

He said that would do. And that give him another idea, and he says:

'Borrow a shirt too.'

'What do we want of a shirt, Tom?'

'Want it for Jim to keep a journal on.'

'Journal your granny—*Jim* can't write.'

'S'pose he *can't* write—he can make marks on the shirt, can't he, if we make him a pen out of an old pewter spoon or a piece of an old iron barrel-hoop?'

'Why, Tom, we can pull a feather out of a goose and make him a better one; and quicker, too.'

'*Prisoners* don't have geese running around the donjonkeep to pull pens out of, you muggins. They *always* make their pens out of the hardest, toughest, troublesomest piece of old brass candlestick or something like that they can get their hands on; and it takes them weeks and weeks, and months and months, to file it out, too, because they've got to do it by rubbing it on the wall. *They* wouldn't use a goose-quill if they had it. It ain't regular.'

'Well, then, what'll we make him the ink out of?'

'Many makes it out of iron-rust and tears; but that's the common sort and women; the best authorities uses their own blood. Jim can do that; and when he wants to send any little common ordinary mysterious message to let the world know where he's captivated, he can write it on the bottom of a tin plate with a fork and throw it out of the window. The Iron Mask always done that, and it's a blame' good way too.'

'Jim ain't got no tin plates. They feed him in a pan.'

'That ain't anything; we can get him some.'

'Can't nobody *read* his plates?'

'That ain't got nothing to *do* with it, Huck Finn. All *he's* got to do is to write on the plate and throw it out. You don't *have* to be able to read it. Why, half the time you can't read anything a prisoner writes on a tin plate, or anywhere else.'

'Well, then, what's the sense in wasting the plates?'

'Why, blame' it all, it ain't the *prisoner's* plates.'

'But it's *somebody's* plates, ain't it?'

'Well, s'pos'n it is? What does the *prisoner* care whose——'

He broke off there, because we heard the breakfast-horn blowing. So we cleared out for the house.

Along during that morning I borrowed a sheet and a white shirt off of the clothes-line; and I found an old sack and put them in it, and we went down and got the fox-fire, and put that in too. I called it borrowing, because that was what pap always called it; but Tom said it warn't borrowing, it was stealing. He said we was representing prisoners; and prisoners don't care how they get a thing so they get it, and nobody don't blame them for it, either. It ain't no crime in a prisoner to steal the thing he needs to get away with, Tom said; it's his right; and so, as long as we was representing a prisoner we had a perfect right to steal anything on this place we had the least use for, to get ourselves out of prison with. He said if we warn't prisoners it would be a very different thing, and nobody but a mean ornery person would steal when he warn't a prisoner. So we allowed we would steal everything there was that come handy. And yet he made a mighty fuss, one day, after that, when I stole a watermelon out of the nigger patch and eat it; and he made me go and give the niggers a dime, without telling them what it was for. Tom said that what he meant was, we could steal anything we *needed*. Well, I says, I needed the watermelon. But he said I didn't need it to get out of prison with, there's where the difference was. He said if I'd a wanted it to hide a knife in, and smuggle it to Jim to kill the seneskal with, it would a been all right. So I let it go at that, though I couldn't see no advantage in my representing a prisoner, if I got to set down and chaw over a lot of gold-leaf distinctions like that, every time I see a chance to hog a watermelon.

Well, as I was saying, we waited that morning till everybody was settled down to business, and nobody in sight around the yard; then Tom he carried the sack into the lean-to whilst I stood off a piece to keep watch. By-and-by he come out, and we went and set down on the wood-pile, to talk. He says:

'Everything's all right, now, except tools; and that's easy fixed.'

'Tools?' I says.

'Yes.'

'Tools for what?'

'Why, to dig with. We ain't agoing to *gnaw* him out, are we?'

'Ain't them old crippled picks and things in there good enough to dig a nigger out with?' I says.

He turns on me looking pitying enough to make a body cry, and says:

'Huck Finn, did you *ever* hear of a prisoner having picks and shovels, and all the modern conveniences in his wardrobe to dig himself out with? Now I want to ask you—if you got any reasonableness in you at all—what kind of a show would *that* give him to be a hero? Why, they might as well lend him the key, and done with it. Picks and shovels—why, they wouldn't furnish 'em to a king.'

'Well, then,' I says, 'if we don't want the picks and shovels, what do we want?'

'A couple of case-knives.'

'To dig the foundations out from under that cabin with?'

'Yes.'

'Confound it, it's foolish, Tom.'

'It don't make no difference how foolish it is, it's the *right* way—and it's the regular way. And there ain't no *other* way, that ever *I* heard of, and I've read all the books that gives any information about these things. They always dig out with a case-knife—and not through dirt, mind you; generly it's through solid rock. And it takes them weeks and weeks and weeks, and for ever and ever. Why, look at one of them prisoners in the bottom dungeon of the Castle Deef, in the harbour of Marseilles, that dug himself out that way; how long was *he* at it, you reckon?'

'I don't know.'

'Well, guess.'

'I don't know. A month and a half?'

'*Thirty-seven year*—and he come out in China. *That's* the kind. I wish the bottom of *this* fortress was solid rock.'

'*Jim* don't know nobody in China.'

'What's *that* got to do with it? Neither did that other fellow. But you're always a-wandering off on a side issue. Why can't you stick to the main point?'

'All right—*I* don't care where he comes out, so he *comes* out; and Jim don't, either, I reckon. But there's one thing, anyway—Jim's too old to be dug out with a case-knife. He won't last.'

'Yes he will *last*, too. You don't reckon it's going to take thirty-seven years to dig out through a *dirt* foundation, do you?'

'How long will it take, Tom?'

'Well, we can't resk being as long as we ought to, because it mayn't take very long for Uncle Silas to hear from down there by New Orleans. He'll hear Jim ain't from there. Then his next move will be to advertise Jim, or something like that. So we can't resk being as long digging him out as we ought to. By rights I reckon we ought to be a couple of years; but we can't. Things being so uncertain, what I recommend is this: that we really dig right in, as quick as we can; and after that, we can *let on*, to ourselves, that we was at it thirty-seven years. Then we can snatch him out and rush him away the first time there's an alarm. Yes, I reckon that'll be the best way.'

'Now, there's *sense* in that,' I says. 'Letting on don't cost nothing; letting on ain't no trouble; and if it's any objcct, I don't mind letting on we was at it a hundred and fifty year. It wouldn't strain me none, after I got my hand in. So I'll mosey along now, and smouch a couple of case-knives.'

'Smouch three,' he says; 'we want one to make a saw out of.'

'Tom, if it ain't unregular and irreligious to sejest it,' I says, 'there's an old rusty saw-blade around yonder sticking under the weather-boarding behind the smoke-house.'

He looked kind of weary and discouraged-like, and says:

'It ain't no use to try to learn you nothing, Huck. Run along and smouch the knives—three of them.' So I done it.

## *Chapter 36*

THE LIGHTNING-ROD—HIS LEVEL BEST—A BEQUEST TO POSTERITY—STEALING SPOONS—AMONGST THE DOGS—A HIGH FIGURE

As soon as we reckoned everybody was asleep, that night, we went down the lightning-rod, and shut ourselves up in the lean-to, and got out our pile of fox-fire, and went to work. We cleared everything out of the way, about four or five foot along the middle of the bottom log. Tom said he was right behind Jim's bed now, and we'd dig in under it, and when we got through there couldn't nobody in the cabin ever know there was any hole there, because Jim's counterpin hung down most to the ground, and you'd have to raise it up and look under to see the hole. So we dug and dug, with the case-knives, till most midnight; and then we was dog-tired, and our hands was blistered, and yet you couldn't see we'd done anything, hardly. At last I says:

'This ain't no thirty-seven-year job, this is a thirty-eight-year job, Tom Sawyer.'

He never said nothing. But he sighed, and pretty soon he stopped digging, and then for a good little while I knowed he was thinking. Then he says:

'It ain't no use, Huck, it ain't agoing to work. If we was prisoners it would, because then we'd have as many years as we wanted, and no hurry; and we wouldn't get but a few minutes to dig, every day, while they was changing watches, and so our hands wouldn't get blistered, and we could keep it up right along, year in and year out, and do it right, and the way it ought to be done. But *we* can't fool along, we got to rush; we ain't got no time to spare. If we was to put in another night this way, we'd have to knock off for a week to let our hands get well—couldn't touch a case-knife with them sooner.'

'Well, then, what we going to do, Tom?'

'I'll tell you. It ain't right, and it ain't moral, and I wouldn't like it to get out—but there ain't only just the one way; we got to dig him out with the picks, and *let on* it's case-knives.'

'*Now* you're *talking*!' I says; 'your head gets leveller and leveller all the time, Tom Sawyer,' I says. 'Picks is the thing, moral or no moral; and as for me, I don't care shucks for the morality of it, nohow. When I start in to steal a nigger, or a watermelon, or a Sunday-school book, I ain't no ways particular how it's done so it's done. What I want is my nigger; or what I want is my watermelon; or what I want is my Sunday-school book; and if a pick's the handiest thing, that's the thing I'm agoing to dig that nigger or that watermelon or that Sunday-school book out with; and I don't give a dead rat what the authorities thinks about it nuther.'

'Well,' he says, 'there's excuse for picks and letting-on in a case like this; if it warn't so, I wouldn't approve of it, nor I wouldn't stand by and see the rules broke—because right is right, and wrong is wrong, and a body ain't got no business doing wrong when he ain't ignorant and knows better. It might answer for *you* to dig Jim out with a pick, *without* any letting-on, because you don't know no better; but it wouldn't for me, because I do know better. Gimme a case-knife.'

He had his own by him, but I handed him mine. He flung it down, and says:

'Gimme a *case-knife*.'

I didn't know just what to do—but then I thought. I scratched around amongst the old tools, and got a pick-axe and give it to him, and he took it and went to work, and never said a word.

He was always just that particular. Full of principle.

So then I got a shovel, and then we picked and shovelled, turn about, and made the fur fly. We stuck to it about a half an hour, which was as long as we could stand up; but we had a good deal of a hole to show for it. When I got upstairs, I looked out at the window and see Tom doing his level best with the lightning-rod, but he couldn't come it, his hands was so sore. At last he says:

'It ain't no use, it can't be done. What you reckon I better do? Can't you think up no way?'

'Yes,' I says, 'but I reckon it ain't regular. Come up the stairs, and let on it's a lightning-rod.'

So he done it.

Next day Tom stole a pewter spoon and a brass candlestick in the house, for to make some pens for Jim out of, and six tallow candles; and I hung around the nigger cabins, and laid for a chance, and stole three tin plates. Tom said it wasn't enough; but I said nobody wouldn't ever see the plates that Jim throwed out, because they'd fall in the dog-fennel and jimpson weeds under the window-hole—then we could tote them back and he could use them over again. So Tom was satisfied. Then he says:

'Now, the thing to study out is, how to get the things to Jim.'

'Take them in through the hole,' I says, 'when we get it done.'

He only just looked scornful, and said something about nobody ever heard of such an idiotic idea, and then he went to studying. By-and-by he said he had ciphered out two or three ways, but there warn't no need to decide on any of them yet. Said we'd got to post Jim first.

That night we went down the lightning-rod a little after ten, and took one of the candles along, and listened under the window-hole, and heard Jim snoring; so we pitched it in, and it didn't wake him. Then we whirled in with the pick and shovel, and in about two hours and a half the job was done. We crept in under Jim's bed and into the cabin, and pawed around and found the candle and lit it, and stood over Jim awhile, and found him looking hearty and healthy, and then we woke him up gentle and gradual. He was so glad to see us he most cried; and called us honey, and all the pet-names he could think of; and was for having us hunt up a cold chisel to cut the chain off of his leg with, right away, and clearing out without losing any time. But Tom he showed him how unregular it would be, and set down and told him all about our plans, and how we could alter them in a minute any time there was an alarm; and not to be the least afraid, because we would see he got away, *sure*. So Jim he said it was all right, and we set there and talked over old times awhile, and then Tom asked a lot of questions, and when Jim told him Uncle Silas come in every day or two to pray with him, and Aunt Sally come in to see if he was comfortable and had plenty to eat, and both of them was kind as they could be, Tom says:

'*Now* I know how to fix it. We'll send you some things by them.'

I said, 'Don't do nothing of the kind; it's one of the most jackass ideas I ever struck'; but he never paid no attention to me; went right on. It was his way when he'd got his plans set.

So he told Jim how we'd have to smuggle in the rope-ladder pie, and other large things, by Nat, the nigger that fed him, and he must be on the look-out, and not be surprised, and not let Nat see him open them; and we would put small things in uncle's coat pockets and he must steal them out; and we would tie things to aunt's apron-strings or put them in her apron pocket, if we got a chance; and told him what they would be and what they was for. And told him how to keep a journal on the shirt with his blood, and all that. He told him everything. Jim he couldn't see no sense in the most of it, but he allowed we was white folks and knowed better than him; so he was satisfied, and said he would do it all just as Tom said.

Jim had plenty corn-cob pipes and tobacco; so we had a right-down good sociable time; then we crawled out through the hole, and so home to bed, with hands that looked like they'd been chawed. Tom was in high spirits. He said it was the best fun he ever had in his life, and the most intellectural; and said if he only could see his way to it we would keep it up all the rest of our lives and leave Jim to our children to get out; for he believed Jim would come to like it better and better the more he got used to it. He said that in that way it could be strung out to as much as eighty year, and would be the best time on record. And he said it would make us all celebrated that had a hand in it.

In the morning we went out to the wood-pile and chopped up the brass candlestick into handy sizes, and Tom put them and the pewter spoon in his pocket. Then we went to the nigger cabins, and while I got Nat's notice off, Tom shoved a piece of candlestick into the middle of a corn-pone that was in Jim's pan, and we went along with Nat to see how it would work, and it just worked noble; when Jim bit into it it most mashed all his teeth out; and there warn't ever anything could a worked better. Tom said so himself. Jim he never let on but what it was only just a piece of rock or something like that that's always getting into bread, you know; but after that he never bit into nothing but what he jabbed his fork into it in three or four places, first.

And whilst we was a-standing there in the dimmish light, here comes a couple of the hounds bulging in, from under Jim's bed; and they kept on piling in till there was eleven of them, and there warn't hardly room in there to get your breath. By jings, we forgot to fasten that lean-to door. The nigger Nat he only just hollered 'witches!' once, and keeled over on to the floor amongst the dogs, and begun to groan like he was dying. Tom jerked the door open and flung out a slab of Jim's meat, and the dogs went for it, and in two seconds he was out himself and back again and shut the door, and I knowed he'd fixed the other door too. Then he went to work on the nigger, coaxing him and petting him, and asking him if he'd been imagining he saw something again. He raised up, and blinked his eyes around, and says:

'Mars Sid, you'll say I's a fool, but if I didn't b'lieve I see most a million dogs, er devils, er some'n, I wisht I may die right heah in dese tracks. I did, mos' sholy. Mars Sid, I *felt* um—I *felt* um, sah; dey was all over me. Dad fetch it, I jis' wisht I could git my han's on one er dem witches jis' wunst—on'y jis' wunst—it's all *I'd* ast. But mos'ly I wisht dey'd lemme 'lone, I does.'

Tom says:

'Well, I tell you what *I* think. What makes them come here just at this runaway nigger's breakfast-time? It's because they're hungry; that's the reason. You make them a witch pie; that's the thing for *you* to do.'

'But my lan', Mars Sid, how's *I* gwyne to make 'm a witch pie? I doan' know how to make it. I hain't ever hearn er sich a thing b'fo'.'

'Well, then, I'll have to make it myself.'

'Will you do it, honey?—will you? I'll wusshup de groun' und' yo' foot, I will!'

'All right, I'll do it, seeing it's you, and you've been good to us and showed us the runaway nigger. But you got to be mighty careful. When we come around, you turn your back; and then whatever we've put in the pan, don't you let on you see it at all. And don't you look, when Jim unloads the pan—something might happen, I don't know what. And above all, don't you *handle* the witch-things.'

'*Hannel* 'm, Mars Sid? What *is* you a-talkin' 'bout? I wouldn't lay de weight er my finger on um, not f'r ten hund'd thous'n' billion dollars, I wouldn't.'

## *Chapter 37*

THE LAST SHIRT—MOONING AROUND—'IN A TEARING WAY'—SAILING ORDERS—THE WITCH PIE

THAT was all fixed. So then we went away and went to the rubbage-pile in the back yard where they keep the old boots, and rags, and pieces of bottles, and wore-out tin things, and all such truck, and scratched around and found an old tin wash-pan and stopped up the holes as well as we could, to bake the pie in, and took it down cellar and stole it full of flour, and started for breakfast and found a couple of shingle-nails that Tom said would be handy for a prisoner to scrabble his name and sorrows on the dungeon walls with, and dropped one of them in Aunt Sally's apron pocket which was hanging on a chair, and t'other we stuck in the band of Uncle Silas's hat, which was on the bureau, because we heard the children say their pa and ma was going to the runaway nigger's house this morning, and then went to breakfast, and Tom dropped the pewter spoon in Uncle Silas's coat pocket, and Aunt Sally wasn't come yet, so we had to wait a little while.

And when she come she was hot, and red, and cross, and couldn't hardly wait for the blessing; and then she went to sluicing out coffee with one hand and cracking the handiest child's head with her thimble with the other, and says:

'I've hunted high, and I've hunted low, and it does beat all, what *has* become of your other shirt.'

My heart fell down amongst my lungs and livers and things, and a hard piece of corn-crust started down my throat after it and got met on the road with a cough and was shot across the table and took one of the children in the eye and curled him up like a fishing-worm, and let a cry out of him the size of a war-whoop, and Tom he turned kinder blue around the gills, and it all amounted to a considerable state of things for about a quarter of a minute or as much as that, and I would a sold out for half price if there was a bidder. But after that we was all right again—it was the sudden surprise of it that knocked us so kind of cold. Uncle Silas he says:

'It's most uncommon curious, I can't understand it. I know perfectly well I took it *off*, because——'

'Because you hain't got but one *on*. Just *listen* at the man! *I* know you took it off, and know it by a better way than your wool-gethering memory, too, because it was on the clo'es-line yesterday—I see it there myself. But it's gone—that's the long and the short of it, and you'll just have to change to a red flann'l one till I can get time to make a new one. And it'll be the third I've made in two years; it just keeps a body on the jump to keep you in shirts; and whatever you do manage to *do* with 'm all, is more'n *I* can make out. A body'd think you *would* learn to take some sort of care of 'em, at your time of life.'

'I know it, Sally, and I do try all I can. But it oughtn't to be altogether my fault, because you know I don't see them nor have nothing to do with them except when they're on me; and I don't believe I've ever lost one of them *off* of me.'

'Well, it ain't *your* fault if you haven't, Silas—you'd a done it if you could, I reckon. And the shirt ain't all that's gone, nuther. Ther's a spoon gone; and *that* ain't all. There was ten, and now ther's only nine. The calf got the shirt I reckon, but the calf never took the spoon, *that's* certain.'

'Why, what else is gone, Sally?'

'Ther's six *candles* gone—that's what. The rats could a got the candles, and I reckon they did; I wonder they don't walk off with the whole place, the way you're always going to stop their holes and don't do it; and if they warn't fools they'd sleep in your hair, Silas—*you'd* never find it out; but you can't lay the *spoon* on the rats, and that I *know*.'

'Well, Sally, I'm in fault, and I acknowledge it; I've been remiss; but I won't let to-morrow go by without stopping up them holes.'

'Oh I wouldn't hurry, next year'll do. Matilda Angelina Araminta *Phelps*!'

Whack comes the thimble, and the child snatches her claws out of the sugar-bowl without fooling around any. Just then, the nigger woman steps on to the passage, and says:

'Missus, dey 's a sheet gone.'

'A *sheet* gone! Well, for the land's sake!'

'I'll stop up them holes *to-day*,' says Uncle Silas, looking sorrowful.

'Oh, *do* shet up!—s'pose the rats took the *sheet*? *Where 's* it gone, Lize?'

'Clah to goodness I hain't no notion, Miss Sally. She wuz on de clo's-line yistiddy, but she done gone; she ain' dah no mo', now.'

'I reckon the world *is* coming to an end. I *never* see the beat of it, in all my born days. A shirt, and a sheet, and a spoon, and six can——'

'Missus,' comes a young yaller wench, 'dey 's a brass cannelstick miss'n.'

'Cler out from here, you hussy, er I'll take a skillet to ye!'

Well, she was just a-biling. I begun to lay for a chance; I reckoned I would sneak out and go for the woods till the weather moderated. She kept a-raging right along, running her insurrection all by herself, and everybody else mighty meek and quiet; and at last Uncle Silas, looking kind of foolish, fishes up that spoon out of his pocket. She stopped, with her mouth open and her hands up; and as for me, I wished I was in Jerusalem or somewheres. But not long; because she says:

'It's *just* as I expected. So you had it in your pocket all the time; and like as not you've got the other things there too. How'd it get there?'

'I reely don't know, Sally,' he says, kind of apologizing, 'or you know I would tell. I was a-studying over my text in Acts Seventeen, before breakfast, and I reckon I put it in there, not noticing, meaning to put my Testament in, and it must be so, because my Testament ain't in, but I'll go and see, and if the Testament is where I had it, I'll know I didn't put it in, and that will show that I laid the Testament down and took up the spoon, and——'

'Oh, for the land's sake! Give a body a rest! Go 'long now, the whole kit and biling of ye; and don't come nigh me again till I've got back my peace of mind.'

*I'd* a heard her, if she'd a said it to herself, let alone speaking it out; and I'd a got up and obeyed her, if I'd a been dead. As we was passing through the setting-room, the old man he took up his hat, and the shingle-nail fell out on the floor, and he just merely picked it up and laid it on the mantelshelf, and never said nothing, and went out. Tom see him do it, and remembered about the spoon, and says:

'Well, it ain't no use to send things by *him* no more, he ain't reliable.' Then he says: 'But he done us a good turn with the spoon, anyway, without knowing it, and so we'll go and do him one without *him* knowing it—stop up his rat-holes.'

There was a noble good lot of them, down cellar, and it took us a whole hour, but we done the job tight and good, and shipshape. Then we heard steps on the stairs, and blowed out our light, and hid; and here comes the old man, with a candle in one hand and a bundle of stuff in t'other, looking as absent-minded as year before last. He went a-mooning around, first to one rat-hole and then another, till he'd been to them all. Then he stood about five minutes, picking tallow-drip off his candle and thinking. Then he turns off slow and dreamy towards the stairs, saying:

'Well, for the life of me I can't remember when I done it. I could show her now that I warn't to blame on account of the rats. But never mind—let it go. I reckon it wouldn't do no good.'

And so he went on a-mumbling upstairs, and then we left. He was a mighty nice old man. And always is.

Tom was a good deal bothered about what to do for a spoon, but he said we'd got to have it; so he took a think. When he had ciphered it out, he told me how we was to do; then we went and waited around the spoon-basket till we see Aunt Sally coming, and then Tom went to counting the spoons and laying them out to one side, and I slid one of them up my sleeve, and Tom says:

'Why, Aunt Sally, there ain't but nine spoons, *yet*.'

She says:

'Go 'long to your play, and don't bother me. I know better, I counted 'm myself.'

'Well, I've counted them twice, Aunty, and *I* can't make but nine.'

She looked out of all patience, but of course she come to count—anybody would.

'I declare to gracious ther' *ain't* but nine!' she says. 'Why, what in the world—plague *take* the things, I'll count 'm again.'

So I slipped back the one I had, and when she got done counting, she says:

'Hang the troublesome rubbage, ther's *ten*, now!' and she looked huffy and bothered both. But Tom says:

'Why, Aunty, *I* don't think there's ten.'

'You numskull, didn't you see me *count* 'm?'

'I know, but——'

'Well, I'll count 'm *again*.'

So I smouched one, and they come out nine same as the other time. Well, she *was* in a tearing way—just a-trembling all over, she was so mad. But she counted and counted, till she got that addled she'd start to count-in the *basket* for a spoon, sometimes; and so, three times they come out right, and three times they come out wrong. Then she grabbed up the basket and slammed it across the house and knocked the cat galley-west; and she said cle'r out and let her have some peace, and if we come bothering around her again betwixt that and dinner, she'd skin us. So we had the odd spoon; and dropped it in her apron pocket whilst she was a-giving us our sailing-orders, and Jim got it all right, along with her shingle-nail, before noon. We was very well satisfied with this business, and Tom allowed it was worth twice the trouble it took, because he said *now* she couldn't ever count them spoons twice alike again to save her life; and wouldn't believe she'd counted them right, if she *did*; and said that after she'd about counted her head off, for the next three days, he judged she'd give it up and offer to kill anybody that wanted her to ever count them any more.

So we put the sheet back on the line, that night, and stole one out of her closet; and kept on putting it back and stealing it again, for a couple of days, till she didn't know how many sheets she had, any more, and said she didn't *care,* and warn't agoing to bullyrag the rest of her soul out about it, and wouldn't count them again not to save her life, she druther die first.

So we was all right now, as to the shirt and the sheet and the spoon and the candles, by the help of the calf and the rats and the mixed-up counting; and as to the candlestick, it warn't no consequence, it would blow over by-and-by.

But that pie was a job; we had no end of trouble with that pie. We fixed it up away down in the woods, and cooked it there; and we got it done at last, and very satisfactory, too; but not all in one day; and we had to use up three wash-pans full of flour, before we got through, and we got burnt pretty much all over, in places, and eyes put out with the smoke; because, you see, we didn't want nothing but a crust, and we couldn't prop it up right, and she would always cave in. But of course we thought of the right way at last; which was to cook the ladder, too, in the pie. So then we laid in with Jim, the second night, and tore up the sheet all in little strings, and twisted them together, and long before daylight we had a lovely rope, that you could a hung a person with. We let on it took nine months to make it.

And in the forenoon we took it down to the woods, but it wouldn't go in the pie. Being made of a whole sheet, that way, there was rope enough for forty pies, if we'd a wanted them, and plenty left over for soup, or sausage, or anything you choose. We could a had a whole dinner.

But we didn't need it. All we needed was just enough for the pie, and so we throwed the rest away. We didn't cook none of the pies in the wash-pan, afraid the solder would melt; but Uncle Silas he had a noble brass warming-pan which he thought considerable of, because it belonged to one of his ancestors with a long wooden handle that come over from England with William the Conqueror in the *Mayflower* or one of them early ships and was hid away up garret with a lot of other old pots and things that was valuable, not on account of being any account because they warn't, but on account of them being relicts, you know, and we snaked her out, private, and took her down there, but she failed on the first pies, because we didn't know how, but she come up smiling on the last one. We took and lined her with dough, and set her in the coals, and loaded her up with rag-rope, and put on a dough roof, and shut down the lid, and put hot embers on top, and stood off five foot, with the long handle, cool and comfortable, and in fifteen minutes she turned out a pie that was a satisfaction to look at. But the person that et it would want to fetch a couple of kags of toothpicks along, for if that rope-ladder wouldn't cramp him down to business, I don't know nothing what I'm talking about, and lay him in enough stomach-ache to last him till next time, too.

Nat didn't look, when we put the witch pie in Jim's pan; and we put the three tin plates in the bottom of the pan under the vittles; and so Jim got everything all right, and as soon as he was by himself he busted into the pie and hid the rope-ladder inside of his straw tick, and scratched some marks on a tin plate and throwed it out of the window-hole.

## *Chapter 38*

### THE COAT OF ARMS—A SKILLED SUPERINTENDENT—UNPLEASANT GLORY—A TEARFUL SUBJECT

MAKING them pens was a distressid-tough job, and so was the saw; and Jim allowed the inscription was going to be the toughest of all. That's the one which the prisoner has to scrabble on the wall. But we had to have it; Tom said we'd *got* to: there warn't no case of a State prisoner not scrabbling his inscription to leave behind, and his coat of arms.

'Look at Lady Jane Grey,' he says; 'look at Gilford Dudley; look at old Northumberland! Why, Huck, s'pose it *is* considerble trouble?—what you going to do?—how you going to get around it? Jim's *got* to do his inscription and coat of arms. They all do.'

Jim says:

'Why, Mars Tom, I hain't got no coat o' arms; I hain't got nuffn but dish-yer ole shirt, en you knows I got to keep de journal on dat.'

'Oh, you don't understand, Jim; a coat of arms is very different.'

'Well,' I says, 'Jim's right, anyway, when he says he hain't got no coat of arms, because he hain't.'

'I reckon *I* knowed that,' Tom says, 'but you bet he'll have one before he goes out of this—because he's going out *right*, and there ain't going to be no flaws in his record.'

So whilst me and Jim filed away at the pens on a brickbat apiece, Jim a-making his'n out of the brass and I making mine out of the spoon, Tom set to work to think out the coat of arms. By-and-by he said he'd struck so many good ones he didn't hardly know which to take, but there was one which he reckoned he'd decide on. He says:

'On the scutcheon we'll have a bend *or* in the dexter base, a saltire *murrey* in the fess, with a dog, couchant, for common charge, and under his foot a chain embattled, for slavery, with a chevron *vert* in a chief engrailed, and three invected lines on a field *azure*, with the nombril points rampant on a dancette indented; crest, a runaway nigger, *sable*, with his bundle over his shoulder, on a bar sinister; and a couple of gules for supporters, which is you and me; motto, *Maggiore fretta, minore atto*. Got it out of a book—means, the more haste, the less speed.'

'Geewhillikins,' I says, 'but what does the rest of it mean?'

'We ain't got no time to bother over that,' he says, 'we got to dig in like all git-out.'

'Well, anyway,' I says, 'what's *some* of it? What's a fess?'

'A fess—a fess is—*you* don't need to know what a fess is. I'll show him how to make it when he gets to it.'

'Shucks, Tom,' I says, 'I think you might tell a person. What's a bar sinister?'

'Oh, *I* don't know. But he's got to have it. All the nobility does.'

That was just his way. If it didn't suit him to explain a thing to you, he wouldn't do it. You might pump at him a week, it wouldn't make no difference.

He'd got all that coat of arms business fixed, so now he started in to finish up the rest of that part of the work, which was to plan out a mournful inscription—said Jim got to have one, like they all done. He made up a lot, and wrote them out on a paper, and read them off, so:

1. *Here a captive heart busted.*
2. *Here a poor prisoner, forsook by the world and friends, fretted out his sorrowful life.*
3. *Here a lonely heart broke, and a worn spirit went to its rest, after thirty-seven years of solitary captivity.*
4. *Here, homeless and friendless, after thirty-seven years of bitter captivity, perished a noble stranger, natural son of Louis XIV.*

Tom's voice trembled, whilst he was reading them, and he most broke down. When he got home, he couldn't no way make up his mind which one for Jim to scrabble on to the wall, they was all so good; but at last he allowed he would let him scrabble them all on. Jim said it would take him a year to scrabble such a lot of truck on to the logs with a nail, and he didn't know how to make letters, besides; but Tom said he would block them out for him, and then he wouldn't have nothing to do but just follow the lines. Then pretty soon he says:

'Come to think, the logs ain't agoing to do; they don't have log walls in a dungeon: we got to dig the inscriptions into a rock. We'll fetch a rock.'

Jim said the rock was worse than the logs; he said it would take him such a pison long time to dig them into a rock, he wouldn't ever get out. But Tom said he would let me help him do it. Then he took a look to see how me and Jim was getting along with the pens. It was most pesky tedious hard work and slow, and didn't give my hands no show to get well of the sores, and we didn't seem to make no headway, hardly. So Tom says:

'I know how to fix it. We got to have a rock for the coat of arms and mournful inscriptions, and we can kill two birds with that same rock. There's a gaudy big grindstone down at the mill, and we'll smouch it, and carve the things on it, and file out the pens and the saw on it, too.'

It warn't no slouch of an idea; and it warn't no slouch of a grindstone nuther; but we allowed we'd tackle it. It warn't quite midnight, yet, so we cleared out for the mill, leaving Jim at work. We smouched the grindstone, and set out to roll her home, but it was a most nation tough job. Sometimes, do what we could, we couldn't keep her from falling over, and she come mighty near mashing us, every time. Tom said she was going to get one of us, sure, before we got through. We got her half-way; and then we was plumb played out, and most drownded with sweat. We see it warn't no use, we got to go and fetch Jim. So he raised up his bed and slid the chain off of the bed-leg, and wrapt it round and round his neck, and we crawled out through our hole and down there, and Jim and me laid into that grindstone and walked her along like nothing; and Tom superintended. He could out-superintend any boy I ever see. He knowed how to do everything.

Our hole was pretty big, but it warn't big enough to get the grindstone through; but Jim he took the pick and soon made it big enough. Then Tom marked out them things on it with the nail, and set Jim to work on them, with the nail for a chisel and an iron bolt from the rubbage in the lean-to for a hammer, and told him to work till the rest of his candle quit on him, and then he could go to bed, and hide the grindstone under his straw tick and sleep on it. Then we helped him fix his chain back on the bed-leg, and was ready for bed ourselves. But Tom thought of something, and says:

'You got any spiders in here, Jim?'

'No, sah, thanks to goodness I hain't, Mars Tom.'

'All right, we'll get you some.'

'But bless you, honey, I doan' *want* none. I's afeard un um. I jis' 's soon have rattlesnakes aroun'.'

Tom thought a minute or two, and says:

'It's a good idea. And I reckon it's been done. It *must* a been done; it stands to reason. Yes, it's a prime good idea. Where could you keep it?'

'Keep what, Mars Tom?'

'Why, a rattlesnake.'

'De goodness gracious alive, Mars Tom! Why, if dey was a rattlesnake to come in heah, I'd take en bust right out thoo dat log wall, I would, wid my head.'

'Why, Jim, you wouldn't be afraid of it, after a little. You could tame it.'

'*Tame* it!'

'Yes—easy enough. Every animal is grateful for kindness and petting, and they wouldn't *think* of hurting a person that pets them. Any book will tell you that. You try—that's all I ask; just try for two or three days. Why, you can get him so, in a little while, that he'll love you; and sleep with you; and won't stay away from you a minute; and will let you wrap him round your neck and put his head in your mouth.'

'*Please*, Mars Tom—doan' talk so! I can't *stan'* it! He'd *let* me shove his head in my mouf—fer a favour, hain't it? I lay he'd wait a pow'ful long time 'fo' I *ast* him. En mo' en dat, I doan' *want* him to sleep wid me.'

'Jim, don't act so foolish. A prisoner's *got* to have some kind of a dumb pet, and if a rattlesnake hain't ever been tried, why, ther's more glory to be gained in your being the first to ever try it than any other way you could ever think of to save your life.'

'Why, Mars Tom, I doan' *want* no sich glory. Snake take 'n bite Jim's chin off, den *whah* is de glory? No, sah, I doan' want no sich doin's.'

'Blame it, can't you *try*? I only *want* you to try—you needn't keep it up if it don't work.'

'But de trouble all *done*, ef de snake bite me while I's a-tryin' him. Mars Tom, I's willin' to tackle mos' anything 'at ain't onreasonablc, but ef you en Huck fetches a rattlesnake in heah for me to tame, I's gwyne to *leave*, dat's *shore*.'

'Well, then, let it go, let it go, if you're so bullheaded about it. We can get you some garter-snakes and you can tie some buttons on their tails, and let on they're rattlesnakes, and I reckon that'll have to do.'

'I k'n stan' *dem*, Mars Tom, but blame' 'f I couldn' get along widout um, I tell you dat. I never knowed b'fo', 't was so much bother and trouble to be a prisoner.'

'Well, it *always* is, when it's done right. You got any rats around here?'

'No, sah, I hain't seed none.'

'Well, we'll get you some rats.'

'Why, Mars Tom, I doan' *want* no rats. Dey's de dad-blamedest creturs to 'sturb a body, en rustle roun' over 'im, en bite his feet, when he's tryin' to sleep, I ever see. No, sah, gimme g'yarter-snakes 'f I's got to have 'm, but doan' gimme no rats, I ain' got no use f'r um, skasely.'

'But Jim, you *got* to have 'em—they all do. So don't make no more fuss about it. Prisoners ain't ever without rats. There ain't no instance of it. And they train them, and pet them, and learn them tricks, and they get to be as sociable as flies. But you got to play music to them. You got anything to play music on?'

'I ain't got nuffn but a coase comb en a piece o' paper, en a juice-harp; but I reck'n dey wouldn' take no stock in a juice-harp.'

'Yes, they would. *They* don't care what kind of music 'tis. A jews-harp's plenty good enough for a rat. All animals likes music—in a prison they dote on it. Specially, painful music; and you can't get no other kind out of a jews-harp. It always interests them; they come out to see what's the matter with you. Yes, you're all right; you're fixed very well. You want to set on your bed, nights, before you go to sleep, and early in the mornings, and play your jews-harp; play The Last Link is Broken—that's the thing that'll scoop a rat, quicker'n anything else; and when you've played about two minutes, you'll see all the rats, and the snakes, and spiders, and things begin to feel worried about you, and come. And they'll just fairly swarm over you, and have a noble good time.'

'Yes, *dey* will, I reck'n, Mars Tom, but what kine er time is *Jim* havin'? Blest if I kin see de pint. But I'll do it ef I got to. I reck'n I better keep de animals satisfied, en not have no trouble in de house.'

Tom waited to think over, and see if there wasn't nothing else; and pretty soon he says:

'Oh—there's one thing I forgot. Could you raise a flower here, do you reckon?'

'I doan' know, but maybe I could, Mars Tom; but it's tolable dark in heah, en I ain' got no use f'r no flower, nohow, en she'd be a pow'ful sight o' trouble.'

'Well, you try it, anyway. Some other prisoners has done it.'

'One er dem big cat-tail-lookin' mullen-stalks would grow in heah, Mars Tom, I reck'n, but she wouldn' be wuth half de trouble she'd coss.'

'Don't you believe it. We'll fetch you a little one, and you plant it in the corner, over there, and raise it. And don't call it mullen, call it Pitchiola—that's its right name, when it's in a prison. And you want to water it with your tears.'

'Why, I got plenty spring water, Mars Tom.'

'You don't *want* spring water; you want to water it with your tears. It's the way they always do.'

'Why, Mars Tom, I lay I kin raise one er dem mullen-stalks twyste wid spring water whiles another man's a *start'n* one wid tears.'

'That ain't the idea. You *got* to do it with tears.'

'She'll die on my han's, Mars Tom, she sholy will; kase I doan' skasely ever cry.'

So Tom was stumped. But he studied it over, and then said Jim would have to worry along the best he could with an onion. He promised he would go to the nigger cabins and drop one, private, in Jim's coffee-pot, in the morning. Jim said he would 'jis' 's soon have tobacker in his coffee'; and found so much fault with it, and with the work and bother of raising the mullen, and jews-harping the rats, and petting and flattering up the snakes and spiders and things, on top of all the other work he had to do on pens, and inscriptions, and journals, and things, which made it more trouble and worry and responsibility to be a prisoner than anything he ever undertook, that Tom most lost all patience with him; and said he was just loadened down with more gaudier chances than a prisoner ever had in the world to make a name for himself, and yet he didn't know enough to appreciate them, and they was just about wasted on him. So Jim he was sorry, and said he wouldn't behave so no more, and then me and Tom shoved for bed.

## *Chapter 39*

### RATS—LIVELY BEDFELLOWS—THE STRAW DUMMY

In the morning we went up to the village and bought a wire rat-trap and fetched it down, and unstopped the best rat-hole, and in about an hour we had fifteen of the bulliest kind of ones; and then we took it and put it in a safe place under Aunt Sally's bed. But while we was gone for spiders, little Thomas Franklin Benjamin Jefferson Elexander Phelps found it there, and opened the door of it to see if the rats would come out, and they did; and Aunt Sally she come in, and when we got back she was a-standing on top of the bed raising Cain, and the rats was doing what they could to keep off the dull times for her. So she took and dusted us both with the hickry, and we was as much as two hours catching another fifteen or sixteen, drat that meddlesome cub, and they warn't the likeliest, nuther, because the first haul was the pick of the flock. I never see a likelier lot of rats than what that first haul was.

We got a splendid stock of sorted spiders, and bugs, and frogs, and caterpillars, and one thing or another; and we like to got a hornet's nest, but we didn't. The family was at home. We didn't give it right up, but staid with them as long as we could; because we allowed we'd tire them out or they'd got to tire us out, and they done it. Then we got allycumpain and rubbed on the places, and was pretty near all right again, but couldn't set down convenient. And so we went for the snakes, and grabbed a couple of dozen garters and house-snakes, and put them in a bag, and put it in our room, and by that time it was supper-time, and a rattling good honest day's work; and hungry?—oh, no, I reckon not! And there warn't a blessed snake up there, when we went back—we didn't half tie the sack, and they worked out, somehow, and left. But it didn't matter much, because they was still on the premises somewheres. So we judged we could get some of them again. No, there warn't no real scarcity of snakes about the house for a considerble spell. You'd see them dripping from the rafters and places, every now and then; and they generly landed in your plate, or down the back of your neck, and most of the time where you didn't want them. Well, they was handsome, and striped, and there warn't no harm in a million of them; but that never made no difference to Aunt Sally, she despised snakes, be the breed what they might, and she couldn't stand them no way you could fix it; and every time one of them flopped down on her, it didn't make no difference what she was doing, she would just lay that work down and light out. I never see such a woman. And you could hear her whoop to Jericho. You couldn't get her to take aholt of one of them with the tongs. And if she turned over and found one in bed, she would scramble out and lift a howl that you would think the house was afire. She disturbed the old man so, that he said he could most wish there hadn't ever been no snakes created. Why, after every last snake had been gone clear out of the house for as much as a week, Aunt Sally warn't over it yet; she warn't near over it; when she was setting thinking about something, you could touch her on the back of her neck with a feather and she would jump right out of her stockings. It was very curious. But Tom said all women was just so. He said they was made that way; for some reason or other.

We got a licking every time one of our snakes come in her way; and she allowed these lickings warn't nothing to what she would do if we ever loaded up the place again with them. I didn't mind the lickings, because they didn't amount to nothing; but I minded the trouble we had, to lay in another lot. But we got them laid in, and all the other things; and you never see a cabin as blithesome as Jim's was when they'd all swarm out for music and go for him. Jim didn't like the spiders, and the spiders didn't like Jim; and so they'd lay for him and make it mighty warm for him. And he said that between the rats, and the snakes, and the grindstone, there warn't no room in bed for him, skasely; and when there was, a body couldn't sleep, it was so lively, and it was always lively, he said, because *they* never all slept at one time, but took turn about, so when the snakes was asleep the rats was on deck, and when the rats turned in the snakes come on watch, so he always had one gang under him, in his way, and t'other gang having a circus over him, and if he got up to hunt a new place, the spiders would take a chance at him as he crossed over. He said if he ever got out, this time, he wouldn't ever be a prisoner again, not for a salary.

Well, by the end of three weeks, everything was in pretty good shape. The shirt was sent in early, in a pie, and every time a rat bit Jim he would get up and write a little in his journal whilst the ink was fresh; the pens was made, the inscriptions and so on was all carved on the grindstone; the bed-leg was sawed in two, and we had et up the sawdust, and it give us a most amazing stomach-ache. We reckoned we was all going to die, but didn't. It was the most undigestible sawdust I ever see; and Tom said the same. But as I was saying, we'd got all the work done, now, at last; and we was all pretty much fagged out, too, but mainly Jim. The old man had wrote a couple of times to the plantation below Orleans to come and get their runaway nigger, but hadn't got no answer, because there warn't no such plantation; so he allowed he would advertise Jim in the St. Louis and New Orleans papers; and when he mentioned the St. Louis ones, it give me the cold shivers, and I see we hadn't no time to lose. So Tom said, now for the nonnamous letters.

'What's them?' I says.

'Warnings to the people that something is up. Sometimes it's done one way, sometimes another. But there's always somebody spying around, that gives notice to the governor of the castle. When Louis XVI was going to light out of the Tooleries, a servant-girl done it. It's a very good way, and so is the nonnamous letters. We'll use them both. And it's usual for the prisoner's mother to change clothes with him, and she stays in, and he slides out in her clothes. We'll do that too.'

'But looky here, Tom, what do we want to *warn* anybody for, that something's up? Let them find it out for themselves—it's their look-out.'

'Yes, I know; but you can't depend on them. It's the way they've acted from the very start—left us to do *everything*. They're so confiding and mullet-headed they don't take notice of nothing at all. So if we don't *give* them notice, there won't be nobody nor nothing to interfere with us, and so after all our hard work and trouble this escape'll go off perfectly flat: won't amount to nothing—won't be nothing *to* it.'

'Well, as for me, Tom, that's the way I'd like.'

'Shucks,' he says, and looked disgusted. So I says:

'But I ain't going to make no complaint. Anyway that suits you suits me. What you going to do about the servant-girl?'

'You'll be her. You slide in, in the middle of the night, and hook that yaller girl's frock.'

'Why, Tom, that'll make trouble next morning; because, of course, she prob'bly hain't got any but that one.'

'I know; but you don't want it but fifteen minutes, to carry the nonnamous letter and shove it under the front door.'

'All right, then, I'll do it; but I could carry it just as handy in my own togs.'

'You wouldn't look like a servant-girl, *then*, would you?'

'No, but there won't be nobody to see what I look like, *anyway*.'

'That ain't got nothing to do with it. The thing for us to do, is just to do our *duty*, and not worry about whether anybody *sees* us do it or not. Hain't you got no principle at all?'

'All right, I ain't saying nothing; I'm the servant-girl. Who's Jim's mother?'

'I'm his mother. I'll hook a gown from Aunt Sally.'

'Well, then, you'll have to stay in the cabin when me and Jim leaves.'

'Not much. I'll stuff Jim's clothes full of straw and lay it on his bed to represent his mother in disguise, and Jim'll take the nigger woman's gown off of me and wear it, and we'll all evade together. When a prisoner of style escapes, it's called an evasion. It's always so called when a king escapes, f'r instance. And the same with a king's son; it don't make no difference whether he's a natural one or an unnatural one.'

So Tom he wrote the nonnamous letter, and I smouched the yaller wench's frock, that night, and put it on, and shoved it under the front door, the way Tom told me to. It said:

*Beware. Trouble is brewing. Keep a sharp look-out.*

UNKNOWN FRIEND

Next night we stuck a picture which Tom drawed in blood, of a skull and crossbones, on the front door; and next night another one of a coffin, on the back door. I never see a family in such a sweat. They couldn't a been worse scared if the place had a been full of ghosts laying for them behind everything and under the beds and shivering through the air. If a door banged, Aunt Sally she jumped, and said 'ouch!' If anything fell, she jumped, and said 'ouch!' If you happened to touch her, when she warn't noticing, she done the same; she couldn't face noway and be satisfied, because she allowed there was something behind her every time—so she was always a-whirling around, sudden, and saying 'ouch!' and before she'd get two-thirds around, she'd whirl back again, and say it again; and she was afraid to go to bed, but she dasn't set up. So the thing was working very well, Tom said; he said he never see a thing work more satisfactory. He said it showed it was done right.

So he said, now for the grand bulge! So the very next morning at the streak of dawn we got another letter ready, and was wondering what we better do with it, because we heard them say at supper they was going to have a nigger on watch at both doors all night. Tom he went down the lightning-rod to spy around; and the nigger at the back door was asleep, and he stuck it in the back of his neck and come back. This letter said:

*Don't betray me, I wish to be your friend. There is a desprate gang of cut-throats from over in the Ingean Territory going to steal your runaway nigger to-night, and they have been trying to scare you so as you will stay in the house and not bother them. I am one of the gang, but have got religgion and wish to quit it and lead a honest life again, and will betray the helish design. They will sneak down from northards, along the fence, at midnight exact, with a false key, and go in the nigger's cabin to get him. I am to be off a piece and blow a tin horn if I see any danger; but stead of that, I will* BA *like a sheep soon as they get in and not blow at all; then whilst they are getting his chains loose, you slip there and lock them in, and can kill them at your leasure. Don't do anything but just the way I am telling you, if you do they will suspicion something and raise whoopjamboreehoo. I do not wish any reward but to know I have done the right thing.*

UNKNOWN FRIEND

## *Chapter 40*

FISHING—THE VIGILANCE COMMITTEE—A LIVELY RUN—
JIM ADVISES A DOCTOR

WE was feeling pretty good, after breakfast, and took my canoe and went over the river a-fishing, with a lunch, and had a good time, and took a look at the raft and found her all right, and got home late to supper, and found them in such a sweat and worry they didn't know which end they was standing on, and made us go right off to bed the minute we was done supper, and wouldn't tell us what the trouble was, and never let on a word about the new letter, but didn't need to, because we knowed as much about it as anybody did, and as soon as we was half upstairs and her back was turned, we slid for the cellar cubboard and loaded up a good lunch and took it up to our room and went to bed, and got up about half-past eleven, and Tom put on Aunt Sally's dress that he stole and was going to start with the lunch, but says:

'Where's the butter?'

'I laid out a hunk of it,' I says, 'on a piece of a corn-pone.'

'Well, you *left* it laid out, then—it ain't here.'

'We can get along without it,' I says.

'We can get along *with* it, too,' he says; 'just you slide down cellar and fetch it. And then mosey right down the lightning-rod and come along. I'll go and stuff the straw into Jim's clothes to represent his mother in disguise, and be ready to *ba* like a sheep and shove soon as you get there.'

So out he went, and down cellar went I. The hunk of butter, big as a person's fist, was where I had left it, so I took up the slab of corn-pone with it on, and blowed out my light, and started upstairs, very stealthy, and got up to the main floor all right, but here comes Aunt Sally with a candle, and I clapped the truck in my hat, and clapped my hat on my head, and the next second she see me; and she says:

'You been down cellar?'

'Yes'm.'

'What you been doing down there?'

'Noth'n.'

'*Noth'n!*'

'No'm.'

'Well, then, what possessed you to go down there, this time of night?'

'I don't know'm.'

'You don't *know*? Don't answer me that way, Tom. I want to know what you been *doing* down there?'

'I hain't been doing a single thing, Aunt Sally, I hope to gracious if I have.'

I reckoned she'd let me go, now, and as a generl thing she would; but I s'pose there was so many strange things going on she was just in a sweat about every little thing that warn't yard-stick straight; so she says, very decided:

'You just march into that setting-room and stay there till I come. You been up to something you no business to, and I lay I'll find out what it is before *I'm* done with you.'

So she went away as I opened the door and walked into the setting-room. My, but there was a crowd there! Fifteen farmers, and every one of them had a gun. I was most powerful sick, and slunk to a chair and set down. They was setting around, some of them talking a little, in a low voice, and all of them fidgety and uneasy, but trying to look like they warn't; but I knowed they was, because they was always taking off their hats, and putting them on, and scratching their heads, and changing their seats, and fumbling with their buttons. I warn't easy myself, but I didn't take my hat off, all the same.

I did wish Aunt Sally would come, and get done with me, and lick me, if she wanted to, and let me get away and tell Tom how we'd overdone this thing, and what a thundering hornet's nest we'd got ourselves into, so we could stop fooling around, straight off, and clear out with Jim before these rips got out of patience and come for us.

At last she come, and begun to ask me questions, but I *couldn't* answer them straight, I didn't know which end of me was up; because these men was in such a fidget now, that some was wanting to start right *now* and lay for them desperadoes, and saying it warn't but a few minutes to midnight; and others was trying to get them to hold on and wait for the sheep-signal; and here was Aunty pegging away at the questions, and me a-shaking all over and ready to sink down in my tracks I was that scared; and the place getting hotter and hotter, and the butter beginning to melt and run down my neck and behind my ears; and pretty soon, when one of them says, '*I'm* for going and getting in the cabin *first*, and right *now*, and catching them when they come,' I most dropped; and a streak of butter come a-trickling down my forehead, and Aunt Sally she see it, and turns white as a sheet, and says:

'For the land's sake what *is* the matter with the child!—he's got the brain-fever as shore as you're born, and they're oozing out!'

And everybody runs to see, and she snatches off my hat, and out comes the bread, and what was left of the butter, and she grabbed me, and hugged me, and says:

'Oh, what a turn you did give me! and how glad and grateful I am it ain't no worse; for luck's against us, and it never rains but it pours, and when I see that truck I thought we'd lost you, for I knowed by the colour and all, it was just like your brains would be if—— Dear, dear, whydn't you *tell* me that was what you'd been down there for, *I* wouldn't a cared. Now cler out to bed, and don't lemme see no more of you till morning!'

I was upstairs in a second, and down the lightning-rod in another one, and shinning through the dark for the lean-to. I couldn't hardly get my words out, I was so anxious; but I told Tom as quick as I could, we must jump for it, now, and not a minute to lose—the house full of men, yonder, with guns!

His eyes just blazed; and he says:

'No!—is that so? *Ain't* it bully! Why, Huck, if it was to do over again, I bet I could fetch two hundred! If we could put it off till——'

'Hurry! *hurry*!' I says. 'Where's Jim?'

'Right at your elbow; if you reach out your arm you can touch him. He's dressed, and everything's ready. Now we'll slide out and give the sheep-signal.'

But then we heard the tramp of men, coming to the door, and heard them begin to fumble with the padlock; and heard a man say:

'I *told* you we'd be too soon; they haven't come—the door is locked. Here, I'll lock some of you into the cabin and you lay for 'em in the dark and kill 'em when they come; and the rest scatter around a piece, and listen if you can hear 'em coming.'

So in they come, but couldn't see us in the dark, and most trod on us whilst we was hustling to get under the bed. But we got under all right, and out through the hole, swift but soft—Jim first, me next, and Tom last, which was according to Tom's orders. Now we was in the lean-to, and heard trampings close by outside. So we crept to the door, and Tom stopped us there and put his eye to the crack, but couldn't make out nothing, it was so dark; and whispered and said he would listen for the steps to get further, and when he nudged us Jim must glide out first, and him last. So he set his ear to the crack and listened, and listened, and listened, and the steps a-scraping around, out there, all the time; and at last he nudged us, and we slid out, and stooped down, not breathing, and not making the least noise, and slipped stealthy towards the fence, in Injun file, and got to it, all right, and me and Jim over it; but Tom's britches catched fast on a splinter on the top rail, and then he hears the steps coming, so he had to pull loose, which snapped the splinter and made a noise; and as he dropped in our tracks and started, somebody sings out:

'Who's that? Answer, or I'll shoot!'

But we didn't answer; we just unfurled our heels and shoved. Then there was a rush, and a *bang*, *bang*, *bang*! and the bullets fairly whizzed around us! We heard them sing out:

'Here they are! They've broke for the river! After 'em, boys! And turn loose the dogs!'

So here they come, full tilt. We could hear them, because they wore boots, and yelled, but we didn't wear no boots, and didn't yell. We was in the path to the mill; and when they got pretty close on to us, we dodged into the bush and let them go by, and then dropped in behind them. They'd had all the dogs shut up, so they wouldn't scare off the robbers; but by this time somebody had let them loose, and here they come, making pow-wow enough for a million; but they was our dogs; so we stopped in our tracks till they catched up; and when they see it warn't nobody but us, and no excitement to offer them, they only just said howdy, and tore right ahead towards the shouting and clattering; and then we up steam again and whizzed along after them till we was nearly to the mill, and then struck up through the bush to where my canoe was tied, and hopped in and pulled for dear life towards the middle of the river, but didn't make no more noise than we was obleeged to. Then we struck out, easy and comfortable, for the island where my raft was; and we could hear them yelling and barking at each other all up and down the bank, till we was so far away the sounds got dim and died out. And when we stepped on to the raft, I says:

'*Now*, old Jim, you're a free man *again*, and I bet you won't ever be a slave no more.'

'En a mighty good job it wuz, too, Huck. It 'uz planned beautiful, en it 'uz *done* beautiful; en dey ain't *nobody* kin git up a plan dat's mo' mixed-up en splendid den what dat one wuz.'

We was all as glad as we could be, but Tom was the gladdest of all, because he had a bullet in the calf of his leg.

When me and Jim heard that, we didn't feel so brash as what we did before. It was hurting him considerble, and bleeding; so we laid him in the wigwam and tore up one of the duke's shirts for to bandage him, but he says:

'Gimme the rags, I can do it myself. Don't stop, now; don't fool around here, and the evasion booming along so handsome; man the sweeps, and set her loose! Boys, we done it elegant!—'deed we did. I wish *we'd* a had the handling of Louis XVI, there wouldn't a been no "Son of Saint Louis, ascend to heaven!" wrote down in *his* biography: no, sir, we'd a whooped him over the *border*—that's what we'd a done with *him*—and done it just as slick as nothing at all, too. Man the sweeps—man the sweeps!'

But me and Jim was consulting—and thinking. And after we'd thought a minute, I says:

'Say it, Jim.'

So he says:

'Well, den, dis is de way it look to me, Huck. Ef it wuz *him* dat 'uz bein' sot free, en one er de boys wuz to git shot, would he say, "Go on en save me, nemmine 'bout a doctor f'r to save dis one"? Is dat like Mars Tom Sawyer? Would he say dat? You *bet* he wouldn't! *Well*, den, is *Jim* gwyne to say it? No, sah—I doan' budge a step out'n dis place, 'dout a *doctor*; not if it's forty year!'

I knowed he was white inside, and I reckoned he'd say what he did say—so it was all right, now, and I told Tom I was agoing for a doctor. He raised considerble row about it, but me and Jim stuck to it and wouldn't budge; so he was for crawling out and setting the raft loose himself; but we wouldn't let him. Then he give us a piece of his mind—but it didn't do no good.

So when he sees me getting the canoe ready, he says:

'Well, then, if you're bound to go, I'll tell you the way to do, when you get to the village. Shut the door, and blindfold the doctor tight and fast, and make him swear to be silent as the grave, and put a purse full of gold in his hand, and then take and lead him all around the back alleys and everywheres, in the dark, and then fetch him here in the canoe, in a round-about way amongst the islands, and search him, and take his chalk away from him, and don't give it back to him till you get him back to the village, or else he will chalk this raft so he can find it again. It's the way they all do.'

So I said I would, and left, and Jim was to hide in the woods when he see the doctor coming, till he was gone again.

## *Chapter 41*

### THE DOCTOR—UNCLE SILAS—SISTER HOTCHKISS—AUNT SALLY IN TROUBLE

THE doctor was an old man; a very nice, kind-looking old man, when I got him up. I told him me and my brother was over on Spanish Island hunting, yesterday afternoon, and camped on a piece of a raft we found, and about midnight he must a kicked his gun in his dreams, for it went off and shot him in the leg, and we wanted him to go over there and fix it and not say nothing about it, nor let anybody know, because we wanted to come home this evening, and surprise the folks.

'Who is your folks?' he says.

'The Phelpses, down yonder.'

'Oh,' he says. And after a minute, he says: 'How'd you say he got shot?'

'He had a dream,' I says, 'and it shot him.'

'Singular dream,' he says.

So he lit up his lantern, and got his saddle-bags, and we started. But when he see the canoe, he didn't like the look of her—said she was big enough for one, but didn't look pretty safe for two. I says:

'Oh, you needn't be afeard, sir, she carried the three of us, easy enough.'

'What three?'

'Why, me and Sid, and—and—and *the guns*; that's what I mean.'

'Oh,' he says.

But he put his foot on the gunnel, and rocked her; and shook his head, and said he reckoned he'd look around for a bigger one. But they was all locked and chained; so he took my canoe, and said for me to wait till he come back, or I could hunt around further, or maybe I better go down home and get them ready for the surprise, if I wanted to. But I said I didn't; so I told him just how to find the raft, and then he started.

I struck an idea, pretty soon. I says to myself, spos'n he can't fix that leg just in three shakes of a sheep's tail, as the saying is? spos'n it takes him three or four days? What are we going to do?—lay around there till he lets the cat out of the bag? No, sir, I know what *I'll* do. I'll wait, and when he comes back, if he says he's got to go any more,

I'll get down there, too, if I swim; and we'll take and tie him, and keep him, and shove out down the river; and when Tom's done with him, we'll give him what it's worth, or all we got, and then let him get ashore.

So then I crept into a lumber pile to get some sleep; and next time I waked up the sun was away up over my head! I shot out and went for the doctor's house, but they told me he'd gone away in the night, some time or other, and warn't back yet. Well, thinks I, that looks powerful bad for Tom, and I'll dig out for the island, right off. So away I shoved, and turned the corner, and nearly rammed my head into Uncle Silas's stomach! He says:

'Why, *Tom*! Where you been, all this time, you rascal?'

'*I* hain't been nowheres,' I says, 'only just hunting for the runaway nigger—me and Sid.'

'Why, where ever did you go?' he says. 'Your aunt's been mighty uneasy.'

'She needn't,' I says, 'because we was all right. We followed the men and the dogs, but they outrun us, and we lost them; but we thought we heard them on the water, so we got a canoe and took out after them, and crossed over but couldn't find nothing of them; so we cruised along up-shore till we got kind of tired and beat out; and tied up the canoe and went to sleep, and never waked up till about an hour ago, then we paddled over here to hear the news, and Sid's at the post office to see what he can hear, and I'm a-branching out to get something to eat for us, and then we're going home.'

So then we went to the post office to get 'Sid'; but just as I suspicioned, he warn't there; so the old man he got a letter out of the office, and we waited a while longer but Sid didn't come; so the old man said come along, let Sid foot it home, or canoe it, when he got done fooling around—but we would ride. I couldn't get him to let me stay and wait for Sid; and he said there warn't no use in it, and I must come along, and let Aunt Sally see we was all right.

When we got home, Aunt Sally was that glad to see me she laughed and cried both, and hugged me, and give me one of them lickings of hern that don't amount to shucks, and said she'd serve Sid the same when he come.

And the place was plumb full of farmers and farmers' wives, to dinner; and such another clack a body never heard. Old Mrs. Hotchkiss was the worst; her tongue was agoing all the time. She says:

'Well, Sister Phelps, I've ransacked that-air cabin over an' I b'lieve the nigger was crazy. I says so to Sister Damrell—didn't I, Sister Damrell?—s'I, he's crazy, s'I—them's the very words I said. You all hearn me: he's crazy, s'I; everything shows it, s'I. Look at that-air grindstone, s'I; want to tell *me* 't any cretur 'ts in his right mind's agoin' to scrabble all them crazy things on to a grindstone, s'I? Here sich 'n' sich a person busted his heart; 'n' here so 'n' so pegged along for thirty-seven year, 'n' all that—natcherl son o' Louis somebody, 'n' sich everlast'n rubbage. He's plumb crazy, s'I; it's what I says in the fust place, it's what I says in the middle, 'n' it's what I says last 'n' all the time—the nigger's crazy—crazy 's Nebokoodneezer, s'I.'

'An' look at that-air ladder made out'n rags, Sister Hotchkiss,' says old Mrs. Damrell, 'what in the name o' goodness *could* he ever want of——'

'The very words I was a-sayin' no longer ago th'n this minute to Sister Utterback, 'n' she'll tell you so herself. Sh-she, look at that-air rag ladder, sh-she; 'n' s'I, yes, *look* at it, s'I—what *could* he a wanted of it, s'I? Sh-she, Sister Hotchkiss, sh-she——'

'But how in the nation'd they ever *git* that grindstone *in* there, *any*-way? 'n' who dug that-air *hole*? 'n' who——'

'My very words, Brer Penrod! I was a-sayin'—pass that-air sasser o' m'lasses, won't ye?—I was a-sayin' to Sister Dunlap, jist this minute, how *did* they git that grindstone in there, s'I. Without *help*, mind you—'thout *help*! *Thar's* wher' 'tis. Don't tell *me*, s'I; there *wuz* help, s'I; 'n' ther' wuz a *plenty* help, too, s'I; ther's ben a *dozen* a-helpin' that nigger, 'n' I lay I'd skin every last nigger on this place, but *I'd* find out who done it, s'I; 'n' moreover, s'I——'

'A *dozen* says you!—*forty* couldn't a done everything that's been done. Look at them case-knife saws and things, how tedious they've been made; look at that bed-leg sawed off with 'm, a week's work for six men; look at that nigger made out'n straw on the bed; and look at——'

'You may *well* say it, Brer Hightower! It's jist as I was a-sayin' to Brer Phelps, his own self. S'e, what do *you* think of it, Sister Hotchkiss, s'e? think o' what, Brer Phelps, s'I? think o' that bed-leg sawed off that a way, s'e? *think* of it, s'I? I lay it never sawed *itself* off, s'I—somebody *sawed* it, s'I; that's my opinion, take it or leave it, it mayn't be no 'count, s'I, but sich as 't is, it's my opinion, s'I, 'n' if anybody k'n start a better one, s'I, let him *do* it, s'I, that's all. I says to Sister Dunlap, s'I——'

'Why, dog my cats, they must a ben a house-full o' niggers in there every night for four weeks, to a done all that work, Sister Phelps. Look at that shirt—every last inch of it kivered over with secret African writ'n done with blood! Must a ben a raft uv 'm at it right along, all the time, amost. Why, I'd give two dollars to have it read to me; 'n' as for the niggers that wrote it, I 'low I'd take 'n' lash 'm t'll——'

'People to *help* him, Brother Marples! Well, I reckon you'd *think* so, if you'd a been in this house for awhile back. Why, they've stole everything they could lay their hands on—and we a-watching, all the time, mind you. They stole that shirt right off o' the line! and as for that sheet they made the rag ladder out of ther' ain't no telling how many times they *didn't* steal that; and flour, and candles, and candle-sticks, and spoons, and the old warming-pan, and most a thousand things that I disremember, now, and my new calico dress; and me, and

Silas, and my Sid and Tom on the constant watch day *and* night, as I was a-telling you, and not a one of us could catch hide nor hair, nor sight nor sound of them; and here at the last minute, lo and behold you, they slides right in under our noses, and fools us, and not only fools *us* but the Injun Territory robbers too, and actuly gets *away* with that nigger, safe and sound, and that with sixteen men and twenty-two dogs on their very heels at that very time! I tell you, it just bangs anything I ever *heard* of. Why, *sperits* couldn't a done better, and been no smarter. And I reckon they must a *been* sperits—because, *you* know our dogs, and ther' ain't no better; well, them dogs never even got on the *track* of 'm, once! You explain *that* to me, if you can!—*any* of you!'

'Well, it does beat——'

'Laws alive, I never——'

'So help me, I wouldn't a be——'

'*House*-thieves as well as——'

'Goodnessgracioussakes, I'd a ben afeard to *live* in sich a——'

' 'Fraid to *live*!—why, I was that scared I dasn't hardly go to bed, or get up, or lay down, or *set* down, Sister Ridgeway. Why, they'd steal the very—why, goodness sakes, you can guess what kind of a fluster *I* was in by the time midnight come, last night. I hope to gracious if I warn't afraid they'd steal some o' the family! I was just to that pass, I didn't have no reasoning faculties no more. It looks foolish enough, *now*, in the day-time; but I says to myself, there's my two poor boys asleep, 'way upstairs in that lonesome room, and I declare to goodness I was that uneasy 't I crep' up there and locked 'em in! I *did*. And anybody would. Because, you know, when you get scared, that way, and it keeps running on, and getting worse and worse, all the time, and your wits gets to addling, and you get to doing all sorts o' wild things, and by-and-by you think to yourself, spos'n *I* was a boy, and was away up there, and the door ain't locked, and you——' She stopped, looking kind of wondering, and then she turned her head around slow, and when her eye lit on me—I got up and took a walk.

Says I to myself, I can explain better how we come to not be in that room this morning, if I go out to one side and study over it a little. So I done it. But I dasn't go fur, or she'd a sent for me. And when it was late in the day, the people all went, and then I come in and told her the noise and shooting waked up me and 'Sid,' and the door was locked, and we wanted to see the fun, so we went down the lightning-rod, and both of us got hurt a little, and we didn't never want to try *that* no more. And then I went on and told her all what I told Uncle Silas before; and then she said she'd forgive us, and maybe it was all right enough anyway, and about what a body might expect of boys, for all boys was a pretty harumscarum lot, as fur as she could see; and so, as long as no harm hadn't come of it, she judged she better put in her time being grateful we was alive and well and she had us still, 'stead of fretting over what was past and done. So then she kissed me, and patted me on the head, and dropped into a kind of a brown study; and pretty soon jumps up, and says:

'Why, lawsamercy, it's most night, and Sid not come yet! What *has* become of that boy?'

I see my chance ; so I skips up and says:

'I'll run right up to town and get him,' I says.

'No, you won't,' she says. 'You'll stay right wher' you are; *one's* enough to be lost at a time. If he ain't here to supper, your uncle'll go.'

Well, he warn't there to supper; so right after supper uncle went.

He come back about ten, a little bit uneasy; hadn't run across Tom's track. Aunt Sally was a good *deal* uneasy; but Uncle Silas he said there warn't no occasion to be—boys will be boys, he said, and you'll see this one turn up in the morning, all sound and right. So she had to be satisfied. But she said she'd set up for him awhile, anyway, and keep a light burning, so he could see it.

And then when I went up to bed she come up with me and fetched her candle, and tucked me in, and mothered me so good I felt mean, and like I couldn't look her in the face; and she set down on the bed and talked with me a long time, and said what a splendid boy Sid was, and didn't seem to want to ever stop talking about him; and kept asking me every now and then, if I reckoned he could a got lost, or hurt, or maybe drownded, and might be laying at this minute, somewheres, suffering or dead, and she not by him to help him, and so the tears would drip down, silent, and I would tell her that Sid was all right, and would be home in the morning, sure; and she would squeeze my hand, or maybe kiss me, and tell me to say it again, and keep on saying it, because it done her good, and she was in so much trouble. And when she was going away, she looked down in my eyes, so steady and gentle, and says:

'The door ain't going to be locked, Tom; and there's the window and the rod; but you'll be good, *won't* you? And you won't go? For *my* sake.'

Laws knows I *wanted* to go, bad enough, to see about Tom, and was all intending to go; but after that, I wouldn't a went, not for kingdoms.

But she was on my mind, and Tom was on my mind; so I slept very restless. And twice I went down the rod, away in the night, and slipped around front, and see her setting there by her candle in the window with her eyes towards the road and the tears in them; and I wished I could do something for her, but I couldn't, only to swear that I wouldn't never do nothing to grieve her any more. And the third time, I waked up at dawn, and slid down, and she was there yet, and her candle was most out, and her old grey head was resting on her hand, and she was asleep.

## *Chapter 42*

TOM SAWYER WOUNDED—THE DOCTOR'S STORY—DOING JIM A GOOD TURN—TOM CONFESSES—AUNT POLLY ARRIVES —'HAND OUT THEM LETTERS'

THE old man was up town again, before breakfast, but couldn't get no track of Tom: and both of them set at the table, thinking, and not saying nothing, and looking mournful, and their coffee getting cold, and not eating anything. And by-and-by the old man says:

'Did I give you the letter?'

'What letter?'

'The one I got yesterday out of the post office.'

'No, you didn't give me no letter.'

'Well, I must a forgot it.'

So he rummaged his pockets, and then went off somewheres where he had laid it down, and fetched it, and give it to her. She says:

'Why, it's from St. Petersburg—it's from Sis.'

I allowed another walk would do me good; but I couldn't stir. But before she could break it open, she dropped it and run—for she see something. And so did I. It was Tom Sawyer on a mattress; and that old doctor; and Jim, in *her* calico dress, with his hands tied behind him; and a lot of people. I hid the letter behind the first thing that come handy, and rushed. She flung at Tom, crying, and says:

'Oh, he's dead, he's dead, I know he's dead!'

And Tom he turned his head a little, and muttered something or other, which showed he warn't in his right mind; then she flung up her hands, and says:

'He's alive, thank God! And that's enough!' and she snatched a kiss of him, and flew for the house to get the bed ready, and scattering orders right and left at the niggers and everybody else, as fast as her tongue could go, every jump of the way.

I followed the men to see what they was going to do with Jim; and the old doctor and Uncle Silas followed after Tom into the house. The men was very huffy, and some of them wanted to hang Jim, for an example to all the other niggers around there, so they wouldn't be trying to run away, like Jim done, and making such a raft of trouble, and keeping a whole family scared most to death for days and nights. But the others said, don't do it, it wouldn't answer at all, he ain't our nigger, and his owner would turn up and make us pay for him sure. So that cooled them down a little, because the people that's always the most anxious for to hang a nigger that hain't done just right, is always the very ones that ain't the most anxious to pay for him when they've got their satisfaction out of him.

They cussed Jim considerble, though, and give him a cuff or two, side the head, once in a while, but Jim never said nothing, and he never let on to know me, and they took him to the same cabin, and put his own clothes on him, and chained him again, and not to no bed-leg, this time, but to a big staple drove into the bottom log, and chained his hands, too, and both legs, and said he warn't to have nothing but bread and water to eat, after this, till his owner come or he was sold at auction, because he didn't come in a certain length of time, and filled up our hole, and said a couple of farmers with guns must stand watch around about the cabin every night, and a bull-dog tied to the door in the day-time; and about this time they was through with the job and was tapering off with a kind of generl good-bye cussing, and then the old doctor comes and takes a look, and says:

'Don't be no rougher on him than you're obleeged to, because he ain't a bad nigger. When I got to where I found the boy, I see I couldn't cut the bullet out without some help, and he warn't in no condition for me to leave, to go and get help; and he got a little worse and a little worse, and after a long time he went out of his head, and wouldn't let me come anigh him, any more, and said if I chalked his raft he'd kill me, and no end of wild foolishness like that, and I see I couldn't do anything at all with him; so I says, I got to have *help*, somehow; and the minute I says it, out crawls this nigger from somewheres, and says he'll help, and he done it, too, and done it very well. Of course I judged he must be a runaway nigger, and there I *was*! and there I had to stick, right straight along all the rest of the day, and all night. It was a fix, I tell you! I had a couple of patients with the chills, and of course I'd of liked to run up to town and see them, but I dasn't, because the nigger might get away, and then I'd be to blame; and yet never a skiff come close enough for me to hail. So there I had to stick, plum till daylight this morning; and I never see a nigger that was a better nuss or faithfuller, and yet he was resking his freedom to do it, and was all tired out, too, and I see plain enough he'd been worked main hard, lately. I liked the nigger for that; I tell you, gentlemen, a nigger like that is worth a thousand dollars—and kind treatment, too. I had everything I needed, and the boy was doing as well there as he would a done at home—better, maybe, because it was so quiet; but there I *was*, with both of 'm on my hands; and there I had to stick, till about dawn this morning; then some men in a skiff come by, and as good luck would have it, the nigger was setting by the pallet with his head propped on his knees, sound asleep; so I motioned them in, quiet, and they slipped up on him and grabbed him and tied him before he knowed what he was about, and we never had no trouble. And the boy being in a kind of a flighty sleep, too, we muffled the oars and hitched the raft on, and towed her over very nice and quiet, and the nigger never made the least row nor said a word, from the start. He ain't no bad nigger, gentlemen; that's what I think about him.'

Somebody says:

'Well, it sounds very good, doctor, I'm obleeged to say.'

Then the others softened up a little, too, and I was mighty thankful to that old doctor for doing Jim that good turn; and I was glad it was according to my judgment of him, too; because I thought he had a good heart in him and was a good man, the first time I see him. Then they all agreed that Jim had acted very well, and was deserving to have some notice took of it, and reward. So every one of them promised, right out and hearty that they wouldn't cuss him no more.

Then they come out and locked him up. I hoped they was going to say he could have one or two of the chains took off, because they was rotten heavy, or could have meat and greens with his bread and water, but they didn't think of it, and I reckoned it warn't best for me to mix in, but I judged I'd get the doctor's yarn to Aunt Sally, somehow or other, as soon as I'd got through the breakers that was laying just ahead of me. Explanations, I mean, of how I forgot to mention about Sid being shot, when I was telling how him and me put in that dratted night paddling around hunting the runaway nigger.

But I had plenty time. Aunt Sally she stuck to the sick-room all day and all night; and every time I see Uncle Silas mooning around, I dodged him.

Next morning I heard Tom was a good deal better, and they said Aunt Sally was gone to get a nap. So I slips to the sick-room, and if I found him awake I reckoned we could put up a yarn for the family that would wash. But he was sleeping, and sleeping very peaceful, too; and pale, nor fire-faced the way he was when he come. So I set down and laid for him to wake. In about a half an hour, Aunt Sally comes gliding in, and there I was, up a stump again! She motioned me to be still, and set down by me, and begun to whisper, and said we could all be joyful now, because all the symptoms was first-rate, and he'd been sleeping like that for ever so long, and looking better and peacefuller all the time, and ten to one he'd wake up in his right mind.

So we set there watching, and by-and-by he stirs a bit, and opened his eyes very natural, and takes a look, and says:

'Hello, why I'm at *home*! How's that? Where's the raft?'

'It's all right,' I says.

'And *Jim*?'

'The same,' I says, but couldn't say it pretty brash. But he never noticed, but says:

'Good! Splendid! *Now* we're all right and safe! Did you tell Aunty?'

I was going to say yes; but she chipped in and says:

'About what, Sid?'

'Why, about the way the whole thing was done.'

'What whole thing?'

'Why, *the* whole thing. There ain't but one; how we set the runaway nigger free—me and Tom.'

'Good land! Set the run—— What *is* the child talking about! Dear, dear, out of his head again!'

'*No*, I ain't out of my HEAD; I know all what I'm talking about. We *did* set him free—me and Tom. We laid out to do it, and we *done* it. And we done it elegant, too.' He'd got a start, and she never checked him up, just set and stared and stared, and let him clip along, and I see it warn't no use for *me* to put in. 'Why, Aunty, it cost us a power of work—weeks of it—hours and hours, every night, whilst you was all asleep. And we had to steal candles, and the sheet, and the shirt, and your dress, and spoons, and tin plates, and case-knives, and the warming-pan, and the grindstone, and flour, and just no end of things, and you can't think what work it was to make the saws, and pens, and inscriptions, and one thing or another, and you can't think *half* the fun it was. And we had to make up the pictures of coffins and things, and nonnamous letters from the robbers, and get up and down the lightning-rod, and dig the hole into the cabin, and make the rope-ladder and send it in cooked up in a pie, and send in spoons and things to work with, in your apron pocket——'

'Mercy sakes!'

'—and load up the cabin with rats and snakes and so on, for company for Jim; and then you kept Tom here so long with the butter in his hat that you come near spiling the whole business, because the men come before we was out of the cabin, and we had to rush, and they heard us and let drive at us, and I got my share, and we dodged out of the path and let them go by, and when the dogs come they warn't interested in us, but went for the most noise, and we got our canoe, and made for the raft, and was all safe, and Jim was a free man, and we done it all by ourselves, and *wasn't* it bully, Aunty!'

'Well, I never heard the likes of it in all my born days! So it was *you*, you little rapscallions, that's been making all this trouble, and turned everbody's wits clean inside out and scared us all most to death. I've as good a notion as ever I had in my life to take it out o' you this very minute. To think, here I've been, night after night, a—*you* just get well once, you young scamp, and I lay I'll tan the Old Harry out o' both o' ye!'

But Tom, he *was* so proud and joyful, he just *couldn't* hold in, and his tongue just *went* it—she a-chipping in, and spitting fire all along, and both of them going it at once, like a cat-convention; and she says:

'*Well*, you get all the enjoyment you can out of it *now*, for mind I tell you if I catch you meddling with him again——'

'Meddling with *who*?' Tom says, dropping his smile, and looking surprised.

'With *who*? Why, the runaway nigger, of course. Who'd you reckon?'

Tom looks at me very grave, and says:

'Tom, didn't you just tell me he was all right? Hasn't he got away?'

'*Him?*' says Aunt Sally; 'the runaway nigger? 'Deed he hasn't. They've got him back, safe and sound, and he's in that cabin again, on bread and water, and loaded down with chains, till he's claimed or sold!'

Tom rose square up in bed, with his eye hot, and his nostrils opening and shutting like gills, and sings out to me:

'They hain't no *right* to shut him up! *Shove*!—and don't you lose a minute. Turn him loose! he ain't no slave; he's as free as any cretur that walks this earth!'

'What *does* the child mean?'

'I mean every word I *say*, Aunt Sally, and if somebody don't go, *I'll* go. I've knowed him all his life, and so has Tom, there. Old Miss Watson died two months ago, and she was ashamed she ever was going to sell him down the river, and *said* so; and she set him free in her will.'

'Then what on earth did *you* want to set him free for, seeing he was already free?'

'Well, that *is* a question, I must say; and *just* like women! Why, I wanted the *adventure* of it; and I'd a waded neck-deep in blood to—goodness alive—AUNT POLLY!'

If she warn't standing right there, just inside the door, looking as sweet and contented as an angel half full of pie, I wish I may never!

Aunt Sally jumped for her, and most hugged the head off of her, and cried over her, and I found a good enough place for me under the bed, for it was getting pretty sultry for *us*, seemed to me. And I peeped out, and in a little while Tom's Aunt Polly shook herself loose and stood there looking across at Tom over her spectacles—kind of grinding him into the earth, you know. And then she says:

'Yes, you *better* turn y'r head away—I would if I was you, Tom.'

'Oh, deary me!' says Aunt Sally; '*is* he changed so? Why, that ain't *Tom*, it's Sid; Tom's—Tom's—why, where is Tom? He was here a minute ago.'

'You mean where's Huck *Finn*—that's what you mean! I reckon I hain't raised such a scamp as my Tom all these years, not to know him when I *see* him. That *would* be a pretty howdy-do. Come out from under that bed, Huck Finn.'

So I done it. But not feeling brash.

Aunt Sally she was one of the mixed-upest-looking persons I ever see; except one, and that was Uncle Silas, when he come in, and they told it all to him. It kind of made him drunk, as you may say, and he didn't know nothing at all the rest of the day, and preached a prayer-meeting sermon that night that give him a rattling ruputation, because the oldest man in the world couldn't a understood it. So Tom's Aunt Polly, she told all about who I was, and what; and I had to up and tell how I was in such a tight place that when Mrs. Phelps took me for Tom Sawyer—she chipped in and says, 'Oh, go on and call me Aunt

Sally, I'm used to it, now, and 'tain't no need to change'—that when Aunt Sally took me for Tom Sawyer, I had to stand it—there warn't no other way, and I knowed he wouldn't mind, because it would be nuts for him, being a mystery, and he'd make an adventure out of it and be perfectly satisfied. And so it turned out, and he let on to be Sid, and made things as soft as he could for me.

And his Aunt Polly she said Tom was right about old Miss Watson setting Jim free in her will; and so, sure enough, Tom Sawyer had gone and took all that trouble and bother to set a free nigger free! and I couldn't ever understand, before, until that minute and that talk, how he *could* help a body set a nigger free, with his bringing-up.

Well, Aunt Polly she said that when Aunt Sally wrote to her that Tom and *Sid* had come, all right and safe, she says to herself:

'Look at that, now! I might have expected it, letting him go off that way without anybody to watch him. So now I got to go and trapse all the way down the river, eleven hundred mile, and find out what that creetur 's up to, *this* time; as long as I couldn't seem to get any answer out of you about it.'

'Why, I never heard nothing from you,' says Aunt Sally.

'Well, I wonder! Why, I wrote to you twice, to ask you what you could mean by Sid being here.'

'Well, I never got 'em, Sis.'

Aunt Polly, she turns around slow and severe, and says:

'You, Tom!'

'Well—*what*?' he says, kind of pettish.

'Don't you what *me*, you impudent thing—hand out them letters.'

'What letters?'

'*Them* letters. I be bound, if I have to take aholt of you I'll——'

'They're in the trunk. There, now. And they're just the same as they was when I got them out of the office. I hain't looked into them, I hain't touched them. But I knowed they'd make trouble, and I thought if you warn't in no hurry, I'd——'

'Well, you *do* need skinning, there ain't no mistake about it. And I wrote another one to tell you I was coming; and I s'pose he——'

'No, it come yesterday; I hain't read it yet, but *it* 's all right, I've got that one.'

I wanted to offer to bet two dollars she hadn't, but I reckoned maybe it was just as safe to not to. So I never said nothing.

## *Chapter the Last*

### OUT OF BONDAGE—PAYING THE CAPTIVE—YOURS TRULY, HUCK FINN

THE first time I catched Tom, private, I asked him what was his idea, time of the evasion?—what it was he'd planned to do if the evasion worked all right and he managed to set a nigger free that was already free before? And he said, what he had planned in his head, from the start, if we got Jim out all safe, was for us to run him down the river, on the raft, and have adventures plumb to the mouth of the river, and then tell him about his being free, and take him back up home on a steamboat, in style, and pay him for his lost time, and write word ahead and get out all the niggers around, and have them waltz him into town with a torchlight procession and a brass band, and then he would be a hero, and so would we. But I reckoned it was about as well the way it was.

We had Jim out of the chains in no time, and when Aunt Polly and Uncle Silas and Aunt Sally found out how good he helped the doctor nurse Tom, they made a heap of fuss over him, and fixed him up prime, and give him all he wanted to eat, and a good time, and nothing to do. And we had him up to the sick-room; and had a high talk; and Tom give Jim forty dollars for being prisoner for us so patient, and doing it up so good, and Jim was pleased most to death, and busted out, and says:

'*Dah*, now, Huck, what I tell you?—what I tell you up dah on Jackson islan'? I *tole* you I got a hairy breas', en what's de sign un it; en I *tole* you I ben rich wunst, en gwineter to be rich *agin*; en it's come true, en heah she *is*! *Dah*, now! doan' talk to *me*—signs is *signs*, mine I tell you; en I knowed jis' 's well 'at I 'uz gwineter be rich agin as I 's a stannin' heah dis minute!'

And then Tom he talked along, and talked along, and says, let's all three slide out of here, one of these nights, and get an outfit, and go for howling adventures amongst the Injuns, over in the Territory, for a couple of weeks or so; and I says, all right, that suits me, but I ain't got no money for to buy the outfit, and I reckon I couldn't get none from home, because it's likely pap 's been back before now, and got it all away from Judge Thatcher and drunk it up.

'No, he hain't,' Tom says; 'it's all there, yet—six thousand dollars and more; and your pap hain't ever been back since. Hadn't when I come away, anyhow.'

Jim says, kind of solemn:

'He ain't a-comin' back no mo', Huck.'

I says:

'Why, Jim?'

'Nemmine why, Huck—but he ain't comin' back no mo'.'

But I kept at him ; so at last he says:

'Doan' you 'member de house dat was float'n down de river, en dey was a man in dah, kivered up, en I went in en unkivered him and didn' let you come in? Well, den, you k'n git yo' money when you wants it; kase dat wuz him.'

Tom 's most well, now, and got his bullet around his neck on a watch-guard for a watch, and is always seeing what time it is, and so there ain't nothing more to write about, and I am rotten glad of it, because if I'd a knowed what a trouble it was to make a book I wouldn't a tackled it and ain't agoing to no more. But I reckon I got to light out for the Territory ahead of the rest, because Aunt Sally she's going to adopt me and sivilize me, and I can't stand it. I been there before.

THE END

YOURS TRULY,

HUCK FINN

*1884*

# JEROME K. JEROME

## *The Heroine*

SHE is always in trouble—and don't she let you know it, too. Her life is undeniably a hard one. Nothing goes right with her. We all have our troubles, but the Stage heroine never has anything else. If she only got one afternoon a week off from trouble, or had her Sundays free, it would be something.

But no: misfortune stalks beside her from week's beginning to week's end.

After her husband has been found guilty of murder, which is about the least thing that can ever happen to him, and her white-haired father has become a bankrupt, and has died of a broken heart, and the home of her childhood has been sold up, then her infant goes and contracts a lingering fever.

She weeps a good deal during the course of her troubles, which, we suppose, is only natural enough, poor woman. But it is depressing from the point of view of the audience, and we almost wish, before the evening is out, that she had not got quite so much trouble.

It is over the child that she does most of her weeping. The child has a damp time of it, altogether. We sometimes wonder that it never catches rheumatism.

She is very good, is the Stage heroine. The comic man expresses a belief that she is a born angel. She reproves him for this with a tearful smile (it wouldn't be her smile if it wasn't tearful).

'Oh no,' she says (sadly of course), 'I have many, many faults.'

We rather wish that she would show them a little more. Her excessive goodness seems somehow to pall upon us. Our only consolation, while watching her, is that there are not many good women off the stage. Life is bad enough, as it is; if there were many women, in real life, as good as the Stage heroine, it would be unbearable.

The Stage heroine's only pleasure in life is to go out in a snowstorm without an umbrella, and with no bonnet on. She has a bonnet, we know (rather a tasteful little thing), we have seen it hanging up behind the door of her room; but when she comes out for a night stroll, during a heavy snowstorm (accompanied by thunder), she is most careful to leave it at home. Maybe she fears the snow will spoil it, and she is a careful girl.

She always brings her child out with her on these excursions. She seems to think that it will freshen it up. The child does not appreciate the snow so much as she does. He says it's cold.

One thing that must irritate the Stage heroine very much, on these occasions, is the way in which the snow seems to lie in wait for her, and follow her about. It is quite a fine night, before she comes on the scene: the moment she appears, it begins to snow. It snows heavily all the while she remains about, and, the instant she goes, it clears up again, and keeps dry for the rest of the evening.

The way the snow 'goes' for that poor woman is most unfair. It always snows much heavier in the particular spot where she is sitting, than it does anywhere else in the whole street. Why we have sometimes seen a heroine, sitting in the midst of a blinding snowstorm, while the other side of the road was as dry as a bone. And it never seemed to occur to her to cross over.

We have cven known a more than usually malignant snowstorm to follow a heroine three times round the stage, and then go off R. with her.

Of course, you can't get away from a snowstorm like that! A Stage snowstorm is the sort of snowstorm that would follow you upstairs, and want to come into bed with you.

Another curious thing about these Stage snowstorms is that the moon is always shining brightly throughout the whole of them. And it shines only on the heroine, and it follows her about, just like the snow does.

Nobody fully understands what a wonderful work of nature the moon is except people acquainted with the stage. Astronomy teaches you something about the moon, but you learn a good deal more from a few visits to a theatre. You will find from the latter that the moon only shines on heroes and heroines, with, perhaps, an occasional beam on the comic man: it always goes out when it sees the villain coming.

It is surprising, too, how quickly the moon *can* go out on the stage. At one moment it is riding in full radiance in the midst of a cloudless sky, and the next instant it is gone! Just as though it had been turned off at the meter. It makes you quite giddy at first, until you get used to it.

The Stage heroine is inclined to thoughtfulness rather than gaiety.

In her cheerful moments the Stage heroine thinks she sees the spirit of her mother, or the ghost of her father, or she dreams of her dead baby.

But this is only in her very merry moods. As a rule, she is too much occupied with weeping to have time for frivolous reflections.

She has a great flow of language, and a wonderful gift of metaphor and simile—more forcible than elegant—and this might be rather trying in a wife, under ordinary circumstances. But as the hero is generally sentenced to ten years' penal servitude, on his wedding morn, he escapes, for a period, from a danger that might well appal a less fortunate bridegroom.

Sometimes the Stage heroine has a brother, and, if so, he is sure to be mistaken for her lover. We never come across a brother and sister, in real life, who ever gave the most suspicious person any grounds for mistaking them for lovers; but the Stage brother and sister are so affectionate that the error is excusable.

And when the mistake does occur, and the husband comes in suddenly and finds them kissing, and raves, she doesn't turn round and say:

'Why, you silly cuckoo, it's only my brother.'

That would be simple and sensible, and would not suit the Stage heroine at all. No, she does all in her power to make everybody believe it is true, so that she can suffer in silence.

She does so love to suffer.

Marriage is undoubtedly a failure in the case of the Stage heroine.

If the Stage heroine were well advised she would remain single. Her husband means well. He is decidedly affectionate. But he is unfortunate and inexperienced in worldly affairs. Things come right for him at the end of the play, it is true; but we would not recommend the heroine to place too much reliance upon the continuance of this happy state of affairs. From what we have seen of her husband and his business capabilities, during the five acts preceding, we are inclined to doubt the possibility of his being anything but unfortunate to the end of his career.

True, he has at last got his 'rights' (which he would never have lost had he had a head instead of a sentimental bladder on his shoulders), the villain is handcuffed, and he and the heroine have settled down comfortably, next door to the comic man.

But this heavenly existence will never last. The Stage hero was built for trouble, and he will be in it again in another month, you bet. They'll get up another mortgage for him on the 'estates'; and he won't know, bless you, whether he really did sign it, or whether he didn't, and out he will go.

And he'll slop his name about to documents without ever looking to see what he's doing, and be let in for Lord knows what; and another wife will turn up for him that he had married, when a boy, and forgotten all about.

And the next corpse that comes to the village he'll get mixed up with—sure to—and have it laid to his door, and there'll be all the old business over again.

No, our advice to the Stage heroine is, to get rid of the hero, as soon as possible, marry the villain, and go and live abroad, somewhere where the comic man won't come fooling around.

She will be much happier.

*1889*

# ARTHUR CONAN DOYLE

## *Captain Hamilton Miggs of the Black Eagle*

FROM 'THE FIRM OF GIRDLESTONE'

THE head of the firm had hardly recovered his mental serenity after the painful duty of explaining her financial position to the Widow Hudson, when his quick ear caught the sound of a heavy foot-step in the counting-house. A gruff voice was audible at the same time, which demanded in rather more energetic language than was usually employed in that orderly establishment, whether the principal was to be seen or not. The answer was evidently in the affirmative, for the lumbering tread came rapidly nearer, and a powerful double knock announced that the visitor was at the other side of the door.

'Come in,' cried Mr. Girdlestone, laying down his pen.

This invitation was so far complied with that the handle turned, and the door revolved slowly upon its hinges. Nothing more substantial than a strong smell of spirituous liquors, however, entered the apart-ment.

'Come in,' the merchant repeated impatiently.

At this second mandate a great tangled mass of black hair was slowly protruded round the angle of the door. Then a copper-coloured fore-head appeared, with a couple of very shaggy eyebrows and eventually a pair of eyes, which protruded from their sockets and looked yellow and unhealthy. These took a long look, first at the senior partner and then at his surroundings, after which, as if reassured by the inspection, the remainder of the face appeared—a flat nose, a large mouth with a lower lip which hung down and exposed a line of tobacco-stained teeth, and finally a thick black beard which bristled straight out from the chin, and bore abundant traces of an egg having formed part of its owner's morning meal. The head having appeared, the body soon followed it, though all in the same anacondalike style of progression, until the individual stood revealed. He was a stoutly-built seafaring man, dressed in a pea jacket and blue trousers and holding his tarpaulin hat in his hand. With a rough scrape and a most unpleasant leer he advanced towards the merchant, a tattooed and hairy hand outstretched in sign of greeting.

'Why, captain,' said the head of the firm, rising and grasping the other's hand with effusion, 'I am glad to see you back safe and well.'

'Glad to see ye, sir—glad to see ye.'

His voice was thick and husky, and there was an indecision about his gait as though he had been drinking heavily. 'I came in sort o' cautious,' he continued, ''cause I didn't know who might be about. When you and me speaks together we likes to speak alone, you bet.'

The merchant raised his bushy eyebrows a little, as though he did not relish the idea of mutual confidences suggested by his companion's remark. 'Hadn't you better take a seat?' he said.

The other took a cane-bottomed chair and carried it into the extreme corner of the office. Then having looked steadily at the wall behind him, and rapped it with his knuckles, he sat down, still throwing an occasional apprehensive glance over his shoulder. 'I've got a touch of the jumps,' he remarked apologetically to his employer. 'I likes to *know* as there ain't no one behind me.'

'You should give up this shocking habit of drinking,' Mr. Girdlestone said seriously. 'It is a waste of the best gifts with which Providence has endowed us. You are the worse for it both in this world and in the next.'

Captain Hamilton Miggs did not seem to be at all impressed by this very sensible piece of advice. On the contrary, he chuckled boisterously to himself, and slapping his thigh, expressed his opinion that his employer was a 'rum 'un'—a conviction which he repeated to himself several times with various symptoms of admiration.

'Well, well,' Girdlestone said, after a short pause, 'boys will be boys, and sailors, I suppose, will be sailors. After eight months of anxiety and toil, ending in success, captain—I am proud to be able to say the words—some little licence must be allowed. I do not judge others by the same hard and fast lines by which I regulate my own conduct.'

This admirable sentiment also failed to elicit any response from the obdurate Miggs, except the same manifestations of mirth and the same audible aside as to the peculiarities of his master's character.

'I must congratulate you on your cargo, and wish you the same luck for your next voyage,' the merchant continued.

'Ivory, an' gold dust, an' skins, an' resin, an' cochineal, an' gums, an' ebony, an' rice, an' tobacco, an' fruits, an' nuts in bulk. If there's a better cargo about, I'd like to see it,' the sailor said defiantly.

'An excellent cargo, captain; very good indeed. Three of your men died, I believe?'

'Ay, three of the lubbers went under. Two o' fever and one o' snakebite. It licks me what sailors are comin' to in these days. When I was afore the mast we'd ha' been ashamed to die o' a trifle like that. Look at me. I've been down wi' coast fever sixteen times, and I've had yellow jack an' dysentery, an' I've been bit by the black cobra in the Andamans. I've had cholera, too. It broke out in a brig when I was in the Sandwich Island trade, and I was shipmates wi' seven dead out o' a crew o' ten. But I ain't none the worse for it—no, nor never will be. But I say, gov'nor, hain't you got a drop of something about the office.'

The senior partner rose, and taking a bottle from the cupboard filled out a stiff glass of rum. The sailor drank it off eagerly, and laid down the empty tumbler with a sigh of satisfaction.

'Say, now,' he said, with an unpleasant confidential leer, 'weren't you surprised to see us come back—eh? Straight now, between man and man?'

'The old ship hangs together well, and has lots of work in her yet,' the merchant answered.

'Lots of work! God's truth, I thought she was gone in the bay! We'd a dirty night with a gale from the west-sou'-west, an' had been goin' by dead reckonin' for three days, so we weren't over and above sure o' ourselves. She wasn't much of a sea-going craft when we left England, but the sun had dried all the pitch out o' her seams, and you might ha' put your finger through some of them. Two days an' a night we were at the pumps, for she leaked like a sieve. We lost the fore topsail, blown clean out o' the ringbolts. I never thought to see Lunnon again.'

'If she could weather a gale like that she could make another voyage.'

'She could start on another,' the sailor said gloomily, 'but as like as not she'd never see the end o't.'

'Come, come, you're not quite yourself this morning, Miggs. We value you as a dashing, fearless fellow—let me fill your glass again—who doesn't fear a little risk where there's something to be gained. You'll lose your good name if you go on like that.'

'She's in a terrible bad way,' the captain insisted. 'You'll have to do something before she can go.'

'What shall we have to do?'

'Dry dock her and give her a thorough overhaul. She might sink before she got out o' the Channel if she went as she is just now.'

'Very well,' the merchant said coldly. 'If you insist on it, it must be done. But, of course, it would make a great difference in your salary.'

'Eh?'

'You are at present getting fifteen pounds a month, and five per cent. commission. These are exceptional terms in consideration of any risk that you may run. We shall dry dock the *Black Eagle*, and your salary is now ten pounds a month and two and a half commission.'

'Belay, there, belay!' the sailor shouted. His coppery face was a shade darker than usual, and his bilious eyes had a venomous gleam in them.

'Don't you beat me down, curse you!' he hissed, advancing to the table and leaning his hands upon it while he pushed his angry face forward until it was within a foot of that of the merchant. 'Don't you try that game on, mate, for I am a freeborn British seaman, and I am under the thumb of no man.'

'You're drunk,' said the senior partner. 'Sit down!'

'You'd reduce my screw, would ye?' roared Captain Hamilton Miggs, working himself into a fury. 'Me that has worked for ye, and slaved for ye, and risked my life for ye. You try it on, guv'nor; just you try it on! Suppose I let out that little story o' the painting out o' the marks—where would the firm of Girdlestone be then! I guess you'd rather double my wage than have that yarn goin' about.'

'What do you mean?'

'What do I mean? You don't know what I mean, do you? Of course not. It wasn't you as set us on to go at night and paint out the Government Plimsoll marks and then paint 'em in again higher up, so as to be able to over-load. That wasn't you, was it?'

'Do you mean to assert that it was?'

'In course I do,' thundered the angry seaman.

The senior partner struck the gong which stood upon the table. 'Gilray,' he said quietly, 'go out and bring in a policeman.'

Captain Hamilton Miggs seemed to be somewhat startled by this sudden move of his antagonist. 'Steady your helm, governor,' he said. 'What are ye up to now?'

'I'm going to give you in charge.'

'What for?'

'For intimidation and using threatening language, and endeavouring to extort money under false pretences.'

'There's no witnesses,' the sailor said in a half-cringing, half-defiant manner.

'Oh yes, there are,' Ezra Girdlestone remarked, coming into the room. He had been standing between the two doors which led to the counting-house, and had overheard the latter portion of the conversation. 'Don't let me interrupt you. You were saying that you would blacken my father's character unless he increased your salary.'

'I didn't mean no harm' said Captain Hamilton Miggs, glancing nervously from the one to the other. He had been fairly well known to the law in his younger days, and had no desire to renew the acquaintance.

'Who painted out those Plimsoll marks?' asked the merchant.

'It was me.'

'Did any one suggest it to you?'

'No.'

'Shall I send in the policeman, sir?' asked Gilray, opening the door.

'Ask him to wait for a moment,' Girdlestone answered. 'And now, captain, to return to the original point, shall we dry dock the *Black*

*Eagle* and reduce the salary, or do you see your way to going back in her on the same terms?'

'I'll go back and be damned to it!' said the captain recklessly, plunging his hands into the pockets of his pea jacket and plumping back into his chair.

'That's right,' his grim employer remarked approvingly. 'But swearing is a most sinful practice. Send the policeman away, Ezra.'

The young man went out with an amused smile, and the two were left together again.

'You'll not be able to pass the Government inspector unless you do something to her,' the seaman said after a long pause, during which he brooded over his wrongs.

'Of course we shall do something. The firm is not mean, though it avoids unnecessary expense. We'll put a coat of paint on her, and some pitch, and do up the rigging. She's a stout old craft, and with one of the smartest sailors afloat in command of her—for we always give you credit for being that—she'll run many a voyage yet.'

'I'm paid for the risk, guv'nor, as you said just now,' the sailor remarked. 'But don't it seem kind o' hard on them as isn't—on the mates an' the hands?'

'There is always a risk, my dear captain. There is nothing in the world without risk. You remember what is said about those who go down to the sea in ships. They see the wonders of the deep, and in return they incur some little danger. My house in Eccleston Square might be shaken down by an earthquake, or a gale might blow in the walls, but I'm not always brooding over the chance of it. There's no use your taking it for granted that some misfortune will happen to the *Black Eagle*.'

The sailor was silenced, but not convinced by his employer's logic. 'Well, well,' he said, sulkily, 'I am going, so there's an end of it, and there's no good in having any more palaver about it. You have your object in running rotten ships, and you make it worth my while to take my chances in them. I'm suited, and you're suited, so there's no more to be said.'

'That's right. Have some more rum?'

'No, not a spot.'

'Why not?'

'Because I likes to keep my head pretty clear when I'm a-talkin' to you, Muster Girdlestone. Out o' your office I'll drink to further orders, but I won't do business and muddle myself at the same time. When d'ye want me to start?'

'When she's unloaded and loaded up again. Three weeks or a month yet. I expect that Spender will have come in with the *Maid of Athens* by that time.'

'Unless some accident happens on the way,' said Captain Hamilton Miggs, with his old leer. 'He was at Sierra Leone when we came up the coast. I couldn't put in there, for the swabs have got a warrant out ag'in me for putting a charge o' shot into a nigger.'

'That was a wicked action—very wrong, indeed,' the merchant said gravely. 'You must consider the interests of the firm, Miggs. We can't afford to have a good port blocked against our ships in this fashion. Did they serve this writ on you?'

'Another nigger brought it aboard.'

'Did you read it?'

'No; I threw it overboard.'

'And what became of the negro?'

'Well,' said Miggs with a grin, 'when I threw the writ overboard he happened to be holdin' on to it. So, ye see, he went over, too. Then I up anchor and scooted.'

'There are sharks about there?'

'A few.'

'Really, Miggs,' the merchant said, 'you must restrain your sinful passions. You have broken the fifth commandment, and closed the trade of Freetown to the *Black Eagle*.'

'It never was worth a rap,' the sailor answered. 'I wouldn't give a cuss for any of the British settlements. Give me real niggers, chaps as knows nothing of law or civilizing, or any rot of the sort. I can pull along with them.'

'I have often wondered how you managed it,' Girdlestone said curiously. 'You succeed in picking up a cargo where the steadiest and best men can't get as much as a bag of nuts. How do you work it?'

'There's many would like to know that,' Miggs answered, with an expressive wink.

'Is it a secret, then?'

'Well, it ain't a secret to you, 'cause you ain't a skipper, and it don't matter if you knows it or not. I don't want to have 'em all at the same game.'

'How is it, then?'

'I'll tell ye,' said Miggs. He seemed to have recovered his serenity by this time, and his eyes twinkled as he spoke of his own exploits. 'I gets drunk with them. That's how I does it.'

'Oh, indeed.'

'Yes, that's how it's worked. Lord love ye, when these fust-class certificated, second-cousin-to-an-earl-merchant skippers comes out they move about among the chiefs and talks down to them as if they was tin Methuselahs on wheels. The Almighty's great coat wouldn't make a waistcoat for some o' these blokes. Now when I gets among 'em I has 'em all into the cabin, though they're black an' naked, an' the smell ain't over an' above pleasant. Then I out with the rum and it's "help yourself an' pass the bottle." Pretty soon, d'ye see, their tongues get loosened, and as I lie low an' keep dark I gets a pretty good idea o' what's in the market. Then when I knows what's to be got, it's queer if I don't manage to get it. Besides, they like a little notice, just as Christians does, and they remembers me because I treat them well.'

'An excellent plan, Miggs—a capital plan!' said the senior partner. 'You are an invaluable servant.'

'Well,' the captain said, rising from his chair, 'I'm getting a great deal too dry with all this palaver. I don't mind gettin' drunk with nigger chiefs, but I'm darned if I'll ——' He paused, but the grim smile on his companion's face showed that he appreciated the compliment.

'I say,' he continued, giving his employer a confidential nudge with his elbow, 'suppose we'd gone down in the bay this last time, you'd ha' been a bit out in your reckoning—eh, what?'

'Why so?'

'Well, we were over-insured on our outward passage. An accident then might ha' put thousands in your pocket, I know. Coming back, though, the cargo was worth more than the insurance, I reckon. You'd ha' been out o' pocket if we'd foundered. It would ha' been a case o' the engineer hoisted on his own Peter, as Shakespeare says.'

'We take our chance of these things,' the merchant said with dignity.

'Well, good morning, guv'nor,' Captain Hamilton Miggs said brusquely. 'When you wants me you can lay your hands on me at the old crib, the Cock and Cowslip, Rotherhithe.'

As he passed out through the Office, Ezra rejoined his father.

'He's a curious chap,' he remarked, jerking his head in the direction which Miggs had taken. 'I heard him bellowing like a bull, so I thought I had best listen to what he had to say. He's a useful servant, though.'

'The fellow's half a savage himself,' his father said. 'He's in his element among them. That's why he gets on so well with them.'

'He doesn't seem much the worse for the climate, either.'

'His body does not, but his soul, Ezra, his soul! However, to return to business. I wish you to see the underwriters and pay the premium of the *Black Eagle*. If you see your way to it, increase the policy; but do it carefully, Ezra, and with tact. She will start about the time of the equinoctial gales. If anything *should* happen to her, it would be as well that the firm should have a margin on the right side.'

*1890*

# THOMAS HARDY

## *Going the Rounds*

### FROM 'UNDER THE GREENWOOD TREE'*

SHORTLY after ten o'clock, the singing-boys arrived at the tranter's house, which was invariably the place of meeting, and preparations were made for the start. The older men and musicians wore thick coats, with stiff perpendicular collars, and coloured handkerchiefs wound round and round the neck till the end came to hand, over all which they just showed their ears and noses, like people looking over a wall. The remainder, stalwart ruddy men and boys, were mainly dressed in snow-white smock-frocks, embroidered upon the shoulders and breasts in ornamental forms of hearts, diamonds, and zigzags. The cider-mug was emptied for the ninth time, the music-books were arranged and the pieces finally decided upon. The boys in the meantime put the old horn-lanterns in order, cut candles into short lengths to fit the lanterns; and a thin fleece of snow having fallen since the early part of the evening, those who had no leggings went to the stable and wound wisps of hay round their ankles to keep the insidious flakes from the interior of their boots.

Mellstock was a parish of considerable acreage, the hamlets composing it lying at a much greater distance from each other than is ordinarily the case. Hence several hours were consumed in playing and singing within hearing of every family, even if but a single air were bestowed on each. There was East Mellstock, the main village; half a mile from this were the church and the vicarage, called West Mellstock, and originally the most thickly-populated portion. A mile north-east lay the hamlet of Lewgate, where the tranter lived; and at other points knots of cottages, besides solitary farmsteads and dairies.

Old William Dewy, with the violoncello, played the bass; his grandson Dick the treble violin; and Reuben and Michael Mail the tenor and second violins respectively. The singers consisted of four men and seven boys, upon whom devolved the task of carrying and attending to the lanterns, and holding the books open for the players. Directly music was the theme, old William ever and instinctively came to the front.

'Now mind, naibours,' he said, as they all went out one by one at the door, he himself holding it ajar and regarding them with a critical face as they passed, like a shepherd counting out his sheep. 'You two counter-boys, keep your ears open to Michael's fingering, and don't

* *First published by Tinsley in 1872; taken over by Chatto & Windus in 1878 and included in their Piccadilly Library in 1891.*

you go straying into the treble part along o' Dick and his set, as ye did last year; and mind this especially when we be in 'Arise, and hail.' Billy Chimlen, don't you sing quite so raving mad as you fain would; and, all o' ye, whatever ye do, keep from making a great scuffle on the ground when we go in at people's gates; but go quietly, so as to strik' up all of a sudden, like spirits.'

'Farmer Ledlow's first?'

'Farmer Ledlow's first; the rest as usual.'

'And, Voss,' said the tranter terminatively, 'you keep house here till about half-past two; then heat the metheglin and cider in the warmer you'll find turned up upon the copper; and bring it wi' the victuals to church-porch, as th'st know.'

Just before the clock struck twelve, they lighted the lanterns and started. The moon, in her third quarter, had risen since the snow-storm; but the dense accumulation of snow-cloud weakened her power to a faint twilight, which was rather pervasive of the landscape than traceable to the sky. The breeze had gone down, and the rustle of their feet, and tones of their speech, echoed with an alert rebound from every post, boundary-stone, and ancient wall they passed, even where the distance of the echo's origin was less than a few yards. Beyond their own slight noises nothing was to be heard, save the occasional howl of foxes in the direction of Yalbury Wood, or the brush of a rabbit among the grass now and then, as it scampered out of their way.

Most of the outlying homesteads and hamlets had been visited by about two o'clock: they then passed across the Home Plantation toward the main village. Pursuing no recognised track, great care was necessary in walking lest their faces should come in contact with the low-hanging boughs of the old trees, which in many spots formed dense overgrowths of interlaced branches.

'Times have changed from the times they used to be,' said Mail, regarding nobody can tell what interesting old panoramas with an inward eye, and letting his outward glance rest on the ground, because it was as convenient a position as any. 'People don't care much about us now! I've been thinking, we must be almost the last left in the county of the old string players. Barrel-organs, and they next door to 'em that you blow wi' your foot, have come in terribly of late years.'

'Ah!' said Bowman, shaking his head; and old William, on seeing him, did the same thing.

'More's the pity,' replied another. 'Time was—long and merry ago now!—when not one of the varmints was to be heard of; but it served some of the choirs right. They should have stuck to strings as we did, and keep out clar'nets, and done away with serpents. If you'd thrive in musical religion, stick to strings, says I.'

'Strings are well enough, as far as that goes,' said Mr. Spinks.

'There's worse things than serpents,' said Mr. Penny. 'Old things pass away, 'tis true; but a serpent was a good old note: a deep rich note was the serpent.'

'Clar'nets, however, be bad at all times,' said Michael Mail. 'One Christmas—years agone now, years—I went the rounds wi' the Dib-beach choir. 'Twas a hard frosty night, and the keys of all the clar'nets froze—ah, they did freeze!—so that 'twas like drawing a cork every time a key was opened; the players o' 'em had to go into a hedger and ditcher's chimley-corner, and thaw their clar'nets every now and then. An icicle o' spet hung down from the end of every man's clar'net a span long; and as to fingers—well, there, if ye'll believe me, we had no fingers at all, to our knowledge.'

'I can well bring back to my mind,' said Mr. Penny, 'what I said to poor Joseph Ryme (who took the tribble part in High-Story Church for two-and-forty year) when they thought of having clar'nets there. "Joseph," I said, says I, "depend upon't, if so be you have them tooting clar'nets you'll spoil the whole set-out. Clar'nets were not made for the service of Providence; you can see it by looking at 'em," I said. And what came o't? Why, my dear souls, the parson set up a barrel-organ on his own account within two years o' the time I spoke, and the old choir came to nothing.'

'As far as look is concerned,' said the tranter, 'I don't for my part see that a fiddle is much nearer heaven than a clar'net. 'Tis farther off. There's always a rakins, scampish countenance about a fiddle that seems to say the Wicked One had a hand in making o' en; while angels be supposed to play clar'nets in heaven, or som'at like 'em, if ye may believe picters.'

'Robert Penny, you were in the right,' broke in the oldest Dewy. 'They should ha' stuck to strings. Your brass-man, is brass—well and good; your reed-man, is reed—well and good; your percussion-man, is percussion—good again. But I don't care who hears me say it, nothing will speak to your heart wi' the sweetness of the man of strings!'

'Strings for ever!' said little Jimmy.

'Strings alone would have held their ground against all the new-comers in creation.' ('True, true!' said Bowman.) 'But clar'nets was death.' ('Death they was!' said Mr. Penny.) 'And harmoniums,' William continued in a louder voice, and getting excited by these signs of approval, 'harmoniums and barrel-organs' ('Ah!' and groans from Spinks) 'be miserable—what shall I call 'em?—miserable—'

'Sinners,' suggested Jimmy, who made large strides like the men, and did not lag behind like the other little boys.

'Miserable machines for such a divine thing as music!'

'Right, William, and so they be!' said the choir with earnest unanimity.

By this time they were crossing to a wicket in the direction of the school, which, standing on a slight eminence on the opposite side of a cross lane, now rose in unvarying and dark flatness against the sky.

The instruments were retuned, and all the band entered the enclosure, enjoined by old William to keep upon the grass.

'Number seventy-eight,' he softly gave out as they formed round in a semicircle, the boys opening the lanterns to get a clearer light, and directing their rays on the books.

Then passed forth into the quiet night an ancient and well-worn hymn, embodying Christianity in words peculiarly befitting the simple and honest hearts of the quaint characters who sang them so earnestly.

Remember Adam's fall,
O thou man:
Remember Adam's fall
From Heaven to Hell.
Remember Adam's fall;
How he hath condemn'd all
In Hell perpetual
Therefore to dwell.

Remember God's goodnesse,
O thou man:
Remember God's goodnesse,
His promise made.
Remember God's goodnesse;
He sent his Son sinlesse
Our ails for to redress,
Our hearts to aid.

In Bethlehem he was born,
O thou man:
In Bethlehem he was born,
For mankind's sake.
In Bethlehem he was born,
Christmas-day i' the morn:
Our Saviour did not scorn
Our faults to take.

Give thanks to God alway,
O thou man:
Give thanks to God alway
With heart-felt joy.
Give thanks to God alway
On this our joyful day:
Let all men sing and say,
Holy, Holy!

Having concluded the last note, they listened for a minute or two, but found that no sound issued from the school-house.

'Forty breaths, and then, "O, what unbounded goodness!" number fifty-nine,' said William.

This was duly gone through, and no notice whatever seemed to be taken of the performance.

'Surely 'tisn't an empty house, as befell us in the year thirty-nine and forty-three!' said old Dewy, with much disappointment.

'Perhaps she's jist come from some noble city, and sneers at our doings,' the tranter whispered.

' 'Od rabbit her!' said Mr. Penny, with an annihilating look at a corner of the school chimney, 'I don't quite stomach her, if this is it. Your plain music well done is as worthy as your other sort done bad, a' b'lieve souls; so say I.'

'Forty breaths, and then the last,' said the leader authoritatively. '"Rejoice, ye tenants of the earth," number sixty-four.'

At the close, waiting yet another minute, he said in a clear loud voice, as he had said in the village at that hour and season for the previous forty years:

'A merry Christmas to ye!'

*1891*

# OUIDA

## *The Queen of Lilies*

FROM 'CHANDOS'

LADY VALENCIA ST. ALBANS stood beside one of the palms in the conservatory of her sister Lady Chesterton's house. It was the day of the Drawing-Room; she waited for her sister, with her white train carelessly caught over one arm, and a shower of lace and silk falling to the ground and trailing there in a perfumy billowy cloud. She was a picture perfect as the eye could ask or the heart could conceive in the glowing colours of the blossoms round; and a painter would have given her to his canvas as the Ordella or the Evadne of Fletcher's dramas in all their sweet and delicate grace, or, if passion could pass over those luminous, thoughtful eyes, as Vittoria Corrombona in her royal and imperious beauty.

Passion had never troubled their stillness as yet. Some touch of calamity had indeed cast a shadow on her; the pressure of improvidence and of impoverishment had sent her father to the Roman air that she had breathed so long, and his decease had left her, for an earl's daughter, almost penniless, while his title and estates had passed away to a distant heir male. Her poverty was bitter, terribly bitter, to the Queen of Lilies, daughter of the once splendid house of Ivors. She was little better than dependent on the generosity of her brother-in-law, Lord

Chesterton, and the nature in her was born for the magnificence of dominion, the consciousness of inalienable power.

She stood now under the curled, hanging leaves of the palms, their pale Eastern green contrasting, as though she had been posed there by a painter's skill, with the exquisite colouring of her own beauty, and the snowy, trailing robes that fell about her. Of that beauty she was too proud to be vain; she was simply conscious of it as an empress is conscious of the extent of the sway of her sceptre.

'We're rather early,' said her sister, a brusque, abrupt, showy woman. 'Who sent you those flowers? Clydesmore? Admirable person, very admirable; great pity he's such a bore. How well you look, Valencia! *On ne pouvait mieux*. Chandos will be at the palace, you know, this morning.'

'Are you sure?'

'Perfectly. He is everywhere. It is the most difficult thing to secure his presence at any time. He is so fastidious, too! He has sent me a most courtly note, however. I wrote to say you had just arrived from Rome, and that I would bring you with me to his ball to-night; and there is his answer. It is an immense deal from *him*!'

Lady Valencia took the white, scented paper her sister tossed to her, and a faint, gratified flush passed over the pure fairness of her face; her lips parted with a slight smile. She had heard so much of the writer—of his fame, of his conquests, of his homage to beauty, of his omnipotence in fashion.

'He is very rich, is he not?'

'Rich!' said Lady Chesterton. 'A thousand men are rich; money's made so fast in these days. Chandos is very much more than only rich. He could make us all eat acorns and drink cider, if he chose to set the fashion of it. He rules the *ton* entirely, and lives far more *en roi* than some royalties we know.'

'Yes; I heard that in Rome. Men spoke of being "friends with Chandos," as they might speak of being invited to the court.'

'Chandos gives much greater fashion than the palace ever confers. Bores and parvenus go *there*, but they never visit *him*,' responded Lady Chesterton, with an impressive accentuation almost thrilling. 'Nothing will ever make him marry, you know. He would hold it in absolute horror. The Princess Marie of Albe is terribly in love with him—almost dying, they say; very beautiful creature she is, too, and would bring a magnificent dower.'

The Lily Queen smiled slightly, her thoughtful, half-haughty smile. She knew, as though they were uttered aloud, the motives of her sister's little detour into this little sketch of sentiment.

'With so much distinction, he could be raised to the peerage any day, of course?' she inquired, half absently, drawing to her the deep purple bells of an Oriental plant. She declined to pursue the more poetic track, yet she looked a poem herself.

'Raised!' echoed her sister. 'My dear, he would call it anything but raised. The Chandos were Marquises of Clarencieux, you remember, until the title was attaindered in the Forty-Five. Philip Chandos, the premier, could have had it restored at any time, of course; but he invariably declined. Ernest Chandos is like his father; he would not accept a peerage.'

'Not a new one. But he might revive his own.'

'He might, of course; nothing would be refused to him; they would be glad to have him in the Lords. But he has often replied that, like his father, he declines it. He has some peculiar notions, you know; there has been some oath or other taken in the family, I believe, about it —great nonsense, of course—utter Quixotism. But men of genius *are* Quixotic: it never does to contradict them. They are like that mare of mine, Million: give them their head, and they will be sweet-tempered enough—take you over some very queer places sometimes, to be sure, but still tolerably even goers; but once give them a check, they rear and throw you directly. I never disagree with authors, any more than with maniacs.'

With which expression of her compassionate consideration for genius, Lady Chesterton, who was very well known across the grass-countries and with the buckhounds, shook out her violet velvets and black Spanish laces, well content with the warning she had adroitly conveyed to her sister never to disagree with the eminent leader of society, whom women idolised as they idolised Jermyn and Grammont in the splendid days of Hampton Court.

The Queen of Lilies did not answer; she stood silent, looking still at the note she held, as though the paper could tell her of its writer, while her other hand ruthlessly drew the purple bells of the flower down in a shower at her feet.

'Is he so much spoilt, then? Can he not bear contradiction?' she said at length.

'My dear, he has never tried it,' retorted her sister, with some petulance. 'Bear it! of course he would bear it: he is the first gentleman in Europe: but the woman who teased him with it would never see him again. He is so used to being followed, he would not know what it was to be opposed. He is the most graceful, the most brilliant, the most generous person in the world: at the same time he is the most difficult to please. Guess, yourself, whether a man whose ideal is *Lucrèce* is very likely to be easily enslaved. But it is time to go.'

And having cast that arrow to hit her sister's vanity or pique her pride, as it might happen, Lady Chesterton floated out of the drawing-room, followed by the Lily Queen, who laid the note down with a lingering farewell glance as she swept away. She had heard much of its writer some years past in Rome, although they had never met; and she had seen his eyes give her an eloquent mute homage the night before —eyes that it was said looked on no woman without awakening love.

'How beautiful his face is!' she thought, recalling the night just passed, and that momentary glance of one long famous to her by reputation. 'Lord Clarencieux—Marquis of Clarencieux:—it is a fine title.'

'Going to the Drawing-Room?' said Trevenna, entering one of the morning-rooms in Park Lane to take his meditated second breakfast. Chandos was taking his first, the chamber scented and shaded, and cooled with rose-water, and his attendants, Georgian and Circassian girls he had bought in the East and appointed to his household. The world had been a little scandalised at those lovely slaves; but Chandos had soon converted his friends to his own views regarding them. 'Why have men to wait on you,' he had argued, 'when you can have women—soft of foot, soft of voice, and charming to look at? To take your chocolate from James or Adolphe is no gratification at all; to take it from Leila or Zelma is a great one.' And his pretty Easterns were certainly irresistible living proofs of the force of his arguments. They were fluttering about him now with silver trays of coffee, sweetmeats, liqueurs, and fruit, dressed in their Oriental costume, and serving him with most loving obedience. A French duke and two or three Guardsmen were breakfasting with him, playing at lansquenet at noon, from which they had just risen. Men were very fond of coming to take a cup of chocolate from those charming young odalisques.

'Cards at noon, Chandos?' cried Trevenna, as he sauntered in the room, regardless alike of the presence of fashionable men who looked coldly on him, and of the charms of the Turkish attendants. 'Fie! fie! The only legitimate gaming before dinner is the sanctioned and sanctified swindling done upon 'Change.'

'Business is holier than pleasure, I suppose,' laughed Chandos. 'Business ruins a host of others; pleasure only ruins yourself: of course the world legitimates the first. How are you to-day? Yes, I am going to the Drawing-Room; I am going to see the Queen of Lilies. I will endure the crush and *ennui* of St. James's for her. Take something to eat, Trevenna?'

'All too light and too late for me. I'm a John Bull,' said Trevenna, taking a glass of curaçoa, nevertheless, with some Strasbourg *pâté*. 'Have you heard the last news of Lady Carallynne?'

'No. Gone off with poor Bodon?'

'Precisely. Went off with him from Lillingstone House last night. Never missed till just now. Carallynne's started in pursuit, swearing to shoot poor Bo dead. Dare say he will, too: 'bon sang ne peut mentir': it must break the criminal law rather than break its word.'

'Hard upon Bo,' murmured Cosmo Grenvil of the Coldstreams. 'She made such fast running on him, and a fellow can't always say no.'

'Well, the mischief's her mother's fault; she made her marry a man she hated,' said Chandos, drawing one of the bright braids of the

Circassian near him through his hand. 'Poor Car! he is quite *à l'antique*: that sort of revenge has gone out with hair-powder, highwaymen, patches, and cock-fighting.'

'Beauty of a commercial age: we can turn damaged honour and broken carriage-panels into money, nowadays,' said Trevenna. 'Carallynne's *rococo*. Liberty all, say I. If my wife runs away with a penniless hussar, why the deuce am I to make a fuss about it? I think I should be the gainer far and away.'

'*Noblesse oblige*,' said Grenvil, softly. 'Car don't like his name stained; Old-World prejudice; great bosh, of course, and Mr. Trevenna can't understand the weakness—very naturally.'

'Mr. Trevenna doesn't understand it, Lord Cosmo. Why standing up to have an ounce of lead shot into you across a handkerchief should be considered to atone to you for another man's having the amusement of making love to your property, is beyond my practical comprehension. If I were a bellicose fellow, now, I should call *you* out for that pretty speech.'

'I only go out with my equals,' yawned the handsome Guardsman, indolently turning to resume his flirtation in Turkish with a Georgian.

'Where do you ever find them—for insolence?' said Trevenna, tranquilly.

'Clearly hit, Cos,' laughed Chandos, to arrest whatever sharper words might have ensued. 'So Lady Car has gone off at last! I declare, Trevenna, you are the most industrious *chiffonnier* for collecting naughty stories that ever existed. You must come across some very dirty tatters sometimes. I do believe you know everything half an hour before it happens.'

'Scandals are like dandelion-seeds,' said Trevenna, with the brevity of an Ecclesiasticus. 'A breath scatters them to the four winds of heaven; but they are arrow-headed, and stick, where they fall, and bring forth and multiply fourfold.'

'And scandals and dandelions are both only weeds that are relished by nothing but donkeys.'

'You know nothing at all about either. You don't want scandal for your pastime, nor taraxacum for your liver; but when you are septuagenarian, dyspeptic, and bored, you'll be glad of the assistance of both.'

'My dear fellow, what unimaginable horrors you suggest! Whenever I feel the days of darkness coming, I shall gently retire from existence in a warm bath, or breathe in chloroform from a bouquet of heliotrope. The world is a very pleasant club; but, if once it gets dull, take your name off the books. Nothing easier; and your friends won't dine the worse.'

'Rather the better, if your suicide is piquant. Something to censure, flavours your curry better than all the cayenne. We never enjoy our *entremets* so thoroughly as when we murmur over it, "Very sad! terribly wrong!" Apropos of censure, even the *Hypercritic* won't censure *you*: there are three columns of superb laudation to *Lucrèce*.'

'Never read critiques, my dear Trevenna,—

> Such is our pride, our folly, or our *cru*,
> That only those who cannot write, *review*!

I am sorry to hear they praise me. I fear, after all, then, I must write very badly. Reviewers puff bad books, as ladies praise plain women.'

'To show their own superiority: very likely. However, whether you please it or not, Jim Jocelyn is so lavish of his milk and honey that the *Hypercritic* will have to atone for his weakness by chopping up novels in vinegar all the rest of the season. I am sure he will expect to dine with you at Richmond.'

'Indeed? Then he may continue to—expect it. I neither buy a Boswell with a *bouillabaisse*, nor play Maecenas by giving a *matelote*. Praise hired with a *pâté*! what a droll state of literature!'

'Not at all. Everything's bought and sold, from the dust of the cinder-heaps to the favour of Heaven—which last little trifle is bid for with all sorts of things, from a piece of plate for the rector, to a new church for St. Paul, it being considered that the Creator of the Universe is peculiarly gratified by small pepper-pots in silver, and big pepper-pots in stucco, as propitiatory and dedicatory offerings. Pooh! everybody's bribed. The only blunder ever made is in the bribe not being suited to the recipient.'

*1893*

June 17. 1879.

Dear Mr Chatto —

I return the Proofs.

I think it should be the first article in the number of the Magazine, because you have no author there of equal rank in Literature with myself.

It would illustrate well.

Wd you like an article occasionally / signed / for the Gentleman's on various topics? What price? —

Thank you for June cheque duly received.

Ever sincerely yrs

Ouida

# E. A. VIZETELLY

## *Zola on the Run**

FROM 'WITH ZOLA IN ENGLAND'

ON Tuesday, July 19, I went to London on business, and did not return to my home in the south-western suburbs until nearly seven o'clock in the evening. My wife immediately placed in my hands an envelope addressed to me in the handwriting of M. Zola. At first, having noticed neither the stamp nor the postmark, I imagined that the communication had come from Paris.

On opening the envelope, however, I found that it contained a card on which was written in French and in pencil:

'My dear confrère,—Tell nobody in the world, and particularly no newspaper, that I am in London. And oblige me by coming to see me to-morrow, Wednesday, at eleven o'clock, at Grosvenor Hotel. You will ask for M. Pascal. And above all, absolute silence, for the most serious interests are at stake.

Cordially,

'EMILE ZOLA.'

I was for a moment amazed and also somewhat affected by this message, the first addressed by M. Zola to anybody after his departure from France. Since the publication of his novel *Paris*, which had followed his first trial, I had not seen him, and we had exchanged but few letters. I had written to express my sympathy over the outcome of the proceedings at Versailles, but owing to his sudden flitting my note had failed to reach him. And now here he was in London—in exile, as, curiously enough, I myself had foretold as probable some time before in a letter to one of the newspapers.

My first impulse was to hurry to the Grosvenor immediately, but I reflected that I might not find him there, and that even if I did I might inconvenience him, as he had appointed the following day for my call. So I contented myself with telegraphing as follows: 'Pascal, Grosvenor Hotel.—Rely on me, to-morrow, eleven o'clock.' And, as a precautionary measure, I signed my telegram merely with my Christian name.

As I afterwards learnt, M. Zola had spent that day companionless, walking about the Mall and St. James's Park, and purchasing a shirt, a

* *Zola disappeared from France on 19th July 1898 after he had been sentenced in absence the previous day to twelve months' imprisonment for having libelled the military tribunal in his letter* J'ACCUSE. D. M. L.

collar, and a pair of socks at a shop in or near Buckingham Palace Road, where, knowing no English, he explained his requirements by pantomime. He had further studied several street scenes, and had given some time to wondering what purpose might be served by a certain ugly elongated building, overlooking a drive and a park. There was a sentry at the gate, but the place had such a gaunt, clumsy, and mournful aspect, that M. Zola could not possibly picture it as the London palace of her most Gracious Majesty the Queen.

However, evening found him once more in his room at the Grosvenor; and feeling tired and feverish he lay down and dozed. When he awoke between nine and ten o'clock he perceived a buff envelope on the carpet near by him. It had been thrust under the door during his sleep, and its presence greatly astonished him, for he expected neither letter nor telegram. For a moment, as he has told me, he imagined this to be some trap; wondered if he had been watched and followed to London, and almost made up his mind to leave the hotel that night. But when, after a little hesitation, he had opened the envelope and read my telegram, he realized how groundless had been his alarm.

On the morrow, when I reached the Grosvenor and inquired at the office there for M. Pascal, I was asked my name, on giving which I received a note from M. Zola saying that he unexpectedly found himself obliged to go out, but would return at 2.30 P.M. As I stood reading this note, I espied a couple of individuals scrutinizing me in what I deemed a most suspicious manner. Both were Frenchmen evidently; they wore billycock hats and carried stout sticks; and one of them, swarthy and almost brigandish of aspect, had the ribbon of the Legion of Honour in his buttonhole. It was easy to take these individuals for French detectives, and I hastily jumped to the conclusion that they were on 'M. Pascal's' track.

To make matters even more suspicious, when, after placing Zola's note in my pocket, I began to cross the vestibule, the others deliberately followed me, and in all likelihood I should have fled never to return if a well-known figure in a white billycock and grey suit had not suddenly advanced towards us from the direction of the staircase. In another moment I had exchanged greetings with M. Zola, and my suspicious scrutinisers had been introduced to me as friends. One of them was none other than M. Fernand Desmoulin. They had arrived from Paris that morning, and were about to sally forth with M. Zola in search of Mr. Fletcher Moulton, Q.C., to whom they had brought a letter of introduction from Maître Labori.

Hence the note which M. Zola had already deposited for me at the hotel office. Had I been a moment later I should have found them gone.

My arrival led to a change in the programme. It was resolved to begin matters with lunch at the hotel itself, and to postpone the quest for Mr. Fletcher Moulton until the afternoon. I made, at the time, a note of our menu. The 'bitter bread of exile' consisted on this occasion of an omelet, fried soles, fillet of beef, and potatoes. To wash down this anchoretic fare M. Desmoulin and myself ordered Sauterne and Apollinaris; but the contents of the waterbottle sufficed for M. Zola and the other gentleman.

With waiters moving to and fro, nearly always within hearing, there was little conversation at table, but we afterwards chatted in all freedom in M. Zola's room just under the roof. Ah! that room. I have already referred to the dingy aspect which it presented. Around the Grosvenor Hotel, encompassing its roof, runs a huge ornamental cornice, behind which are the windows of rooms assigned, I suppose, to luggageless visitors. From the rooms themselves there is nothing to be seen unless you throw back your head, when a tiny patch of sky above the top line of the cornice becomes visible. You are, as it were, in a gloomy well. The back of the cornice, with its plaster stained and cracked, confronts your eyes; and with a little imagination you can easily fancy yourself in a dungeon looking into some castle moat.

'*Le fossé de Vincennes*,' so M. Zola suggested, and that summed up everything. Yet it seemed to him very appropriate to his circumstances, and he absolutely refused to exchange rooms with M. Desmoulin, who was somewhat more comfortably lodged.

* * * * *

That evening, then, I called upon my friend—Mr. F. W. Wareham of Wimbledon, and Ethelburga House, Bishopsgate Street—and laid before him the legal points. I afterwards arranged to see him on the following morning in town, when I hoped to fix a meeting between him and M. Zola. My first call on Thursday, July 21, was made to the Grosvenor Hotel, where I found both the master and M. Desmoulin in a state of anxiety. M. Zola, for his part, felt altogether out of his element. After the excitement of his trial and his journey to England, and the novelty of finding himself stranded in a strange city, a kind of reaction had set in and he was extremely depressed. M. Desmoulin, on his side, having procured several morning newspapers, had explored their columns to ascertain whether the ladies by whom the master had been recognized in the street on the previous day, had by any chance noised the circumstance abroad. However, the Press was still on the Norway and Holland scents, and as yet not a paper so much as suggested M. Zola's presence in England.

'There has hardly been time,' said Desmoulin to me, 'but there will probably be something fresh this afternoon. Those actresses are certain to tell people, and we shall have to make ourselves scarce.'

I tried to cheer and tranquillise both him and M. Zola, and then arranged that Wareham should come to the hotel at 2 P.M. Meantime, said I, whatever M. Desmoulin might do, it would be as well for M. Zola to remain indoors. Several commissions were entrusted to me, and I went off, promising to return about noon.

I betook myself first to Messrs. Chatto and Windus's in St. Martin's Lane, where I arrived a few minutes before ten o'clock. Neither Mr. Chatto nor his partner, Mr. Percy Spalding, had as yet arrived, and I therefore had to wait a few minutes. When Mr. Spalding made his appearance he greeted me with a smile, and while leading the way to his private room exclaimed, 'So our friend Zola is in London!'

To describe my amazement is beyond my powers. I could only just gasp, 'How do you know that?'

'Why, my wife saw him yesterday in Buckingham Palace Road.'

I was confounded. For my part I had scarcely glanced at the ladies whom Desmoulin had conjectured to be French actresses—simply because they were young, prepossessing, and spoke French!—and certainly I should not readily have recognized Mrs. Spalding, whom I had only met once some years previously. It now seemed to me rather fortunate that she should be the person who had recognized M. Zola, since she would naturally be discreet as soon as the situation should be made clear to her.

After I had explained the position, I ascertained that the only persons besides herself who knew anything so far were her husband and the lady friend who had accompanied her on the previous day.

'I will telegraph to my wife at once,' said Mr. Spalding, 'and you may be sure that the matter will go no further. We certainly had a hearty laugh at breakfast this morning when we read in the *Telegraph* of Zola bicycling over the Swiss frontier; but, of course, as from what you tell me, the matter is serious, neither my wife nor myself will speak of it.'

'And her friend?' I exclaimed, 'she knows nothing of the necessity for secrecy, and may perhaps gossip about it.'

'She is going to Hastings to-day.'

'Hastings!' said I, 'why, M. Desmoullin, Zola's companion, does nothing but talk of going to Hastings! I am glad I know this. Hastings is barred for good, so far as Zola is concerned.'

*1899*

# ARNOLD BENNETT

## *The Elixir of Youth*

IT was Monday afternoon of Bursley Wakes—not our modern rectified festival, but the wild and naïve orgy of seventy years ago, the days of bear-baiting and of bull-baiting, from which latter phrase, they say, the town derives its name. In those times there was a town-bull, a sort of civic beast; and a certain notorious character kept a bear in his pantry. The 'beating' (baiting) occurred usually on Sunday mornings at six o'clock, with formidable hungry dogs; and little boys used to look forward eagerly to the day when they would be old enough to be permitted to attend. On Sunday afternoons colliers and potters, gathered round the jawbone of a whale which then stood as a natural curiosity on the waste space near the corn-mill, would discuss the fray, and make bets for next Sunday, while the exhausted dogs licked their wounds, or died. During the Wakes week bull and bear were baited at frequent intervals, according to popular demand, for thousands of sportsmen from neighbouring villages seized the opportunity of the fair to witness the fine beatings for which Bursley was famous throughout the country of the Five Towns. In that week the Wakes took possession of the town, which yielded itself with savage abandonment to all the frenzies of licence. The public-houses remained continuously open night and day, and the barmen and barmaids never went to bed: every inn engaged special 'talent' in order to attract custom, and for a hundred hours the whole thronged town drank, drank, until the supply of coin of George IV, converging gradually into the coffers of a few persons, ceased to circulate. Towards the end of the Wakes, by way of a last ecstasy, the cockfighters would carry their birds, which had already fought and been called off, perhaps, half a dozen times, to the town-field (where the discreet 40 per cent. brewery now stands), and there match them to a finish. It was a spacious age.

On this Monday afternoon in June the less fervid activities of the Wakes were proceeding as usual in the market-place, overshadowed by the Town Hall—not the present stone structure with its gold angel, but a brick edifice built on an ashlar basement. Hobby-horses and revolving swing-boats, propelled, with admirable economy to the proprietors, by privileged boys who took their pay in an occasional ride, competed successfully with the skeleton man, the fat or bearded woman, and Aunt Sally. The long toy-tents, artfully roofed with a tinted cloth which permitted only a soft, mellow light to illuminate the wares displayed, were crowded with jostling youth and full of the sound of whistles,' squarkers,' and various pipes; and multitudes surrounded the gingerbread, nut, and savoury stalls which lined both sides of the roadway as far as Duck Bank. In front of the numerous boxing-booths experts of the 'fancy', obviously out of condition, offered to fight all comers, and were not seldom well thrashed by impetuous champions of local fame. There were no photographic studios and no cocoanut-shies, for these things had not been thought of; and to us moderns the fair, despite its uncontrolled exuberance of revelry, would have seemed strangely quiet, since neither steam-organ nor hooter nor hurdy-gurdy was there to overwhelm the ear with crashing waves of gigantic sound. But if the special phenomena of a later day were missing from the carnival, others, as astonishing to us as the steam-organ would have been to those uncouth roisterers, were certainly present. Chief, perhaps, among these was the man who retailed the elixir of youth, the veritable *eau de jouvence*, to credulous drinkers at sixpence a bottle. This magician, whose dark mysterious face and glittering eyes indicated a strain of Romany blood, and whose accent proved that he had at any rate lived much in Yorkshire, had a small booth opposite the watch-house under the Town Hall. On a banner suspended in front of it was painted the legend:

THE INCA OF PERU'S
ELIXIR OF YOUTH
SOLD HERE.
ETERNAL YOUTH FOR ALL.
DRINK THIS AND YOU WILL NEVER GROW OLD
AS SUPPLIED TO THE NOBILITY & GENTRY
SIXPENCE PER BOT.
WALK IN, WALK IN, &
CONSULT THE INCA OF PERU

The Inca of Peru, dressed in black velveteens, with a brilliant scarf round his neck, stood at the door of his tent, holding an empty glass in one jewelled hand, and with the other twirling a long and silken moustache. Handsome, graceful, and thoroughly inured to the public gaze, he fronted a small circle of gapers like an actor adroit to make the best of himself, and his tongue wagged fast enough to wag a man's leg off. At a casual glance he might have been taken for thirty, but his age was fifty and more—if you could catch him in the morning before he had put the paint on.

'Ladies and gentlemen of Bursley, this enlightened and beautiful town which I am now visiting for the first time,' he began in a hard, metallic voice, employing again with the glib accuracy of a machine the exact phrases which he had been using all day, 'look at me—look well at me. How old do you think I am? How old do I seem? Twenty, my dear, do you say?' and he turned with practised insolence to a pot-girl in a red shawl who could not have uttered an audible word to save her soul, but who blushed and giggled with pleasure at this mark of attention. 'Ah! you flatter, fair maiden! I look more than twenty, but

I think I may say that I do not look thirty. Does any lady or gentleman think I look thirty? No! As a matter of fact, I was twenty-nine years of age when, in South America, while exploring the ruins of the most ancient civilization of the world—of the world, ladies and gentlemen—I made my wonderful discovery, the Elixir of Youth!'

'What art blethering at, Licksy?' a drunken man called from the back of the crowd, and the nickname stuck to the great discoverer during the rest of the Wakes.

'That, ladies and gentlemen,' the Inca of Peru continued unperturbed, 'was—seventy-two years ago. I am now a hundred and one years old precisely, and as fresh as a kitten, all along of my marvellous elixir. Far older, for instance, than this good dame here.'

He pointed to an aged and wrinkled woman, in blue cotton and a white mutch, who was placidly smoking a short cutty. This creature, bowed and satiate with monotonous years, took the pipe from her indrawn lips, and asked in a weary, trembling falsetto:

'How many wives hast had?'

'Seventane,' the Inca retorted quickly, dropping at once into broad dialect, 'and now lone and lookin' to wed again. Wilt have me?'

'Nay,' replied the crone. 'I've buried four mysen, and no man o' mine shall bury me.'

There was a burst of laughter, amid which the Inca, taking the crowd archly into his confidence, remarked:

'I've never administered my elixir to any of my wives, ladies and gentlemen. You may blame me, but I freely confess the fact;' and he winked.

'Licksy! Licksy!' the drunken man idiotically chanted.

'And now,' the Inca proceeded, coming at length to the practical part of his ovation, 'see here!' With the rapidity of a conjurer he whipped from his pocket a small bottle, and held it up before the increasing audience. It contained a reddish fluid, which shone bright and rich in the sunlight. 'See here!' he cried magnificently, but he was destined to interruption.

A sudden cry arose of 'Black Jack! Black Jack! 'Tis him! He's caught!' And the Inca's crowd, together with all the other crowds filling the market-place, surged off eastward in a dense, struggling mass.

The cynosure of every eye was a springless clay-cart, which was being slowly driven past the newly-erected 'big house' of Enoch Wood, Esquire, towards the Town Hall. In this cart were two constables, with their painted staves drawn, and between the constables sat a man securely chained—Black Jack of Moorthorne, the mining village which lies over the ridge a mile or so east of Bursley. The captive was a ferocious and splendid young Hercules, tall, with enormous limbs and hands and heavy black brows. He was dressed in his soiled working attire of a collier, the trousers strapped under the knees, and his feet shod in vast clogs. With open throat, small head, great jaws, and bold beady eyes, he looked what he was, the superb brute—the brute reckless of all save the instant satisfaction of his desires. He came of a family of colliers, the most debased class in a lawless district. Jack's father had been a colliery-serf, legally enslaved to his colliery, legally liable to be sold with the colliery as a chattel, and legally bound to bring up all his sons as colliers, until the Act of George III put an end to this incredible survival from the customs of the Dark Ages. Black Jack was now a hero to the crowd, and knew it, for those vast clogs had kicked a woman to death on the previous day. She was a Moorthorne woman, not his wife, but his sweetheart, older than he; people said that she nagged him, and that he was tired of her. The murderer had hidden for a night, and then, defiantly, surrendered to the watch, and the watch were taking him to the watch-house in the ashlar basement of the Town Hall. The feeble horse between the shafts of the cart moved with difficulty through the press, and often the coloured staves of the constables came down thwack on the heads of heedless youth. At length the cart reached the space between the watch-house and the tent of the Inca of Peru, where it stopped while the constables unlocked a massive door; the prisoner remained proudly in the cart, accepting, with obvious delight, the tribute of cheers and jeers, hoots and shouts, from five thousand mouths.

The Inca of Peru stood at the door of his tent and surveyed Black Jack, who was not more than a few feet away from him.

'Have a glass of my elixir,' he said to the death-dealer; 'no one in this town needs it more than thee, by all accounts. Have a glass, and live for ever. Only sixpence.'

The man in the cart laughed aloud.

'I've nowt on me—not a farden,' he answered, in a strong grating voice.

At that moment a girl, half hidden by the cart, sprang forward, offering something in her outstretched palm to the Inca; but he, misunderstanding her intention, merely glanced with passing interest at her face, and returned his gaze to the prisoner.

'I'll give thee a glass, lad,' he said quickly, 'and then thou canst defy Jack Ketch.'

The crowd yelled with excitement, and the murderer held forth his great hand for the potion. Using every art to enhance the effect of this dramatic advertisement, the Inca of Peru raised his bottle on high, and said in a loud, impressive tone:

'This precious liquid has the property, possessed by no other liquid on earth, of frothing twice. I shall pour it into the glass, and it will froth. Black Jack will drink it, and after he has drunk it will froth again. Observe!'

He uncorked the bottle and filled the glass with the reddish fluid, which after a few seconds duly effervesced, to the vague wonder of the populace. The Inca held the glass till the froth had subsided, and then solemnly gave it to Black Jack.

'Drink!' commanded the Inca.

Black Jack took the draught at a gulp, and instantly flung the glass at the Inca's face. It missed him, however. There were signs of a fracas, but the door of the watch-house swung opportunely open, and Jack was dragged from the cart and hustled within. The crowd, with a crowd's fickleness, turned to other affairs.

That evening the ingenious Inca of Peru did good trade for several hours, but towards eleven o'clock the attraction of the public-houses and of a grand special combined bull and bear beating by moonlight in the large yard of the Cock Inn drew away the circle of his customers until there was none left. He retired inside the tent with several pounds in his pocket and a god's consciousness of having made immortal many of the sons and daughters of Adam.

As he was counting out his gains on the tub of eternal youth by the flicker of a dip, someone lifted the flap of the booth and stealthily entered. He sprang up, fearing robbery with violence, which was sufficiently common during the Wakes; but it was only the young girl who had stood behind the cart when he offered to Black Jack his priceless boon. The Inca had noticed her with increasing interest several times during the evening as she loitered restless near the door of the watch-house.

'What do you want?' he asked her, with the ingratiating affability of the rake who foresees everything.

'Give me a drink.'

'A drink of what, my dear?'

'Licksy.'

He raised the dip, and by its light examined her face. It was a kind of face which carries no provocative signal for nine men out of ten, but which will haunt the tenth: a child's face with a passionate woman's eyes burning and dying in it—black hair, black eyes, thin pale cheeks, equine nostrils, red lips, small ears, and the smallest chin conceivable. He smiled at her, pleased.

'Can you pay for it?' he said pleasantly.

The girl evidently belonged to the poorest class. Her shaggy, uncovered head, lean frame, torn gown, and bare feet, all spoke of hardship and neglect.

'I've a silver groat,' she answered, and closed her small fist tighter.

'A silver groat!' he exclaimed, rather astonished. 'Where did you get that from?'

'He give it me for a-fairing yesterday.'

'Who?'

'Him yonder'—she jerked her head back to indicate the watch-house—'Black Jack.'

'What for?'

'He kissed me,' she said boldly; 'I'm his sweetheart.'

'Eh!' The Inca paused a moment, startled. 'But he killed his sweetheart yesterday.'

'What! Meg!' the girl exclaimed with deep scorn. 'Her weren't his true sweetheart. Her druv him to it. Serve her well right! Owd Meg!'

'How old are you, my dear?'

'Don't know. But feyther said last Wakes I was fourtane. I mun keep young for Jack. He wunna have me if I'm owd.'

'But he'll be hanged, they say.'

She gave a short, satisfied laugh.

'Not now he's drunk Licksy—hangman won't get him. I heard a man say Jack'd get off wi' twenty year for manslaughter, most like.'

'And you'll wait twenty years for him?'

'Yes,' she said; 'I'll meet him at prison gates. But I mun be young. Give me a drink o' Licksy.'

He drew the red draught in silence, and after it had effervesced offered it to her.

''Tis raight?' she questioned, taking the glass.

The Inca nodded, and, lifting the vessel, she opened her eager lips and became immortal. It was the first time in her life that she had drunk out of a glass, and it would be the last.

Struck dumb by the trusting joy in those profound eyes, the Inca took the empty glass from her trembling hand. Frail organism and prey of love! Passion had surprised her too young. Noon had come before the flower could open. She went out of the tent.

'Wench!' the Inca called after her, thy groat!'

She paid him and stood aimless for a second, and then started to cross the roadway. Simultaneously there was a rush and a roar from the Cock yard close by. The raging bull, dragging its ropes, and followed by a crowd of alarmed pursuers, dashed out. The girl was plain in the moonlight. Many others were abroad, but the bull seemed to see nothing but her, and, lowering his huge head, he charged with shut eyes and flung her over the Inca's booth.

'Thou's gotten thy wish: thou'rt young for ever!' the Inca of Peru, made a poet for an instant by this disaster, murmured to himself as he bent with the curious crowd over the corpse.

Black Jack was hanged.

Many years after all this Bursley built itself a new Town Hall (with a spire, and a gold angel on the top in the act of crowning the bailiwick with a gold crown), and began to think about getting up in the world.

*1905*

# CLIVE BELL

## *The Aesthetic Hypothesis*

FROM 'ART'

ABOUT music most people are as willing to be humble as I am. If they cannot grasp musical form and win from it a pure aesthetic emotion, they confess that they understand music imperfectly or not at all. They recognise quite clearly that there is a difference between the feeling of the musician for pure music and that of the cheerful concert-goer for what music suggests. The latter enjoys his own emotions, as he has every right to do, and recognises their inferiority. Unfortunately, people are apt to be less modest about their powers of appreciating visual art. Everyone is inclined to believe that out of pictures, at any rate, he can get all that there is to be got; everyone is ready to cry 'humbug' and 'impostor' at those who say that more can be had. The good faith of people who feel pure aesthetic emotions is called in queston by those who have never felt anything of the sort. It is the prevalence of the representative element, I suppose, that makes the man in the street so sure that he knows a good picture when he sees one. For I have noticed that in matters of architecture, pottery, textiles, &c., ignorance and ineptitude are more willing to defer to the opinions of those who have been blest with peculiar sensibility. It is a pity that cultivated and intelligent men and women cannot be induced to believe that a great gift of aesthetic appreciation is at least as rare in visual as in musical art. A comparison of my own experience in both has enabled me to discriminate very clearly between pure and impure appreciation. Is it too much to ask that others should be as honest about their feelings for pictures as I have been about mine for music? For I am certain that most of those who visit galleries do feel very much what I feel at concerts. They have their moments of pure ecstasy; but the moments are short and unsure. Soon they fall back into the world of human interests and feel emotions, good no doubt, but inferior. I do not dream of saying that what they get from art is bad or nugatory; I say that they do not get the best that art can give. I do not say that they cannot understand art; rather I say that they cannot understand the state of mind of those who understand it best. I do not say that art means nothing or little to them; I say they miss its full significance. I do not suggest for one moment that their appreciation of art is a thing to be ashamed of; the majority of the charming and intelligent people with whom I am acquainted appreciate visual art impurely; and, by the way, the appreciation of almost all great writers has been impure. But provided that there be some fraction of pure aesthetic emotion, even a mixed and minor appreciation of art is, I am sure, one of the most valuable things in the world—so valuable, indeed, that in my giddier moments I have been tempted to believe that art might prove the world's salvation.

Yet, though the echoes and shadows of art enrich the life of the plains, her spirit dwells on the mountains. To him who woos, but woos impurely, she returns enriched what is brought. Like the sun, she warms the good seed in good soil and causes it to bring forth good fruit. But only to the perfect lover does she give a new strange gift—a gift beyond all price. Imperfect lovers bring to art and take away the ideas and emotions of their own age and civilisation. In twelfth-century Europe a man might have been greatly moved by a Romanesque church and found nothing in a T'ang picture. To a man of a later age, Greek sculpture meant much and Mexican nothing, for only to the former could he bring a crowd of associated ideas to be the objects of familiar emotions. But the perfect lover, he who can feel the profound significance of form, is raised above the accidents of time and place. To him the problems of archaeology, history, and hagiography are impertinent. If the forms of a work are significant its provenance is irrelevant. Before the grandeur of those Sumerian figures in the Louvre he is carried on the same flood of emotion to the same aesthetic ecstasy as, more than four thousand years ago, the Chaldean lover was carried. It is the mark of great art that its appeal is universal and eternal. Significant form stands charged with the power to provoke aesthetic emotion in anyone capable of feeling it. The ideas of men go buzz and die like gnats; men change their institutions and their customs as they change their coats; the intellectual triumphs of one age are the follies of another; only great art remains stable and unobscure. Great art remains stable and unobscure because the feelings that it awakens are independent of time and place, because its kingdom is not of this world. To those who have and hold a sense of the significance of form what does it matter whether the forms that move them were created in Paris the day before yesterday or in Babylon fifty centuries ago? The forms of art are inexhaustible; but all lead by the same road of aesthetic emotion to the same world of aesthetic ecstasy.

*1914*

The Young Visiters
or Mr Salteenas plan

by Daisy Ashford

Chap 1

Quite a young girl

Mr Salteena was an elderly man of 42 and was fond of asking peaple to stay with him. He had quite a young girl staying with him of 17 named Ethel Monticue. Mr Salteena had dark short hair and mustache and wiskers which were very black and twisty. He was middle sized and he

The first page of the original MS. of Daisy Ashford's

THE YOUNG VISITERS

First published in 1919 with an Introduction by J. M. Barrie, this authentic work by a child of 9 created a sensation at the time and has been universally popular ever since.

# ANTON TCHEHOV

## *The Chorus Girl*

ONE day when she was younger and better-looking, and when her voice was stronger, Nikolay Petrovitch Kolpakov, her adorer, was sitting in the outer room in her summer villa. It was intolerably hot and stifling. Kolpakov, who had just dined and drunk a whole bottle of inferior port, felt ill-humoured and out of sorts. Both were bored and waiting for the heat of the day to be over in order to go for a walk.

All at once there was a sudden ring at the door. Kolpakov, who was sitting with his coat off, in his slippers, jumped up and looked enquiringly at Pasha.

'It must be the postman or one of the girls,' said the singer.

Kolpakov did not mind being found by the postman or Pasha's lady friends, but by way of precaution gathered up his clothes and went into the next room, while Pasha ran to open the door. To her great surprise in the doorway stood, not the postman and not a girl friend, but an unknown woman, young and beautiful, who was dressed like a lady, and from all outward signs was one.

The stranger was pale and was breathing heavily as though she had been running up a steep flight of stairs.

'What is it?' asked Pasha.

The lady did not at once answer. She took a step forward, slowly looked about the room, and sat down in a way that suggested that from fatigue, or perhaps illness, she could not stand; then for a long time her pale lips quivered as she tried in vain to speak.

'Is my husband here?' she asked at last, raising to Pasha her big eyes with their red tear-stained lids.

'Husband?' whispered Pasha, and was suddenly so frightened that her hands and feet turned cold. 'What husband?' she repeated, beginning to tremble.

'My husband . . . Nikolay Petrovitch Kolpakov.'

'N . . . no, madam. . . . I . . . I don't know any husband.'

A minute passed in silence. The stranger several times passed her handkerchief over her pale lips and held her breath to stop her inward trembling, while Pasha stood before her motionless, like a post, and looked at her with astonishment and terror.

'So you say he is not here?' the lady asked, this time speaking with a firm voice and smiling oddly.

'I . . . I don't know who it is you are asking about.'

'You are horrid, mean, vile . . .' the stranger muttered, scanning

Pasha with hatred and repulsion. 'Yes, yes . . . you are horrid. I am very, very glad that at last I can tell you so!'

Pasha felt that on this lady in black with the angry eyes and white slender fingers she produced the impression of something horrid and unseemly, and she felt ashamed of her chubby red cheeks, the pock-mark on her nose, and the fringe on her forehead, which never could be combed back. And it seemed to her that if she had been thin, and had had no powder on her face and no fringe on her forehead, then she could have disguised the fact that she was not 'respectable', and she would not have felt so frightened and ashamed to stand facing this unknown, mysterious lady.

'Where is my husband?' the lady went on. 'Though I don't care whether he is here or not, but I ought to tell you that the money has been missed, and they are looking for Nikolay Petrovitch. . . . They mean to arrest him. That's your doing!'

The lady got up and walked about the room in great excitement. Pasha looked at her and was so frightened that she could not understand.

'He'll be found and arrested to-day,' said the lady, and she gave a sob, and in that sound could be heard her resentment and vexation. 'I know who has brought him to this awful position! Low, horrid creature! Loathsome, mercenary hussy!' The lady's lips worked and her nose wrinkled up with disgust. 'I am helpless, do you hear, you low woman? . . . I am helpless; you are stronger than I am, but there is One to defend me and my children! God sees all! He is just! He will punish you for every tear I have shed, for all my sleepless nights! The time will come; you will think of me . . .!'

Silence followed again. The lady walked about the room and wrung her hands, while Pasha still gazed blankly at her in amazement, not understanding and expecting something terrible.

'I know nothing about it, madam,' she said, and suddenly burst into tears.

'You are lying!' cried the lady, and her eyes flashed angrily at her. 'I know all about it! I've known you a long time. I know that for the last month he has been spending every day with you!'

'Yes. What then? What of it? I have a great many visitors, but I don't force anyone to come. He is free to do as he likes.'

'I tell you they have discovered that money is missing! He has embezzled money at the office! For the sake of such a . . . creature as you, for your sake he has actually committed a crime. Listen,' said the lady in a resolute voice, stopping short, facing Pasha. 'You can have no principles; you live simply to do harm—that's your object; but one can't imagine you have fallen so low that you have no trace of human feeling left! He has a wife, children. . . . If he is condemned and sent into exile we shall starve, the children and I. . . . Understand that! And yet there is a chance of saving him and us from destitution and disgrace. If I take them nine hundred roubles to-day they will let him alone. Only nine hundred roubles!'

'What nine hundred roubles?' Pasha asked softly. 'I . . . I don't know. . . . I haven't taken it.'

'I am not asking you for nine hundred roubles. . . . You have no money, and I don't want your money. I ask you for something else. . . . Men usually give expensive things to women like you. Only give me back the things my husband has given you!'

'Madam, he has never made me a present of anything!' Pasha wailed, beginning to understand.

'Where is the money? He has squandered his own and mine and other people's. . . . What has become of it all? Listen, I beg you! I was carried away by indignation and said a lot of nasty things to you, but I apologize. You must hate me, I know, but if you are capable of sympathy, put yourself in my position! I implore you to give me back the things!'

'H'm!' said Pasha, and she shrugged her shoulders. 'I would with pleasure, but, God is my witness, he never made me a present of anything. Believe me, on my conscience. However, you are right, though,' said the singer in confusion, 'he did bring me two little things. Certainly I will give them back, if you wish it.'

Pasha pulled out one of the drawers in the toilet-table and took out of it a hollow gold bracelet and a thin ring with a ruby in it.

'Here, madam!' she said, handing the visitor these articles.

The lady flushed and her face quivered. She was offended.

'What are you giving me?' she said. 'I am not asking for charity, but for what does not belong to you . . . what you have taken advantage of your position to squeeze out of my husband . . . that weak, unhappy man. . . . On Thursday, when I saw you with my husband at the harbour you were wearing expensive brooches and bracelets. So it's no use your playing the innocent lamb to me! I ask you for the last time: will you give me the things, or not?'

'You are a queer one, upon my word,' said Pasha, beginning to feel offended. 'I assure you that, except the bracelet and this little ring, I've never seen a thing from your Nikolay Petrovitch. He brings me nothing but sweet cakes.'

'Sweet cakes!' laughed the stranger. 'At home the children have nothing to eat, and here you have sweet cakes. You absolutely refuse to restore the presents?'

Receiving no answer, the lady sat down and stared into space, pondering.

'What's to be done now?' she said. 'If I don't get nine hundred roubles, he is ruined, and the children and I are ruined, too. Shall I kill this low woman or go down on my knees to her?'

The lady pressed her handkerchief to her face and broke into sobs.

'I beg you!' Pasha heard through the stranger's sobs. 'You see you have plundered and ruined my husband. Save him. . . . You have no feeling for him, but the children . . . the children. . . . What have the children done?'

Pasha imagined little children standing in the street, crying with hunger, and she, too, sobbed.

'What can I do, madam?' she said. 'You say that I am a low woman and that I have ruined Nikolay Petrovitch, and I assure you . . . before God Almighty, I have had nothing from him whatever. . . . There is only one girl in our chorus who has a rich admirer; all the rest of us live from hand to mouth on bread and kvass. Nikolay Petrovitch is a highly educated, refined gentleman, so I've made him welcome. We are bound to make gentlemen welcome.'

'I ask you for the things! Give me the things! I am crying. . . . I am humiliating myself. . . . If you like I will go down on my knees! If you wish it!'

Pasha shrieked with horror and waved her hands. She felt that this pale, beautiful lady who expressed herself so grandly, as though she were on the stage, really might go down on her knees to her, simply from pride, from grandeur, to exalt herself and humiliate the chorus girl.

'Very well, I will give you things!' said Pasha, wiping her eyes and bustling about. 'By all means. Only they are not from Nikolay Petrovitch. . . . I got these from other gentlemen. As you please. . . .'

Pasha pulled out the upper drawer of the chest, took out a diamond brooch, a coral necklace, some rings and bracelets, and gave them all to the lady.

'Take them if you like, only I've never had anything from your husband. Take them and grow rich,' Pasha went on, offended at the threat to go down on her knees. 'And if you are a lady . . . his lawful wife, you should keep him to yourself. I should think so! I did not ask him to come; he came of himself.'

Through her tears the lady scrutinized the articles given her and said:

'This isn't everything. . . . There won't be five hundred roubles' worth here.'

Pasha impulsively flung out of the chest a gold watch, a cigar-case and studs, and said, flinging up her hands:

'I've nothing else left. . . . You can search!'

The visitor gave a sigh, with trembling hands twisted the things up in her handkerchief, and went out without uttering a word, without even nodding her head.

The door from the next room opened and Kolpakov walked in. He was pale and kept shaking his head nervously, as though he had swallowed something very bitter; tears were glistening in his eyes.

'What presents did you make me?' Pasha asked, pouncing upon him. 'When did you allow me to ask you?'

'Presents . . . that's no matter!' said Kolpakov, and he tossed his head. 'My God! She cried before you, she humbled herself. . . .'

'I am asking you, what presents did you make me?' Pasha cried.

'My God! She, a lady, so proud, so pure. . . . She was ready to go down on her knees to . . . to this wench! And I've brought her to this! I've allowed it!'

He clutched his head in his hands and moaned.

'No, I shall never forgive myself for this! I shall never forgive myself! Get away from me . . . you low creature!' he cried with repulsion, backing away from Pasha, and thrusting her off with trembling hands. 'She would have gone down on her knees, and . . . and to you! Oh, my God!'

He rapidly dressed, and pushing Pasha aside contemptuously, made for the door and went out.

Pasha lay down and began wailing aloud. She was already regretting her things which she had given away so impulsively, and her feelings were hurt. She remembered how three years ago a merchant had beaten her for no sort of reason, and she wailed more loudly than ever.

*1920*

# ROBERT NICHOLS

## *The Flower of Flame*

I LOVE a flower which has no lover,
  The yellow sea-poppy is its name;
Spined leaves its glaucous green stem cover,
  Its flower is a yellow fitful flame.

Stung by the spray which leaps the shingle,
  Torn by the winds that scour the beach,
Its roots with the salt sea-wrack mingle,
  Its leaves upon the bleached stones bleach.

Its desperate growth but few remember,
  None misses it when it has died—
Scorched by the sun to a scant ember
  Or wholly ravaged by the tide.

Yet I elect this weed to cherish,
  Nor any other would desire
Than this, which must so shortly perish
  Tortured by sea-foam or sky-fire.

Above this flower we two once bended,
  Drawn to it by a subtle spell,
On whom the fire of heaven descended,
  Over whom the wave arose from hell.

Frantic, she snatched the ragged blossom,
  Kissed it then with a wild, fierce kiss,
Pressed spine and flame into her bosom,
  Crying, 'The flower! our love is this!'

The grey waves crash. The wind whirls over.
  The flower is withered from the beach,
Whose waves divide the loved and lover,
  Whose wind blows louder than their speech.

*1920*

## ROGER FRY

### *Art and Life*

WHEN we look at ancient works of art we habitually treat them not merely as objects of æsthetic enjoyment but also as successive deposits of the human imagination. It is indeed this view of works of art as crystallised history that accounts for much of the interest felt in ancient art by those who have but little æsthetic feeling and who find nothing to interest them in the work of their contemporaries, where the historical motive is lacking, and they are left face to face with bare æsthetic values.

I once knew an old gentleman who had retired from his city office to a country house—a fussy, feeble little being, who had cut no great figure in life. He had built himself a house which was preternaturally hideous; his taste was deplorable and his manners indifferent; but he had a dream, the dream of himself as an exquisite and refined intellectual dandy living in a society of elegant frivolity. To realise this dream he had spent large sums in buying up every scrap of eighteenth-century French furniture which he could lay hands on. These he stored in an immense upper floor in his house, which was always locked except when he went up to indulge in his dream and to become for a time a courtier at Versailles doing homage to the du Barry, whose toilet-tables and whatnots were strewn pell-mell about the room without order or effect of any kind. Such is an extreme instance of the historical way of looking at works of art. For this old gentleman, as for how many an American millionaire, art was merely a help to an imagined dream life.

To many people then it seems an easy thing to pass thus directly from the work of art to the life of the time which produced it. We all in fact weave an imagined Middle Ages around the parish church and an imagined Renaissance haunts us in the college courts of Oxford and Cambridge. We don't, I fancy, stop to consider very closely how true the imagined life is: we are satisfied with the prospect of another sort of life which we might have lived, which we often think we might have preferred to our actual life. We don't stop to consider much how far the pictured past corresponds to any reality, certainly not to consider what proportion of the whole reality of the past life gets itself embalmed in this way in works of art. Thus we picture our Middle Ages as almost entirely occupied with religion and war, our Renaissance as occupied in learning, and our eighteenth century as occupied in gallantry and wit. Whereas, as a matter of fact, all of these things were going on all the time while the art of each period has for some reason been mainly taken up with the expression of one or another activity. There is indeed a certain danger in accepting too naïvely the general atmosphere —the ethos, which the works of art of a period exhale. Thus when we look at the thirteenth-century sculpture of Chartres or Beauvais we feel at once the expression of a peculiar gracious piety, a smiling and gay devoutness which we are tempted to take for the prevailing mood of the time—and which we perhaps associate with the revelation of just such a type of character in S. Francis of Assisi. A study of Salimbeni's chronicle with its interminable record of squalid avarice and meanness, or of the fierce brutalities of Dante's Inferno is a necessary corrective of such a pleasant dream.

It would seem then that the correspondence between art and life which we so habitually assume is not at all constant and requires much correction before it can be trusted. Let us approach the same question from another point and see what result we obtain. Let us consider the great revolutions in art and the revolutions in life and see if they coincide. And here let me try to say what I mean by life as contrasted with art. I mean the general intellectual and instinctive reaction to their surroundings of those men of any period whose lives rise to complete self-consciousness. Their view of the universe as a whole and their conception of their relations to their kind. Of course their conception of the nature and function of art will itself be one of the most varying aspects of life and may in any particular period profoundly modify the correspondence of art to life.

Perhaps the greatest revolution in life that we know of at all intimately was that which effected the change from Paganism to Christianity. That this was no mere accident is evident from the fact that Christianity was only one of many competing religions, all of which represented a closely similar direction of thought and feeling. Any one of these would have produced practically the same effect, that of focussing men's minds on the spiritual life as opposed to the material life which had preoccupied them for so long. One cannot doubt then that here was a change which denoted a long prepared and inevitable readjustment of men's attitude to their universe. Now the art of the Roman Empire showed no trace whatever of this influence; it went on with precisely the same motives and principles which had satisfied Paganism. The subjects changed and became mainly Christian, but the treatment was so exactly similar that it requires more than a cursory glance to say if the figure on a sarcophagus is Christ or Orpheus, Moses or Aesculapius.

The next great turning-point in history is that which marks the triumph of the forces of reaction towards the close of the twelfth century—a reaction which destroyed the promising hopes of freedom of thought and manners which make the twelfth century appear as a foretaste of modern enlightenment. Here undoubtedly the change in life corresponds very closely with a great change in art—the change from the Romanesque to the Gothic, and at first sight we might suppose a causal connection between the two. But when we consider the nature of the changes in the two sequences, this becomes very doubtful. For whereas in the life of the Middle Ages the change was one of reaction—the sharp repression by the reactionary forces of a gradual growth of freedom—the change in art is merely the efflorescence of certain long prepared and anticipated effects. The forms of Gothic architecture were merely the answer to certain engineering problems which had long occupied the inventive ingenuity of twelfth-century architects, while in the figurative arts the change merely showed a new self-confidence in the rendering of the human figure, a newly developed mastery in the handling of material. In short, the change in art was in the opposite direction to that in life. Whereas in life the direction of movement was sharply bent backwards, in art the direction followed on in a continuous straight line.

It is true that in one small particular the reaction did have a direct effect on art. The preaching of S. Bernard of Clairvaux did impose on the architects who worked for the Cistercian order a peculiar architectural hypocrisy. They were bound by his traditional influence to make their churches have an appearance of extreme simplicity and austerity, but they wanted nevertheless to make them as magnificent and imposing as possible. The result was a peculiar style of ostentatious simplicity. Paray le Monial is the only church left standing in which this curious and, in point of fact, depressing evidence of the direct influence of the religious reaction on art is to be seen, and, as a curiosity in psychological expression, it is well worth a visit. For the rest the movement of art went on entirely unaffected by the new orientation of thought.

We come now to the Renaissance, and here for the first time in our survey we may, I think, safely admit a true correspondence between the change in life and the change in art. The change in life, if one may generalise on such a vast subject, was towards the recognition of the rights of the individual, towards complete self-realisation and the recognition of the objective reality of the material universe which implied the whole scientific attitude—and in both these things the exemplar which men put before themselves was the civilisation of Greece and Rome. In art the change went *pari passu* with the change in life, each assisting and directing the other—the first men of science were artists like Brunelleschi, Ucello, Piero della Francesca and Leonardo da Vinci. The study of classical literature was followed in strict connection with the study of classical canons of art, and the greater sense of individual importance found its expression in the new naturalism which made portraiture in the modern sense possible.

For once then art and the other functions of the human spirit found themselves in perfect harmony and direct alliance, and to that harmony we may attribute much of the intensity and self-assurance of the work of the great Renaissance artists. It is one of the rarest of good fortunes for an artist to find himself actually understood and appreciated by the mass of his educated contemporaries, and not only that, but moving alongside of and in step with them towards a similar goal.

The Catholic reaction retarded and impeded the main movement of Renaissance thought, but it did not really succeed either in suppressing it or changing the main direction of its current. In art it undoubtedly had some direct effect, it created a new kind of insincerity of expression, a florid and sentimental religiosity—a new variety of bad taste, the rhetorical and over-emphatic. And I suspect that art was already prepared for this step by a certain exhaustion of the impulsive energy of the Renaissance—so that here too we may admit a correspondence.

The seventeenth century shows us no violent change in life, but rather the gradual working out of the principles implicit in the Renaissance and the Catholic reaction. But here we come to another curious want of correspondence between art and life, for in art we have a violent revolution, followed by a bitter internecine struggle among artists. This revolution was inaugurated by Caravaggio, who first discovered the surprising emotional possibilities of chiaroscuro and who combined with this a new idea of realism—realism in the modern sense, viz., the literal acceptance of what is coarse, common, squalid or undistinguished in life—realism in the sense of the novelists of Zola's time. To Caravaggio's influence we might trace not only a great deal of Rembrandt's art but the whole of that movement in favour of the extravagantly impressive and picturesque, which culminated in the romantic movement of the nineteenth century. Here, then, is another surprising want of correspondence between art and life.

In the eighteenth century we get a curious phenomenon. Art goes to court, identifies itself closely with a small aristocratic clique, becomes the exponent of their manners and their tastes. It becomes a luxury. It is no longer in the main stream of spiritual and intellectual effort, and this seclusion of art may account for the fact that the next great change in life—the French Revolution and all its accompanying intellectual ferment—finds no serious correspondence in art. We get a change, it is true; the French Republicans believed they were the counterpart of the Romans, and so David had to invent for them that peculiarly distressing type of the ancient Roman—always in heroic attitudes, always immaculate, spotless and with a highly polished 'Mme. Tussaud' surface. By-the-by, I was almost forgetting that we do owe Mme. Tussaud to the French Revolution. But the real movement of art in quite other directions to David—lay in the gradual unfolding of the Romanticist conception of the world—a world of violent emotional effects, of picturesque accidents, of wild nature, and this was a long prepared reaction from the complacent sophistication of eighteenth-century life. It is possible that one may associate this with the general state of mind that produced the Revolution, since both were a revolt against the established order of the eighteenth century; but curiously enough it found its chief ally in the reaction which followed the Revolution, in the neo-Christianism of Chateaubriand and the new sentimental respect for the age of faith—which, incidentally, appeared so much more picturesque than the age of reason.

It would be interesting at this point to consider how far during the nineteenth century reactionary political and religious thought was inspired primarily by æsthetic considerations—a curious instance of the counter-influence of art on life might perhaps be discovered in the devotees of the Oxford Movement. But this would take us too far afield.

The foregoing violently foreshortened view of history and art will show, I hope, that the usual assumption of a direct and decisive connection between life and art is by no means correct. It may, I hope, give pause to those numerous people who have already promised themselves a great new art as a result of the present war, though perhaps it is as well to let them enjoy it in anticipation, since it is, I fancy, the only way in which they are likely to enjoy a great art of any kind. What this survey suggests to me is that if we consider this special spiritual activity of art we find it no doubt open at times to influences from life, but in the main self-contained—we find the rhythmic sequences of change determined much more by its own internal forces—and by the readjustment within it, of its own elements—than by external forces. I admit, of course, that it is always conditioned more or less by economic changes, but these are rather conditions of its existence at all than directive influences. I also admit that under certain conditions the rhythms of life and of art may coincide with great effect on both; but in the main the two rhythms are distinct, and as often as not play against each other.

We have, I hope, gained some experience with which to handle the real subject of my inquiry, the relation of the modern movement in art to life. To understand it we must go back to the impressionist movement, which dates from about 1870. The artists who called themselves impressionists combined two distinct ideas. On the one hand they upheld, more categorically than ever before, the complete detachment of the artistic vision from the values imposed on vision by everyday life —they claimed, as Whistler did in his '10 o'clock,' to be pure artists. On the other hand a group of them used this freedom for the quasi-scientific description of new effects of atmospheric colour and atmospheric perspective, thereby endowing painting with a quite new series of colour harmonies, or at least of harmonies which had not been cultivated by European painters for many hundreds of years. They did more than this—the effects thus explored were completely unfamiliar to the ordinary man, whose vision is limited to the mere recognition of objects with a view to the uses of everyday life. He was forced, in looking at their pictures, to accept as artistic representation something very remote from all his previous expectations, and thereby he also acquired in time a new tolerance in his judgments on works of art, a tolerance which was destined to bear a still further strain in succeeding developments.

As against these great advantages which art owes to impressionism we must set the fact that the pseudo-scientific and analytic method of these painters forced artists to accept pictures which lacked design and formal co-ordination to a degree which had never before been permitted. They, or rather some of them, reduced the artistic vision to a continuous patchwork or mosaic of coloured patches without architectural framework or structural coherence. In this, impressionism marked the climax of a movement which had been going on more or less steadily from the thirteenth century—the tendency to approximate the forms of art more and more exactly to the representation of the totality of appearance. When once representation had been pushed to this point where further development was impossible, it was inevitable that artists should turn round and question the validity of the fundamental assumption that art aimed at representation; and the moment the question was fairly posed it became clear that the pseudo-scientific assumption that fidelity to appearance was the measure of art had no logical foundation. From that moment on it became evident that art had arrived at a critical point, and that the greatest revolution in art that had taken place since Graeco-Roman impressionism became converted into Byzantine formalism was inevitable. It was this revolution that Cézanne inaugurated and that Gauguin and van Goch continued. There is no need here to give in detail the characteristics of this new movement: they are sufficiently familiar. But we may summarise them as the re-establishment of purely æsthetic criteria in place of the criterion of conformity to appearance—the rediscovery of the principles of structural design and harmony.

The new movement has also led to a new canon of criticism, and this has changed our attitude to the arts of other times and countries. So long as representation was regarded as the end of art, the skill of the artist and his proficiency in this particular feat of representation were regarded with an admiration which was in fact mainly non-æsthetic. With the new indifference to representation we have become much less interested in skill and not at all interested in knowledge. We are thus no longer cut off from a great deal of barbaric and primitive art the very meaning of which escaped the understanding of those who demanded a certain standard of skill in representation before they could give serious consideration to a work of art. In general the effect of the movement has been to render the artist intensely conscious of the æsthetic unity of the work of art, but singularly naïve and simple as regards other considerations.

It remains to be considered whether the life of the past fifty years has shown any such violent re-orientation as we have found in the history of modern art. If we look back to the days of Herbert Spencer and Huxley, what changes are there in the general tendencies of life? The main ideas of rationalism seem to me to have steadily made way—there have been minor counter-revolutions, it is true, but the main current of active thought has surely moved steadily along the lines already laid down. I mean that the scientific attitude is more and more widely accepted. The protests of organised religion and of various mysticisms seem to grow gradually weaker and to carry less weight. Hardly any writers or thinkers of first-rate calibre now appear in the reactionary camp. I see, in short, no big change in direction, no evident revulsion of feeling.

None the less I suppose that a Spencer would be impossible now, and that the materialism of to-day is recognisably different from the materialism of Spencer. It would be very much less naïvely self-confident. It would admit far greater difficulties in presenting its picture of the universe than would have occurred to Spencer. The fact is that scepticism has turned on itself and has gone behind a great many of the axioms that seemed self-evident to the earlier rationalists. I do not see that it has at any point threatened the superstructure of the rationalist position, but it has led us to recognise the necessity of a continual revision and reconstruction of these data. Rationalism has become less arrogant and less narrow in its vision. And this is partly due also to the adventure of the scientific spirit into new regions. I refer to all that immense body of study and speculation which starts from Robertson Smith's *Religion of the Israelites*. The discovery of natural law in what seemed to earlier rationalists the chaotic fancies and caprices of the human imagination. The assumption that man is a mainly rational animal has given place to the discovery that he is, like other animals, mainly instinctive. This modifies immensely the attitude of the rationalist—it gives him a new charity and a new tolerance. What seemed like the wilful follies of mad or wicked men to the earlier rationalists are now seen to be inevitable responses to fundamental instinctive needs. By observing mankind the man of science has lost his contempt for him. Now this I think has had an important bearing on the new movement in art. In the first place I find something analogous in the new orientation of scientific and artistic endeavour. Science has turned its instruments in on human nature and begun to investigate its fundamental needs, and art has also turned its vision inwards, has begun to work upon the fundamental necessities of man's æsthetic functions.

But besides this analogy, which may be merely accidental and not causal, I think there can be little doubt that the new scientific development—for it is in no sense a revolution—has modified men's attitude to art. To Herbert Spencer, religion was primitive fear of the unknown and art was sexual attraction—he must have contemplated with perfect equanimity, almost with satisfaction, a world in which both these functions would disappear. I suppose that the scientific man of today would be much more ready to admit not only the necessity but the great importance of æsthetic feeling for the spiritual existence of man. The general conception of life in the mid-nineteenth century ruled out art as noxious, or at best, a useless frivolity, and above all as a mere survival of more primitive stages of evolution.

On the other hand, the artist of the new movement is moving into a sphere more and more remote from that of the ordinary man. In proportion as art becomes purer the number of people to whom it appeals gets less. It cuts out all the romantic overtones of life which are the usual bait by which men are induced to accept a work of art. It appeals only to the æsthetic sensibility, and that in most men is comparatively weak.

In the modern movement in art, then, as in so many cases in past history, the revolution in art seems to be out of all proportion to any corresponding change in life as a whole. It seems to find its sources, if at all, in what at present seem like minor movements. Whether the difference between the nineteenth and twentieth centuries will in retrospect seem as great in life as they already do in art I cannot guess—at least it is curious to note how much more conscious we are of the change in art than we are of the general change in thought and feeling.

*1920*

# ALDOUS HUXLEY

## *Crome Yellow*

### *Chapter 1*

ALONG this particular stretch of line no express had ever passed. All the trains—the few that there were—stopped at all the stations. Denis knew the names of those stations by heart. Bole, Tritton, Spavin Delawarr, Knipswich for Timpany, West Bowlby, and, finally, Camlet-on-the-Water. Camlet was where he always got out, leaving the train to creep indolently onward, goodness only knew whither, into the green heart of England.

They were snorting out of West Bowlby now. It was the next station, thank Heaven. Denis took his chattels off the rack and piled them neatly in the corner opposite his own. A futile proceeding. But one must have something to do. When he had finished, he sank back into his seat and closed his eyes. It was extremely hot.

Oh, this journey! It was two hours cut clean out of his life; two hours in which he might have done so much, so much—written the perfect poem, for example, or read the one illuminating book. Instead of which—his gorge rose at the smell of the dusty cushions against which he was leaning.

Two hours. One hundred and twenty minutes. Anything might be done in that time. Anything. Nothing. Oh, he had had hundreds of hours, and what had he done with them? Wasted them, spilt the precious minutes as though his reservoir were inexhaustible. Denis groaned in the spirit, condemned himself utterly with all his works. What right had he to sit in the sunshine, to occupy corner seats in third-class carriages, to be alive? None, none, none.

Misery and a nameless nostalgic distress possessed him. He was twenty-three, and oh! so agonizingly conscious of the fact.

The train came bumpingly to a halt. Here was Camlet at last. Denis jumped up, crammed his hat over his eyes, deranged his pile of baggage, leaned out of the window and shouted for a porter, seized a bag in either hand, and had to put them down again in order to open the door. When at last he had safely bundled himself and his baggage on to the platform, he ran up the train towards the van.

'A bicycle, a bicycle!' he said breathlessly to the guard. He felt himself a man of action. The guard paid no attention, but continued methodically to hand out, one by one, the packages labelled to Camlet. 'A bicycle!' Denis repeated. 'A green machine, cross-framed, name of Stone. S–T–O–N–E.'

'All in good time, sir,' said the guard soothingly. He was a large, stately man with a naval beard. One pictured him at home, drinking tea, surrounded by a numerous family. It was in that tone that he must have spoken to his children when they were tiresome. 'All in good time, sir.' Denis's man of action collapsed, punctured.

He left his luggage to be called for later, and pushed off on his bicycle. He always took his bicycle when he went into the country. It was part of the theory of exercise. One day one would get up at six o'clock and pedal away to Kenilworth, or Stratford-on-Avon—anywhere. And within a radius of twenty miles there were always Norman churches and Tudor mansions to be seen in the course of an afternoon's excursion. Somehow they never did get seen, but all the same it was nice to feel that the bicycle was there, and that one fine morning one really might get up at six.

Once at the top of the long hill which led up from Camlet station, he felt his spirits mounting. The world, he found, was good. The far-away blue hills, the harvests whitening on the slopes of the ridge along which his road led him, the treeless sky-lines that changed as he moved—yes, they were all good. He was overcome by the beauty of those deeply embayed combes, scooped in the flanks of the ridge beneath him. Curves, curves: he repeated the word slowly, trying as he did so to find some term in which to give expression to his appreciation. Curves—no, that was inadequate. He made a gesture with his hand, as though to scoop the achieved expression out of the air, and almost fell off his bicycle. What was the word to describe the curves of those little valleys? They were as fine as the lines of a human body, they were informed with the subtlety of art. . . .

*Galbe.* That was a good word; but it was French. *Le galbe évasé de ses hanches*: had one ever read a French novel in which that phrase didn't occur? Some day he would compile a dictionary for the use of novelists. *Galbe, gonflé, goulu: parfum, peau, pervers, potelé, pudeur: vertu, volupté.*

But he really must find that word. Curves, curves. . . . Those little valleys had the lines of a cup moulded round a woman's breast; they seemed the dinted imprints of some huge divine body that had rested on these hills. Cumbrous locutions, these; but through them he seemed to be getting nearer to what he wanted. Dinted, dimpled, wimpled—his mind wandered down echoing corridors of assonance and alliteration ever further and further from the point. He was enamoured with the beauty of words.

Becoming once more aware of the outer world, he found himself on the crest of a descent. The road plunged down, steep and straight, into a considerable valley. There, on the opposite slope, a little higher up the valley, stood Crome, his destination. He put on his brakes; this view of Crome was pleasant to linger over. The façade with its three projecting towers rose precipitously from among the dark trees of the garden. The house basked in full sunlight; the old brick rosily glowed.

How ripe and rich it was, how superbly mellow! And at the same time, how austere! The hill was becoming steeper and steeper; he was gaining speed in spite of his brakes. He loosed his grip of the levers, and in a moment was rushing headlong down. Five minutes later he was passing through the gate of the great courtyard. The front door stood hospitably open. He left his bicycle leaning against the wall and walked in. He would take them by surprise.

## *Chapter 2*

HE took nobody by surprise; there was nobody to take. All was quiet; Denis wandered from room to empty room, looking with pleasure at the familiar pictures and furniture, at all the little untidy signs of life that lay scattered here and there. He was rather glad that they were all out; it was amusing to wander through the house as though one were exploring a dead, deserted Pompeii. What sort of life would the excavator reconstruct from these remains; how would he people these empty chambers? There was the long gallery, with its rows of respectable and (though, of course, one couldn't publicly admit it) rather boring Italian primitives, its Chinese sculptures, its unobtrusive, dateless furniture. There was the panelled drawing-room, where the huge chintz-covered arm-chairs stood, oases of comfort among the austere flesh-mortifying antiques. There was the morning-room, with its pale lemon walls, its painted Venetian chairs and rococo tables, its mirrors, its modern pictures. There was the library, cool, spacious, and dark, book-lined from floor to ceiling, rich in portentous folios. There was the dining-room, solidly, portwinily English, with its great mahogany table, its eighteenth-century chairs and sideboard, its eighteenth-century pictures—family portraits, meticulous animal paintings. What could one reconstruct from such data? There was much of Henry Wimbush in the long gallery and the library, something of Anne, perhaps, in the morning-room. That was all. Among the accumulations of ten generations the living had left but few traces.

Lying on the table in the morning-room he saw his own book of poems. What tact! He picked it up and opened it. It was what the reviewers call 'a slim volume'. He read at hazard:

. . . But silence and the topless dark
Vault in the lights of Luna Park
And Blackpool from the nightly gloom
Hollows a bright tumultuous tomb.

He put it down again, shook his head, and sighed. 'What genius I had then!' he reflected, echoing the aged Swift. It was nearly six months since the book had been published; he was glad to think he would never write anything of the same sort again. Who could have been reading it, he wondered? Anne, perhaps; he liked to think so. Perhaps, too, she had at last recognized herself in the Hamadryad of the poplar sapling; the slim Hamadryad whose movements were like the swaying of a young tree in the wind. 'The Woman who was a Tree' was what he had called the poem. He had given her the book when it came out, hoping that the poem would tell her what he hadn't dared to say. She had never referred to it.

He shut his eyes and saw a vision of her in a red velvet cloak, swaying into the little restaurant where they sometimes dined together in London—three quarters of an hour late, and he at his table, haggard with anxiety, irritation, hunger. Oh, she was damnable!

It occurred to him that perhaps his hostess might be in her boudoir. It was a possibility; he would go and see. Mrs. Wimbush's boudoir was in the central tower on the garden front. A little staircase corkscrewed up to it from the hall. Denis mounted, tapped at the door. 'Come in.' Ah, she was there; he had rather hoped she wouldn't be. He opened the door.

Priscilla Wimbush was lying on the sofa. A blotting-pad rested on her knees and she was thoughtfully sucking the end of a silver pencil.

'Hullo,' she said, looking up. 'I'd forgotten you were coming.'

'Well, here I am, I'm afraid,' said Denis deprecatingly. 'I'm awfully sorry.'

Mrs. Wimbush laughed. Her voice, her laughter, were deep and masculine. Everything about her was manly. She had a large, square, middle-aged face, with a massive projecting nose and little greenish eyes, the whole surmounted by a lofty and elaborate coiffure of a curiously improbable shade of orange. Looking at her, Denis always thought of Wilkie Bard as the cantatrice.

> That's why I'm going to
> Sing in op'ra, sing in op'ra,
> Sing in op-pop-pop-pop-popera.

To-day she was wearing a purple silk dress with a high collar and a row of pearls. The costume, so richly dowagerish, so suggestive of the Royal Family, made her look more than ever like something on the Halls.

'What have you been doing all this time?' she asked.

'Well,' said Denis, and he hesitated, almost voluptuously. He had a tremendously amusing account of London and its doings all ripe and ready in his mind. It would be a pleasure to give it utterance. 'To begin with,' he said . . .

But he was too late. Mrs. Wimbush's question had been what the grammarians call rhetorical; it asked for no answer. It was a little conversational flourish, a gambit in the polite game.

'You find me busy at my horoscopes,' she said, without even being aware that she had interrupted him.

A little pained, Denis decided to reserve his story for more receptive ears. He contented himself, by way of revenge, with saying 'Oh?' rather icily.

'Did I tell you how I won four hundred on the Grand National this year?'

'Yes,' he replied, still frigid and monosyllabic. She must have told him at least six times.

'Wonderful, isn't it? Everything is in the Stars. In the Old Days, before I had the Stars to help me, I used to lose thousands. Now'—she paused an instant—'well, look at that four hundred on the Grand National. That's the Stars.'

Denis would have liked to hear more about the Old Days. But he was too discreet and, still more, too shy to ask. There had been something of a bust up; that was all he knew. Old Priscilla—not so old then, of course, and sprightlier—had lost a great deal of money, dropped it in handfuls and hatfuls on every racecourse in the country. She had gambled too. The number of thousands varied in the different legends, but all put it high. Henry Wimbush was forced to sell some of his Primitives—a Taddeo da Poggibonsi, an Amico di Taddeo, and four or five nameless Sienese—to the Americans. There was a crisis. For the first time in his life Henry asserted himself, and with good effect, it seemed.

Priscilla's gay and gadding existence had come to an abrupt end. Nowadays she spent almost all her time at Crome, cultivating a rather ill-defined malady. For consolation she dallied with New Thought and the Occult. Her passion for racing still possessed her, and Henry, who was a kind-hearted fellow at bottom, allowed her forty pounds a month betting money. Most of Priscilla's days were spent in casting the horoscopes of horses, and she invested her money scientifically, as the Stars dictated. She betted on football too, and had a large notebook in which she registered the horoscopes of all the players in all the teams of the League. The process of balancing the horoscopes of two elevens one against the other was a very delicate and difficult one. A match between the Spurs and the Villa entailed a conflict in the heavens so vast and so complicated that it was not to be wondered at if she sometimes made a mistake about the outcome.

'Such a pity you don't believe in these things, Denis, such a pity,' said Mrs. Wimbush in her deep, distinct voice.

'I can't say I feel it so.'

'Ah, that's because you don't know what it's like to have faith. You've no idea how amusing and exciting life becomes when you do believe. All that happens means something; nothing you do is ever insignificant. It makes life so jolly, you know. Here am I at Crome. Dull as ditchwater, you'd think; but no, I don't find it so. I don't regret the Old Days a bit. I have the Stars . . .' She picked up the sheet of paper that was lying on the blotting-pad. 'Inman's horoscope,' she explained. '(I thought I'd like to have a little fling on the billiards championship this autumn.) I have the Infinite to keep in tune with,' she waved her hand. 'And then there's the next world and all the spirits, and one's Aura, and Mrs. Eddy and saying you're not ill, and the Christian Mysteries and Mrs. Besant. It's all splendid. One's never dull for a moment. I can't think how I used to get on before—in the Old Days. Pleasure?—running about, that's all it was; just running about. Lunch, tea, dinner, theatre, supper, every day. It was fun, of course, while it lasted. But there wasn't much left of it afterwards. There's rather a good thing about that in Barbecue-Smith's new book. Where is it?'

She sat up and reached for a book that was lying on the little table by the head of the sofa.

'Do you know him, by the way?' she asked.

'Who?'

'Mr. Barbecue-Smith.'

Denis knew of him vaguely. Barbecue-Smith was a name in the Sunday papers. He wrote about the Conduct of Life. He might even be the author of *What a Young Girl Ought to Know.*

'No, not personally,' he said.

'I've invited him for next week-end.' She turned over the pages of the book. 'Here's the passage I was thinking of. I marked it. I always mark the things I like.'

Holding the book almost at arm's length, for she was somewhat long-sighted, and making suitable gestures with her free hand, she began to read, slowly, dramatically.

' "What are thousand pound fur coats, what are quarter million incomes?" ' She looked up from the page with a histrionic movement of the head; her orange coiffure nodded portentously. Denis looked at it, fascinated. Was it the Real Thing and henna, he wondered, or was it one of those Complete Transformations one sees in the advertisements?

' "What are Thrones and Sceptres?" '

The orange Transformation—yes, it must be a Transformation—bobbed up again.

' "What are the gaieties of the Rich, the splendours of the Powerful, what is the pride of the Great, what are the gaudy pleasures of High Society?" '

The voice, which had risen in tone, questioningly, from sentence to sentence, dropped suddenly and boomed reply.

' "They are nothing. Vanity, fluff, dandelion seed in the wind, thin vapours of fever. The things that matter happen in the heart. Seen things are sweet, but those unseen are a thousand times more significant. It is the Unseen that counts in Life." '

Mrs. Wimbush lowered the book. 'Beautiful, isn't it?' she said.

Denis preferred not to hazard an opinion, but uttered a non-committal 'H'm.'

'Ah, it's a fine book this, a beautiful book,' said Priscilla, as she let the pages flick back, one by one, from under her thumb. 'And here's the passage about the Lotus Pool. He compares the Soul to a Lotus Pool, you know.' She held up the book again and read. ' "A Friend of mine has a Lotus Pool in his garden. It lies in a little dell embowered with wild roses and eglantine, among which the nightingale pours forth its amorous descant all the summer long. Within the pool the Lotuses blossom, and the birds of the air come to drink and bathe themselves in its crystal waters. . . ." Ah, and that reminds me,' Priscilla exclaimed, shutting the book with a clap and uttering her big profound laugh—'that reminds me of the things that have been going on in our bathing-pool since you were here last. We gave the village people leave to come and bathe here in the evenings. You've no idea of the things that happened.'

She leaned forward, speaking in a confidential whisper; every now and then she uttered a deep gurgle of laughter. '. . . mixed bathing . . . saw them out of my window . . . sent for a pair of field-glasses to make sure . . . no doubt of it. . . .' The laughter broke out again. Denis laughed too. Barbecue-Smith was tossed on the floor.

'It's time we went to see if tea's ready,' said Priscilla. She hoisted herself up from the sofa and went swishing off across the room, striding beneath the trailing silk. Denis followed her, faintly humming to himself:

That's why I'm going to
Sing in op'ra, sing in op'ra,
Sing in op-pop-pop-pop-popera.

And then the little twiddly bit of accompaniment at the end: 'ra-ra.'

## *Chapter 3*

THE terrace in front of the house was a long narrow strip of turf, bounded along its outer edge by a graceful stone balustrade. Two little summer-houses of brick stood at either end. Below the house the ground sloped very steeply away, and the terrace was a remarkably high one; from the balusters to the sloping lawn beneath was a drop of thirty feet. Seen from below, the high unbroken terrace wall, built like the house itself of brick, had the almost menacing aspect of a fortification—a castle bastion, from whose parapet one looked out across airy depths to distances level with the eye. Below, in the foreground, hedged in by solid masses of sculptured yew trees, lay the stone-brimmed swimming-pool. Beyond it stretched the park, with its massive elms, its green expanses of grass, and, at the bottom of the valley, the gleam of the narrow river. On the farther side of the stream the land rose again in a long slope, chequered with cultivation. Looking up the valley, to the right, one saw a line of blue, far-off hills.

The tea-table had been planted in the shade of one of the little summer-houses, and the rest of the party was already assembled about it when Denis and Priscilla made their appearance. Henry Wimbush had begun to pour out the tea. He was one of those ageless, unchanging men on the farther side of fifty, who might be thirty, who might be anything. Denis had known him almost as long as he could remember. In all those years his pale, rather handsome face had never grown any older; it was like the pale grey bowler hat which he always wore, winter and summer—unageing, calm, serenely without cxpression.

Next him, but separated from him and from the rest of the world by the almost impenetrable barriers of her deafness, sat Jenny Mullion. She was perhaps thirty, had a tilted nose and a pink-and-white complexion, and wore her brown hair plaited and coiled in two lateral buns over her ears. In the secret tower of her deafness she sat apart, looking down at the world through sharply piercing eyes. What did she think of men and women and things? That was something that Denis had never been able to discover. In her enigmatic remoteness Jenny was a little disquieting. Even now some interior joke seemed to be amusing her, for she was smiling to herself, and her brown eyes were like very bright round marbles.

On his other side the serious, moon-like innocence of Mary Bracegirdle's face shone pink and childish. She was nearly twenty-three, but one wouldn't have guessed it. Her short hair, clipped like a page's, hung in a bell of elastic gold about her cheeks. She had large blue china eyes, whose expression was one of ingenuous and often puzzled earnestness.

Next to Mary a small gaunt man was sitting, rigid and erect in his chair. In appearance Mr. Scogan was like one of those extinct bird-lizards of the Tertiary. His nose was beaked, his dark eye had the shining quickness of a robin's. But there was nothing soft or gracious or feathery about him. The skin of his wrinkled brown face had a dry and scaly look; his hands were the hands of a crocodile. His movements were marked by the lizard's disconcertingly abrupt clockwork speed; his speech was thin, fluty, and dry. Henry Wimbush's schoolfellow and exact contemporary, Mr. Scogan looked far older and, at the same time, far more youthfully alive than did that gentle aristocrat with the face like a grey bowler.

Mr. Scogan might look like an extinct saurian, but Gombauld was altogether and essentially human. In the old-fashioned natural histories of the 'thirties he might have figured in a steel engraving as a type of Homo Sapiens—an honour which at that time commonly fell to Lord Byron. Indeed, with more hair and less collar, Gombauld would have been completely Byronic—more than Byronic, even, for Gombauld was of Provençal descent, a black-haired young corsair of thirty, with flashing teeth and luminous large dark eyes. Denis looked at him enviously. He was jealous of his talent: if only he wrote verse as well as Gombauld painted pictures! Still more, at the moment, he envied Gombauld his looks, his vitality, his easy confidence of manner. Was it surprising that Anne should like him? Like him?—it might even be something worse, Denis reflected bitterly, as he walked at Priscilla's side down the long grass terrace.

Between Gombauld and Mr. Scogan a very much lowered deck-chair presented its back to the new arrivals as they advanced towards the tea-table. Gombauld was leaning over it; his face moved vivaciously; he smiled, he laughed, he made quick gestures with his hands. From the depths of the chair came up a sound of soft, lazy laughter. Denis started as he heard it. That laughter—how well he knew it! What emotions it evoked in him! He quickened his pace.

In her low deck-chair Anne was nearer to lying than to sitting. Her long, slender body reposed in an attitude of listless and indolent grace. Within its setting of light brown hair her face had a pretty regularity that was almost doll-like. And indeed there were moments when she seemed nothing more than a doll; when the oval face, with its long-lashed, pale blue eyes, expressed nothing; when it was no more than a lazy mask of wax. She was Henry Wimbush's own niece; that bowler-like countenance was one of the Wimbush heirlooms; it ran in the family, appearing in its female members as a blank doll-face. But across this dollish mask, like a gay melody dancing over an unchanging fundamental bass, passed Anne's other inheritance—quick laughter, light ironic amusement, and the changing expressions of many moods. She was smiling now as Denis looked down at her: her cat's smile, he called it, for no very good reason. The mouth was compressed, and on either side of it two tiny wrinkles had formed themselves in her cheeks. An infinity of slightly malicious amusement lurked in those little folds, in the puckers about the half-closed eyes, in the eyes themselves, bright and laughing between the narrowed lids.

The preliminary greetings spoken, Denis found an empty chair between Gombauld and Jenny and sat down.

'How are you, Jenny?' he shouted at her.

Jenny nodded and smiled in mysterious silence, as though the subject of her health were a secret that could not be publicly divulged.

'How's London been since I went away?' Anne inquired from the depth of her chair.

The moment had come; the tremendously amusing narrative was waiting for utterance. 'Well,' said Denis, smiling happily, 'to begin with . . .'

'Has Priscilla told you of our great antiquarian find?' Henry Wimbush leaned forward; the most promising of buds was nipped.

'To begin with,' said Denis desperately, 'there was the Ballet . . .'

'Last week,' Mr. Wimbush went on softly and implacably, 'we dug up fifty yards of oaken drain-pipes; just tree trunks with a hole bored through the middle. Very interesting indeed. Whether they were laid down by the monks in the fifteenth century, or whether . . .'

Denis listened gloomily. 'Extraordinary!' he said, when Mr. Wimbush had finished; 'quite extraordinary!' He helped himself to another slice of cake. He didn't even want to tell his tale about London now; he was damped.

For some time past Mary's grave blue eyes had been fixed upon him. 'What have you been writing lately?' she asked. It would be nice to have a little literary conversation.

'Oh, verse and prose,' said Denis—'just verse and prose.'

'Prose?' Mr. Scogan pounced alarmingly on the word. 'You've been writing prose?'

'Yes.'

'Not a novel?'

'Yes.'

'My poor Denis!' exclaimed Mr. Scogan. 'What about?'

Denis felt rather uncomfortable. 'Oh, about the usual things, you know.'

'Of course,' Mr. Scogan groaned. 'I'll describe the plot for you. Little Percy, the hero, was never good at games, but he was always clever. He passes through the usual public school and the usual university and comes to London, where he lives among the artists. He is bowed down with melancholy thought; he carries the whole weight of the universe upon his shoulders. He writes a novel of dazzling brilliance; he dabbles delicately in Amour and disappears, at the end of the book, into the luminous Future.'

Denis blushed scarlet. Mr. Scogan had described the plan of his novel with an accuracy that was appalling. He made an effort to laugh. 'You're entirely wrong,' he said. 'My novel is not in the least like that.' It was a heroic lie. Luckily, he reflected, only two chapters were written. He would tear them up that very evening when he unpacked.

Mr. Scogan paid no attention to his denial, but went on: 'Why will you young men continue to write about things that are so entirely uninteresting as the mentality of adolescents and artists? Professional anthropologists might find it interesting to turn sometimes from the beliefs of the Blackfellow to the philosophical preoccupations of the undergraduate. But you can't expect an ordinary adult man, like myself, to be much moved by the story of his spiritual troubles. And after all, even in England, even in Germany and Russia, there are more adults than adolescents. As for the artist, he is preoccupied with problems that are so utterly unlike those of the ordinary adult man—problems of pure aesthetics which don't so much as present themselves to people like myself—that a description of his mental processes is as boring to the ordinary reader as a piece of pure mathematics. A serious book about artists regarded as artists is unreadable; and a book about artists regarded as lovers, husbands, dipsomaniacs, heroes, and the like is really not worth writing again. Jean-Christophe is the stock artist of literature, just as Professor Radium of *Comic Cuts* is its stock man of science.'

'I'm sorry to hear I'm as uninteresting as all that,' said Gombauld.

'Not at all, my dear Gombauld,' Mr. Scogan hastened to explain. 'As a lover or a dipsomaniac, I've no doubt of your being a most fascinating specimen. But as a combiner of forms, you must honestly admit it, you're a bore.'

'I entirely disagree with you,' exclaimed Mary. She was somehow always out of breath when she talked, and her speech was punctuated by little gasps. 'I've known a great many artists, and I've always found their mentality very interesting. Especially in Paris. Tschuplitski, for example—I saw a great deal of Tschuplitski in Paris this spring. . . .'

'Ah, but then you're an exception, Mary, you're an exception,' said Mr. Scogan. 'You are a *femme supérieure*.'

A flush of pleasure turned Mary's face into a harvest moon.

## *Chapter 4*

DENIS woke up next morning to find the sun shining, the sky serene. He decided to wear white flannel trousers—white flannel trousers and a black jacket, with a silk shirt and his new peach-coloured tie. And what shoes? White was the obvious choice, but there was something rather pleasing about the notion of black patent leather. He lay in bed for several minutes considering the problem.

Before he went down—patent leather was his final choice—he looked at himself critically in the glass. His hair might have been more golden, he reflected. As it was, its yellowness had the hint of a greenish tinge in it. But his forehead was good. His forehead made up in height what his chin lacked in prominence. His nose might have been longer, but it would pass. His eyes might have been blue and not green. But his coat was very well cut and, discreetly padded, made him seem robuster than he actually was. His legs, in their white casing, were long and elegant. Satisfied, he descended the stairs. Most of the party had already finished their breakfast. He found himself alone with Jenny.

'I hope you slept well,' he said.

'Yes, isn't it lovely?' Jenny replied, giving two rapid little nods. 'But we had such awful thunderstorms last week.'

Parallel straight lines, Denis reflected, meet only at infinity. He might talk for ever of care-charmer sleep and she of meteorology till the end of time. Did one ever establish contact with anyone? We are all parallel straight lines. Jenny was only a little more parallel than most.

'They are very alarming, these thunderstorms,' he said, helping himself to porridge. 'Don't you think so? Or are you above being frightened?'

'No. I always go to bed in a storm. One is so much safer lying down.'

'Why?'

'Because,' said Jenny, making a descriptive gesture, 'because lightning goes downwards and not flat ways. When you're lying down you're out of the current.'

'That's very ingenious.'

'It's true.'

There was a silence. Denis finished his porridge and helped himself to bacon. For lack of anything better to say, and because Mr. Scogan's absurd phrase was for some reason running in his head, he turned to Jenny and asked:

'Do you consider yourself a *femme supérieure*?' He had to repeat the question several times before Jenny got the hang of it.

'No,' she said, rather indignantly, when at last she heard what Denis was saying. 'Certainly not. Has anyone been suggesting that I am?'

'No,' said Denis. 'Mr. Scogan told Mary she was one.'

'Did he?' Jenny lowered her voice. 'Shall I tell you what I think of that man? I think he's slightly sinister.'

Having made this pronouncement, she entered the ivory tower of her deafness and closed the door. Denis could not induce her to say anything more, could not induce her even to listen. She just smiled at him, smiled and occasionally nodded.

Denis went out on to the terrace to smoke his after-breakfast pipe and to read his morning paper. An hour later, when Anne came down, she found him still reading. By this time he had got to the Court Circular and the Forthcoming Weddings. He got up to meet her as she approached, a Hamadryad in white muslin, across the grass.

'Why, Denis,' she exclaimed, 'you look perfectly sweet in your white trousers.'

Denis was dreadfully taken aback. There was no possible retort. 'You speak as though I were a child in a new frock,' he said, with a show of irritation.

'But that's how I feel about you, Denis dear.'

'Then you oughtn't to.'

'But I can't help it. I'm so much older than you.'

'I like that,' he said. 'Four years older.'

'And if you do look perfectly sweet in your white trousers, why shouldn't I say so? And why did you put them on, if you didn't think you were going to look sweet in them?'

'Let's go into the garden,' said Denis. He was put out; the conversation had taken such a preposterous and unexpected turn. He had planned a very different opening, in which he was to lead off with, 'You look adorable this morning,' or something of the kind, and she was to answer, 'Do I?' and then there was to be a pregnant silence.

And now she had got in first with the trousers. It was provoking; his pride was hurt.

That part of the garden that sloped down from the foot of the terrace to the pool had a beauty which did not depend on colour so much as on forms. It was as beautiful by moonlight as in the sun. The silver of water, the dark shapes of yew and ilex trees remained, at all hours and seasons, the dominant features of the scene. It was a landscape in black and white. For colour there was the flower-garden; it lay to one side of the pool, separated from it by a huge Babylonian wall of yews. You passed through a tunnel in the hedge, you opened a wicket in a wall, and you found yourself, startlingly and suddenly, in the world of colour. The July borders blazed and flared under the sun. Within its high brick walls the garden was like a great tank of warmth and perfume and colour.

Denis held open the little iron gate for his companion. 'It's like passing from a cloister into an Oriental palace,' he said, and took a deep breath of the warm, flower-scented air. ' "In fragrant volleys they let fly . . ." How does it go?

> Well shot, ye firemen! O how sweet
> And round your equal fires do meet;
> Whose shrill report no ear can tell,
> But echoes to the eye and smell . . .'

'You have a bad habit of quoting,' said Anne. 'As I never know the context or author, I find it humiliating.'

Denis apologized. 'It's the fault of one's education. Things somehow seem more real and vivid when one can apply somebody else's ready-made phrase about them. And then there are lots of lovely names and words—Monophysite, Iamblichus, Pomponazzi; you bring them out triumphantly, and feel you've clinched the argument with the mere magical sound of them. That's what comes of the higher education.'

'You may regret your education,' said Anne; 'I'm ashamed of my lack of it. Look at those sunflowers! Aren't they magnificent?'

'Dark faces and golden crowns—they're kings in Ethiopia. And I like the way the tits cling to the flowers and pick out the seeds, while the other loutish birds, grubbing dirtily for their food, look up in envy from the ground. Do they look up in envy? That's the literary touch, I'm afraid. Education again. It always comes back to that.' He was silent.

Anne had sat down on a bench that stood in the shade of an old apple tree. 'I'm listening,' she said.

He did not sit down, but walked backwards and forwards in front of the bench, gesticulating a little as he talked. 'Books,' he said—'books. One reads so many, and one sees so few people and so little of the world. Great thick books about the universe and the mind and ethics. You've no idea how many there are. I must have read twenty or thirty tons of them in the last five years. Twenty tons of ratiocination. Weighted with that, one's pushed out into the world.'

He went on walking up and down. His voice rose, fell, was silent a moment, and then talked on. He moved his hands, sometimes he waved his arms. Anne looked and listened quietly, as though she were at a lecture. He was a nice boy, and to-day he looked charming—charming!

One entered the world, Denis pursued, having ready-made ideas about everything. One had a philosophy and tried to make life fit into it. One should have lived first and then made one's philosophy to fit life. . . . Life, facts, things were horribly complicated; ideas, even the most difficult of them, deceptively simple. In the world of ideas everything was clear; in life all was obscure, embroiled. Was it surprising that one was miserable, horribly unhappy? Denis came to a halt in front of the bench, and as he asked this last question he stretched out his arms and stood for an instant in an attitude of crucifixion, then let them fall again to his sides.

'My poor Denis!' Anne was touched. He was really too pathetic as he stood there in front of her in his white flannel trousers. 'But does one suffer about these things? It seems very extraordinary.'

'You're like Scogan,' cried Denis bitterly. 'You regard me as a specimen for an anthropologist. Well, I suppose I am.'

'No, no,' she protested, and drew in her skirt with a gesture that indicated that he was to sit down beside her. He sat down. 'Why can't you just take things for granted and as they come?' she asked. 'It's so much simpler.'

'Of course it is,' said Denis. 'But it's a lesson to be learnt gradually. There are the twenty tons of ratiocination to be got rid of first.'

'I've always taken things as they come,' said Anne. 'It seems so obvious. One enjoys the pleasant things, avoids the nasty ones. There's nothing more to be said.'

'Nothing—for you. But, then, you were born a pagan; I am trying laboriously to make myself one. I can take nothing for granted, I can enjoy nothing as it comes along. Beauty, pleasure, art, women—I have to invent an excuse, a justification for everything that's delightful. Otherwise I can't enjoy it with an easy conscience. I make up a little story about beauty and pretend that it has something to do with truth and goodness. I have to say that art is the process by which one reconstructs the divine reality out of chaos. Pleasure is one of the mystical roads to union with the infinite—the ecstasies of drinking, dancing, love-making. As for women, I am perpetually assuring myself that they're the broad highway to divinity. And to think that I'm only just beginning to see through the silliness of the whole thing! It's incredible to me that anyone should have escaped these horrors.'

'It's still more incredible to me,' said Anne, 'that anyone should have been a victim to them. I should like to see myself believing that men are the highway to divinity.' The amused malice of her smile planted two little folds on either side of her mouth, and through their half-closed lids her eyes shone with laughter. 'What you need, Denis, is a nice plump young wife, a fixed income, and a little congenial but regular work.'

'What I need is you.' That was what he ought to have retorted, that was what he wanted passionately to say. He could not say it. His desire fought against his shyness. 'What I need is you.' Mentally he shouted the words, but not a sound issued from his lips. He looked at her despairingly. Couldn't she see what was going on inside him? Couldn't she understand? 'What I need is you.' He would say it, he would—he would.

'I think I shall go and bathe,' said Anne. 'It's so hot.' The opportunity had passed.

## *Chapter 5*

Mr. Wimbush had taken them to see the sights of the Home Farm, and now they were standing, all six of them—Henry Wimbush, Mr. Scogan, Denis, Gombauld, Anne, and Mary—by the low wall of the piggery, looking into one of the styes.

'This is a good sow,' said Henry Wimbush. 'She had a litter of fourteen.'

'Fourteen?' Mary echoed incredulously. She turned astonished blue eyes towards Mr. Wimbush, then let them fall on to the seething mass of *élan vital* that fermented in the sty.

An immense sow reposed on her side in the middle of the pen. Her round, black belly, fringed with a double line of dugs, presented itself to the assault of an army of small, brownish-black swine. With a frantic greed they tugged at their mother's flank. The old sow stirred sometimes uneasily or uttered a little grunt of pain. One small pig, the runt, the weakling of the litter, had been unable to secure a place at the banquet. Squealing shrilly, he ran backwards and forwards, trying to push in among his stronger brothers or even to climb over their tight little black backs towards the maternal reservoir.

'There *are* fourteen,' said Mary. 'You're quite right. I counted. It's extraordinary.'

'The sow next door,' Mr. Wimbush went on, 'has done very badly. She only had five in her litter. I shall give her another chance. If she does no better next time, I shall fat her up and kill her. There's the boar,' he pointed towards a farther sty. 'Fine old beast, isn't he? But he's getting past his prime. He'll have to go too.'

'How cruel!' Anne exclaimed.

'But how practical, how eminently realistic!' said Mr. Scogan. 'In this farm we have a model of sound paternal government. Make them breed, make them work, and when they're past working or breeding or begetting, slaughter them.'

'Farming seems to be mostly indecency and cruelty,' said Anne.

With the ferrule of his walking-stick Denis began to scratch the boar's long bristly back. The animal moved a little so as to bring himself within easier range of the instrument that evoked in him such delicious sensations; then he stood stock still, softly grunting his contentment. The mud of years flaked off his sides in a grey powdery scurf.

'What a pleasure it is,' said Denis, 'to do somebody a kindness. I believe I enjoy scratching this pig quite as much as he enjoys being scratched. If only one could always be kind with so little expense or trouble. . . .'

A gate slammed; there was a sound of heavy footsteps.

'Morning, Rowley!' said Henry Wimbush.

'Morning, sir,' old Rowley answered. He was the most venerable of the labourers on the farm—a tall, solid man, still unbent, with grey side-whiskers and a steep, dignified profile. Grave, weighty in his manner, splendidly respectable, Rowley had the air of a great English statesman of the mid-nineteenth century. He halted on the outskirts of the group, and for a moment they all looked at the pigs in a silence that was only broken by the sound of grunting or the squelch of a sharp hoof in the mire. Rowley turned at last, slowly and ponderously and nobly, as he did everything, and addressed himself to Henry Wimbush.

'Look at them, sir,' he said, with a motion of his hand towards the wallowing swine. 'Rightly is they called pigs.'

'Rightly indeed,' Mr. Wimbush agreed.

'I am abashed by that man,' said Mr. Scogan, as old Rowley plodded off slowly and with dignity. 'What wisdom, what judgment, what a sense of values! "Rightly are they called swine." Yes. And I wish I could, with as much justice, say, "Rightly are we called men." '

They walked on towards the cowsheds and the stables of the cart-horses. Five white geese, taking the air this fine morning, even as they were doing, met them in the way. They hesitated, cackled; then, converting their lifted necks into rigid, horizontal snakes, they rushed off in disorder, hissing horribly as they went. Red calves paddled in the dung and mud of a spacious yard. In another enclosure stood the bull, massive as a locomotive. He was a very calm bull, and his face wore an expression of melancholy stupidity. He gazed with reddish-brown eyes at his visitors, chewed thoughtfully at the tangible memories of an earlier meal, swallowed and regurgitated, chewed again. His tail lashed savagely from side to side; it seemed to have nothing to do with his impassive bulk. Between his short horns was a triangle of red curls, short and dense.

'Splendid animal,' said Henry Wimbush. 'Pedigree stock. But he's getting a little old, like the boar.'

'Fat him up and slaughter him,' Mr. Scogan pronounced, with a delicate old-maidish precision of utterance.

'Couldn't you give the animals a little holiday from producing children?' asked Anne. 'I'm so sorry for the poor things.'

Mr. Wimbush shook his head. 'Personally,' he said, 'I rather like seeing fourteen pigs grow where only one grew before. The spectacle of so much crude life is refreshing.'

'I'm glad to hear you say so,' Gombauld broke in warmly. 'Lots of life: that's what we want. I like pullulation; everything ought to increase and multiply as hard as it can.'

Gombauld grew lyrical. Everybody ought to have children—Anne ought to have them, Mary ought to have them—dozens and dozens. He emphasized his point by thumping with his walking-stick on the bull's leather flanks. Mr. Scogan ought to pass on his intelligence to little Scogans, and Denis to little Denises. The bull turned his head to see what was happening, regarded the drumming stick for several seconds, then turned back again satisfied, it seemed, that nothing was happening. Sterility was odious, unnatural, a sin against life. Life, life, and still more life. The ribs of the placid bull resounded.

Standing with his back against the farmyard pump, a little apart, Denis examined the group. Gombauld, passionate and vivacious, was its centre. The others stood round, listening—Henry Wimbush, calm and polite beneath his grey bowler; Mary, with parted lips and eyes that shone with the indignation of a convinced birth-controller. Anne looked on through half-shut eyes, smiling; and beside her stood Mr. Scogan, bolt upright in an attitude of metallic rigidity that contrasted strangely with that fluid grace of hers which even in stillness suggested a soft movement.

Gombauld ceased talking, and Mary, flushed and outraged, opened her mouth to refute him. But she was too slow. Before she could utter a word Mr. Scogan's fluty voice had pronounced the opening phrases of a discourse. There was no hope of getting so much as a word in edgeways; Mary had perforce to resign herself.

'Even your eloquence, my dear Gombauld,' he was saying—'even your eloquence must prove inadequate to reconvert the world to a belief in the delights of mere multiplication. With the gramophone, the cinema, and the automatic pistol, the goddess of Applied Science has presented the world with another gift, more precious even than these—the means of dissociating love from propagation. Eros, for those who wish it, is now an entirely free god; his deplorable associations with Lucina may be broken at will. In the course of the next few centuries, who knows? the world may see a more complete severance. I look forward to it optimistically. Where the great Erasmus Darwin and Miss Anna Seward, Swan of Lichfield, experimented—and, for all their scientific ardour, failed—our descendants will experiment and succeed. An impersonal generation will take the place of Nature's hideous system. In vast state incubators, rows upon rows of gravid bottles will supply the world with the population it requires. The family system will disappear; society, sapped at its very base, will have to find new foundations; and Eros, beautifully and irresponsibly free, will flit like a gay butterfly from flower to flower through a sunlit world.'

'It sounds lovely,' said Anne.

'The distant future always does.'

Mary's china blue eyes, more serious and more astonished than ever, were fixed on Mr. Scogan. 'Bottles?' she said. 'Do you really think so? Bottles. . . .'

## *Chapter 6*

MR. BARBECUE-SMITH arrived in time for tea on Saturday afternoon. He was a short and corpulent man, with a very large head and no neck. In his earlier middle age he had been distressed by this absence of neck, but was comforted by reading in Balzac's *Louis Lambert* that all the world's great men have been marked by the same peculiarity, and for a simple and obvious reason: Greatness is nothing more nor less than the harmonious functioning of the faculties of the head and heart; the shorter the neck, the more closely these two organs approach one another; *argal* . . . It was convincing.

Mr. Barbecue-Smith belonged to the old school of journalists. He sported a leonine head with a greyish-black mane of oddly unappetizing hair brushed back from a broad but low forehead. And somehow he always seemed slightly, ever so slightly, soiled. In younger days he had gaily called himself a Bohemian. He did so no longer. He was a teacher now, a kind of prophet. Some of his books of comfort and spiritual teaching were in their hundred and twentieth thousand.

Priscilla received him with every mark of esteem. He had never been to Crome before; she showed him round the house. Mr. Barbecue-Smith was full of admiration.

'So quaint, so old-world,' he kept repeating. He had a rich, rather unctuous voice.

Priscilla praised his latest book. 'Splendid, I thought it was,' she said in her large, jolly way.

'I'm happy to think you found it a comfort,' said Mr. Barbecue-Smith.

'Oh, tremendously! And the bit about the Lotus Pool—I thought that so beautiful.'

'I knew you would like that. It came to me, you know, from without.' He waved his hand to indicate the astral world.

They went out into the garden for tea. Mr. Barbecue-Smith was duly introduced.

'Mr. Stone is a writer too,' said Priscilla, as she introduced Denis.

'Indeed!' Mr. Barbecue-Smith smiled benignly, and, looking up at

Denis with an expression of Olympian condescension, 'And what sort of things do you write?'

Denis was furious, and to make matters worse, he felt himself blushing hotly. Had Priscilla no sense of proportion? She was putting them in the same category—Barbecue-Smith and himself. They were both writers, they both used pen and ink. To Mr. Barbecue-Smith's question he answered, 'Oh, nothing much, nothing,' and looked away.

'Mr. Stone is one of our younger poets.' It was Anne's voice. He scowled at her, and she smiled back exasperatingly.

'Excellent, excellent,' said Mr. Barbecue-Smith, and he squeezed Denis's arm encouragingly. 'The Bard's is a noble calling.'

As soon as tea was over Mr. Barbecue-Smith excused himself; he had to do some writing before dinner. Priscilla quite understood. The prophet retired to his chamber.

Mr. Barbecue-Smith came down to the drawing-room at ten to eight. He was in a good humour, and, as he descended the stairs, he smiled to himself and rubbed his large white hands together. In the drawing-room someone was playing softly and ramblingly on the piano. He wondered who it could be. One of the young ladies, perhaps. But no, it was only Denis, who got up hurriedly and with some embarrassment as he came into the room.

'Do go on, do go on,' said Mr. Barbecue-Smith. 'I am very fond of music.'

'Then I couldn't possibly go on,' Denis replied. 'I only make noises.'

There was a silence. Mr. Barbecue-Smith stood with his back to the hearth, warming himself at the memory of last winter's fires. He could not control his interior satisfaction, but still went on smiling to himself. At last he turned to Denis.

'You write,' he asked, 'don't you?'

'Well, yes—a little, you know.'

'How many words do you find you can write in an hour?'

'I don't think I've ever counted.'

'Oh, you ought to, you ought to. It's most important.'

Denis exercised his memory. 'When I'm in good form,' he said, 'I fancy I do a twelve-hundred-word review in about four hours. But sometimes it takes me much longer.'

Mr. Barbecue-Smith nodded. 'Yes, three hundred words an hour at your best.' He walked out into the middle of the room, turned round on his heels, and confronted Denis again. 'Guess how many words I wrote this evening between five and half-past seven.'

'I can't imagine.'

'No, but you must guess. Between five and half-past seven—that's two and a half hours.'

'Twelve hundred words,' Denis hazarded.

'No, no, no.' Mr. Barbecue-Smith's expanded face shone with gaiety. 'Try again.'

'Fifteen hundred.'

'No.'

'I give it up,' said Denis. He found he couldn't summon up much interest in Mr. Barbecue-Smith's writing.

'Well, I'll tell you. Three thousand eight hundred.'

Denis opened his eyes. 'You must get a lot done in a day,' he said.

Mr. Barbecue-Smith suddenly became extremely confidential. He pulled up a stool to the side of Denis's arm-chair, sat down in it, and began to talk softly and rapidly.

'Listen to me,' he said, laying his hand on Denis's sleeve. 'You want to make your living by writing; you're young, you're inexperienced. Let me give you a little sound advice.'

What was the fellow going to do? Denis wondered: give him an introduction to the editor of *John o' London's Weekly*, or tell him where he could sell a light middle for seven guineas? Mr. Barbecue-Smith patted his arm several times and went on.

'The secret of writing,' he said, breathing it into the young man's ear—'the secret of writing is Inspiration.'

Denis looked at him in astonishment.

'Inspiration . . .' Mr. Barbecue-Smith repeated.

'You mean the native wood-note business?'

Mr. Barbecue-Smith nodded.

'Oh, then I entirely agree with you,' said Denis. 'But what if one hasn't got Inspiration?'

'That was precisely the question I was waiting for,' said Mr. Barbecue-Smith. 'You ask me what one should do if one hasn't got Inspiration. I answer: you have Inspiration; everyone has Inspiration. It's simply a question of getting it to function.'

The clock struck eight. There was no sign of any of the other guests; everybody was always late at Crome. Mr. Barbecue-Smith went on.

'That's my secret,' he said. 'I give it you freely.' (Denis made a suitably grateful murmur and grimace.) 'I'll help you to find your Inspiration, because I don't like to see a nice, steady young man like you exhausting his vitality and wasting the best years of his life in a grinding intellectual labour that could be completely obviated by Inspiration. I did it myself, so I know what it's like. Up till the time I was thirty-eight I was a writer like you—a writer without Inspiration. All I wrote I squeezed out of myself by sheer hard work. Why, in those days I was never able to do more than six-fifty words an hour, and what's more, I often didn't sell what I wrote.' He sighed. 'We artists,' he said parenthetically, 'we intellectuals aren't much appreciated here in England.' Denis wondered if there was any method, consistent, of course, with politeness, by which he could dissociate himself from Mr. Barbecue-Smith's 'we.' There was none; and besides, it was too late now, for Mr. Barbecue-Smith was once more pursuing the tenor of his discourse.

'At thirty-eight I was a poor, struggling, tired, overworked, unknown journalist. Now, at fifty . . .' He paused modestly and made a little gesture, moving his fat hands outwards, away from one another, and expanding his fingers as though in demonstration. He was exhibiting himself. Denis thought of that advertisement of Nestlé's milk—the two cats on the wall, under the moon, one black and thin, the other white, sleek, and fat. Before Inspiration and after.

'Inspiration has made the difference,' said Mr. Barbecue-Smith solemnly. 'It came quite suddenly—like a gentle dew from heaven.' He lifted his hand and let it fall back on to his knee to indicate the descent of the dew. 'It was one evening. I was writing my first little book about the Conduct of Life—*Humble Heroisms*. You may have read it; it has been a comfort—at least I hope and think so—a comfort to many thousands. I was in the middle of the second chapter, and I was stuck. Fatigue, overwork—I had only written a hundred words in the last hour, and I could get no further. I sat biting the end of my pen and looking at the electric light, which hung above my table, a little above and in front of me.' He indicated the position of the lamp with elaborate care. 'Have you ever looked at a bright light intently for a long time?' he asked, turning to Denis. Denis didn't think he had. 'You can hypnotize yourself that way,' Mr. Barbecue-Smith went on.

The gong sounded in a terrific crescendo from the hall. Still no sign of the others. Denis was horribly hungry.

'That's what happened to me,' said Mr. Barbecue-Smith. 'I was hypnotized. I lost consciousness like that.' He snapped his fingers. 'When I came to, I found that it was past midnight, and I had written four thousand words. Four thousand,' he repeated, opening his mouth very wide on the *ou* of thousand. 'Inspiration had come to me.'

'What a very extraordinary thing,' said Denis.

'I was afraid of it at first. It didn't seem to me natural. I didn't feel, somehow, that it was quite right, quite fair, I might almost say, to produce a literary composition unconsciously. Besides, I was afraid I might have written nonsense.'

'And had you written nonsense?' Denis asked.

'Certainly not,' Mr. Barbecue-Smith replied, with a trace of annoyance. 'Certainly not. It was admirable. Just a few spelling mistakes and slips, such as there generally are in automatic writing. But the style, the thought—all the essentials were admirable. After that, Inspiration came to me regularly. I wrote the whole of *Humble Heroisms* like that. It was a great success, and so has everything been that I have written since.' He leaned forward and jabbed at Denis with his finger. 'That's my secret,' he said, 'and that's how you could write too, if you tried—without effort, fluently, well.'

'But how?' asked Denis, trying not to show how deeply he had been insulted by that final 'well.'

'By cultivating your Inspiration, by getting into touch with your

Subconscious. Have you ever read my little book, *Pipe-Lines to the Infinite*?'

Denis had to confess that that was, precisely, one of the few, perhaps the only one, of Mr. Barbecue-Smith's works he had not read.

'Never mind, never mind,' said Mr. Barbecue-Smith. 'It's just a little book about the connection of the Subconscious with the Infinite. Get into touch with the Subconscious and you are in touch with the Universe. Inspiration, in fact. You follow me?'

'Perfectly, perfectly,' said Denis. 'But don't you find that the Universe sometimes sends you very irrelevant messages?'

'I don't allow it to,' Mr. Barbecue-Smith replied. 'I canalize it. I bring it down through pipes to work the turbines of my conscious mind.'

'Like Niagara,' Denis suggested. Some of Mr. Barbecue-Smith's remarks sounded strangely like quotations—quotations from his own works, no doubt.

'Precisely. Like Niagara. And this is how I do it.' He leaned forward, and with a raised forefinger marked his points as he made them, beating time, as it were, to his discourse. 'Before I go off into my trance, I concentrate on the subject I wish to be inspired about. Let us say I am writing about the humble heroisms; for ten minutes before I go into the trance I think of nothing but orphans supporting their little brothers and sisters, of dull work well and patiently done, and I focus my mind on such great philosophical truths as the purification and uplifting of the soul by suffering, and the alchemical transformation of leaden evil into golden good.' (Denis again hung up his little festoon of quotation marks.) 'Then I pop off. Two or three hours later I wake up again, and find that inspiration has done its work. Thousands of words, comforting, uplifting words, lie before me. I type them out neatly on my machine and they are ready for the printer.'

'It all sounds wonderfully simple,' said Denis.

'It is. All the great and splendid and divine things of life are wonderfully simple.' (Quotation marks again.) 'When I have to do my aphorisms,' Mr. Barbecue-Smith continued, 'I prelude my trance by turning over the pages of any Dictionary of Quotations or Shakespeare Calendar that comes to hand. That sets the key, so to speak; that ensures that the Universe shall come flowing in, not in a continuous rush, but in aphorismic drops. You see the idea?'

Denis nodded. Mr. Barbecue-Smith put his hand in his pocket and pulled out a notebook. 'I did a few in the train to-day,' he said, turning over the pages. 'Just dropped off into a trance in the corner of my carriage. I find the train very conducive to good work. Here they are.' He cleared his throat and read:

'*The Mountain Road may be steep, but the air is pure up there, and it is from the Summit that one gets the view.*'

'*The Things that Really Matter happen in the Heart.*'

It was curious, Denis reflected, the way the Infinite sometimes repeated itself.

'*Seeing is Believing. Yes, but Believing is also Seeing. If I believe in God, I see God, even in the things that seem to be evil.*'

Mr. Barbecue-Smith looked up from his notebook. 'That last one,' he said, 'is particularly subtle and beautiful, don't you think? Without Inspiration I could never have hit on that.' He re-read the apophthegm with a slower and more solemn utterance. 'Straight from the Infinite,' he commented reflectively, then addressed himself to the next aphorism.

'*The flame of a candle gives Light, but it also Burns.*'

Puzzled wrinkles appeared on Mr. Barbecue-Smith's forehead. 'I don't exactly know what that means,' he said. 'It's very gnomic. One could apply it, of course, to the Higher Education—illuminating, but provoking the Lower Classes to discontent and revolution. Yes, I suppose that's what it is. But it's gnomic, it's gnomic.' He rubbed his chin thoughtfully. The gong sounded again, clamorously, it seemed imploringly: dinner was growing cold. It roused Mr. Barbecue-Smith from meditation. He turned to Denis.

'You understand me now when I advise you to cultivate your Inspiration. Let your Subconscious work for you; turn on the Niagara of the Infinite.'

There was the sound of feet on the stairs. Mr. Barbecue-Smith got up, laid his hand for an instant on Denis's shoulder, and said:

'No more now. Another time. And remember, I rely absolutely on your discretion in this matter. There are intimate, sacred things that one doesn't wish to be generally known.'

'Of course,' said Denis. 'I quite understand.'

## *Chapter 7*

At Crome all the beds were ancient hereditary pieces of furniture. Huge beds, like four-masted ships, with furled sails of shining coloured stuff. Beds carved and inlaid, beds painted and gilded. Beds of walnut and oak, of rare exotic woods. Beds of every date and fashion from the time of Sir Ferdinando, who built the house, to the time of his namesake in the late eighteenth century, the last of the family, but all of them grandiose, magnificent.

The finest of all was now Anne's bed. Sir Julius, son to Sir Ferdinando, had had it made in Venice against his wife's first lying-in. Early *seicento* Venice had expended all its extravagant art in the making of it. The body of the bed was like a great square sarcophagus. Clustering roses were carved in high relief on its wooden panels, and luscious *putti* wallowed among the roses. On the black groundwork of the panels the carved reliefs were gilded and burnished. The golden roses twined in spirals up the four pillar-like posts, and cherubs, seated at the top of each column, supported a wooden canopy fretted with the same carved flowers.

Anne was reading in bed. Two candles stood on the little table beside her. In their rich light her face, her bare arm and shoulder took on warm hues and a sort of peach-like quality of surface. Here and there in the canopy above her carved golden petals shone brightly among profound shadows, and the soft light, falling on the sculptured panel of the bed, broke restlessly among the intricate roses, lingered in a broad caress on the blown cheeks, the dimpled bellies, the tight, absurd little posteriors of the sprawling *putti*.

There was a discreet tap at the door. She looked up. 'Come in, come in.' A face, round and childish within its sleek bell of golden hair, peered round the opening door. More childish-looking still, a suit of mauve pyjamas made its entrance.

It was Mary. 'I thought I'd just look in for a moment to say good-night,' she said, and sat down on the edge of the bed.

Anne closed her book. 'That was very sweet of you.'

'What are you reading?' She looked at the book. 'Rather second-rate, isn't it?' The tone in which Mary pronounced the word 'second-rate' implied an almost infinite denigration. She was accustomed in London to associate only with first-rate people who liked first-rate things, and she knew that there were very, very few first-rate things in the world, and that those were mostly French.

'Well, I'm afraid I like it,' said Anne. There was nothing more to be said. The silence that followed was a rather uncomfortable one. Mary fiddled uneasily with the bottom button of her pyjama jacket. Leaning back on her mound of heaped-up pillows, Anne waited and wondered what was coming.

'I'm so awfully afraid of repressions,' said Mary at last, bursting suddenly and surprisingly into speech. She pronounced the words on the tail-end of an expiring breath, and had to gasp for new air almost before the phrase was finished.

'What's there to be depressed about?'

'I said repressions, not depressions.'

'Oh, repressions; I see,' said Anne. 'But repressions of what?'

Mary had to explain. 'The natural instincts of sex . . .' she began didactically. But Anne cut her short.

'Yes, yes. Perfectly. I understand. Repressions; old maids and all the rest. But what about them?'

'That's just it,' said Mary. 'I'm afraid of them. It's always dangerous to repress one's instincts. I'm beginning to detect in myself symptoms like the ones you read of in the books. I constantly dream that I'm falling down wells; and sometimes I even dream that I'm climbing up ladders. It's most disquieting. The symptoms are only too clear.'

'Are they?'

'One may become a nymphomaniac if one's not careful. You've no idea how serious these repressions are if you don't get rid of them in time.'

'It sounds too awful,' said Anne. 'But I don't see that I can do anything to help you.'

'I thought I'd just like to talk it over with you.'

'Why, of course; I'm only too happy, Mary darling.'

Mary coughed and drew a deep breath. 'I presume,' she began sententiously, 'I presume we may take for granted that an intelligent young woman of twenty-three who has lived in civilized society in the twentieth century has no prejudices.'

'Well, I confess I still have a few.'

'But not about repressions.'

'No, not many about repressions; that's true.'

'Or, rather, about getting rid of repressions.'

'Exactly.'

'So much for our fundamental postulate,' said Mary. Solemnity was expressed in every feature of her round young face, radiated from her large blue eyes. 'We come next to the desirability of possessing experience. I hope we are agreed that knowledge is desirable and that ignorance is undesirable.'

Obedient as one of those complaisant disciples from whom Socrates could get whatever answer he chose, Anne gave her assent to this proposition.

'And we are equally agreed, I hope, that marriage is what it is.'

'It is.'

'Good!' said Mary. 'And repressions being what they are . . .'

'Exactly.'

'There would therefore seem to be only one conclusion.'

'But I knew that,' Anne exclaimed, 'before you began.'

'Yes, but now it's been proved,' said Mary. 'One must do things logically. The question is now . . .'

'But where does the question come in? You've reached your only possible conclusion—logically, which is more than I could have done. All that remains is to impart the information to someone you like—someone you like really rather a lot, someone you're in love with, if I may express myself so baldly.'

'But that's just where the question comes in,' Mary exclaimed. 'I'm not in love with anybody.'

'Then, if I were you, I should wait till you are.'

'But I can't go on dreaming night after night that I'm falling down a well. It's too dangerous.'

'Well, if it really is *too* dangerous, then of course you must do something about it; you must find somebody else.'

'But who?' A thoughtful frown puckered Mary's brow. 'It must be somebody intelligent, somebody with intellectual interests that I can share. And it must be somebody with a proper respect for women, somebody who's prepared to talk seriously about his work and his ideas and about my work and my ideas. It isn't, as you see, at all easy to find the right person.'

'Well,' said Anne, 'there are three unattached and intelligent men in the house at the present time. There's Mr. Scogan, to begin with; but perhaps he's rather too much of a genuine antique. And there are Gombauld and Denis. Shall we say that the choice is limited to the last two?'

Mary nodded. 'I think we had better,' she said, and then hesitated, with a certain air of embarrassment.

'What is it?'

'I was wondering,' said Mary, with a gasp, 'whether they really were unattached. I thought that perhaps you might . . . you might . . .'

'It was very nice of you to think of me, Mary darling,' said Anne, smiling the tight cat's smile. 'But as far as I'm concerned, they are both entirely unattached.'

'I'm very glad of that,' said Mary, looking relieved. 'We are now confronted with the question: Which of the two?'

'I can give no advice. It's a matter for your taste.'

'It's not a matter of my taste,' Mary pronounced, 'but of their merits. We must weigh them and consider them carefully and dispassionately.'

'You must do the weighing yourself,' said Anne; there was still the trace of a smile at the corners of her mouth and round the half-closed eyes. 'I won't run the risk of advising you wrongly.'

'Gombauld has more talent,' Mary began, 'but he is less civilized than Denis.' Mary's pronunciation of 'civilized' gave the word a special and additional significance. She uttered it meticulously, in the very front of her mouth, hissing delicately on the opening sibilant. So few people were civilized, and they, like the first-rate works of art, were mostly French. 'Civilization is most important, don't you think?'

Anne held up her hand. 'I won't advise,' she said. 'You must make the decision.'

'Gombauld's family,' Mary went on reflectively, 'comes from Marseilles. Rather a dangerous heredity, when one thinks of the Latin attitude towards women. But then, I sometimes wonder whether Denis is altogether serious-minded, whether he isn't rather a dilettante. It's very difficult. What do you think?'

'I'm not listening,' said Anne. 'I refuse to take any responsibility.'

Mary sighed. 'Well,' she said, 'I think I had better go to bed and think about it.'

'Carefully and dispassionately,' said Anne.

At the door Mary turned round. 'Good-night,' she said, and

wondered as she said the words why Anne was smiling in that curious way. It was probably nothing, she reflected. Anne often smiled for no apparent reason; it was probably just a habit. 'I hope I shan't dream of falling down wells again to-night,' she added.

'Ladders are worse,' said Anne.

Mary nodded. 'Yes, ladders are much graver.'

## *Chapter 8*

BREAKFAST on Sunday morning was an hour later than on week-days, and Priscilla, who usually made no public appearance before luncheon, honoured it by her presence. Dressed in black silk, with a ruby cross as well as her customary string of pearls round her neck, she presided. An enormous Sunday paper concealed all but the extreme pinnacle of her coiffure from the outer world.

'I see Surrey has won,' she said, with her mouth full, 'by four wickets. The sun is in Leo: that would account for it!'

'Splendid game, cricket,' remarked Mr. Barbecue-Smith heartily to no one in particular; 'so thoroughly English.'

Jenny, who was sitting next to him, woke up suddenly with a start. 'What?' she said. 'What?'

'So English,' repeated Mr. Barbecue-Smith.

Jenny looked at him, surprised. 'English? Of course I am.'

He was beginning to explain, when Mrs. Wimbush vailed her Sunday paper, and appeared, a square, mauve-powdered face in the midst of orange splendours. 'I see there's a new series of articles on the next world just beginning,' she said to Mr. Barbecue-Smith. 'This one's called "Summer Land and Gehenna." '

'Summer Land,' echoed Mr. Barbecue-Smith, closing his eyes. 'Summer Land. A beautiful name. Beautiful—beautiful.'

Mary had taken the seat next to Denis's. After a night of careful consideration she had decided on Denis. He might have less talent than Gombauld, he might be a little lacking in seriousness, but somehow he was safer.

'Are you writing much poetry here in the country?' she asked, with a bright gravity.

'None,' said Denis curtly. 'I haven't brought my typewriter.'

'But do you mean to say you can't write without a typewriter?'

Denis shook his head. He hated talking at breakfast, and, besides, he wanted to hear what Mr. Scogan was saying at the other end of the table.

'. . . My scheme for dealing with the Church,' Mr. Scogan was saying, 'is beautifully simple. At the present time the Anglican clergy wear their collars the wrong way round. I would compel them to wear, not only their collars, but all their clothes, turned back to front—coat, waistcoat, trousers, boots—so that every clergyman should present to the world a smooth façade, unbroken by stud, button, or lace. The enforcement of such a livery would act as a wholesome deterrent to those intending to enter the Church. At the same time it would enormously enhance, what Archbishop Laud so rightly insisted on, the "beauty of holiness" in the few incorrigibles who could not be deterred.'

'In hell, it seems,' said Priscilla, reading in her Sunday paper, 'the children amuse themselves by flaying lambs alive.'

'Ah, but, dear lady, that's only a symbol,' exclaimed Mr. Barbecue-Smith, 'a material symbol of a h-piritual truth. Lambs signify . . .'

'Then there are military uniforms,' Mr. Scogan went on. 'When scarlet and pipeclay were abandoned for khaki, there were some who trembled for the future of war. But then, finding how elegant the new tunic was, how closely it clipped the waist, how voluptuously, with the lateral bustles of the pockets, it exaggerated the hips; when they realized the brilliant potentialities of breeches and top-boots, they were reassured. Abolish these military elegances, standarize a uniform of sack-cloth and mackintosh, you will very soon find that . . .'

'Is anyone coming to church with me this morning?' asked Henry Wimbush. No one responded. He baited his bare invitation. 'I read the lessons, you know. And there's Mr. Bodiham. His sermons are sometimes worth hearing.'

'Thank you, thank you,' said Mr. Barbecue-Smith. 'I for one prefer to worship in the infinite church of Nature. How does our Shakespeare put it? "Sermons in books, stones in the running brooks." ' He waved his arm in a fine gesture towards the window, and even as he did so he became vaguely, but none the less insistently, none the less uncomfortably aware that something had gone wrong with the quotation. Something—what could it be? Sermons? Stones? Books?

## *Chapter 9*

MR. BODIHAM was sitting in his study at the Rectory. The nineteenth-century Gothic windows, narrow and pointed, admitted the light grudgingly; in spite of the brilliant July weather, the room was sombre. Brown varnished bookshelves lined the walls, filled with row upon row of those thick, heavy theological works which the second-hand booksellers generally sell by weight. The mantelpiece, the overmantel, a towering structure of spindly pillars and little shelves, were brown and varnished. The writing-desk was brown and varnished. So were the chairs, so was the door. A dark red-brown carpet with patterns covered the floor. Everything was brown in the room, and there was a curious brownish smell.

In the midst of this brown gloom Mr. Bodiham sat at his desk. He was the man in the Iron Mask. A grey metallic face with iron cheekbones and a narrow iron brow; iron folds, hard and unchanging, ran perpendicularly down his cheeks; his nose was the iron beak of some thin, delicate bird of rapine. He had brown eyes, set in sockets rimmed with iron; round them the skin was dark, as though it had been charred. Dense wiry hair covered his skull; it had been black, it was turning grey. His ears were very small and fine. His jaws, his chin, his upper lip were dark, iron-dark, where he had shaved. His voice, when he spoke and especially when he raised it in preaching, was harsh, like the grating of iron hinges when a seldom-used door is opened.

It was nearly half-past twelve. He had just come back from church, hoarse and weary with preaching. He preached with fury, with passion, an iron man beating with a flail upon the souls of his congregation. But the souls of the faithful at Crome were made of india-rubber, solid rubber; the flail rebounded. They were used to Mr. Bodiham at Crome. The flail thumped on india-rubber, and as often as not the rubber slept.

That morning he had preached, as he had often preached before, on the nature of God. He had tried to make them understand about God, what a fearful thing it is to fall into His hands. God—they thought of something soft and merciful. They blinded themselves to facts; still more, they blinded themselves to the Bible. The passengers on the *Titanic* sang 'Nearer my God to Thee' as the ship was going down. Did they realize what they were asking to be brought nearer to? A white fire of righteousness, an angry fire. . . .

When Savonarola preached, men sobbed and groaned aloud. Nothing broke the polite silence with which Crome listened to Mr. Bodiham—only an occasional cough and sometimes the sound of heavy breathing. In the front pew sat Henry Wimbush, calm, well-bred, beautifully dressed. There were times when Mr. Bodiham wanted to jump down from the pulpit and shake him into life,—times when he would have liked to beat and kill his whole congregation.

He sat at his desk dejectedly. Outside the Gothic windows the earth was warm and marvellously calm. Everything was as it had always been. And yet, and yet . . . It was nearly four years now since he had preached that sermon on Matthew xxiv. 7: 'For nation shall rise up against nation, and kingdom against kingdom: and there shall be famines, and pestilences, and earthquakes, in divers places.' It was nearly four years. He had had the sermon printed; it was so terribly, so vitally important that all the world should know what he had to say. A copy of the little pamphlet lay on his desk—eight small grey pages, printed by a fount of type that had grown blunt, like an old dog's teeth, by the endless champing and champing of the press. He opened it and began to read it yet once again.

' "For nation shall rise up against nation, and kingdom against kingdom: and there shall be famines, and pestilences, and earthquakes, in divers places."

'Nineteen centuries have elapsed since Our Lord gave utterance to those words, and not a single one of them has been without wars, plagues, famines, and earthquakes. Mighty empires have crashed in ruin to the ground, diseases have unpeopled half the globe, there have been vast natural cataclysms in which thousands have been overwhelmed by flood and fire and whirlwind. Time and again, in the course of these nineteen centuries, such things have happened, but they have not brought Christ back to earth. They were "signs of the times" inasmuch as they were signs of God's wrath against the chronic wickedness of mankind, but they were not signs of the times in connection with the Second Coming.

'If earnest Christians have regarded the present war as a true sign of the Lord's approaching return, it is not merely because it happens to be a great war involving the lives of millions of people, not merely because famine is tightening its grip on every country in Europe, not merely because disease of every kind, from syphilis to spotted fever, is rife among the warring nations; no, it is not for these reasons that we regard this war as a true Sign of the Times, but because in its origin and its progress it is marked by certain characteristics which seem to connect it almost beyond a doubt with the predictions in Christian Prophecy relating to the Second Coming of the Lord.

'Let me enumerate the features of the present war which most clearly suggest that it is a Sign foretelling the near approach of the Second Advent. Our Lord said that "this Gospel of the Kingdom shall be preached in all the world for a witness unto all nations; and then shall the end come." Although it would be presumptuous for us to say what degree of evangelization will be regarded by God as sufficient, we may at least confidently hope that a century of unflagging missionary work has brought the fulfilment of this condition at any rate near. True, the larger number of the world's inhabitants have remained deaf to the preaching of the true religion; but that does not vitiate the fact that the Gospel *has* been preached "for a witness" to all unbelievers from the Papist to the Zulu. The responsibility for the continued prevalence of unbelief lies, not with the preachers, but with those preached to.

'Again, it has been generally recognized that "the drying up of the waters of the great river Euphrates," mentioned in the sixteenth chapter of Revelations, refers to the decay and extinction of Turkish power, and is a sign of the near approaching end of the world as we know it. The capture of Jerusalem and the successes in Mesopotamia are great strides forward in the destruction of the Ottoman Empire; though it must be admitted that the Gallipoli episode proved that the Turk still possesses a "notable horn" of strength. Historically speaking, this drying up of Ottoman power has been going on for the past century; the last two years have witnessed a great acceleration of the process, and there can be no doubt that complete desiccation is within sight.

'Closely following on the words concerning the drying up of Euphrates comes the prophecy of Armageddon, that world war with which the Second Coming is to be so closely associated. Once begun, the world war can end only with the return of Christ, and His coming will be sudden and unexpected, like that of a thief in the night.

'Let us examine the facts. In history, exactly as in St. John's Gospel, the world war is immediately preceded by the drying up of Euphrates, or the decay of Turkish power. This fact alone would be enough to connect the present conflict with the Armageddon of Revelations and therefore to point to the near approach of the Second Advent. But further evidence of an even more solid and convincing nature can be adduced.

'Armageddon is brought about by the activities of three unclean spirits, as it were toads, which come out of the mouths of the Dragon, the Beast, and the False Prophet. If we can identify these three powers of evil much light will clearly be thrown on the whole question.

'The Dragon, the Beast, and the False Prophet can all be identified in history. Satan, who can only work through human agency, has used these three powers in the long war against Christ which has filled the last nineteen centuries with religious strife. The Dragon, it has been sufficiently established, is pagan Rome, and the spirit issuing from its mouth is the spirit of Infidelity. The Beast, alternatively symbolized as a Woman, is undoubtedly the Papal power, and Popery is the spirit which it spews forth. There is only one power which answers to the description of the False Prophet, the wolf in sheep's clothing, the agent of the devil working in the guise of the Lamb, and that power is the so-called "Society of Jesus." The spirit that issues from the mouth of the False Prophet is the spirit of False Morality.

'We may assume, then, that the three evil spirits are Infidelity, Popery, and False Morality. Have these three influences been the real cause of the present conflict? The answer is clear.

'The spirit of Infidelity is the very spirit of German criticism. The Higher Criticism, as it is mockingly called, denies the possibility of miracles, prediction, and real inspiration, and attempts to account for the Bible as a natural development. Slowly but surely, during the last eighty years, the spirit of Infidelity has been robbing the Germans of their Bible and their faith, so that Germany is to-day a nation of unbelievers. Higher Criticism has thus made the war possible; for it would be absolutely impossible for any Christian nation to wage war as Germany is waging it.

'We come next to the spirit of Popery, whose influence in causing the war was quite as great as that of Infidelity, though not, perhaps, so immediately obvious. Since the Franco-Prussian War the Papal power has steadily declined in France, while in Germany it has steadily increased. To-day France is an anti-papal state, while Germany possesses a powerful Roman Catholic minority. Two papally controlled states, Germany and Austria, are at war with six anti-papal states—England, France, Italy, Russia, Serbia, and Portugal. Belgium is, of course, a thoroughly papal state, and there can be little doubt that the presence on the Allies' side of an element so essentially hostile has done much to hamper the righteous cause and is responsible for our comparative ill-success. That the spirit of Popery is behind the war is thus seen clearly enough in the grouping of the opposed powers, while the rebellion in the Roman Catholic parts of Ireland has merely confirmed a conclusion already obvious to any unbiased mind.

'The spirit of False Morality has played as great a part in this war as the two other evil spirits. The Scrap of Paper incident is the nearest and most obvious example of Germany's adherence to this essentially unchristian or Jesuitical morality. The end is German world-power, and in the attainment of this end, any means are justifiable. It is the true principle of Jesuitry applied to international politics.

'The identification is now complete. As was predicted in Revelations, the three evil spirits have gone forth just as the decay of the Ottoman power was nearing completion, and have joined together to make the world war. The warning, "Behold, I come as a thief," is therefore meant for the present period—for you and me and all the world. This war will lead on inevitably to the war of Armageddon, and will only be brought to an end by the Lord's personal return.

'And when He returns, what will happen? Those who are in Christ, St. John tells us, will be called to the Supper of the Lamb. Those who are found fighting against Him will be called to the Supper of the Great God—that grim banquet where they shall not feast, but be feasted on. "For," as St. John says, "I saw an angel standing in the sun; and he cried in a loud voice, saying to all the fowls that fly in the midst of heaven, Come and gather yourselves together unto the supper of the Great God; that ye may eat the flesh of kings, and the flesh of captains, and the flesh of mighty men, and the flesh of horses, and of them that sit on them, and the flesh of all men, both free and bond, both small and great." All the enemies of Christ will be slain with the sword of him that sits upon the horse, "and all the fowls will be filled with their flesh." That is the Supper of the Great God.

'It may be soon or it may, as men reckon time, be long; but sooner or later, inevitably, the Lord will come and deliver the world from its present troubles. And woe unto them who are called, not to the Supper of the Lamb, but to the Supper of the Great God. They will realize then, but too late, that God is a God of Wrath as well as a God of Forgiveness. The God who sent bears to devour the mockers of Elisha, the God who smote the Egyptians for their stubborn wickedness, will assuredly smite them too, unless they make haste to repent. But perhaps it is already too late. Who knows but that to-morrow, in a moment even, Christ may be upon us unawares, like a thief? In a little while, who knows? the angel standing in the sun may be summoning the ravens and vultures from their crannies in the rocks to feed upon the putrefying flesh of the millions of unrighteous whom God's wrath has destroyed. Be ready, then; the coming of the Lord is at hand. May it be for all of you an object of hope, not a moment to be looked forward to with terror and trembling.'

Mr. Bodiham closed the little pamphlet and leaned back in his chair. The argument was sound, absolutely compelling; and yet—it was four years since he had preached that sermon; four years, and England was at peace, the sun shone, the people of Crome were as wicked and indifferent as ever—more so, indeed, if that were possible. If only he could understand, if the heavens would but make a sign! But his questionings remained unanswered. Seated there in his brown varnished chair under the Ruskinian window, he could have screamed aloud. He gripped the arms of his chair—gripping, gripping for control. The knuckles of his hands whitened; he bit his lip. In a few seconds he was able to relax the tension; he began to rebuke himself for his rebellious impatience.

Four years, he reflected; what were four years, after all? It must inevitably take a long time for Armageddon to ripen, to yeast itself up. The episode of 1914 had been a preliminary skirmish. And as for the war having come to an end—why, that, of course, was illusory. It was still going on, smouldering away in Silesia, in Ireland, in Anatolia; the discontent in Egypt and India was preparing the way, perhaps, for a great extension of the slaughter among the heathen peoples. The Chinese boycott of Japan, and the rivalries of that country and America in the Pacific, might be breeding a great new war in the East. The prospect, Mr. Bodiham tried to assure himself, was hopeful; the real, the genuine Armageddon might soon begin, and then, like a thief in the night . . . But, in spite of all his comfortable reasoning, he remained unhappy, dissatisfied. Four years ago he had been so confident; God's intention seemed then so plain. And now? Now, he did well to be angry. And now he suffered too.

Sudden and silent as a phantom Mrs. Bodiham appeared, gliding noiselessly across the room. Above her black dress her face was pale with an opaque whiteness, her eyes were pale as water in a glass, and her strawy hair was almost colourless. She held a large envelope in her hand.

'This came for you by the post,' she said softly.

The envelope was unsealed. Mechanically Mr. Bodiham tore it open. It contained a pamphlet, larger than his own and more elegant in appearance. 'The House of Sheeny, Clerical Outfitters, Birmingham.' He turned over the pages. The catalogue was tastefully and ecclesiastically printed in antique characters with illuminated Gothic initials. Red marginal lines, crossed at the corners after the manner of an Oxford picture frame, enclosed each page of type; little red crosses took the place of full stops. Mr. Bodiham turned the pages.

*Soutane in best black merino. Ready to wear; in all sizes.*

*Clerical frock-coats. From nine guineas. A dressy garment, tailored by our own experienced ecclesiastical cutters.*

Half-tone illustrations represented young curates, some dapper, some Rugbeian and muscular, some with ascetic faces and large ecstatic eyes, dressed in jackets, in frock-coats, in surplices, in clerical evening dress, in black Norfolk suitings.

*A large assortment of chasubles.*

*Rope girdles.*

*Sheeny's Special Skirt Cassocks. Tied by a string about the waist. . . . When worn under a surplice presents an appearance indistinguishable from that of a complete cassock. . . . Recommended for summer wear and hot climates.*

With a gesture of horror and disgust Mr. Bodiham threw the catalogue into the waste-paper basket. Mrs. Bodiham looked at him; her pale, glaucous eyes reflected his action without comment.

'The village,' she said in her quiet voice, 'the village grows worse and worse every day.'

'What has happened now?' asked Mr. Bodiham, feeling suddenly very weary.

'I'll tell you.' She pulled up a brown varnished chair and sat down. In the village of Crome, it seemed, Sodom and Gomorrah had come to a second birth.

The sermon attributed to "*Mr. Bodiham*" in Chapter 9 is a reproduction of the substance of an Address, given by the Rev. E. H. Horne, in A.D. 1916, to a meeting of clergy, and then published. It is now reprinted as an Appendix in a small book by him, entitled *The Significance of Air War* (Marshall, Morgan and Scott).

## *Chapter 10*

DENIS did not dance, but when ragtime came squirting out of the pianola in gushes of treacle and hot perfume, in jets of Bengal light, then things began to dance inside him. Little black nigger corpuscles jigged and drummed in his arteries. He became a cage of movement, a walking *palais de danse*. It was very uncomfortable, like the preliminary symptoms of a disease. He sat in one of the window-seats, glumly pretending to read.

At the pianola, Henry Wimbush, smoking a long cigar through a tunnelled pillar of amber, trod out the shattering dance music with serene patience. Locked together, Gombauld and Anne moved with a harmoniousness that made them seem a single creature, two-headed and four-legged. Mr. Scogan, solemnly buffoonish, shuffled round the room with Mary. Jenny sat in the shadow behind the piano, scribbling, so it seemed, in a big red notebook. In arm-chairs by the fireplace, Priscilla and Mr. Barbecue-Smith discussed higher things, without, apparently, being disturbed by the noise of the Lower Plane.

'Optimism,' said Mr. Barbecue-Smith, with a tone of finality, speaking through strains of the 'Wild, Wild Women'—'optimism is the opening out of the soul towards the light; it is an expansion towards and into God, it is a h-piritual self-unification with the Infinite.'

'How true!' sighed Priscilla, nodding the baleful splendours of her coiffure.

'Pessimism, on the other hand, is the contraction of the soul towards darkness; it is a focusing of the self upon a point in the Lower Plane; it is a h-piritual slavery to mere facts, to gross physical phenomena.'

'They're making a wild man of me.' The refrain sang itself over in Denis's mind. Yes, they were; damn them! A wild man, but not wild enough; that was the trouble. Wild inside; raging, writhing—yes, 'writhing' was the word, writhing with desire. But outwardly he was hopelessly tame; outwardly—baa, baa, baa.

There they were, Anne and Gombauld, moving together as though they were a single supple creature. The beast with two backs. And he sat in a corner, pretending to read, pretending he didn't want to dance, pretending he rather despised dancing. Why? It was the baa-baa business again.

Why was he born with a different face? Why *was* he? Gombauld had a face of brass—one of those old, brazen rams that thumped against the walls of cities till they fell. He was born with a different face—a woolly face.

The music stopped. The single harmonious creature broke in two. Flushed, a little breathless, Anne swayed across the room to the pianola, laid her hand on Mr. Wimbush's shoulder.

'A waltz this time, please, Uncle Henry,' she said.

'A waltz,' he repeated, and turned to the cabinet where the rolls were kept. He trod off the old roll and trod on the new, a slave at the mill, uncomplaining and beautifully well bred. 'Rum; Tum; Rum-ti-ti-; Tum-ti-ti. . . .' The melody wallowed oozily along, like a ship moving forward over a sleek and oily swell. The four-legged creature, more graceful, more harmonious in its movements than ever, slid across the floor. Oh, why was he born with a different face?

'What are you reading?'

He looked up, startled. It was Mary. She had broken from the uncomfortable embrace of Mr. Scogan, who had now seized on Jenny for his victim.

'What are you reading?'

'I don't know,' said Denis truthfully. He looked at the title page; the book was called *The Stock Breeder's Vade Mecum.*

'I think you are so sensible to sit and read quietly,' said Mary, fixing him with her china eyes. 'I don't know why one dances. It's so boring.'

Denis made no reply; she exacerbated him. From the arm-chair by the fireplace he heard Priscilla's deep voice.

'Tell me, Mr. Barbecue-Smith—you know all about science, I know——' A deprecating noise came from Mr. Barbecue-Smith's chair. 'This Einstein theory. It seems to upset the whole starry universe. It makes me so worried about my horoscopes. You see . . .'

Mary renewed her attack. 'Which of the contemporary poets do you like best?' she asked. Denis was filled with fury. Why couldn't this pest of a girl leave him alone? He wanted to listen to the horrible music, to watch them dancing—oh, with what grace, as though they had been made for one another!—to savour his misery in peace. And she came and put him through this absurd catechism! She was like 'Mangold's Questions': 'What are the three diseases of wheat?'—'Which of the contemporary poets do you like best?'

'Blight, Mildew, and Smut,' he replied, with the laconism of one who is absolutely certain of his own mind.

It was several hours before Denis managed to go to sleep that night. Vague but agonizing miseries possessed his mind. It was not only Anne who made him miserable; he was wretched about himself, the future, life in general, the universe. 'This adolescence business,' he repeated to himself every now and then, 'is horribly boring.' But the fact that he knew his disease did not help him to cure it.

After kicking all the clothes off the bed, he got up and sought relief in composition. He wanted to imprison his nameless misery in words. At the end of an hour, nine more or less complete lines emerged from among the blots and scratchings.

I do not know what I desire
When summer nights are dark and still,
When the wind's many-voicéd quire
Sleeps among the muffled branches.
I long and know not what I will:
And not a sound of life or laughter stanches
Time's black and silent flow.
I do not know what I desire,
I do not know.

He read it through aloud; then threw the scribbled sheet into the waste-paper basket and got into bed again. In a very few minutes he was asleep.

## *Chapter 11*

Mr. Barbecue-Smith was gone. The motor had whirled him away to the station; a faint smell of burning oil commemorated his recent departure. A considerable detachment had come into the courtyard to speed him on his way; and now they were walking back, round the side of the house, towards the terrace and the garden. They walked in silence; nobody had yet ventured to comment on the departed guest.

'Well?' said Anne, at last, turning with raised inquiring eyebrows to Denis. 'Well?' It was time for someone to begin.

Denis declined the invitation; he passed it on to Mr. Scogan. 'Well?' he said.

Mr. Scogan did not respond; he only repeated the question, 'Well?'

It was left for Henry Wimbush to make a pronouncement. 'A very agreeable adjunct to the week-end,' he said. His tone was obituary.

They had descended, without paying much attention where they were going, the steep yew-walk that went down, under the flank of the terrace, to the pool. The house towered above them, immensely tall, with the whole height of the built-up terrace added to its own seventy feet of brick façade. The perpendicular lines of the three towers soared up, uninterrupted, enhancing the impression of height until it became overwhelming. They paused at the edge of the pool to look back.

'The man who built this house knew his business,' said Denis. 'He was an architect.'

'Was he?' said Henry Wimbush reflectively. 'I doubt it. The builder of this house was Sir Ferdinando Lapith, who flourished during the reign of Elizabeth. He inherited the estate from his father, to whom it had been granted at the time of the dissolution of the monasteries; for Crome was originally a cloister of monks and this swimming-pool their fish-pond. Sir Ferdinando was not content merely to adapt the old monastic buildings to his own purposes; but using them as a stone quarry for his barns and byres and outhouses, he built for himself a grand new house of brick—the house you see now.'

He waved his hand in the direction of the house and was silent. Severe, imposing, almost menacing, Crome loomed down on them.

'The great thing about Crome,' said Mr. Scogan, seizing the opportunity to speak, 'is the fact that it's so unmistakably and aggressively a work of art. It makes no compromise with nature, but affronts it and rebels against it. It has no likeness to Shelley's tower, in the "Epipsychidion," which, if I remember rightly—

> Seems not now a work of human art,
> But as it were titanic, in the heart
> Of earth having assumed its form and grown
> Out of the mountain, from the living stone,
> Lifting itself in caverns light and high.

No, no; there isn't any nonsense of that sort about Crome. That the hovels of the peasantry should look as though they had grown out of the earth, to which their inmates are attached, is right, no doubt, and suitable. But the house of an intelligent, civilized, and sophisticated man should never seem to have sprouted from the clods. It should rather be an expression of his grand unnatural remoteness from the cloddish life. Since the days of William Morris that's a fact which we in England have been unable to comprehend. Civilized and sophisticated men have solemnly played at being peasants. Hence quaintness, arts and crafts, cottage architecture, and all the rest of it. In the suburbs of our cities you may see, reduplicated in endless rows, studiedly quaint imitations and adaptations of the village hovel. Poverty, ignorance, and a limited range of materials produced the hovel, which possesses undoubtedly, in suitable surroundings, its own "as it were titanic" charm. We now employ our wealth, our technical knowledge, our rich variety of materials for the purpose of building millions of imitation hovels in totally unsuitable surroundings. Could imbecility go further?'

Henry Wimbush took up the thread of his interrupted discourse. 'All that you say, my dear Scogan,' he began, 'is certainly very just, very true. But whether Sir Ferdinando shared your views about architecture or if, indeed, he had any views about architecture at all, I very much doubt. In building this house, Sir Ferdinando was, as a matter of fact, preoccupied by only one thought—the proper placing of his privies. Sanitation was the one great interest of his life. In 1573 he even published, on this subject, a little book—now extremely scarce—called, *Certaine Priuy Counsels* by *One of Her Maiestie's Most Honourable Priuy Counsel, F. L. Knight*, in which the whole matter is treated with great learning and elegance. His guiding principle in arranging the sanitation of a house was to secure that the greatest possible distance should separate the privy from the sewage arrangements. Hence it followed inevitably that the privies were to be placed at the top of the house, being connected by vertical shafts with pits or channels in the ground. It must not be thought that Sir Ferdinando was moved only by material and merely sanitary considerations; for the placing of his privies in an exalted position he had also certain excellent spiritual reasons. For, he argues in the third chapter of his *Priuy Counsels*, the necessities of nature are so base and brutish that in obeying them we are apt to forget that we are the noblest creatures of the universe. To counteract these degrading effects he advised that the privy should be in every house the room nearest to heaven, that it should be well provided with windows commanding an extensive and noble prospect, and that the walls of the chamber should be lined with book-shelves containing all the ripest products of human wisdom, such as the Proverbs of Solomon, Boëthius's *Consolations of Philosophy*, the apophthegms of Epictetus and Marcus Aurelius, the *Enchiridion* of Erasmus, and all other works, ancient or modern, which testify to the nobility of the human soul. In Crome he was able to put his theories into practice. At the top of each of the three projecting towers he placed a privy. From these a shaft went down the whole height of the house, that is to say, more than seventy feet, through the cellars, and into a series of conduits provided with flowing water tunnelled in the ground on a level with the base of the raised terrace. These conduits emptied themselves into the stream several hundred yards below the fish-pond. The total depth of the shafts from the top of the towers to their subterranean conduits was a hundred and two feet. The eighteenth century, with its passion for modernization, swept away these monuments of sanitary ingenuity. Were it not for tradition and the explicit account of them left by Sir Ferdinando, we should be unaware that these noble privies had ever existed. We should even suppose that Sir Ferdinando built his house after this strange and splendid model for merely æsthetic reasons.'

The contemplation of the glories of the past always evoked in Henry Wimbush a certain enthusiasm. Under the grey bowler his face worked and glowed as he spoke. The thought of these vanished privies moved him profoundly. He ceased to speak; the light gradually died out of his face, and it became once more the replica of the grave, polite hat which shaded it. There was a long silence; the same gently melancholy thoughts seemed to possess the mind of each of them. Permanence, transience—Sir Ferdinando and his privies were gone, Crome still stood. How brightly the sun shone and how inevitable was death! The ways of God were strange; the ways of man were stranger still. . . .

'It does one's heart good,' exclaimed Mr. Scogan at last, 'to hear of these fantastic English aristocrats. To have a theory about privies and to build an immense and splendid house in order to put it into practice—it's magnificent, beautiful! I like to think of them all: the eccentric milords rolling across Europe in ponderous carriages, bound on extraordinary errands. One is going to Venice to buy La Bianchi's larynx; he won't get it till she's dead, of course, but no matter; he's prepared to wait; he has a collection, pickled in glass bottles, of the throats of famous opera singers. And the instruments of renowned virtuosi—he goes in for them too; he will try to bribe Paganini to part with his little Guarnerio, but he has small hope of success. Paganini won't sell his fiddle; but perhaps he might sacrifice one of his guitars. Others are bound on crusades—one to die miserably among the savage Greeks, another, in his white top hat, to lead Italians against their oppressors. Others have no business at all; they are just giving their oddity a continental airing. At home they cultivate themselves at leisure and with greater elaboration. Beckford builds towers, Portland digs holes in the ground, Cavendish, the millionaire, lives in a stable, eats nothing but mutton, and amuses himself—oh, solely for his private delectation—by anticipating the electrical discoveries of half a century. Glorious eccentrics! Every age is enlivened by their presence. Some day, my dear Denis,' said Mr. Scogan, turning a beady bright regard in his direction—'some day you must become their biographer—"The Lives of Queer Men." What a subject! I should like to undertake it myself.'

Mr. Scogan paused, looked up once more at the towering house, then murmured the word, 'Eccentricity,' two or three times.

'Eccentricity. . . . It's the justification of all aristocracies. It justifies leisured classes and inherited wealth and privilege and endowments and all the other injustices of that sort. If you're to do anything reasonable in this world, you must have a class of people who are secure, safe from public opinion, safe from poverty, leisured, not compelled to waste their time in the imbecile routines that go by the name of Honest Work. You must have a class of which the members can think and, within the obvious limits, do what they please. You must have a class in which people who have eccentricities can indulge them and in which eccentricity in general will be tolerated and understood. That's the important thing about an aristocracy. Not only is it eccentric itself—often grandiosely so; it also tolerates and even encourages eccentricity in others. The eccentricities of the artist and the new-fangled thinker don't inspire it with that fear, loathing, and disgust which the burgesses instinctively feel towards them. It is a sort of Red Indian Reservation planted in the midst of a vast horde of Poor Whites—colonials at that. Within its boundaries wild men disport themselves—often, it must be admitted, a little grossly, a little too flamboyantly; and when kindred spirits are born outside the pale it offers them some sort of refuge from the hatred which the Poor Whites, *en bons bourgeois*, lavish on anything that is wild or out of the ordinary. After the social revolution there will be no Reservations; the Redskins will be drowned in the great sea of Poor Whites. What then? Will they suffer you to go on writing villanelles, my good Denis? Will you, unhappy Henry, be allowed to live in this house of the splendid privies, to continue your quiet delving in the mines of futile knowledge? Will Anne . . .'

'And you,' said Anne, interrupting him, 'will you be allowed to go on talking?'

'You may rest assured,' Mr. Scogan replied, 'that I shall not. I shall have some Honest Work to do.'

## *Chapter 12*

'BLIGHT, Mildew, and Smut. . . .' Mary was puzzled and distressed. Perhaps her ears had played her false. Perhaps what he had really said was, 'Squire, Binyon, and Shanks,' or 'Childe, Blunden, and Earp,' or even 'Abercrombie, Drinkwater, and Rabindranath Tagore.' Perhaps. But then her ears never did play her false. 'Blight, Mildew, and Smut.' The impression was distinct and ineffaceable. 'Blight, Mildew . . .' she was forced to the conclusion, reluctantly, that Denis had indeed pronounced those improbable words. He had deliberately repelled her attempt to open a serious discussion. That was horrible. A man who would not talk seriously to a woman just because she was a woman—oh, impossible! Egeria or nothing. Perhaps Gombauld would be more satisfactory. True, his meridional heredity was a little disquieting; but at least he was a serious worker, and it was with his work that she would associate herself. And Denis? After all, what *was* Denis? A dilettante, an amateur. . . .

Gombauld had annexed for his painting-room a little disused granary that stood by itself in a green close beyond the farmyard. It was a square brick building with a peaked roof and little windows set high up in each of its walls. A ladder of four rungs led up to the door; for the granary was perched above the ground, and out of reach of the rats, on four massive toadstools of grey stone. Within, there lingered a faint smell of dust and cobwebs; and the narrow shaft of sunlight that came slanting in at every hour of the day through one of the little windows was always alive with silvery motes. Here Gombauld worked, with a kind of concentrated ferocity, during six or seven hours of each day. He was pursuing something new, something terrific, if only he could catch it.

During the last eight years, nearly half of which had been spent in the process of winning the war, he had worked his way industriously through cubism. Now he had come out on the other side. He had begun by painting a formalized nature; then, little by little, he had risen from nature into the world of pure form, till in the end he was painting nothing but his own thoughts, externalized in the abstract geometrical forms of the mind's devising. He found the process arduous and exhilarating. And then, quite suddenly, he grew dissatisfied; he felt himself cramped and confined within intolerably narrow limitations. He was humiliated to find how few and crude and uninteresting were the forms he could invent; the inventions of nature were without number, inconceivably subtle and elaborate. He had done with cubism. He was out on the other side. But the cubist discipline preserved him from falling into excesses of nature worship. He took from nature its rich, subtle, elaborate forms, but his aim was always to work them into a whole that should have the thrilling simplicity and formality of an idea; to combine prodigious realism with prodigious simplification. Memories of Caravaggio's portentous achievements haunted him. Forms of a breathing, living reality emerged from darkness, built themselves up into compositions as luminously simple and single as a mathematical idea. He thought of the 'Call of Matthew,' of 'Peter Crucified,' of the 'Lute Players,' of 'Magdalen.' He had the secret, that astonishing ruffian, he had the secret! And now Gombauld was after it, in hot pursuit. Yes, it would be something terrific, if only he could catch it.

For a long time an idea had been stirring and spreading, yeastily, in his mind. He had made a portfolio full of studies, he had drawn a cartoon; and now the idea was taking shape on canvas. A man fallen from a horse. The huge animal, a gaunt white cart-horse, filled the upper half of the picture with its great body. Its head, lowered towards the ground, was in shadow; the immense bony body was what arrested the eye, the body and the legs, which came down on either side of the picture like the pillars of an arch. On the ground, between the legs of the towering beast, lay the foreshortened figure of a man, the head in the extreme foreground, the arms flung wide to right and left. A white, relentless light poured down from a point in the right foreground. The beast, the fallen man, were sharply illuminated; round them, beyond and behind them, was the night. They were alone in the darkness, a universe in themselves.

The picture was more than half finished. Gombauld had been at work all the morning on the figure of the man, and now he was taking a rest—the time to smoke a cigarette. Tilting back his chair till it touched the wall, he looked thoughtfully at his canvas. He was pleased, and at the same time he was desolated. In itself, the thing was good; he knew it. But that something he was after, that something that would be so terrific if only he could catch it—had he caught it? Would he ever catch it?

Three little taps—rat, tat, tat! Surprised, Gombauld turned his eyes towards the door. Nobody ever disturbed him while he was at work; it was one of the unwritten laws. 'Come in!' he called. The door, which was ajar, swung open, revealing, from the waist upwards, the form of Mary. She had only dared to mount half-way up the ladder. If he didn't want her, retreat would be easier and more dignified than if she climbed to the top.

'May I come in?' she asked.

'Certainly.'

She skipped up the remaining two rungs and was over the threshold in an instant. 'A letter came for you by the second post,' she said. 'I thought it might be important, so I brought it out to you.' Her eyes, her childish face were luminously candid as she handed him the letter. There had never been a flimsier pretext.

Gombauld looked at the envelope and put it in his pocket unopened. 'Luckily,' he said, 'it isn't at all important. Thanks very much all the same.'

There was a silence; Mary felt a little uncomfortable. 'May I have a look at what you've been painting?' she had the courage to say at last.

Gombauld had only half smoked his cigarette; in any case he wouldn't begin work again till he had finished. He would give her the five minutes that separated him from the bitter end. 'This is the best place to see it from,' he said.

Mary looked at the picture for some time without saying anything. Indeed, she didn't know what to say; she was taken aback, she was at a loss. She had expected a cubist masterpiece, and here was a picture of a man and a horse, not only recognizable as such, but even aggressively in drawing. *Trompe-l'œil*—there was no other word to describe the delineation of that foreshortened figure under the trampling feet of the horse. What was she to think, what was she to say? Her orientations were gone. One could admire representationalism in the Old Masters. Obviously. But in a modern . . .? At eighteen she might have done so. But now, after five years of schooling among the best judges, her instinctive reaction to a contemporary piece of representation was contempt—an outburst of laughing disparagement. What could Gombauld be up to? She had felt so safe in admiring his work before. But now—she didn't know what to think. It was very difficult, very difficult.

'There's rather a lot of chiaroscuro, isn't there?' she ventured at last, and inwardly congratulated herself on having found a critical formula so gentle and at the same time so penetrating.

'There is,' Gombauld agreed.

Mary was pleased; he accepted her criticism; it was a serious discussion. She put her head on one side and screwed up her eyes. 'I think it's awfully fine,' she said. 'But of course it's a little too . . . too . . . *trompe-l'œil* for my taste.' She looked at Gombauld, who made no response, but continued to smoke, gazing meditatively all the time at his picture. Mary went on gaspingly. 'When I was in Paris this spring I saw a lot of Tschuplitski. I admire his work so tremendously. Of course, it's frightfully abstract now—frightfully abstract and frightfully intellectual. He just throws a few oblongs on to his canvas—quite flat, you know, and painted in pure primary colours. But his design is wonderful. He's getting more and more abstract every day. He'd quite given up the third dimension when I was there and was just thinking of giving up the second. Soon, he says, there'll be just the blank canvas. That's the logical conclusion. Complete abstraction. Painting's finished; he's finishing it. When he's reached pure abstraction he's going to take up architecture. He says it's more intellectual than painting. Do you agree?' she asked, with a final gasp.

Gombauld dropped his cigarette end and trod on it. 'Tschuplitski's finished painting,' he said. 'I've finished my cigarette. But I'm going on painting.' And, advancing towards her, he put his arm round her shoulders and turned her round, away from the picture.

Mary looked up at him; her hair swung back, a soundless bell of gold. Her eyes were serene; she smiled. So the moment had come. His arm was round her. He moved slowly, almost imperceptibly, and she moved with him. It was a peripatetic embracement. 'Do you agree with him?' she repeated. The moment might have come, but she would not cease to be intellectual, serious.

'I don't know. I shall have to think about it.' Gombauld loosened his embrace, his hand dropped from her shoulder. 'Be careful going down the ladder,' he added solicitously.

Mary looked round, startled. They were in front of the open door. She remained standing there for a moment in bewilderment. The hand that had rested on her shoulder made itself felt lower down her back; it administered three or four kindly little smacks. Replying automatically to its stimulus, she moved forward.

'Be careful going down the ladder,' said Gombauld once more.

She was careful. The door closed behind her and she was alone in the little green close. She walked slowly back through the farmyard; she was pensive.

## *Chapter 13*

HENRY WIMBUSH brought down with him to dinner a budget of printed sheets loosely bound together in a cardboard portfolio.

'To-day,' he said, exhibiting it with a certain solemnity, 'to-day I have finished the printing of my *History of Crome*. I helped to set up the type of the last page this evening.'

'The famous History?' cried Anne. The writing and the printing of this *Magnum Opus* had been going on as long as she could remember. All her childhood long Uncle Henry's History had been a vague and fabulous thing, often heard of and never seen.

'It has taken me nearly thirty years,' said Mr. Wimbush. 'Twenty-five years of writing and nearly four of printing. And now it's finished—the whole chronicle, from Sir Ferdinando Lapith's birth to the death of my father William Wimbush—more than three centuries and a half: a history of Crome, written at Crome, and printed at Crome by my own press.'

'Shall we be allowed to read it now it's finished?' asked Denis.

Mr. Wimbush nodded. 'Certainly,' he said. 'And I hope you will not find it uninteresting,' he added modestly. 'Our muniment room is particularly rich in ancient records, and I have some genuinely new light to throw on the introduction of the three-pronged fork.'

'And the people?' asked Gombauld. 'Sir Ferdinando and the rest of them—were they amusing? Were there any crimes or tragedies in the family?'

'Let me see,' Henry Wimbush rubbed his chin thoughtfully. 'I can only think of two suicides, one violent death, four or perhaps five broken hearts, and half a dozen little blots on the scutcheon in the way of misalliances, seductions, natural children, and the like. No, on the whole, it's a placid and uneventful record.'

'The Wimbushes and the Lapiths were always an unadventurous, respectable crew,' said Priscilla, with a note of scorn in her voice. 'If I were to write my family history now! Why, it would be one long continuous blot from beginning to end.' She laughed jovially, and helped herself to another glass of wine.

'If I were to write mine,' Mr. Scogan remarked, 'it wouldn't exist. After the second generation we Scogans are lost in the mists of antiquity.'

'After dinner,' said Henry Wimbush, a little piqued by his wife's disparaging comment on the masters of Crome, 'I'll read you an episode from my History that will make you admit that even the Lapiths, in their own respectable way, had their tragedies and strange adventures.'

'I'm glad to hear it,' said Priscilla.

'Glad to hear what?' asked Jenny, emerging suddenly from her private interior world like a cuckoo from a clock. She received an explanation, smiled, nodded, cuckooed a last 'I see,' and popped back, clapping shut the door behind her.

Dinner was eaten; the party had adjourned to the drawing-room.

'Now,' said Henry Wimbush, pulling up a chair to the lamp. He put on his round pince-nez, rimmed with tortoise-shell, and began cautiously to turn over the pages of his loose and still fragmentary book. He found his place at last. 'Shall I begin?' he asked, looking up.

'Do,' said Priscilla, yawning.

In the midst of an attentive silence Mr. Wimbush gave a little preliminary cough and started to read.

'The infant who was destined to become the fourth baronet of the name of Lapith was born in the year 1740. He was a very small baby, weighing not more than three pounds at birth, but from the first he was sturdy and healthy. In honour of his maternal grandfather, Sir Hercules Occam of Bishop's Occam, he was christened Hercules. His mother, like many other mothers, kept a notebook, in which his progress from month to month was recorded. He walked at ten months, and before his second year was out he had learnt to speak a number of words. At three years he weighed but twenty-four pounds, and at six, though he could read and write perfectly and showed a remarkable aptitude for music, he was no larger and heavier than a well-grown child of two. Meanwhile, his mother had borne two other children, a boy and a girl, one of whom died of croup during infancy, while the other was carried off by smallpox before it reached the age of five. Hercules remained the only surviving child.

'On his twelfth birthday Hercules was still only three feet and two inches in height. His head, which was very handsome and nobly shaped, was too big for his body, but otherwise he was exquisitely proportioned and, for his size, of great strength and agility. His parents, in the hope of making him grow, consulted all the most eminent physicians of the time. Their various prescriptions were followed to the letter, but in vain. One ordered a very plentiful meat diet; another exercise; a third constructed a little rack, modelled on those employed by the Holy Inquisition, on which young Hercules was stretched, with excruciating torments, for half an hour every morning and evening. In the course of the next three years Hercules gained perhaps two inches. After that his growth stopped completely, and he remained for the rest of his life a pigmy of three feet and four inches. His father, who had built the most extravagant hopes upon his son, planning for him in his imagination a military career equal to that of Marlborough, found himself a disappointed man. "I have brought an abortion into the world," he would say, and he took so violent a dislike to his son that the boy dared scarcely come into his presence. His temper, which had been serene, was turned by disappointment to moroseness and savagery.

He avoided all company (being, as he said, ashamed to show himself, the father of a *lusus naturæ*, among normal, healthy human beings), and took to solitary drinking, which carried him very rapidly to his grave; for the year before Hercules came of age his father was taken off by an apoplexy. His mother, whose love for him had increased with the growth of his father's unkindness, did not long survive, but little more than a year after her husband's death succumbed, after eating two dozen of oysters, to an attack of typhoid fever.

'Hercules thus found himself at the age of twenty-one alone in the world, and master of a considerable fortune, including the estate and mansion of Crome. The beauty and intelligence of his childhood had survived into his manly age, and, but for his dwarfish stature, he would have taken his place among the handsomest and most accomplished young men of his time. He was well read in Greek and Latin authors, as well as in all the moderns of any merit who had written in English, French, or Italian. He had a good ear for music, and was no indifferent performer on the violin, which he used to play like a bass viol, seated on a chair with the instrument between his legs. To the music of the harpsichord and clavichord he was extremely partial, but the smallness of his hands made it impossible for him ever to perform upon these instruments. He had a small ivory flute made for him, on which, whenever he was melancholy, he used to play a simple country air or jig, affirming that this rustic music had more power to clear and raise the spirits than the most artificial productions of the masters. From an early age he practised the composition of poetry, but, though conscious of his great powers in this art, he would never publish any specimen of his writing. "My stature," he would say, "is reflected in my verses; if the public were to read them it would not be because I am a poet, but because I am a dwarf." Several MS. books of Sir Hercules's poems survive. A single specimen will suffice to illustrate his qualities as a poet.

In ancient days, while yet the world was young,
Ere Abram fed his flocks or Homer sung;
When blacksmith Tubal tamed creative fire,
And Jabal dwelt in tents and Jubal struck the lyre;
Flesh grown corrupt brought forth a monstrous birth
And obscene giants trod the shrinking earth,
Till God, impatient of their sinful brood,
Gave rein to wrath and drown'd them in the Flood.
Teeming again, repeopled Tellus bore
The lubber Hero and the Man of War;
Huge towers of Brawn, topp'd with an empty Skull,
Witlessly bold, heroically dull.
Long ages pass'd and Man grown more refin'd,
Slighter in muscle but of vaster Mind,
Smiled at his grandsire's broadsword, bow and bill,
And learn'd to wield the Pencil and the Quill.

The glowing canvas and the written page
Immortaliz'd his name from age to age,
His name emblazon'd on Fame's temple wall;
For Art grew great as Humankind grew small.
Thus man's long progress step by step we trace;
The Giant dies, the hero takes his place;
The Giant vile, the dull heroic Block:
At one we shudder and at one we mock.
Man last appears. In him the Soul's pure flame
Burns brightlier in a not inord'nate frame.
Of old when Heroes fought and Giants swarmed,
Men were huge mounds of matter scarce inform'd;
Wearied by leavening so vast a mass,
The spirit slept and all the mind was crass.
The smaller carcase of these later days
Is soon inform'd; the Soul unwearied plays
And like a Pharos darts abroad her mental rays.
But can we think that Providence will stay
Man's footsteps here upon the upward way?
Mankind in understanding and in grace
Advanc'd so far beyond the Giants' race?
Hence impious thought! Still led by God's own Hand,
Mankind proceeds towards the Promised Land.
A time will come (prophetic, I descry
Remoter dawns along the gloomy sky),
When happy mortals of a Golden Age
Will backward turn the dark historic page,
And in our vaunted race of Men behold
A form as gross, a Mind as dead and cold,
As we in Giants see, in warriors of old.
A time will come, wherein the soul shall be
From all superfluous matter wholly free:
When the light body, agile as a fawn's,
Shall sport with grace along the velvet lawns.
Nature's most delicate and final birth,
Mankind perfected shall possess the earth.
But ah, not yet! For still the Giants' race,
Huge, though diminish'd, tramps the Earth's fair face;
Gross and repulsive, yet perversely proud,
Men of their imperfections boast aloud.
Vain of their bulk, of all they still retain
Of giant ugliness absurdly vain;
At all that's small they point their stupid scorn
And, monsters, think themselves divinely born.
Sad is the Fate of those, ah, sad indeed,
The rare precursors of the nobler breed!
Who come man's golden glory to foretell,
But pointing Heav'nwards live themselves in Hell.

'As soon as he came into the estate, Sir Hercules set about remodelling his household. For though by no means ashamed of his deformity—

indeed, if we may judge from the poem quoted above, he regarded himself as being in many ways superior to the ordinary race of man—he found the presence of full-grown men and women embarrassing. Realizing, too, that he must abandon all ambitions in the great world, he determined to retire absolutely from it and to create, as it were, at Crome a private world of his own, in which all should be proportionable to himself. Accordingly, he discharged all the old servants of the house and replaced them gradually, as he w asable to find suitable successors, by others of dwarfish stature. In the course of a few years he had assembled about himself a numerous household, no member of which was above four feet high and the smallest among them scarcely two feet and six inches. His father's dogs, such as setters, mastiffs, greyhounds, and a pack of beagles, he sold or gave away as too large and too boisterous for his house, replacing them by pugs and King Charles spaniels and whatever other breeds of dog were the smallest. His father's stable was also sold. For his own use, whether riding or driving, he had six black Shetland ponies, with four very choice piebald animals of New Forest breed.

'Having thus settled his household entirely to his own satisfaction, it only remained for him to find some suitable companion with whom to share this paradise. Sir Hercules had a susceptible heart, and had more than once, between the ages of sixteen and twenty, felt what it was to love. But here his deformity had been a source of the most bitter humiliation, for, having once dared to declare himself to a young lady of his choice, he had been received with laughter. On his persisting, she had picked him up and shaken him like an importunate child, telling him to run away and plague her no more. The story soon got about—indeed, the young lady herself used to tell it as a particularly pleasant anecdote—and the taunts and mockery it occasioned were a source of the most acute distress to Hercules. From the poems written at this period we gather that he meditated taking his own life. In course of time, however, he lived down this humiliation; but never again, though he often fell in love, and that very passionately, did he dare to make any advances to those in whom he was interested. After coming to the estate and finding that he was in a position to create his own world as he desired it, he saw that, if he was to have a wife—which he very much desired, being of an affectionate and, indeed, amorous temper—he must choose her as he had chosen his servants—from among the race of dwarfs. But to find a suitable wife was, he found, a matter of some difficulty; for he would marry none who was not distinguished by beauty and gentle birth. The dwarfish daughter of Lord Bemboro he refused on the ground that besides being a pigmy she was hunchbacked; while another young lady, an orphan belonging to a very good family in Hampshire, was rejected by him because her face, like that of so many dwarfs, was wizened and repulsive. Finally, when he was almost despairing of success, he heard from a reliable source that Count Titimalo, a Venetian nobleman, possessed a daughter of exquisite beauty and great accomplishments, who was but three feet in height. Setting out at once for Venice, he went immediately on his arrival to pay his respects to the count, whom he found living with his wife and five children in a very mean apartment in one of the poorer quarters of the town. Indeed, the count was so far reduced in his circumstances that he was even then negotiating (so it was rumoured) with a travelling company of clowns and acrobats, who had had the misfortune to lose their performing dwarf, for the sale of his diminutive daughter Filomena. Sir Hercules arrived in time to save her from this untoward fate, for he was so much charmed by Filomena's grace and beauty, that at the end of three days' courtship he made her a formal offer of marriage, which was accepted by her no less joyfully than by her father, who perceived in an English son-in-law a rich and unfailing source of revenue. After an unostentatious marriage, at which the English ambassador acted as one of the witnesses, Sir Hercules and his bride returned by sea to England, where they settled down, as it proved, to a life of uneventful happiness.

'Crome and its household of dwarfs delighted Filomena, who felt herself now for the first time to be a free woman living among her equals in a friendly world. She had many tastes in common with her husband, especially that of music. She had a beautiful voice, of a power surprising in one so small, and could touch A in alt without effort. Accompanied by her husband on his fine Cremona fiddle, which he played, as we have noted before, as one plays a bass viol, she would sing all the liveliest and tenderest airs from the operas and cantatas of her native country. Seated together at the harpsichord, they found that they could with their four hands play all the music written for two hands of ordinary size, a circumstance which gave Sir Hercules unfailing pleasure.

'When they were not making music or reading together, which they often did, both in English and Italian, they spent their time in healthful outdoor exercises, sometimes rowing in a little boat on the lake, but more often riding or driving, occupations in which, because they were entirely new to her, Filomena especially delighted. When she had become a perfectly proficient rider, Filomena and her husband used often to go hunting in the park, at that time very much more extensive than it is now. They hunted not foxes nor hares, but rabbits, using a pack of about thirty black and fawn-coloured pugs, a kind of dog which, when not overfed, can course a rabbit as well as any of the smaller breeds. Four dwarf grooms, dressed in scarlet liveries and mounted on white Exmoor ponies, hunted the pack, while their master and mistress, in green habits, followed either on the black Shetlands or on the piebald New Forest ponies. A picture of the whole hunt—dogs, horses, grooms, and masters—was painted by William Stubbs, whose work Sir Hercules admired so much that he invited him, though a man of ordinary stature, to come and stay at the mansion for the purpose of executing this picture. Stubbs likewise painted a portrait of Sir Hercules and his lady driving in their green enamelled calash drawn by four black Shetlands. Sir Hercules wears a plum-coloured velvet coat and white breeches; Filomena is dressed in flowered muslin and a very large hat with pink feathers. The two figures in their gay carriage stand out sharply against a dark background of trees; but to the left of the picture the trees fall away and disappear, so that the four black ponies are seen against a pale and strangely lurid sky that has the golden-brown colour of thunder-clouds lighted up by the sun.

'In this way four years passed happily by. At the end of that time Filomena found herself great with child. Sir Hercules was overjoyed. "If God is good," he wrote in his day-book, "the name of Lapith will be preserved and our rarer and more delicate race transmitted through the generations until in the fullness of time the world shall recognize the superiority of those beings whom now it uses to make mock of." On his wife's being brought to bed of a son he wrote a poem to the same effect. The child was christened Ferdinando in memory of the builder of the house.

'With the passage of the months a certain sense of disquiet began to invade the minds of Sir Hercules and his lady. For the child was growing with an extraordinary rapidity. At a year he weighed as much as Hercules had weighed when he was three. "Ferdinando goes *crescendo*," wrote Filomena in her diary. "It seems not natural." At eighteen months the baby was almost as tall as their smallest jockey, who was a man of thirty-six. Could it be that Ferdinando was destined to become a man of the normal, gigantic dimensions? It was a thought to which neither of his parents dared yet give open utterance, but in the secrecy of their respective diaries they brooded over it in terror and dismay.

'On his third birthday Ferdinando was taller than his mother and not more than a couple of inches short of his father's height. "To-day for the first time," wrote Sir Hercules, "we discussed the situation. The hideous truth can be concealed no longer: Ferdinando is not one of us. On this, his third birthday, a day when we should have been rejoicing at the health, the strength, and beauty of our child, we wept together over the ruin of our happiness. God give us strength to bear this cross."

'At the age of eight Ferdinando was so large and so exuberantly healthy that his parents decided, though reluctantly, to send him to school. He was packed off to Eton at the beginning of the next half. A profound peace settled upon the house. Ferdinando returned for the summer holidays larger and stronger than ever. One day he knocked down the butler and broke his arm. "He is rough, inconsiderate, unamenable to persuasion," wrote his father. "The only thing that will teach him manners is corporal chastisement." Ferdinando, who at this age was already seventeen inches taller than his father, received no corporal chastisement.

'One summer holidays about three years later Ferdinando returned to Crome accompanied by a very large mastiff dog. He had bought it from an old man at Windsor who found the beast too expensive to feed. It was a savage, unreliable animal; hardly had it entered the house when it attacked one of Sir Hercules's favourite pugs, seizing the creature in its jaws and shaking it till it was nearly dead. Extremely put out by this occurrence, Sir Hercules ordered that the beast should be chained up in the stable-yard. Ferdinando sullenly answered that the dog was his, and he would keep it where he pleased. His father, growing angry, bade him take the animal out of the house at once, on pain of his utmost displeasure. Ferdinando refused to move. His mother at this moment coming into the room, the dog flew at her, knocked her down, and in a twinkling had very severely mauled her arm and shoulder; in another instant it must infallibly have had her by the throat, had not Sir Hercules drawn his sword and stabbed the animal to the heart. Turning on his son, he ordered him to leave the room immediately, as being unfit to remain in the same place with the mother whom he had nearly murdered. So awe-inspiring was the spectacle of Sir Hercules standing with one foot on the carcase of the gigantic dog, his sword drawn and still bloody, so commanding were his voice, his gestures, and the expression of his face, that Ferdinando slunk out of the room in terror and behaved himself for all the rest of the vacation in an entirely exemplary fashion. His mother soon recovered from the bites of the mastiff, but the effect on her mind of this adventure was ineradicable; from that time forth she lived always among imaginary terrors.

'The two years which Ferdinando spent on the Continent, making the Grand Tour, were a period of happy repose for his parents. But even now the thought of the future haunted them; nor were they able to solace themselves with all the diversions of their younger days. The Lady Filomena had lost her voice and Sir Hercules was grown too rheumatical to play the violin. He, it is true, still rode after his pugs, but his wife felt herself too old and, since the episode of the mastiff, too nervous for such sports. At most, to please her husband, she would follow the hunt at a distance in a little gig drawn by the safest and oldest of the Shetlands.

'The day fixed for Ferdinando's return came round. Filomena, sick with vague dreads and presentiments, retired to her chamber and her bed. Sir Hercules received his son alone. A giant in a brown travelling-suit entered the room. "Welcome home, my son," said Sir Hercules in a voice that trembled a little.

' "I hope I see you well, sir." Ferdinando bent down to shake hands, then straightened himself up again. The top of his father's head reached to the level of his hip.

'Ferdinando had not come alone. Two friends of his own age accompanied him, and each of the young men had brought a servant. Not for thirty years had Crome been desecrated by the presence of so many members of the common race of men. Sir Hercules was appalled and indignant, but the laws of hospitality had to be obeyed. He received the young gentlemen with grave politeness and sent the servants to the kitchen, with orders that they should be well cared for.

'The old family dining-table was dragged out into the light and dusted (Sir Hercules and his lady were accustomed to dine at a small table twenty inches high). Simon, the aged butler, who could only just look over the edge of the big table, was helped at supper by the three servants brought by Ferdinando and his guests.

'Sir Hercules presided, and with his usual grace supported a conversation on the pleasures of foreign travel, the beauties of art and nature to be met with abroad, the opera at Venice, the singing of the orphans in the churches of the same city, and on other topics of a similar nature. The young men were not particularly attentive to his discourses; they were occupied in watching the efforts of the butler to change the plates and replenish the glasses. They covered their laughter by violent and repeated fits of coughing or choking. Sir Hercules affected not to notice, but changed the subject of the conversation to sport. Upon this one of the young men asked whether it was true, as he had heard, that he used to hunt the rabbit with a pack of pug dogs. Sir Hercules replied that it was, and proceeded to describe the chase in some detail. The young men roared with laughter.

'When supper was over, Sir Hercules climbed down from his chair and, giving as his excuse that he must see how his lady did, bade them good-night. The sound of laughter followed him up the stairs. Filomena was not asleep; she had been lying on her bed listening to the sound of enormous laughter and the tread of strangely heavy feet on the stairs and along the corridors. Sir Hercules drew a chair to her bedside and sat there for a long time in silence, holding his wife's hand and sometimes gently squeezing it. At about ten o'clock they were startled by a violent noise. There was a breaking of glass, a stamping of feet, with an outburst of shouts and laughter. The uproar continuing for several minutes, Sir Hercules rose to his feet and, in spite of his wife's entreaties, prepared to go and see what was happening. There was no light on the staircase, and Sir Hercules groped his way down cautiously, lowering himself from stair to stair and standing for a moment on each tread before adventuring on a new step. The noise was louder here; the shouting articulated itself into recognizable words and phrases. A line of light was visible under the dining-room door. Sir Hercules tiptoed across the hall towards it. Just as he approached the door there was another terrific crash of breaking glass and jangled metal. What could they be doing? Standing on tiptoe he managed to look through the keyhole. In the middle of the ravaged table old

Simon, the butler, so primed with drink that he could scarcely keep his balance, was dancing a jig. His feet crunched and tinkled among the broken glass, and his shoes were wet with spilt wine. The three young men sat round, thumping the table with their hands or with the empty wine bottles, shouting and laughing encouragement. The three servants leaning against the wall laughed too. Ferdinando suddenly threw a handful of walnuts at the dancer's head, which so dazed and surprised the little man that he staggered and fell down on his back, upsetting a decanter and several glasses. They raised him up, gave him some brandy to drink, thumped him on the back. The old man smiled and hiccoughed, "To-morrow," said Ferdinando, "we'll have a concerted ballet of the whole household." "With father Hercules wearing his club and lion-skin," added one of his companions, and all three roared with laughter.

'Sir Hercules would look and listen no further. He crossed the hall once more and began to climb the stairs, lifting his knees painfully high at each degree. This was the end; there was no place for him now in the world, no place for him and Ferdinando together.

'His wife was still awake; to her questioning glance he answered, "They are making mock of old Simon. To-morrow it will be our turn." They were silent for a time.

'At last Filomena said, "I do not want to see to-morrow."

' "It is better not," said Sir Hercules. Going into his closet he wrote in his day-book a full and particular account of all the events of the evening. While he was still engaged in this task he rang for a servant and ordered hot water and a bath to be made ready for him at eleven o'clock. When he had finished writing he went into his wife's room, and preparing a dose of opium twenty times as strong as that which she was accustomed to take when she could not sleep, he brought it to her, saying, "Here is your sleeping-draught."

'Filomena took the glass and lay for a little time, but did not drink immediately. The tears came into her eyes. "Do you remember the songs we used to sing, sitting out there *sulla terrazza* in summer-time?" She began singing softly in her ghost of a cracked voice a few bars from Stradella's "*Amor, amor, non dormir piu.*" "And you playing on the violin. It seems such a short time ago, and yet so long, long, long. *Addio, amore. A rivederti.*" She drank off the draught and, lying back on the pillow, closed her eyes. Sir Hercules kissed her hand and tiptoed away, as though he were afraid of waking her. He returned to his closet, and having recorded his wife's last words to him, he poured into his bath the water that had been brought up in accordance with his orders. The water being too hot for him to get into the bath at once, he took down from the shelf his copy of Suetonius. He wished to read how Seneca had died. He opened the book at random. "But dwarfs," he read, "he held in abhorrence as being *lusus naturæ* and of evil omen." He winced as though he had been struck. This same Augustus, he remembered, had exhibited in the amphitheatre a young man called Lucius, of good family, who was not quite two feet in height and weighed seventeen pounds, but had a stentorian voice. He turned over the pages. Tiberius, Caligula, Claudius, Nero: it was a tale of growing horror. "Seneca his preceptor, he forced to kill himself." And there was Petronius, who had called his friends about him at the last, bidding them talk to him, not of the consolations of philosophy, but of love and gallantry, while the life was ebbing away through his opened veins. Dipping his pen once more in the ink he wrote on the last page of his diary: "He died a Roman death." Then, putting the toes of one foot into the water and finding that it was not too hot, he threw off his dressing-gown and, taking a razor in his hand, sat down in the bath. With one deep cut he severed the artery in his left wrist, then lay back and composed his mind to meditation. The blood oozed out, floating through the water in dissolving wreaths and spirals. In a little while the whole bath was tinged with pink. The colour deepened; Sir Hercules felt himself mastered by an invincible drowsiness; he was sinking from vague dream to dream. Soon he was sound asleep. There was not much blood in his small body.'

## *Chapter 14*

FOR their after-luncheon coffee the party generally adjourned to the library. Its windows looked east, and at this hour of the day it was the coolest place in the whole house. It was a large room, fitted, during the eighteenth century, with white painted shelves of an elegant design. In the middle of one wall a door, ingeniously upholstered with rows of dummy books, gave access to a deep cupboard, where, among a pile of letter-files and old newspapers, the mummy-case of an Egyptian lady, brought back by the second Sir Ferdinando on his return from the Grand Tour, mouldered in the darkness. From ten yards away and at a first glance, one might almost have mistaken this secret door for a section of shelving filled with genuine books. Coffee-cup in hand, Mr. Scogan was standing in front of the dummy bookshelf. Between the sips he discoursed.

'The bottom shelf,' he was saying, 'is taken up by an Encyclopædia in fourteen volumes. Useful, but a little dull, as is also Caprimulge's *Dictionary of the Finnish Language*. The *Biographical Dictionary* looks much more promising. *Biography of Men who were Born Great*, *Biography of Men who Achieved Greatness*, *Biography of Men who had Greatness Thrust upon Them*, and *Biography of Men who were Never Great at All*. Then there are ten volumes of *Thom's Works and Wanderings*, while the *Wild Goose Chase, a Novel*, by an anonymous author, fills no less than six. But what's this, what's this?' Mr. Scogan stood on tiptoe and peered up. 'Seven volumes of the *Tales of Knockespotch*. The *Tales of Knockespotch*,' he repeated. 'Ah, my dear Henry,' he said, turning round, 'these are your best books. I would willingly give all the rest of your library for them.'

The happy possessor of a multitude of first editions, Mr. Wimbush could afford to smile indulgently.

'Is it possible,' Mr. Scogan went on, 'that they possess nothing more than a back and a title?' He opened the cupboard door and peeped inside, as though he hoped to find the rest of the books behind it. 'Phooh!' he said, and shut the door again. 'It smells of dust and mildew. How symbolical! One comes to the great masterpieces of the past, expecting some miraculous illumination, and one finds, on opening them, only darkness and dust and a faint smell of decay. After all, what is reading but a vice, like drink or venery or any other form of excessive self-indulgence? One reads to tickle and amuse one's mind; one reads, above all, to prevent oneself thinking. Still—the *Tales of Knockespotch* . . .'

He paused, and thoughtfully drummed with his fingers on the backs of the non-existent, unattainable books.

'But I disagree with you about reading,' said Mary. 'About serious reading, I mean.'

'Quite right, Mary, quite right,' Mr. Scogan answered. 'I had forgotten there were any serious people in the room.'

'I like the idea of the Biographies,' said Denis. 'There's room for us all within the scheme; it's comprehensive.'

'Yes, the Biographies are good, the Biographies are excellent,' Mr. Scogan agreed. 'I imagine them written in a very elegant Regency style—Brighton Pavilion in words—perhaps by the great Dr. Lemprière himself. You know his classical dictionary? Ah!' Mr. Scogan raised his hand and let it limply fall again in a gesture which implied that words failed him. 'Read his biography of Helen; read how Jupiter, disguised as a swan, was "enabled to avail himself of his situation" *vis-à-vis* to Leda. And to think that he may have, must have written these biographies of the Great! What a work, Henry! And, owing to the idiotic arrangement of your library, it can't be read.'

'I prefer the *Wild Goose Chase*,' said Anne. 'A novel in six volumes—it must be restful.'

'Restful,' Mr. Scogan repeated. 'You've hit on the right word. A *Wild Goose Chase* is sound, but a bit old-fashioned—pictures of clerical life in the fifties, you know; specimens of the landed gentry; peasants for pathos and comedy; and in the background, always the picturesque beauties of nature soberly described. All very good and solid, but, like certain puddings, just a little dull. Personally, I like much better the notion of *Thom's Works and Wanderings*. The eccentric Mr. Thom of Thom's Hill. Old Tom Thom, as his intimates used to call him. He spent ten years in Tibet organizing the clarified butter industry on modern European lines, and was able to retire at thirty-six with a handsome fortune. The rest of his life he devoted to travel and ratiocination; here is the result.' Mr. Scogan tapped the dummy books. 'And now we come to the *Tales of Knockespotch*. What a masterpiece and what a great man! Knockespotch knew how to write fiction. Ah, Denis, if you could only read Knockespotch you wouldn't be writing a novel about the wearisome development of a young man's character, you wouldn't be describing in endless, fastidious detail, cultured life in Chelsea and Bloomsbury and Hampstead. You would be trying to write a readable book. But then, alas! owing to the peculiar arrangement of our host's library, you never will read Knockespotch.'

'Nobody could regret the fact more than I do,' said Denis.

'It was Knockespotch,' Mr. Scogan continued, 'the great Knockespotch, who delivered us from the dreary tyranny of the realistic novel. My life, Knockespotch said, is not so long that I can afford to spend precious hours writing or reading descriptions of middle-class interiors. He said again, "I am tired of seeing the human mind bogged in a social plenum; I prefer to paint it in a vacuum, freely and sportively bombinating."'

'I say,' said Gombauld, 'Knockespotch was a little obscure sometimes, wasn't he?'

'He was,' Mr. Scogan replied, 'and with intention. It made him seem even profounder than he actually was. But it was only in his aphorisms that he was so dark and oracular. In his Tales he was always luminous. Oh, those Tales—those Tales! How shall I describe them? Fabulous characters shoot across his pages like gaily dressed performers on the trapeze. There are extraordinary adventures and still more extraordinary speculations. Intelligences and emotions, relieved of all the imbecile preoccupations of civilized life, move in intricate and subtle dances, crossing and recrossing, advancing, retreating, impinging. An immense erudition and an immense fancy go hand in hand. All the ideas of the present and of the past, on every possible subject, bob up among the Tales, smile gravely or grimace a caricature of themselves, then disappear to make place for something new. The verbal surface of his writing is rich and fantastically diversified. The wit is incessant. The . . .'

'But couldn't you give us a specimen,' Denis broke in—'a concrete example?'

'Alas!' Mr. Scogan replied, 'Knockespotch's great book is like the sword Excalibur. It remains stuck fast in this door, awaiting the coming of a writer with genius enough to draw it forth. I am not even a writer, I am not so much as qualified to attempt the task. The extraction of Knockespotch from his wooden prison I leave, my dear Denis, to you.'

'Thank you,' said Denis.

## *Chapter 15*

'In the time of the amiable Brantôme,' Mr. Scogan was saying, 'every debutante at the French Court was invited to dine at the King's table, where she was served with wine in a handsome silver cup of Italian workmanship. It was no ordinary cup, this goblet of the debutantes; for, inside, it had been most curiously and ingeniously engraved with a series of very lively amorous scenes. With each draught that the young lady swallowed these engravings became increasingly visible, and the Court looked on with interest, every time she put her nose in the cup, to see whether she blushed at what the ebbing wine revealed. If the debutante blushed, they laughed at her for her innocence; if she did not, she was laughed at for being too knowing.'

'Do you propose,' asked Anne, 'that the custom should be revived at Buckingham Palace?'

'I do not,' said Mr. Scogan. 'I merely quoted the anecdote as an illustration of the customs, so genially frank, of the sixteenth century. I might have quoted other anecdotes to show that the customs of the seventeenth and eighteenth, of the fifteenth and fourteenth centuries, and indeed of every other century, from the time of Hammurabi onward, were equally genial and equally frank. The only century in which customs were not characterized by the same cheerful openness was the nineteenth, of blessed memory. It was the astonishing exception. And yet, with what one must suppose was a deliberate disregard of history, it looked upon its horribly pregnant silences as normal and natural and right; the frankness of the previous fifteen or twenty thousand years was considered abnormal and perverse. It was a curious phenomenon.'

'I entirely agree.' Mary panted with excitement in her effort to bring out what she had to say. 'Havelock Ellis says . . .'

Mr. Scogan, like a policeman arresting the flow of traffic, held up his hand. 'He does; I know. And that brings me to my next point: the nature of the reaction.'

'Havelock Ellis . . .'

'The reaction, when it came—and we may say roughly that it set in a little before the beginning of this century—the reaction was to openness, but not to the same openness as had reigned in the earlier ages. It was to a scientific openness, not to the jovial frankness of the past, that we returned. The whole question of Amour became a terribly serious one. Earnest young men wrote in the public prints that from this time forth it would be impossible ever again to make a joke of any sexual matter. Professors wrote thick books in which sex was sterilized and dissected. It has become customary for serious young women, like Mary, to discuss, with philosophic calm, matters of which the merest hint would have sufficed to throw the youth of the sixties into a delirium of amorous excitement. It is all very estimable, no doubt. But still'—Mr. Scogan sighed—'I for one should like to see, mingled with this scientific ardour, a little more of the jovial spirit of Rabelais and Chaucer.'

'I entirely disagree with you,' said Mary. 'Sex isn't a laughing matter; it's serious.'

'Perhaps,' answered Mr. Scogan, 'perhaps I'm an obscene old man, for I must confess that I cannot always regard it as wholly serious.'

'But I tell you . . .' began Mary furiously. Her face had flushed with excitement. Her cheeks were the cheeks of a great ripe peach.

'Indeed,' Mr. Scogan continued, 'it seems to me one of the few permanently and everlastingly amusing subjects that exist. Amour is the one human activity of any importance in which laughter and pleasure preponderate, if ever so slightly, over misery and pain.'

'I entirely disagree,' said Mary. There was a silence.

Anne looked at her watch. 'Nearly a quarter to eight,' she said. 'I wonder when Ivor will turn up.' She got up from her deck-chair and, leaning her elbows on the balustrade of the terrace, looked out over the valley and towards the farther hills. Under the level evening light the architecture of the land revealed itself. The deep shadows, the bright contrasting lights gave the hills a new solidity. Irregularities of the surface, unsuspected before, were picked out with light and shade. The grass, the corn, the foliage of trees were stippled with intricate shadows. The surface of things had taken on a marvellous enrichment.

'Look!' said Anne suddenly, and pointed. On the opposite side of the valley, at the crest of the ridge, a cloud of dust flushed by the sunlight to rosy gold was moving rapidly along the sky-line. 'It's Ivor. One can tell by the speed.'

The dust cloud descended into the valley and was lost. A horn with the voice of a sea-lion made itself heard, approaching. A minute later Ivor came leaping round the corner of the house. His hair waved in the wind of his own speed; he laughed as he saw them.

'Anne darling,' he cried, and embraced her, embraced Mary, very nearly embraced Mr. Scogan. 'Well, here I am. I've come with incredulous speed.' Ivor's vocabulary was rich, but a little erratic. 'I'm not late for dinner, am I?' He hoisted himself up on to the balustrade, and sat there, kicking his heels. With one arm he embraced a large stone flower-pot, leaning his head sideways against its hard and lichenous flanks in an attitude of trustful affection. He had brown, wavy hair, and his eyes were of a very brilliant, pale, improbable blue. His head was narrow, his face thin and rather long, his nose aquiline. In old age—though it was difficult to imagine Ivor old—he might grow to have an Iron Ducal grimness. But now, at twenty-six, it was not the structure of his face that impressed one; it was its expression. That was charming and vivacious, and his smile was an irradiation. He was for ever moving, restlessly and rapidly, but with an engaging gracefulness. His frail and slender body seemed to be fed by a spring of inexhaustible energy.

'No, you're not late.'

'You're in time to answer a question,' said Mr. Scogan. 'We were arguing whether Amour were a serious matter or no. What do you think? Is it serious?'

'Serious?' echoed Ivor. 'Most certainly.'

'I told you so,' said Mary triumphantly.

'But in what sense serious?' Mr. Scogan asked.

'I mean as an occupation. One can go on with it without ever getting bored.'

'I see,' said Mr. Scogan. 'Perfectly.'

'One can occupy oneself with it,' Ivor continued, 'always and everywhere. Women are always wonderfully the same. Shapes vary a little, that's all. In Spain'—with his free hand he described a series of ample curves—'one can't pass them on the stairs. In England'—he put the tip of his forefinger against the tip of his thumb and, lowering his hand, drew out this circle into an imaginary cylinder—'in England they're tubular. But their sentiments are always the same. At least, I've always found it so.'

'I'm delighted to hear it,' said Mr. Scogan.

## *Chapter 16*

THE ladies had left the room and the port was circulating. Mr. Scogan filled his glass, passed on the decanter, and, leaning back in his chair, looked about him for a moment in silence. The conversation rippled idly round him, but he disregarded it; he was smiling at some private joke. Gombauld noticed his smile.

'What's amusing you?' he asked.

'I was just looking at you all, sitting round this table,' said Mr. Scogan.

'Are we as comic as all that?'

'Not at all,' Mr. Scogan answered politely. 'I was merely amused by my own speculations.'

'And what were they?'

'The idlest, the most academic of speculations. I was looking at you one by one and trying to imagine which of the first six Cæsars you would each resemble, if you were given the opportunity of behaving like a Cæsar. The Cæsars are one of my touchstones,' Mr. Scogan explained. 'They are characters functioning, so to speak, in the void. They are human beings developed to their logical conclusions. Hence their unequalled value as a touchstone, a standard. When I meet someone for the first time, I ask myself this question: Given the Cæsarean environment, which of the Cæsars would this person resemble—Julius,

Augustus, Tiberius, Caligula, Claudius, Nero? I take each trait of character, each mental and emotional bias, each little oddity, and magnify them a thousand times. The resulting image gives me his Cæsarean formula.'

'And which of the Cæsars do you resemble?' asked Gombauld.

'I am potentially all of them,' Mr. Scogan replied, 'all—with the possible exception of Claudius, who was much too stupid to be a development of anything in my character. The seeds of Julius's courage and compelling energy, of Augustus's prudence, of the libidinousness and cruelty of Tiberius, of Caligula's folly, of Nero's artistic genius and enormous vanity, are all within me. Given the opportunities, I might have been something fabulous. But circumstances were against me. I was born and brought up in a country rectory; I passed my youth doing a great deal of utterly senseless hard work for a very little money. The result is that now, in middle age, I am the poor thing that I am. But perhaps it is as well. Perhaps, too, it's as well that Denis hasn't been permitted to flower into a little Nero, and that Ivor remains only potentially a Caligula. Yes, it's better so, no doubt. But it would have been more amusing, as a spectacle, if they had had the chance to develop, untrammelled, the full horror of their potentialities. It would have been pleasant and interesting to watch their tics and foibles and little vices swelling and burgeoning and blossoming into enormous and fantastic flowers of cruelty and pride and lewdness and avarice. The Cæsarean environment makes the Cæsar, as the special food and the queenly cell make the queen bee. We differ from the bees in so far that, given the proper food, they can be sure of making a queen every time. With us there is no such certainty; out of every ten men placed in the Cæsarean environment one will be temperamentally good, or intelligent, or great. The rest will blossom into Cæsars; he will not. Seventy and eighty years ago simple-minded people, reading of the exploits of the Bourbons in South Italy, cried out in amazement: To think that such things should be happening in the nineteenth century! And a few years since we too were astonished to find that in our still more astonishing twentieth century, unhappy blackamoors on the Congo and the Amazon were being treated as English serfs were treated in the time of Stephen. To-day we are no longer surprised at these things. The Black and Tans harry Ireland, the Poles maltreat the Silesians, the bold Fascisti slaughter their poorer countrymen: we take it all for granted. Since the war we wonder at nothing. We have created a Cæsarean environment and a host of little Cæsars has sprung up. What could be more natural?'

Mr. Scogan drank off what was left of his port and refilled the glass.

'At this very moment,' he went on, 'the most frightful horrors are taking place in every corner of the world. People are being crushed, slashed, disembowelled, mangled; their dead bodies rot and their eyes decay with the rest. Screams of pain and fear go pulsing through the air at the rate of eleven hundred feet per second. After travelling for three seconds they are perfectly inaudible. These are distressing facts; but do we enjoy life any the less because of them? Most certainly we do not. We feel sympathy, no doubt; we represent to ourselves imaginatively the sufferings of nations and individuals and we deplore them. But, after all, what are sympathy and imagination? Precious little, unless the person for whom we feel sympathy happens to be closely involved in our affections; and even then they don't go very far. And a good thing too; for if one had an imagination vivid enough and a sympathy sufficiently sensitive really to comprehend and to feel the sufferings of other people, one would never have a moment's peace of mind. A really sympathetic race would not so much as know the meaning of happiness. But luckily, as I've already said, we aren't a sympathetic race. At the beginning of the war I used to think I really suffered, through imagination and sympathy, with those who physically suffered. But after a month or two I had to admit that, honestly, I didn't. And yet I think I have a more vivid imagination than most. One is always alone in suffering; the fact is depressing when one happens to be the sufferer, but it makes pleasure possible for the rest of the world.'

There was a pause. Henry Wimbush pushed back his chair.

'I think perhaps we ought to go and join the ladies,' he said.

'So do I,' said Ivor, jumping up with alacrity. He turned to Mr. Scogan. 'Fortunately,' he said, 'we can share our pleasures. We are not always condemned to be happy alone.'

## *Chapter 17*

IVOR brought his hands down with a bang on to the final chord of his rhapsody. There was just a hint in that triumphant harmony that the seventh had been struck along with the octave by the thumb of the left hand; but the general effect of splendid noise emerged clearly enough. Small details matter little so long as the general effect is good. And, besides, that hint of the seventh was decidedly modern. He turned round in his seat and tossed the hair back out of his eyes.

'There,' he said. 'That's the best I can do for you, I'm afraid.'

Murmurs of applause and gratitude were heard, and Mary, her large china eyes fixed on the performer, cried out aloud, 'Wonderful!' and gasped for new breath as though she were suffocating.

Nature and fortune had vied with one another in heaping on Ivor Lombard all their choicest gifts. He had wealth and he was perfectly independent. He was good looking, possessed an irresistible charm of manner, and was the hero of more amorous successes than he could well remember. His accomplishments were extraordinary for their number and variety. He had a beautiful untrained tenor voice; he could improvise, with a startling brilliance, rapidly and loudly, on the piano. He was a good amateur medium and telepathist, and had a considerable first-hand knowledge of the next world. He could write rhymed verses with an extraordinary rapidity. For painting symbolical pictures he had a dashing style, and if the drawing was sometimes a little weak, the colour was always pyrotechnical. He excelled in amateur theatricals and, when occasion offered, he could cook with genius. He resembled Shakespeare in knowing little Latin and less Greek. For a mind like his, education seemed supererogatory. Training would only have destroyed his natural aptitudes.

'Let's go out into the garden,' Ivor suggested. 'It's a wonderful night.'

'Thank you,' said Mr. Scogan, 'but I for one prefer these still more wonderful arm-chairs.' His pipe had begun to bubble oozily every time he pulled at it. He was perfectly happy.

Henry Wimbush was also happy. He looked for a moment over his pince-nez in Ivor's direction and then, without saying anything, returned to the grimy little sixteenth-century account books which were now his favourite reading. He knew more about Sir Ferdinando's household expenses than about his own.

The outdoor party, enrolled under Ivor's banner, consisted of Anne, Mary, Denis, and, rather unexpectedly, Jenny. Outside it was warm and dark; there was no moon. They walked up and down the terrace, and Ivor sang a Neapolitan song: 'Stretti, stretti'—close, close—with something about the little Spanish girl to follow. The atmosphere began to palpitate. Ivor put his arm round Anne's waist, dropped his head sideways on to her shoulder, and in that position walked on, singing as he walked. It seemed the easiest, the most natural, thing in the world. Denis wondered why he had never done it. He hated Ivor.

'Let's go down to the pool,' said Ivor. He disengaged his embrace and turned round to shepherd his little flock. They made their way along the side of the house to the entrance of the yew-tree walk that led down to the lower garden. Between the blank precipitous wall of the house and the tall yew trees the path was a chasm of impenetrable gloom. Somewhere there were steps down to the right, a gap in the yew hedge. Denis, who headed the party, groped his way cautiously; in this darkness, one had an irrational fear of yawning precipices, of horrible spiked obstructions. Suddenly from behind him he heard a shrill, startled, 'Oh!' and then a sharp, dry concussion that might have been the sound of a slap. After that, Jenny's voice was heard pronouncing, 'I am going back to the house.' Her tone was decided, and even as she pronounced the words she was melting away into the darkness. The incident, whatever it had been, was closed. Denis resumed his forward groping. From somewhere behind Ivor began to sing again, softly:

Phillis plus avare que tendre,<br>
Ne gagnant rien à refuser,<br>
Un jour exigea à Silvandre<br>
Trente moutons pour un baiser.

The melody drooped and climbed again with a kind of easy languor; the warm darkness seemed to pulse like blood about them.

Le lendemain, nouvelle affaire:
Pour le berger, le troc fut bon . . .

'Here are the steps,' cried Denis. He guided his companions over the danger, and in a moment they had the turf of the yew-tree walk under their feet. It was lighter here, or at least it was just perceptibly less dark; for the yew walk was wider than the path that had led them under the lea of the house. Looking up, they could see between the high black hedges a strip of sky and a few stars.

Car il obtint de la bergère . . .

went on Ivor, and then interrupted himself to shout, 'I'm going to run down,' and he was off, full speed, down the invisible slope, singing unevenly as he went:

Trente baisers pour un mouton.

The others followed. Denis shambled in the rear, vainly exhorting everyone to caution: the slope was steep, one might break one's neck. What was wrong with these people, he wondered? They had become like young kittens after a dose of cat-nip. He himself felt a certain kittenishness sporting within him; but it was, like all his emotions, rather a theoretical feeling; it did not overmasteringly seek to express itself in a practical demonstration of kittenishness.

'Be careful,' he shouted once more, and hardly were the words out of his mouth when, thump! there was the sound of a heavy fall in front of him, followed by the long 'F-f-f-f-f' of a breath indrawn with pain and afterwards by a very sincere, 'OO-ooh'! Denis was almost pleased; he had told them so, the idiots, and they wouldn't listen. He trotted down the slope towards the unseen sufferer.

Mary came down the hill like a runaway steam-engine. It was tremendously exciting, this blind rush through the dark; she felt she would never stop. But the ground grew level beneath her feet, her speed insensibly slackened, and suddenly she was caught by an extended arm and brought to an abrupt halt.

'Well,' said Ivor as he tightened his embrace, 'you're caught now, Anne.'

She made an effort to release herself. 'It's not Anne. It's Mary.'

Ivor burst into a peal of amused laughter. 'So it is!' he exclaimed. 'I seem to be making nothing but floaters this evening. I've already made one with Jenny.' He laughed again, and there was something so jolly about his laughter that Mary could not help laughing too. He did not remove his encircling arm, and somehow it was all so amusing and natural that Mary made no further attempt to escape from it. They walked along by the side of the pool, interlaced. Mary was too short for him to be able, with any comfort, to lay his head on her shoulder. He rubbed his cheek, caressed and caressing, against the thick, sleek mass of her hair. In a little while he began to sing again; the night trembled amorously to the sound of his voice. When he had finished he kissed her. Anne or Mary: Mary or Anne. It didn't seem to make much difference which it was. There were differences in detail, of course; but the general effect was the same; and, after all, the general effect was the important thing.

Denis made his way down the hill.

'Any damage done?' he called out.

'Is that you, Denis? I've hurt my ankle so—and my knee, and my hand. I'm all in pieces.'

'My poor Anne,' he said. 'But then,' he couldn't help adding, 'it was silly to start running downhill in the dark.'

'Ass!' she retorted in a tone of tearful irritation; 'of course it was.'

He sat down beside her on the grass, and found himself breathing the faint, delicious atmosphere of perfume that she carried always with her.

'Light a match,' she commanded. 'I want to look at my wounds.'

He felt in his pockets for the match-box. The light spurted and then grew steady. Magically, a little universe had been created, a world of colours and forms—Anne's face, the shimmering orange of her dress, her white, bare arms, a patch of green turf—and round about a darkness that had become solid and utterly blind. Anne held out her hands; both were green and earthy with her fall, and the left exhibited two or three red abrasions.

'Not so bad,' she said. But Denis was terribly distressed, and his emotion was intensified when, looking up at her face, he saw that the trace of tears, involuntary tears of pain, lingered on her eyelashes. He pulled out his handkerchief and began to wipe away the dirt from the wounded hand. The match went out; it was not worth while to light another. Anne allowed herself to be attended to, meekly and gratefully. 'Thank you,' she said, when he had finished cleaning and bandaging her hand; and there was something in her tone that made him feel that she had lost her superiority over him, that she was younger than he, had become, suddenly, almost a child. He felt tremendously large and protective. The feeling was so strong that instinctively he put his arm about her. She drew closer, leaned against him, and so they sat in silence. Then, from below, soft but wonderfully clear through the still darkness, they heard the sound of Ivor's singing. He was going on with his half-finished song:

> Le lendemain Phillis plus tendre,
> Ne voulant déplaire au berger,
> Fut trop heureuse de lui rendre
> Trente moutons pour un baiser.

There was a rather prolonged pause. It was as though time were being allowed for the giving and receiving of a few of those thirty kisses. Then the voice sang on:

> Le lendemain Phillis peu sage
> Aurait donné moutons et chien
> Pour un baiser que le volage
> A Lisette donnait pour rien.

The last note died away into an uninterrupted silence.

'Are you better?' Denis whispered. 'Are you comfortable like this?'

She nodded a Yes to both questions.

'Trente moutons pour un baiser.' The sheep, the woolly mutton—baa, baa, baa . . .? Or the shepherd? Yes, decidedly, he felt himself to be the shepherd now. He was the master, the protector. A wave of courage swelled through him, warm as wine. He turned his head, and began to kiss her face, at first rather randomly, then, with more precision, on the mouth.

Anne averted her head; he kissed the ear, the smooth nape that this movement presented him. 'No,' she protested; 'no, Denis.'

'Why not?'

'It spoils our friendship, and that was so jolly.'

'Bosh!' said Denis.

She tried to explain. 'Can't you see,' she said, 'it isn't . . . it isn't our stunt at all.' It was true. Somehow she had never thought of Denis in the light of a man who might make love; she had never so much as conceived the possibilities of an amorous relationship with him. He was so absurdly young, so . . . so . . . she couldn't find the adjective, but she knew what she meant.

'Why isn't it our stunt?' asked Denis. 'And, by the way, that's a horrible and inappropriate expression.'

'Because it isn't.'

'But if I say it is?'

'It makes no difference. I say it isn't.'

'I shall make you say it is.'

'All right, Denis. But you must do it another time. I must go in and get my ankle into hot water. It's beginning to swell.'

Reasons of health could not be gainsaid. Denis got up reluctantly, and helped his companion to her feet. She took a cautious step. 'Ooh!' She halted and leaned heavily on his arm.

'I'll carry you,' Denis offered. He had never tried to carry a woman, but on the cinema it always looked an easy piece of heroism.

'You couldn't,' said Anne.

'Of course I can.' He felt larger and more protective than ever. 'Put your arms round my neck,' he ordered. She did so and, stooping, he picked her up under the knees and lifted her from the ground. Good heavens, what a weight! He took five staggering steps up the slope, then almost lost his equilibrium, and had to deposit his burden suddenly, with something of a bump.

Anne was shaking with laughter. 'I said you couldn't, my poor Denis.'

'I can,' said Denis, without conviction. 'I'll try again.'

'It's perfectly sweet of you to offer, but I'd rather walk, thanks.' She laid her hand on his shoulder and, thus supported, began to limp slowly up the hill.

'My poor Denis!' she repeated, and laughed again. Humiliated, he was silent. It seemed incredible that, only two minutes ago, he should have been holding her in his embrace, kissing her. Incredible. She was helpless then, a child. Now she had regained all her superiority; she was once more the far-off being, desired and unassailable. Why had he been such a fool as to suggest that carrying stunt? He reached the house in a state of the profoundest depression.

He helped Anne upstairs, left her in the hands of a maid, and came down again to the drawing-room. He was surprised to find them all sitting just where he had left them. He had expected that, somehow, everything would be quite different—it seemed such a prodigious time since he went away. All silent and all damned, he reflected, as he looked at them. Mr. Scogan's pipe still wheezed; that was the only sound. Henry Wimbush was still deep in his account books; he had just made the discovery that Sir Ferdinando was in the habit of eating oysters the whole summer through, regardless of the absence of the justifying R. Gombauld, in horn-rimmed spectacles, was reading. Jenny was mysteriously scribbling in her red notebook. And, seated in her favourite arm-chair at the corner of the hearth, Priscilla was looking through a pile of drawings. One by one she held them out at arm's length and, throwing back her mountainous orange head, looked long and attentively through half-closed eyelids. She wore a pale sea-green dress; on the slope of her mauve-powdered décolletage diamonds twinkled. An immensely long cigarette-holder projected at an angle from her face. Diamonds were embedded in her high-piled coiffure; they glittered every time she moved. It was a batch of Ivor's drawings—sketches of Spirit Life, made in the course of tranced tours through the other world. On the back of each sheet descriptive titles were written: 'Portrait of an Angel, 15th March '20'; 'Astral Beings at Play, 3rd December '19'; 'A Party of Souls on their Way to a Higher Sphere, 21st May '21.' Before examining the drawing on the obverse of each sheet, she turned it over to read the title. Try as she could—and she tried hard—Priscilla had never seen a vision or succeeded in establishing any communication with the Spirit World. She had to be content with the reported experiences of others.

'What have you done with the rest of your party?' she asked, looking up as Denis entered the room.

He explained. Anne had gone to bed, Ivor and Mary were still in the garden. He selected a book and a comfortable chair, and tried, as far as the disturbed state of his mind would permit him, to compose himself for an evening's reading. The lamplight was utterly serene; there was no movement save the stir of Priscilla among her papers. All silent and all damned, Denis repeated to himself, all silent and all damned. . . .

It was nearly an hour later when Ivor and Mary made their appearance.

'We waited to see the moon rise,' said Ivor.

'It was gibbous, you know,' Mary explained, very technical and scientific.

'It was so beautiful down in the garden! The trees, the scent of the flowers, the stars . . .' Ivor waved his arms. 'And when the moon came up, it was really too much. It made me burst into tears.' He sat down at the piano and opened the lid.

'There were a great many meteorites,' said Mary to anyone who would listen. 'The earth must just be coming into the summer shower of them. In July and August . . .'

But Ivor had already begun to strike the keys. He played the garden, the stars, the scent of flowers, the rising moon. He even put in a nightingale that was not there. Mary looked on and listened with parted lips. The others pursued their occupations, without appearing to be seriously disturbed. On this very July day, exactly three hundred and fifty years ago, Sir Ferdinando had eaten seven dozen oysters. The discovery of this fact gave Henry Wimbush a peculiar pleasure. He had a natural piety which made him delight in the celebration of memorial feasts. The three hundred and fiftieth anniversary of the seven dozen oysters. . . . He wished he had known before dinner; he would have ordered champagne.

On her way to bed Mary paid a call. The light was out in Anne's room, but she was not yet asleep.

'Why didn't you come down to the garden with us?' Mary asked.

'I fell down and twisted my ankle. Denis helped me home.'

Mary was full of sympathy. Inwardly, too, she was relieved to find Anne's non-appearance so simply accounted for. She had been vaguely suspicious, down there in the garden—suspicious of what, she hardly knew; but there had seemed to be something a little *louche* in the way she had suddenly found herself alone with Ivor. Not that she minded, of course; far from it. But she didn't like the idea that perhaps she was the victim of a put-up job.

'I do hope you'll be better to-morrow,' she said, and she commiserated with Anne on all she had missed—the garden, the stars, the scent of flowers, the meteorites through whose summer shower the earth was now passing, the rising moon and its gibbosity. And then they had had such interesting conversation. What about? About almost everything.

Nature, art, science, poetry, the stars, spiritualism, the relations of the sexes, music, religion. Ivor, she thought, had an interesting mind.

The two young ladies parted affectionately.

## *Chapter 18*

THE nearest Roman Catholic church was upwards of twenty miles away. Ivor, who was punctilious in his devotions, came down early to breakfast and had his car at the door, ready to start, by a quarter to ten. It was a smart, expensive-looking machine, enamelled a pure lemon yellow and upholstered in emerald green leather. There were two seats—three if you squeezed tightly enough—and their occupants were protected from wind, dust, and weather by a glazed sedan that rose, an elegant eighteenth-century hump, from the midst of the body of the car.

Mary had never been to a Roman Catholic service, thought it would be an interesting experience, and, when the car moved off through the great gates of the courtyard, she was occupying the spare seat in the sedan. The sea-lion horn roared, faintlier, faintlier, and they were gone.

In the parish church of Crome Mr. Bodiham preached on 1 Kings vi. 18: 'And the cedar of the house within was carved with knops'—a sermon of immediate local interest. For the past two years the problem of the War Memorial had exercised the minds of all those in Crome who had enough leisure, or mental energy, or party spirit to think of such things. Henry Wimbush was all for a library—a library of local literature, stocked with county histories, old maps of the district, monographs on the local antiquities, dialect dictionaries, handbooks of the local geology and natural history. He liked to think of the villagers, inspired by such reading, making up parties of a Sunday afternoon to look for fossils and flint arrow-heads. The villagers themselves favoured the idea of a memorial reservoir and water supply. But the busiest and most articulate party followed Mr. Bodiham in demanding something religious in character—a second lich-gate, for example, a stained-glass window, a monument of marble, or, if possible, all three. So far, however, nothing had been done, partly because the memorial committee had never been able to agree, partly for the more cogent reason that too little money had been subscribed to carry out any of the proposed schemes. Every three or four months Mr. Bodiham preached a sermon on the subject. His last had been delivered in March; it was high time that his congregation had a fresh reminder.

'And the cedar of the house within was carved with knops.'

Mr. Bodiham touched lightly on Solomon's temple. From thence he passed to temples and churches in general. What were the characteristics of these buildings dedicated to God? Obviously, the fact of their, from a human point of view, complete uselessness. They were unpractical buildings 'carved with knops.' Solomon might have built a library—indeed, what could be more to the taste of the world's wisest man? He might have dug a reservoir—what more useful in a parched city like Jerusalem? He did neither; he built a house all carved with knops, useless and unpractical. Why? Because he was dedicating the work to God. There had been much talk in Crome about the proposed War Memorial. A War Memorial was, in its very nature, a work dedicated to God. It was a token of thankfulness that the first stage in the culminating world-war had been crowned by the triumph of righteousness; it was at the same time a visibly embodied supplication that God might not long delay the Advent which alone could bring the final peace. A library, a reservoir? Mr. Bodiham scornfully and indignantly condemned the idea. These were works dedicated to man, not to God. As a War Memorial they were totally unsuitable. A lich-gate had been suggested. This was an object which answered perfectly to the definition of a War Memorial: a useless work dedicated to God and carved with knops. One lich-gate, it was true, already existed. But nothing would be easier than to make a second entrance into the churchyard; and a second entrance would need a second gate. Other suggestions had been made. Stained-glass windows, a monument of marble. Both these were admirable, especially the latter. It was high time that the War Memorial was erected. It might soon be too late. At any moment, like a thief in the night, God might come. Meanwhile a difficulty stood in the way. Funds were inadequate. All should subscribe according to their means. Those who had lost relations in the war might reasonably be expected to subscribe a sum equal to that which they would have had to pay in funeral expenses if the relative had died while at home. Further delay was disastrous. The War Memorial must be built at once. He appealed to the patriotism and the Christian sentiments of all his hearers.

Henry Wimbush walked home thinking of the books he would present to the War Memorial Library, if ever it came into existence. He took the path through the fields; it was pleasanter than the road. At the first stile a group of village boys, loutish young fellows all dressed in the hideous ill-fitting black which makes a funeral of every English Sunday and holiday, were assembled, drearily guffawing as they smoked their cigarettes. They made way for Henry Wimbush, touching their caps as he passed. He returned their salute; his bowler and face were one in their unruffled gravity.

In Sir Ferdinando's time, he reflected, in the time of his son, Sir Julius, these young men would have had their Sunday diversions even at Crome, remote and rustic Crome. There would have been archery, skittles, dancing—social amusements in which they would have partaken as members of a conscious community. Now they had nothing, nothing except Mr. Bodiham's forbidding Boys' Club and the rare dances and concerts organized by himself. Boredom or the urban pleasures of the county metropolis were the alternatives that presented themselves to these poor youths. Country pleasures were no more; they had been stamped out by the Puritans.

In Manningham's Diary for 1600 there was a queer passage, he remembered, a very queer passage. Certain magistrates in Berkshire, Puritan magistrates, had had wind of a scandal. One moonlit summer night they had ridden out with their *posse* and there, among the hills, they had come upon a company of men and women, dancing, stark naked, among the sheep-cotes. The magistrates and their men had ridden their horses into the crowd. How self-conscious the poor people must suddenly have felt, how helpless without their clothes against armed and booted horsemen! The dancers are arrested, whipped, gaoled, set in the stocks; the moonlight dance is never danced again. What old, earthy, Panic rite came to extinction here? he wondered. Who knows?—perhaps their ancestors had danced like this in the moonlight ages before Adam and Eve were so much as thought of. He liked to think so. And now it was no more. These weary young men, if they wanted to dance, would have to bicycle six miles to the town. The country was desolate, without life of its own, without indigenous pleasures. The pious magistrates had snuffed out for ever a little happy flame that had burned from the beginning of time.

> And as on Tullia's tomb one lamp burned clear,
> Unchanged for fifteen hundred year . . .

He repeated the lines to himself, and was desolated to think of all the murdered past.

## *Chapter 19*

HENRY WIMBUSH's long cigar burned aromatically. The *History of Crome* lay on his knee; slowly he turned over the pages.

'I can't decide what episode to read you to-night,' he said thoughtfully. 'Sir Ferdinando's voyages are not without interest. Then, of course, there's his son, Sir Julius. It was he who suffered from the delusion that his perspiration engendered flies; it drove him finally to suicide. Or there's Sir Cyprian.' He turned the pages more rapidly. 'Or Sir Henry. Or Sir George. . . . No, I'm inclined to think I won't read about any of these.'

'But you must read something,' insisted Mr. Scogan, taking his pipe out of his mouth.

'I think I shall read about my grandfather,' said Henry Wimbush, 'and the events that led up to his marriage with the eldest daughter of the last Sir Ferdinando.'

'Good,' said Mr. Scogan. 'We are listening.'

'Before I begin reading,' said Henry Wimbush, looking up from the book and taking off the pince-nez which he had just fitted to his nose—'before I begin, I must say a few preliminary words about Sir Ferdinando, the last of the Lapiths. At the death of the virtuous and unfortunate Sir Hercules, Ferdinando found himself in possession of the family fortune, not a little increased by his father's temperance and thrift; he applied himself forthwith to the task of spending it, which he did in an ample and jovial fashion. By the time he was forty he had eaten and, above all, drunk and loved away about half his capital, and would infallibly have soon got rid of the rest in the same manner, if he had not had the good fortune to become so madly enamoured of the Rector's daughter as to make a proposal of marriage. The young lady accepted him, and in less than a year had become the absolute mistress of Crome and her husband. An extraordinary reformation made itself apparent in Sir Ferdinando's character. He grew regular and economical in his habits; he even became temperate, rarely drinking more than a bottle and a half of port at a sitting. The waning fortune of the Lapiths began once more to wax, and that in despite of the hard times (for Sir Ferdinando married in 1809 in the height of the Napoleonic Wars). A prosperous and dignified old age, cheered by the spectacle of his children's growth and happiness—for Lady Lapith had already borne him three daughters, and there seemed no good reason why she should not bear many more of them, and sons as well—a partriarchal decline into the family vault, seemed now to be Sir Ferdinando's enviable destiny. But Providence willed otherwise. To Napoleon, cause already of such infinite mischief, was due, though perhaps indirectly, the untimely and violent death which put a period to this reformed existence.

'Sir Ferdinando, who was above all things a patriot, had adopted, from the earliest days of the conflict with the French, his own peculiar method of celebrating our victories. When the happy news reached London, it was his custom to purchase immediately a large store of liquor and, taking a place on whichever of the outgoing coaches he happened to light on first, to drive through the country proclaiming the good news to all he met on the road and dispensing it, along with the liquor, at every stopping-place to all who cared to listen or drink. Thus, after the Nile, he had driven as far as Edinburgh; and later, when the coaches, wreathed with laurel for triumph, with cypress for mourning, were setting out with the news of Nelson's victory and death, he sat through all a chilly October night on the box of the Norwich *Meteor* with a nautical keg of rum on his knees and two cases of old brandy under the seat. This genial custom was one of the many habits which he abandoned on his marriage. The victories in the Peninsula, the retreat from Moscow, Leipzig, and the abdication of the tyrant all went uncelebrated. It so happened, however, that in the summer of 1815 Sir Ferdinando was staying for a few weeks in the capital. There had been a succession of anxious, doubtful days; then came the glorious news of Waterloo. It was too much for Sir Ferdinando; his joyous youth awoke again within him. He hurried to his wine merchant and bought a dozen bottles of 1760 brandy. The Bath coach was on the point of starting; he bribed his way on to the box and, seated in glory beside the driver, proclaimed aloud the downfall of the Corsican bandit and passed about the warm liquid joy. They clattered through Uxbridge, Slough, Maidenhead. Sleeping Reading was awakened by the great news. At Didcot one of the ostlers was so much overcome by patriotic emotions and the 1760 brandy that he found it impossible to do up the buckles of the harness. The night began to grow chilly, and Sir Ferdinando found that it was not enough to take a nip at every stage: to keep up his vital warmth he was compelled to drink between the stages as well. They were approaching Swindon. The coach was travelling at a dizzy speed—six miles in the last half-hour—when, without having manifested the slightest premonitory symptom of unsteadiness, Sir Ferdinando suddenly toppled sideways off his seat and fell, head foremost, into the road. An unpleasant jolt awakened the slumbering passengers. The coach was brought to a standstill; the guard ran back with a light. He found Sir Ferdinando still alive, but unconscious; blood was oozing from his mouth. The back wheels of the coach had passed over his body, breaking most of his ribs and both arms. His skull was fractured in two places. They picked him up, but he was dead before they reached the next stage. So perished Sir Ferdinando, a victim to his own patriotism. Lady Lapith did not marry again, but determined to devote the rest of her life to the well-being of her three children—Georgiana, now five years old, and Emmeline and Caroline, twins of two.'

Henry Wimbush paused, and once more put on his pince-nez. 'So much by way of introduction,' he said. 'Now I can begin to read about my grandfather.'

'One moment,' said Mr. Scogan, 'till I've refilled my pipe.'

Mr. Wimbush waited. Seated apart in a corner of the room, Ivor was showing Mary his sketches of Spirit Life. They spoke together in whispers.

Mr. Scogan had lighted his pipe again. 'Fire away,' he said.

Henry Wimbush fired away.

'It was in the spring of 1833 that my grandfather, George Wimbush, first made the acquaintance of the "three lovely Lapiths," as they were always called. He was then a young man of twenty-two, with curly yellow hair and a smooth pink face that was the mirror of his youthful and ingenuous mind. He had been educated at Harrow and Christ Church, he enjoyed hunting and all other field sports, and, though his circumstances were comfortable to the verge of affluence, his pleasures were temperate and innocent. His father, an East Indian merchant, had destined him for a political career, and had gone to considerable expense in acquiring a pleasant little Cornish borough as a twenty-first birthday gift for his son. He was justly indignant when, on the very eve of George's majority, the Reform Bill of 1832 swept the borough out of existence. The inauguration of George's political career had to be postponed. At the time he got to know the lovely Lapiths he was waiting; he was not at all impatient.

'The lovely Lapiths did not fail to impress him. Georgiana, the eldest, with her black ringlets, her flashing eyes, her noble aquiline profile, her swan-like neck, and sloping shoulders, was orientally dazzling; and the twins, with their delicately turned-up noses, their blue eyes, and chestnut hair, were an identical pair of ravishingly English charmers.

'Their conversation at this first meeting proved, however, to be so forbidding that, but for the invincible attraction exercised by their beauty, George would never have had the courage to follow up the acquaintance. The twins, looking up their noses at him with an air of languid superiority, asked him what he thought of the latest French poetry and whether he liked the *Indiana* of George Sand. But what was almost worse was the question with which Georgiana opened her conversation with him. "In music," she asked, leaning forward and fixing him with her large dark eyes, "are you a classicist or a transcendentalist?" George did not lose his presence of mind. He had enough appreciation of music to know that he hated anything classical, and so, with a promptitude which did him credit, he replied, "I am a transcendentalist." Georgiana smiled bewitchingly. "I am glad," she said; "so am I. You went to hear Paganini last week, of course. 'The Prayer of Moses'—ah!" She closed her eyes. "Do you know anything more transcendental than that?" "No," said George, "I don't." He hesitated, was about to go on speaking, and then decided that after all it would be wiser not to say—what was in fact true—that he had enjoyed above all Paganini's Farmyard Imitations. The man had made his fiddle bray like an ass, cluck like a hen, grunt, squeal, bark, neigh, quack, bellow, and growl; that last item, in George's estimation, had almost compensated for the tediousness of the rest of the concert. He smiled with pleasure at the thought of it. Yes, decidedly, he was no classicist in music; he was a thoroughgoing transcendentalist.

'George followed up this first introduction by paying a call on the young ladies and their mother, who occupied, during the season, a small but elegant house in the neighbourhood of Berkeley Square. Lady Lapith made a few discreet inquiries, and having found that George's financial position, character, and family were all passably good, she asked him to dine. She hoped and expected that her daughters would all marry into the peerage; but, being a prudent woman, she knew it was advisable to prepare for all contingencies. George Wimbush, she thought, would make an excellent second string for one of the twins.

'At this first dinner, George's partner was Emmeline. They talked of Nature. Emmeline protested that to her high mountains were a feeling and the hum of human cities torture. George agreed that the country was very agreeable, but held that London during the season also had its charms. He noticed with surprise and a certain solicitous distress that Miss Emmeline's appetite was poor, that it didn't, in fact, exist. Two spoonfuls of soup, a morsel of fish, no bird, no meat, and three grapes—that was her whole dinner. He looked from time to time at her two sisters; Georgiana and Caroline seemed to be quite as abstemious. They waved away whatever was offered them with an expression of delicate disgust, shutting their eyes and averting their faces from the proffered dish, as though the lemon sole, the duck, the loin of veal, the trifle, were objects revolting to the sight and smell. George, who thought the dinner capital, ventured to comment on the sisters' lack of appetite.

' "Pray, don't talk to me of eating," said Emmeline, drooping like a sensitive plant. "We find it so coarse, so unspiritual, my sisters and I. One can't think of one's soul while one is eating."

'George agreed; one couldn't. "But one must live," he said.

' "Alas!" Emmeline sighed. "One must. Death is very beautiful, don't you think?" She broke a corner off a piece of toast and began to nibble at it languidly. "But since, as you say, one must live . . ." She made a little gesture of resignation. "Luckily a very little suffices to keep one alive." She put down her corner of toast half eaten.

'George regarded her with some surprise. She was pale, but she looked extraordinarily healthy, he thought; so did her sisters. Perhaps if you were really spiritual you needed less food. He, clearly, was not spiritual.

'After this he saw them frequently. They all liked him, from Lady Lapith downwards. True, he was not very romantic or poetical; but he was such a pleasant, unpretentious, kind-hearted young man, that one couldn't help liking him. For his part, he thought them wonderful, wonderful, especially Georgiana. He enveloped them all in a warm, protective affection. For they needed protection; they were altogether too frail, too spiritual for this world. They never ate, they were always pale, they often complained of fever, they talked much and lovingly of death, they frequently swooned. Georgiana was the most ethereal of all; of the three she ate least, swooned most often, talked most of death, and was the palest—with a pallor that was so startling as to appear positively artificial. At any moment, it seemed, she might loose her precarious hold on this material world and become all spirit. To George the thought was a continual agony. If she were to die . . .

'She contrived, however, to live through the season, and that in spite of the numerous balls, routs, and other parties of pleasure which, in company with the rest of the lovely trio, she never failed to attend. In the middle of July the whole household moved down to the country. George was invited to spend the month of August at Crome.

'The house-party was distinguished; in the list of visitors figured the names of two marriageable young men of title. George had hoped that country air, repose, and natural surroundings might have restored to the three sisters their appetites and the roses of their cheeks. He was mistaken. For dinner, the first evening, Georgiana ate only an olive, two or three salted almonds, and half a peach. She was as pale as ever. During the meal she spoke of love.

'"True love," she said, "being infinite and eternal, can only be consummated in eternity. Indiana and Sir Rodolphe celebrated the mystic wedding of their souls by jumping into Niagara. Love is incompatible with life. The wish of two people who truly love one another is not to live together but to die together."

'"Come, come, my dear," said Lady Lapith, stout and practical. "What would become of the next generation, pray, if all the world acted on your principles?"

'"Mamma! . . ." Georgiana protested, and dropped her eyes.

'"In my young days," Lady Lapith went on, "I should have been laughed out of countenance if I'd said a thing like that. But then in my young days souls weren't as fashionable as they are now and we didn't think death was at all poetical. It was just unpleasant."

'"Mamma! . . ." Emmeline and Caroline implored in unison.

'"In my young days——" Lady Lapith was launched into her subject; nothing, it seemed, could stop her now. "In my young days, if you didn't eat, people told you you needed a dose of rhubarb. Nowadays . . ."

'There was a cry; Georgiana had swooned sideways on to Lord Timpany's shoulder. It was a desperate expedient; but it was successful. Lady Lapith was stopped.

'The days passed in an uneventful round of pleasures. Of all the gay party George alone was unhappy. Lord Timpany was paying his court to Georgiana, and it was clear that he was not unfavourably received. George looked on, and his soul was a hell of jealousy and despair. The boisterous company of the young men became intolerable to him; he shrank from them, seeking gloom and solitude. One morning, having broken away from them on some vague pretext, he returned to the house alone. The young men were bathing in the pool below; their cries and laughter floated up to him, making the quiet house seem lonelier and more silent. The lovely sisters and their mamma still kept their chambers; they did not customarily make their appearance till luncheon, so that the male guests had the morning to themselves. George sat down in the hall and abandoned himself to thought.

'At any moment she might die; at any moment she might become Lady Timpany. It was terrible, terrible. If she died, then he would die too; he would go to seek her beyond the grave. If she became Lady Timpany . . . ah, then! The solution of the problem would not be so simple. If she became Lady Timpany: it was a horrible thought.

But then suppose she were in love with Timpany—though it seemed incredible that anyone could be in love with Timpany—suppose her life depended on Timpany, suppose she couldn't live without him? He was fumbling his way along this clueless labyrinth of suppositions when the clock struck twelve. On the last stroke, like an automaton released by the turning clockwork, a little maid, holding a large covered tray, popped out of the door that led from the kitchen regions into the hall. From his deep arm-chair George watched her (himself, it was evident, unobserved) with an idle curiosity. She pattered across the room and came to a halt in front of what seemed a blank expanse of panelling. She reached out her hand and, to George's extreme astonishment, a little door swung open, revealing the foot of a winding staircase. Turning sideways in order to get her tray through the narrow opening, the little maid darted in with a rapid crablike motion. The door closed behind her with a click. A minute later it opened again and the maid, without her tray, hurried back across the hall and disappeared in the direction of the kitchen. George tried to recompose his thoughts, but an invincible curiosity drew his mind towards the hidden door, the staircase, the little maid. It was in vain he told himself that the matter was none of his business, that to explore the secrets of that surprising door, that mysterious staircase within, would be a piece of unforgivable rudeness and indiscretion. It was in vain; for five minutes he struggled heroically with his curiosity, but at the end of that time he found himself standing in front of the innocent sheet of panelling through which the little maid had disappeared. A glance sufficed to show him the position of the secret door—secret, he perceived, only to those who looked with a careless eye. It was just an ordinary door let in flush with the panelling. No latch nor handle betrayed its position, but an unobtrusive catch sunk in the wood invited the thumb. George was astonished that he had not noticed it before; now he had seen it, it was so obvious, almost as obvious as the cupboard door in the library with its lines of imitation shelves and its dummy books. He pulled back the catch and peeped inside. The staircase, of which the degrees were made not of stone but of blocks of ancient oak, wound up and out of sight. A slit-like window admitted the daylight; he was at the foot of the central tower, and the little window looked out over the terrace; they were still shouting and splashing in the pool below.

'George closed the door and went back to his seat. But his curiosity was not satisfied. Indeed, this partial satisfaction had but whetted its appetite. Where did the staircase lead? What was the errand of the little maid? It was no business of his, he kept repeating—no business of his. He tried to read, but his attention wandered. A quarter-past twelve sounded on the harmonious clock. Suddenly determined, George rose, crossed the room, opened the hidden door, and began to ascend the stairs. He passed the first window, corkscrewed round, and came to another. He paused for a moment to look out; his heart beat uncomfortably, as though he were affronting some unknown danger. What he was doing, he told himself, was extremely ungentlemanly, horribly underbred. He tiptoed onward and upward. One turn more, then half a turn, and a door confronted him. He halted before it, listened; he could hear no sound. Putting his eye to the keyhole, he saw nothing but a stretch of white sunlit wall. Emboldened, he turned the handle and stepped across the threshold. There he halted, petrified by what he saw, mutely gaping.

'In the middle of a pleasantly sunny little room—"it is now Priscilla's boudoir," Mr. Wimbush remarked parenthetically—stood a small circular table of mahogany. Crystal, porcelain, and silver,—all the shining apparatus of an elegant meal—were mirrored in its polished depths. The carcase of a cold chicken, a bowl of fruit, a great ham, deeply gashed to its heart of tenderest white and pink, the brown cannon ball of a cold plum-pudding, a slender Hock bottle, and a decanter of claret jostled one another for a place on this festive board. And round the table sat the three sisters, the three lovely Lapiths—eating!

'At George's sudden entrance they had all looked towards the door, and now they sat, petrified by the same astonishment which kept George fixed and staring. Georgiana, who sat immediately facing the door, gazed at him with dark, enormous eyes. Between the thumb and forefinger of her right hand she was holding a drumstick of the dismembered chicken; her little finger, elegantly crooked, stood apart from the rest of her hand. Her mouth was open, but the drumstick had never reached its destination; it remained, suspended, frozen, in mid-air. The other two sisters had turned round to look at the intruder. Caroline still grasped her knife and fork; Emmeline's fingers were round the stem of her claret glass. For what seemed a very long time, George and the three sisters stared at one another in silence. They were a group of statues. Then suddenly there was movement. Georgiana dropped her chicken bone, Caroline's knife and fork clattered on her plate. The movement propagated itself, grew more decisive; Emmeline sprang to her feet, uttering a cry. The wave of panic reached George; he turned and, mumbling something unintelligible as he went, rushed out of the room and down the winding stairs. He came to a standstill in the hall, and there, all by himself in the quiet house, he began to laugh.

'At luncheon it was noticed that the sisters ate a little more than usual. Georgiana toyed with some French beans and a spoonful of calves'-foot jelly. "I feel a little stronger to-day," she said to Lord Timpany, when he congratulated her on this increase of appetite; "a little more material," she added, with a nervous laugh. Looking up, she caught George's eye; a blush suffused her cheeks and she looked hastily away.

'In the garden that afternoon they found themselves for a moment alone.

' "You won't tell anyone, George? Promise you won't tell anyone," she implored. "It would make us look so ridiculous. And besides, eating *is* unspiritual, isn't it? Say you won't tell anyone.'

' "I will," said George brutally. "I'll tell everyone, unless . . .'

' "It's blackmail."

' "I don't care," said George. "I'll give you twenty-four hours to decide."

'Lady Lapith was disappointed, of course; she had hoped for better things—for Timpany and a coronet. But George, after all, wasn't so bad. They were married at the New Year.

'My poor grandfather!' Mr. Wimbush added, as he closed his book and put away his pince-nez. 'Whenever I read in the papers about oppressed nationalities, I think of him.' He relighted his cigar. 'It was a maternal government, highly centralized, and there were no representative institutions.'

Henry Wimbush ceased speaking. In the silence that ensued Ivor's whispered commentary on the spirit sketches once more became audible. Priscilla, who had been dozing, suddenly woke up.

'What?' she said in the startled tones of one newly returned to consciousness; 'what?'

Jenny caught the words. She looked up, smiled, nodded reassuringly. 'It's about a ham,' she said.

'What's about a ham?'

'What Henry has been reading.' She closed the red notebook lying on her knees and slipped a rubber band round it. 'I'm going to bed,' she announced, and got up.

'So am I,' said Anne, yawning. But she lacked the energy to rise from her arm-chair.

The night was hot and oppressive. Round the open windows the curtains hung unmoving. Ivor, fanning himself with the portrait of an Astral Being, looked out into the darkness and drew a breath.

'The air 's like wool,' he declared.

'It will get cooler after midnight,' said Henry Wimbush, and cautiously added, 'perhaps.'

'I shan't sleep, I know.'

Priscilla turned her head in his direction; the monumental coiffure nodded exorbitantly at her slightest movement. 'You must make an effort,' she said. 'When I can't sleep, I concentrate my will: I say, "I will sleep, I am asleep!" And pop! off I go. That's the power of thought.'

'But does it work on stuffy nights?' Ivor inquired. 'I simply cannot sleep on a stuffy night.'

'Nor can I,' said Mary, 'except out of doors.'

'Out of doors! What a wonderful idea!' In the end they decided to sleep on the towers—Mary on the western tower, Ivor on the eastern. There was a flat expanse of leads on each of the towers, and you could get a mattress through the trap doors that opened on to them. Under the stars, under the gibbous moon, assuredly they would sleep. The mattresses were hauled up, sheets and blankets were spread, and an hour later the two insomniasts, each on his separate tower, were crying their good-nights across the dividing gulf.

On Mary the sleep-compelling charm of the open air did not work with its expected magic. Even through the mattress one could not fail to be aware that the leads were extremely hard. Then there were noises: the owls screeched tirelessly, and once, roused by some unknown terror, all the geese of the farmyard burst into a sudden frenzy of cackling. The stars and the gibbous moon demanded to be looked at, and when one meteorite had streaked across the sky, you could not help waiting, open-eyed and alert, for the next. Time passed; the moon climbed higher and higher in the sky. Mary felt less sleepy than she had when she first came out. She sat up and looked over the parapet. Had Ivor been able to sleep? she wondered. And as though in answer to her mental question, from behind the chimney-stack at the farther end of the roof a white form noiselessly emerged—a form that, in the moonlight, was recognizably Ivor's. Spreading his arms to right and left, like a tight-rope dancer, he began to walk forward along the roof-tree of the house. He swayed terrifyingly as he advanced. Mary looked on speechlessly; perhaps he was walking in his sleep! Suppose he were to wake up suddenly, now! If she spoke or moved it might mean his death. She dared look no more, but sank back on her pillows. She listened intently. For what seemed an immensely long time there was no sound. Then there was a patter of feet on the tiles, followed by a scrabbling noise and a whispered 'Damn!' And suddenly Ivor's head and shoulders appeared above the parapet. One leg followed, then the other. He was on the leads. Mary pretended to wake up with a start.

'Oh?' she said. 'What are you doing here?'

'I couldn't sleep,' he explained, 'so I came along to see if you couldn't. One gets bored by oneself on a tower. Don't you find it so?'

It was light before five. Long, narrow clouds barred the east, their edges bright with orange fire. The sky was pale and watery. With the mournful scream of a soul in pain, a monstrous peacock, flying heavily up from below, alighted on the parapet of the tower. Ivor and Mary started broad awake.

'Catch him!' cried Ivor, jumping up. 'We'll have a feather.' The frightened peacock ran up and down the parapet in an absurd distress, curtseying and bobbing and clucking; his long tail swung ponderously back and forth as he turned and turned again. Then with a flap and swish he launched himself upon the air and sailed magnificently earthward, with a recovered dignity. But he had left a trophy. Ivor had his feather, a long-lashed eye of purple and green, of blue and gold. He handed it to his companion.

'An angel's feather,' he said.

Mary looked at it for a moment, gravely and intently. Her purple pyjamas clothed her with an ampleness that hid the lines of her body; she looked like some large, comfortable, unjointed toy, a sort of Teddy bear—but a Teddy bear with an angel's head, pink cheeks, and hair like a bell of gold. An angel's face, the feather of an angel's wing. . . . Somehow the whole atmosphere of this sunrise was rather angelic.

'It's extraordinary to think of sexual selection,' she said at last, looking up from her contemplation of the miraculous feather.

'Extraordinary!' Ivor echoed. 'I select you, you select me. What luck!'

He put his arm round her shoulders and they stood looking eastward. The first sunlight had begun to warm and colour the pale light of the dawn. Mauve pyjamas and white pyjamas; they were a young and charming couple. The rising sun touched their faces. It was all extremely symbolic; but then, if you choose to think so, nothing in this world is not symbolical. Profound and beautiful truth!

'I must be getting back to my tower,' said Ivor at last.

'Already?'

'I'm afraid so. The varletry will soon be up and about.'

'Ivor. . . .' There was a prolonged and silent farewell.

'And now,' said Ivor, 'I repeat my tight-rope stunt.'

Mary threw her arms round his neck. 'You mustn't, Ivor. It's dangerous. Please.'

He had to yield at last to her entreaties. 'All right,' he said, 'I'll go down through the house and up at the other end.'

He vanished through the trap door into the darkness that still lurked within the shuttered house. A minute later he had reappeared on the farther tower; he waved his hand, and then sank down, out of sight, behind the parapet. From below, in the house, came the thin wasp-like buzzing of an alarum-clock. He had gone back just in time.

## *Chapter 20*

IVOR was gone. Lounging behind the wind-screen in his yellow sedan he was whirling across rural England. Social and amorous engagements of the most urgent character called him from hall to baronial hall, from castle to castle, from Elizabethan manor-house to Georgian mansion, over the whole expanse of the kingdom. To-day in Somerset, to-morrow in Warwickshire, on Saturday in the West Riding, by Tuesday morning in Argyll—Ivor never rested. The whole summer through, from the beginning of July till the end of September, he devoted himself to his engagements; he was a martyr to them. In the autumn he went back to London for a holiday. Crome had been a little incident, an evanescent bubble on the stream of his life; it belonged already to the past. By tea-time he would be at Gobley, and there would be Zenobia's welcoming smile. And on Thursday morning—but that was a long,

long way ahead. He would think of Thursday morning when Thursday morning arrived. Meanwhile there was Gobley, meanwhile Zenobia.

In the visitors' book at Crome Ivor had left, according to his invariable custom in these cases, a poem. He had improvised it magisterially in the ten minutes preceding his departure. Denis and Mr. Scogan strolled back together from the gates of the courtyard, whence they had bidden their last farewells; on the writing-table in the hall they found the visitors' book, open, and Ivor's composition scarcely dry. Mr. Scogan read it aloud:

> The magic of those immemorial kings,
> Who webbed enchantment on the bowls of night,
> Sleeps in the soul of all created things;
> In the blue sea, th' Acroceraunian height,
> In the eyed butterfly's auricular wings
> And orgied visions of the anchorite;
> In all that singing flies and flying sings,
> In rain, in pain, in delicate delight.
> But much more magic, much more cogent spells
> Weave here their wizardries about my soul.
> Crome calls me like the voice of vesperal bells,
> Haunts like a ghostly-peopled necropole.
> Fate tears me hence. Hard fate! since far from Crome
> My soul must weep, remembering its Home.

'Very nice and tasteful and tactful,' said Mr. Scogan, when he had finished. 'I am only troubled by the butterfly's auricular wings. You have a first-hand knowledge of the workings of a poet's mind, Denis; perhaps you can explain.'

'What could be simpler,' said Denis. 'It's a beautiful word, and Ivor wanted to say that the wings were golden.'

'You make it luminously clear.'

'One suffers so much,' Denis went on, 'from the fact that beautiful words don't always mean what they ought to mean. Recently, for example, I had a whole poem ruined, just because the word "carminative" didn't mean what it ought to have meant. Carminative—it's admirable, isn't it?'

'Admirable,' Mr. Scogan agreed. 'And what does it mean?'

'It's a word I've treasured from my earliest infancy,' said Denis, 'treasured and loved. They used to give me cinnamon when I had a cold—quite useless, but not disagreeable. One poured it drop by drop out of narrow bottles, a golden liquor, fierce and fiery. On the label was a list of its virtues, and among other things it was described as being in the highest degree carminative. I adored the word. "Isn't it carminative?" I used to say to myself when I'd taken my dose. It seemed so wonderfully to describe that sensation of internal warmth, that glow, that—what shall I call it?—physical self-satisfaction which followed the drinking of cinnamon. Later, when I discovered alcohol, "carminative" described for me that similar, but nobler, more spiritual glow which wine evokes not only in the body but in the soul as well. The carminative virtues of burgundy, of rum, of old brandy, of Lacryma Christi, of Marsala, of Aleatico, of stout, of gin, of champagne, of claret, of the raw new wine of this year's Tuscan vintage—I compared them, I classified them. Marsala is rosily, downily carminative; gin pricks and refreshes while it warms. I had a whole table of carmination values. And now'—Denis spread out his hands, palm upwards, despairingly—'now I know what carminative really means.'

'Well, what *does* it mean?' asked Mr. Scogan, a little impatiently.

'Carminative,' said Denis, lingering lovingly over the syllables, 'carminative. I imagined vaguely that it had something to do with *carmen-carminis*, still more vaguely with *caro-carnis*, and its derivatives, like carnival and carnation. Carminative—there was the idea of singing and the idea of flesh, rose-coloured and warm, with a suggestion of the jollities of mi-Carême and the masked holidays of Venice. Carminative—the warmth, the glow, the interior ripeness were all in the word. Instead of which . . .'

'Do come to the point, my dear Denis,' protested Mr. Scogan. 'Do come to the point.'

'Well, I wrote a poem the other day,' said Denis; 'I wrote a poem about the effects of love.'

'Others have done the same before you,' said Mr. Scogan. 'There is no need to be ashamed.'

'I was putting forward the notion,' Denis went on, 'that the effects of love were often similar to the effects of wine, that Eros could intoxicate as well as Bacchus. Love, for example, is essentially carminative. It gives one the sense of warmth, the glow.

*And passion carminative as wine . . .*

was what I wrote. Not only was the line elegantly sonorous; it was also, I flattered myself, very aptly and compendiously expressive. Everything was in the word carminative—a detailed, exact foreground, an immense, indefinite hinterland of suggestion.

*And passion carminative as wine . . .*

I was not ill-pleased. And then suddenly it occurred to me that I had never actually looked up the word in a dictionary. Carminative had grown up with me from the days of the cinnamon bottle. It had always been taken for granted. Carminative: for me the word was as rich in content as some tremendous, elaborate work of art; it was a complete landscape with figures.

*And passion carminative as wine . . .*

It was the first time I had ever committed the word to writing, and all at once I felt I would like lexicographical authority for it. A small

English-German dictionary was all I had at hand. I turned up C, ca, car, carm. There it was: "Carminative: *windtreibend.*" *Windtreibend*!' he repeated. Mr. Scogan laughed. Denis shook his head. 'Ah,' he said, 'for me it was no laughing matter. For me it marked the end of a chapter, the death of something young and precious. There were the years—years of childhood and innocence—when I had believed that carminative meant—well, carminative. And now, before me lies the rest of my life—a day, perhaps, ten years, half a century, when I shall know that carminative means *windtreibend.*

Plus ne suis ce qui j'ai été
Et ne le saurai jamais être.

It is a realization that makes one rather melancholy.'

'Carminative,' said Mr. Scogan thoughtfully.

'Carminative,' Denis repeated, and they were silent for a time. 'Words,' said Denis at last, 'words—I wonder if you can realize how much I love them. You are too much preoccupied with mere things and ideas and people to understand the full beauty of words. Your mind is not a literary mind. The spectacle of Mr. Gladstone finding thirty-four rhymes to the name "Margot" seems to you rather pathetic than anything else. Mallarmé's envelopes with their versified addresses leave you cold, unless they leave you pitiful; you can't see that

Apte à ne point te cabrer, hue!
Poste, et j'ajouterai, dia!
Si tu ne fuis onze-bis Rue
Balzac, chez cet Heredia,

is a little miracle.'

'You're right,' said Mr. Scogan. 'I can't.'

'You don't feel it to be magical?'

'No.'

'That's the test for the literary mind,' said Denis; 'the feeling of magic, the sense that words have power. The technical, verbal part of literature is simply a development of magic. Words are man's first and most grandiose invention. With language, he created a whole new universe; what wonder if he loved words and attributed power to them! With fitted, harmonious words the magicians summoned rabbits out of empty hats and spirits from the elements. Their descendants, the literary men, still go on with the process, morticing their verbal formulas together and, before the power of the finished spell, trembling with delight and awe. Rabbits out of empty hats? No, their spells are more subtly powerful, for they evoke emotions out of empty minds. Formulated by their art, the most insipid statements become enormously significant. For example, I proffer the constatation, "Black ladders lack bladders." A self-evident truth, one on which it would not have been worth while to insist, had I chosen to formulate it in such words as "Black fire-escapes have no bladders," or, "Les échelles noires manquent de vessie." But since I put it as I do, "Black ladders lack bladders," it becomes, for all its self-evidence, significant, unforgettable, moving. The creation by word-power of something out of nothing—what is that but magic? And, I may add, what is that but literature? Half the world's greatest poetry is simply "Les échelles noires manquent de vessie," translated into magic significance as, "Black ladders lack bladders." And you can't appreciate words. I'm sorry for you.'

'A mental carminative,' said Mr. Scogan reflectively. 'That's what you need.'

## *Chapter 21*

PERCHED on its four stone mushrooms, the little granary stood two or three feet above the grass of the green close. Beneath it there was a perpetual shade and a damp growth of long, luxuriant grasses. Here, in the shadow, in the green dampness, a family of white ducks had sought shelter from the afternoon sun. Some stood, preening themselves, some reposed with their long bellies pressed to the ground, as though the cool grass were water. Little social noises burst fitfully forth, and from time to time some pointed tail would execute a brilliant Lisztian tremolo. Suddenly their jovial repose was shattered. A prodigious thump shook the wooden flooring above their heads; the whole granary trembled, little fragments of dirt and crumbled wood rained down among them. With a loud, continuous quacking the ducks rushed out from beneath this nameless menace, and did not stay their flight till they were safely in the farmyard.

'Don't lose your temper,' Anne was saying. 'Listen! You've frightened the ducks. Poor dears! no wonder.' She was sitting sideways in a low, wooden chair. Her right elbow rested on the back of the chair and she supported her cheek on her hand. Her long, slender body drooped into curves of lazy grace. She was smiling, and she looked at Gombauld through half-closed eyes.

'Damn you!' Gombauld repeated, and stamped his foot again. He glared at her round the half-finished portrait on the easel.

'Poor ducks!' Anne repeated. The sound of their quacking was faint in the distance; it was inaudible.

'Can't you see you make me lose my time?' he asked. 'I can't work with you dangling about distractingly like this.'

'You'd lose less time if you stopped talking and stamping your feet and did a little painting for a change. After all, what am I dangling about for, except to be painted?'

Gombauld made a noise like a growl. 'You're awful,' he said, with conviction. 'Why do you ask me to come and stay here? Why do you tell me you'd like me to paint your portrait?'

'For the simple reasons that I like you—at least, when you're in a good temper—and that I think you're a good painter.'

'For the simple reason'—Gombauld mimicked her voice—'that you want me to make love to you and, when I do, to have the amusement of running away.'

Anne threw back her head and laughed. 'So you think it amuses me to have to evade your advances! So like a man! If you only knew how gross and awful and boring men are when they try to make love and you don't want them to make love! If you could only see yourselves through our eyes!'

Gombauld picked up his palette and brushes and attacked his canvas with the ardour of irritation. 'I suppose you'll be saying next that you didn't start the game, that it was I who made the first advances, and that you were the innocent victim who sat still and never did anything that could invite or allure me on.'

'So like a man again!' said Anne. 'It's always the same old story about the woman tempting the man. The woman lures, fascinates, invites; and man—noble man, innocent man—falls a victim. My poor Gombauld! Surely you're not going to sing that old song again. It's so unintelligent, and I always thought you were a man of sense.'

'Thanks,' said Gombauld.

'Be a little objective,' Anne went on. 'Can't you see that you're simply externalizing your own emotions? That's what you men are always doing; it's so barbarously naïve. You feel one of your loose desires for some woman, and because you desire her strongly you immediately accuse her of luring you on, of deliberately provoking and inviting the desire. You have the mentality of savages. You might just as well say that a plate of strawberries and cream deliberately lures you on to feel greedy. In ninety-nine cases out of a hundred women are as passive and innocent as the strawberries and cream.'

'Well, all I can say is that this must be the hundredth case,' said Gombauld, without looking up.

Anne shrugged her shoulders and gave vent to a sigh. 'I'm at a loss to know whether you're more silly or more rude.'

After painting for a little time in silence Gombauld began to speak again. 'And then there's Denis,' he said, renewing the conversation as though it had only just been broken off. 'You're playing the same game with him. Why can't you leave that wretched young man in peace?'

Anne flushed with a sudden and uncontrollable anger. 'It's perfectly untrue about Denis,' she said indignantly. 'I never dreamt of playing what you beautifully call the same game with him.' Recovering her calm, she added in her ordinary cooing voice and with her exacerbating smile, 'You've become very protective towards poor Denis all of a sudden.'

'I have,' Gombauld replied, with a gravity that was somehow a little too solemn. 'I don't like to see a young man . . .'

'. . . being whirled along the road to ruin,' said Anne, continuing his sentence for him. 'I admire your sentiments and, believe me, I share them.'

She was curiously irritated at what Gombauld had said about Denis. It happened to be so completely untrue. Gombauld might have some slight ground for his reproaches. But Denis—no, she had never flirted with Denis. Poor boy! He was very sweet. She became somewhat pensive.

Gombauld painted on with fury. The restlessness of an unsatisfied desire, which, before, had distracted his mind, making work impossible, seemed now to have converted itself into a kind of feverish energy. When it was finished, he told himself, the portrait would be diabolic. He was painting her in the pose she had naturally adopted at the first sitting. Seated sideways, her elbow on the back of the chair, her head and shoulders turned at an angle from the rest of her body, towards the front, she had fallen into an attitude of indolent abandonment. He had emphasized the lazy curves of her body; the lines sagged as they crossed the canvas, the grace of the painted figure seemed to be melting into a kind of soft decay. The hand that lay along the knee was as limp as a glove. He was at work on the face now; it had begun to emerge on the canvas, doll-like in its regularity and listlessness. It was Anne's face—but her face as it would be, utterly unillumined by the inward lights of thought and emotion. It was the lazy, expressionless mask which was sometimes her face. The portrait was terribly like; and at the same time it was the most malicious of lies. Yes, it would be diabolic when it was finished, Gombauld decided; he wondered what she would think of it.

## *Chapter 22*

For the sake of peace and quiet Denis had retired earlier on this same afternoon to his bedroom. He wanted to work, but the hour was a drowsy one, and lunch, so recently eaten, weighed heavily on body and mind. The meridian demon was upon him; he was possessed by that bored and hopeless post-prandial melancholy which the cœnobites of old knew and feared under the name of 'accidie.' He felt, like Ernest Dowson, 'a little weary.' He was in the mood to write something rather exquisite and gentle and quietist in tone; something a little droopy and at the same time—how should he put it?—a little infinite. He thought of Anne, of love hopeless and unattainable. Perhaps that was the ideal kind of love, the hopeless kind—the quiet, theoretical kind of love. In this sad mood of repletion he could well believe it. He began to write. One elegant quatrain had flowed from beneath his pen:

A brooding love which is at most
  The stealth of moonbeams when they slide,
Evoking colour's bloodless ghost,
  O'er some scarce-breathing breast or side . . .

when his attention was attracted by a sound from outside. He looked down from his window; there they were, Anne and Gombauld, talking, laughing together. They crossed the courtyard in front, and passed out of sight through the gate in the right-hand wall. That was the way to the green close and the granary; she was going to sit for him again. His pleasantly depressing melancholy was dissipated by a puff of violent emotion; angrily he threw his quatrain into the waste-paper basket and ran downstairs. 'The stealth of moonbeams,' indeed!

In the hall he saw Mr. Scogan; the man seemed to be lying in wait. Denis tried to escape, but in vain. Mr. Scogan's eye glittered like the eye of the Ancient Mariner.

'Not so fast,' he said, stretching out a small saurian hand with pointed nails—'not so fast. I was just going down to the flower garden to take the sun. We'll go together.'

Denis abandoned himself; Mr. Scogan put on his hat and they went out arm in arm. On the shaven turf of the terrace Henry Wimbush and Mary were playing a solemn game of bowls. They descended by the yew-tree walk. It was here, thought Denis, here that Anne had fallen, here that he had kissed her, here—and he blushed with retrospective shame at the memory—here that he had tried to carry her and failed. Life was awful!

'Sanity!' said Mr. Scogan, suddenly breaking a long silence. 'Sanity—that's what's wrong with me and that's what will be wrong with you, my dear Denis, when you're old enough to be sane or insane. In a sane world I should be a great man; as things are, in this curious establishment, I am nothing at all; to all intents and purposes I don't exist. I am just *Vox et prœterea nihil.*'

Denis made no response; he was thinking of other things. 'After all,' he said to himself—'after all, Gombauld is better looking than I, more entertaining, more confident; and, besides, he's already somebody and I'm still only potential. . . .'

'Everything that ever gets done in this world is done by madmen,' Mr. Scogan went on. Denis tried not to listen, but the tireless insistence of Mr. Scogan's discourse gradually compelled his attention. 'Men such as I am, such as you may possibly become, have never achieved anything. We're too sane; we're merely reasonable. We lack the human touch, the compelling enthusiastic mania. People are quite ready to listen to the philosophers for a little amusement, just as they would listen to a fiddler or a mountebank. But as to acting on the advice of the men of reason—never. Wherever the choice has had to be made between the man of reason and the madman, the world has unhesitatingly followed the madman. For the madman appeals to what is fundamental, to passion and the instincts; the philosophers to what is superficial and supererogatory—reason.'

They entered the garden; at the head of one of the alleys stood a green wooden bench, embayed in the midst of a fragrant continent of lavender bushes. It was here, though the place was shadeless and one breathed hot, dry perfume instead of air—it was here that Mr. Scogan elected to sit. He thrived on untempered sunlight.

'Consider, for example, the case of Luther and Erasmus.' He took out his pipe and began to fill it as he talked. 'There was Erasmus, a man of reason if ever there was one. People listened to him at first—a new virtuoso performing on that elegant and resourceful instrument, the intellect; they even admired and venerated him. But did he move them to behave as he wanted them to behave—reasonably, decently, or at least a little less porkishly than usual? He did not. And then Luther appears, violent, passionate, a madman insanely convinced about matters in which there can be no conviction. He shouted, and men rushed to follow him. Erasmus was no longer listened to; he was reviled for his reasonableness. Luther was serious, Luther was reality—like the Great War. Erasmus was only reason and decency; he lacked the power, being a sage, to move men to action. Europe followed Luther and embarked on a century and a half of war and bloody persecution. It's a melancholy story.' Mr. Scogan lighted a match. In the intense light the flame was all but invisible. The smell of burning tobacco began to mingle with the sweetly acrid smell of the lavender.

'If you want to get men to act reasonably, you must set about persuading them in a maniacal manner. The very sane precepts of the founders of religions are only made infectious by means of enthusiasms which to a sane man must appear deplorable. It is humiliating to find how impotent unadulterated sanity is. Sanity, for example, informs us that the only way in which we can preserve civilization is by behaving decently and intelligently. Sanity appeals and argues; our rulers persevere in their customary porkishness, while we acquiesce and obey. The only hope is a maniacal crusade; I am ready, when it comes, to beat a tambourine with the loudest, but at the same time I shall feel a little ashamed of myself. However'—Mr. Scogan shrugged his shoulders and, pipe in hand, made a gesture of resignation—'it's futile to complain that things are as they are. The fact remains that sanity unassisted is useless. What we want, then, is a sane and reasonable exploitation of the forces of insanity. We sane men will have the power yet.' Mr. Scogan's eyes shone with a more than ordinary brightness, and, taking his pipe out of his mouth, he gave vent to his loud, dry, and somehow rather fiendish laugh.

'But I don't want power,' said Denis. He was sitting in limp discomfort at one end of the bench, shading his eyes from the intolerable light. Mr. Scogan, bolt upright at the other end, laughed again.

'Everybody wants power,' he said. 'Power in some form or other. The sort of power you hanker for is literary power. Some people want power to persecute other human beings; you expend your lust for power in persecuting words, twisting them, moulding them, torturing them to obey you. But I divagate.'

'Do you?' asked Denis faintly.

'Yes,' Mr. Scogan continued, unheeding, 'the time will come. We men of intelligence will learn to harness the insanities to the service of reason. We can't leave the world any longer to the direction of chance. We can't allow dangerous maniacs like Luther, mad about dogma, like Napoleon, mad about himself, to go on casually appearing and turning everything upside-down. In the past it didn't so much matter; but our modern machine is too delicate. A few more knocks like the Great War, another Luther or two, and the whole concern will go to pieces. In future, the men of reason must see that the madness of the world's maniacs is canalized into proper channels, is made to do useful work, like a mountain torrent driving a dynamo. . . .'

'Making electricity to light a Swiss hotel,' said Denis. 'You ought to complete the simile.'

Mr. Scogan waved away the interruption. 'There's only one thing to be done,' he said. 'The men of intelligence must combine, must conspire, and seize power from the imbeciles and maniacs who now direct us. They must found the Rational State.'

The heat that was slowly paralysing all Denis's mental and bodily faculties seemed to bring to Mr. Scogan additional vitality. He talked with an ever-increasing energy, his hands moved in sharp, quick, precise gestures, his eyes shone. Hard, dry, and continuous, his voice went on sounding and sounding in Denis's ears with the insistence of a mechanical noise.

'In the Rational State,' he heard Mr. Scogan saying, 'human beings will be separated out into distinct species, not according to the colour of their eyes or the shape of their skulls, but according to the qualities of their mind and temperament. Examining psychologists, trained to what would now seem an almost superhuman clairvoyance, will test each child that is born and assign it to its proper species. Duly labelled and docketed, the child will be given the education suitable to members of its species, and will be set, in adult life, to perform those functions which human beings of his variety are capable of performing.'

'How many species will there be?' asked Denis.

'A great many, no doubt,' Mr. Scogan answered; 'the classification will be subtle and elaborate. But it is not in the power of a prophet to go into details, nor is it his business. I will do no more than indicate the three main species into which the subjects of the Rational State will be divided.'

He paused, cleared his throat, and coughed once or twice, evoking in Denis's mind the vision of a table with a glass and water-bottle, and, lying across one corner, a long white pointer for the lantern pictures.

'The three main species,' Mr. Scogan went on, 'will be these: the Directing Intelligences, the Men of Faith, and the Herd. Among the Intelligences will be found all those capable of thought, those who know how to attain to a certain degree of freedom—and, alas, how limited, even among the most intelligent, that freedom is!—from the mental bondage of their time. A select body of Intelligences, drawn from among those who have turned their attention to the problems of practical life, will be the governors of the Rational State. They will employ as their instruments of power the second great species of humanity—the men of Faith, the Madmen, as I have been calling them, who believe in things unreasonably, with passion, and are ready to die for their beliefs and their desires. These wild men, with their fearful potentialities for good or for mischief, will no longer be allowed to react casually to a casual environment. There will be no more Cæsar Borgias, no more Luthers and Mohammeds, no more Joanna Southcotts, no more Comstocks. The old-fashioned Man of Faith and Desire, that haphazard creature of brute circumstance, who might drive men to tears and repentance, or who might equally well set them on to cutting one another's throats, will be replaced by a new sort of madman, still externally the same, still bubbling with a seemingly spontaneous enthusiasm, but, ah, how very different from the madman of the past! For the new Man of Faith will be expending his passion, his desire, and his enthusiasm in the propagation of some reasonable idea. He will be, all unawares, the tool of some superior intelligence.'

Mr. Scogan chuckled maliciously; it was as though he were taking a revenge, in the name of reason, on the enthusiasts. 'From their earliest years, as soon, that is, as the examining psychologists have assigned them their place in the classified scheme, the Men of Faith will have had their special education under the eye of the Intelligences. Moulded by a long process of suggestion, they will go out into the world, preaching and practising with a generous mania the coldly reasonable projects of the Directors from above. When these projects are accomplished, or when the ideas that were useful a decade ago have ceased to be useful, the Intelligences will inspire a new generation of madmen with a new eternal truth. The principal function of the Men of Faith will be to move and direct the Multitude, that third great species consisting of those countless millions who lack intelligence and are without valuable enthusiasm. When any particular effort is required of the Herd, when it is thought necessary, for the sake of solidarity, that humanity shall be kindled and united by some single enthusiastic desire or idea, the Men of Faith, primed with some simple and satisfying creed, will be sent out on a mission of evangelization. At ordinary times, when the high spiritual temperature of a Crusade would be unhealthy, the Men of Faith will be quietly and earnestly busy with the great work of education. In the upbringing of the Herd humanity's almost boundless suggestibility will be scientifically exploited. Systematically, from earliest infancy, its members will be assured that there is no happiness to be found except in work and obedience; they will be made to believe that they are happy, that they are tremendously important beings, and that everything they do is noble and significant. For the lower species the earth will be restored to the centre of the universe and man to pre-eminence on the earth. Oh, I envy the lot of the commonalty in the Rational State! Working their eight hours a day, obeying their betters, convinced of their own grandeur and significance and immortality, they will be marvellously happy, happier than any race of men has ever been. They will go through life in a rosy state of intoxication, from which they will never awaken. The Men of Faith will play the cup-bearers at this lifelong bacchanal, filling and ever filling again with the warm liquor that the Intelligences, in sad and sober privacy behind the scenes, will brew for the intoxication of their subjects.'

'And what will be my place in the Rational State?' Denis drowsily inquired from under his shading hand.

Mr. Scogan looked at him for a moment in silence. 'It's difficult to see where you would fit in,' he said at last. 'You couldn't do manual work; you're too independent and unsuggestible to belong to the larger Herd; you have none of the characteristics required in a Man of Faith. As for the Directing Intelligences, they will have to be marvellously clear and merciless and penetrating.' He paused and shook his head. 'No, I can see no place for you; only the lethal chamber.'

Deeply hurt, Denis emitted the imitation of a loud Homeric laugh. 'I'm getting sunstroke here,' he said, and got up.

Mr. Scogan followed his example, and they walked slowly away down the narrow path, brushing the blue lavender flowers in their passage. Denis pulled a sprig of lavender and sniffed at it; then some dark leaves of rosemary that smelt like incense in a cavernous church. They passed a bed of opium poppies, dispetaled now; the round, ripe seed-heads were brown and dry—like Polynesian trophies, Denis thought; severed heads stuck on poles. He liked the fancy enough to impart it to Mr. Scogan.

'Like Polynesian trophies. . . .' Uttered aloud, the fancy seemed less charming and significant than it did when it first occurred to him.

There was a silence, and in a growing wave of sound the whir of the reaping machines swelled up from the fields beyond the garden and then receded into a remoter hum.

'It is satisfactory to think,' said Mr. Scogan, as they strolled slowly onward, 'that a multitude of people are toiling in the harvest fields in order that we may talk of Polynesia. Like every other good thing in this world, leisure and culture have to be paid for. Fortunately, however, it is not the leisured and the cultured who have to pay. Let us be duly thankful for that, my dear Denis—duly thankful,' he repeated, and knocked the ashes out of his pipe.

Denis was not listening. He had suddenly remembered Anne. She was with Gombauld—alone with him in his studio. It was an intolerable thought.

'Shall we go and pay a call on Gombauld?' he suggested carelessly. 'It would be amusing to see what he's doing now.'

He laughed inwardly to think how furious Gombauld would be when he saw them arriving.

## *Chapter 23*

GOMBAULD was by no means so furious at their apparition as Denis had hoped and expected he would be. Indeed, he was rather pleased than annoyed when the two faces, one brown and pointed, the other round and pale, appeared in the frame of the open door. The energy born of his restless irritation was dying within him, returning to its emotional elements. A moment more and he would have been losing his temper again—and Anne would be keeping hers, infuriatingly. Yes, he was positively glad to see them.

'Come in, come in,' he called out hospitably.

Followed by Mr. Scogan, Denis climbed the little ladder and stepped over the threshold. He looked suspiciously from Gombauld to his sitter, and could learn nothing from the expression of their faces except that they both seemed pleased to see the visitors. Were they really glad, or were they cunningly simulating gladness? He wondered.

Mr. Scogan, meanwhile, was looking at the portrait.

'Excellent,' he said approvingly, 'excellent. Almost too true to character, if that is possible; yes, positively too true. But I'm surprised to find you putting in all this psychology business.' He pointed to the face, and with his extended finger followed the slack curves of the painted figure. 'I thought you were one of the fellows who went in exclusively for balanced masses and impinging planes.'

Gombauld laughed. 'This is a little infidelity,' he said.

'I'm sorry,' said Mr. Scogan. 'I for one, without ever having had the slightest appreciation of painting, have always taken particular pleasure in Cubismus. I like to see pictures from which nature has been completely banished, pictures which are exclusively the product of the human mind. They give me the same pleasure as I derive from a good piece of reasoning or a mathematical problem or an achievement of engineering. Nature, or anything that reminds me of nature, disturbs me; it is too large, too complicated, above all too utterly pointless and incomprehensible. I am at home with the works of man; if I choose to set my mind to it, I can understand anything that any man has made or thought. That is why I always travel by Tube, never by bus if I can possibly help it. For, travelling by bus, one can't avoid seeing, even in London, a few stray works of God—the sky, for example, an occasional tree, the flowers in the window-boxes. But travel by Tube and you see nothing but the works of man—iron riveted into geometrical forms, straight lines of concrete, patterned expanses of tiles.

All is human and the product of friendly and comprehensible minds. All philosophies and all religions—what are they but spiritual Tubes bored through the universe! Through these narrow tunnels, where all is recognizably human, one travels comfortable and secure, contriving to forget that all round and below and above them stretches the blind mass of earth, endless and unexplored. Yes, give me the Tube and Cubismus every time; give me ideas, so snug and neat and simple and well made. And preserve me from nature, preserve me from all that's inhumanly large and complicated and obscure. I haven't the courage, and, above all, I haven't the time to start wandering in that labyrinth.'

While Mr. Scogan was discoursing, Denis had crossed over to the farther side of the little square chamber, where Anne was sitting, still in her graceful, lazy pose, on the low chair.

'Well?' he demanded, looking at her almost fiercely. What was he asking of her? He hardly knew himself.

Anne looked up at him, and for answer echoed his 'Well?' in another, a laughing key.

Denis had nothing more, at the moment, to say. Two or three canvases stood in the corner behind Anne's chair, their faces turned to the wall. He pulled them out and began to look at the paintings.

'May I see too?' Anne requested.

He stood them in a row against the wall. Anne had to turn round in her chair to look at them. There was the big canvas of the man fallen from the horse, there was a painting of flowers, there was a small landscape. His hands on the back of the chair, Denis leaned over her. From behind the easel at the other side of the room Mr. Scogan was talking away. For a long time they looked at the pictures, saying nothing; or, rather, Anne looked at the pictures, while Denis, for the most part, looked at Anne.

'I like the man and the horse; don't you?' she said at last, looking up with an inquiring smile.

Denis nodded, and then in a queer, strangled voice, as though it had cost him a great effort to utter the words, he said, 'I love you.'

It was a remark which Anne had heard a good many times before and mostly heard with equanimity. But on this occasion—perhaps because they had come so unexpectedly, perhaps for some other reason—the words provoked in her a certain surprised commotion.

'My poor Denis,' she managed to say, with a laugh; but she was blushing as she spoke.

## *Chapter 24*

It was noon. Denis, descending from his chamber, where he had been making an unsuccessful effort to write something about nothing in particular, found the drawing-room deserted. He was about to go out into the garden when his eye fell on a familiar but mysterious object—the large red notebook in which he had so often seen Jenny quietly and busily scribbling. She had left it lying on the window-seat. The temptation was great. He picked up the book and slipped off the elastic band that kept it discreetly closed.

'Private. Not to be opened,' was written in capital letters on the cover. He raised his eyebrows. It was the sort of thing one wrote in one's Latin Grammar while one was still at one's preparatory school.

Black is the raven, black is the rook,
But blacker the thief who steals this book!

It was curiously childish, he thought, and he smiled to himself. He opened the book. What he saw made him wince as though he had been struck.

Denis was his own severest critic; so, at least, he had always believed. He liked to think of himself as a merciless vivisector probing into the palpitating entrails of his own soul; he was Brown Dog to himself. His weaknesses, his absurdities—no one knew them better than he did. Indeed, in a vague way he imagined that nobody beside himself was aware of them at all. It seemed, somehow, inconceivable that he should appear to other people as they appeared to him, inconceivable that they ever spoke of him among themselves in that same freely critical and, to be quite honest, mildly malicious tone in which he was accustomed to talk of them. In his own eyes he had defects, but to see them was a privilege reserved to him alone. For the rest of the world he was surely an image of flawless crystal. It was almost axiomatic.

On opening the red notebook that crystal image of himself crashed to the ground, and was irreparably shattered. He was not his own severest critic after all. The discovery was a painful one.

The fruit of Jenny's unobtrusive scribbling lay before him. A caricature of himself, reading (the book was upside-down). In the background a dancing couple, recognizable as Gombauld and Anne. Beneath, the legend: 'Fable of the Wallflower and the Sour Grapes.' Fascinated and horrified, Denis pored over the drawing. It was masterful. A mute, inglorious Rouveyre appeared in every one of those cruelly clear lines. The expression of the face, an assumed aloofness and superiority tempered by a feeble envy; the attitude of the body and limbs, an attitude of studious and scholarly dignity, given away by the fidgety pose of the turned-in feet—these things were terrible. And, more terrible still, was the likeness, was the magisterial certainty with which his physical peculiarities were all recorded and subtly exaggerated.

Denis looked deeper into the book. There were caricatures of other people: of Priscilla and Mr. Barbecue-Smith; of Henry Wimbush, of Anne and Gombauld; of Mr. Scogan, whom Jenny had represented in a light that was more than slightly sinister, that was, indeed, diabolic; of Mary and Ivor. He scarcely glanced at them. A fearful desire to know the worst about himself possessed him. He turned over the leaves, lingering at nothing that was not his own image. Seven full pages were devoted to him.

'Private. Not to be opened.' He had disobeyed the injunction; he had only got what he deserved. Thoughtfully he closed the book, and slid the rubber band once more into its place. Sadder and wiser, he went out on to the terrace. And so this, he reflected, this was how Jenny employed the leisure hours in her ivory tower apart. And he had thought her a simple-minded, uncritical creature! It was he, it seemed, who was the fool. He felt no resentment towards Jenny. No, the distressing thing wasn't Jenny herself; it was what she and the phenomenon of her red book represented, what they stood for and concretely symbolized. They represented all the vast conscious world of men outside himself; they symbolized something that in his studious solitariness he was apt not to believe in. He could stand at Piccadilly Circus, could watch the crowds shuffle past, and still imagine himself the one fully conscious, intelligent, individual being among all those thousands. It seemed, somehow, impossible that other people should be in their way as elaborate and complete as he in his. Impossible; and yet, periodically he would make some painful discovery about the external world and the horrible reality of its consciousness and its intelligence. The red notebook was one of these discoveries, a footprint in the sand. It put beyond a doubt the fact that the outer world really existed.

Sitting on the balustrade of the terrace, he ruminated this unpleasant truth for some time. Still chewing on it, he strolled pensively down towards the swimming-pool. A peacock and his hen trailed their shabby finery across the turf of the lower lawn. Odious birds! Their necks, thick and greedily fleshy at the roots, tapered up to the cruel inanity of their brainless heads, their flat eyes and piercing beaks. The fabulists were right, he reflected, when they took beasts to illustrate their tractates of human morality. Animals resemble men with all the truthfulness of a caricature. (Oh, the red notebook!) He threw a piece of stick at the slowly pacing birds. They rushed towards it, thinking it was something to eat.

He walked on. The profound shade of a giant ilex tree engulfed him. Like a great wooden octopus, it spread its long arms abroad.

Under the spreading ilex tree . . .

He tried to remember who the poem was by, but couldn't.

The smith, a brawny man is he,
With arms like rubber bands.

Just like his; he would have to try and do his Muller exercises more regularly.

He emerged once more into the sunshine. The pool lay before him, reflecting in its bronze mirror the blue and various green of the summer day. Looking at it, he thought of Anne's bare arms and seal-sleek bathing-dress, her moving knees and feet.

> And little Luce with the white legs,
> And bouncing Barbary . . .

Oh, these rags and tags of other people's making! Would he ever be able to call his brain his own? Was there, indeed, anything in it that was truly his own, or was it simply an education?

He walked slowly round the water's edge. In an embayed recess among the surrounding yew trees, leaning her back against the pedestal of a pleasantly comic version of the Medici Venus, executed by some nameless mason of the *seicento*, he saw Mary pensively sitting.

'Hullo!' he said, for he was passing so close to her that he had to say something.

Mary looked up. 'Hullo!' she answered in a melancholy, uninterested tone.

In this alcove, hewed out of the dark trees, the atmosphere seemed to Denis agreeably elegiac. He sat down beside her under the shadow of the public goddess. There was a prolonged silence.

At breakfast that morning Mary had found on her plate a picture postcard of Gobley Great Park. A stately Georgian pile, with a façade sixteen windows wide; parterres in the foreground; huge, smooth lawns receding out of the picture to right and left. Ten years more of the hard times and Gobley, with all its peers, will be deserted and decaying. Fifty years, and the countryside will know the old landmarks no more. They will have vanished as the monasteries vanished before them. At the moment, however, Mary's mind was not moved by these considerations.

On the back of the postcard, next to the address, was written, in Ivor's bold, large hand, a single quatrain.

> Hail, maid of moonlight! Bride of the sun, farewell!
> Like bright plumes moulted in an angel's flight,
> There sleep within my heart's most mystic cell
> Memories of morning, memories of the night.

There followed a postscript of three lines: 'Would you mind asking one of the housemaids to forward the packet of safety-razor blades I left in the drawer of my washstand. Thanks.—IVOR.'

Seated under the Venus's immemorial gesture, Mary considered life and love. The abolition of her repressions, so far from bringing the expected peace of mind, had brought nothing but disquiet, a new and hitherto unexperienced misery. Ivor, Ivor. . . . She couldn't do without him now. It was evident, on the other hand, from the poem on the back of the picture postcard, that Ivor could very well do without her. He was at Gobley now; so was Zenobia. Mary knew Zenobia. She thought of the last verse of the song he had sung that night in the garden.

> Le lendemain, Phillis peu sage
> Aurait donné moutons et chien
> Pour un baiser que le volage
> A Lisette donnait pour rien.

Mary shed tears at the memory; she had never been so unhappy in all her life before.

It was Denis who first broke the silence. 'The individual,' he began in a soft and sadly philosophical tone, 'is not a self-supporting universe. There are times when he comes into contact with other individuals, when he is forced to take cognizance of the existence of other universes besides himself.'

He had contrived this highly abstract generalization as a preliminary to a personal confidence. It was the first gambit in a conversation that was to lead up to Jenny's caricatures.

'True,' said Mary; and, generalizing for herself, she added, 'When one individual comes into intimate contact with another, she—or he, of course, as the case may be—must almost inevitably receive or inflict suffering.'

'One is apt,' Denis went on, 'to be so spellbound by the spectacle of one's own personality that one forgets that the spectacle presents itself to other people as well as to oneself.'

Mary was not listening. 'The difficulty,' she said, 'makes itself acutely felt in matters of sex. If one individual seeks intimate contact with another individual in the natural way, she is certain to receive or inflict suffering. If, on the other hand, she avoids contacts, she risks the equally grave sufferings that follow on unnatural repressions. As you see, it's a dilemma.'

'When I think of my own case,' said Denis, making a more decided move in the desired direction, 'I am amazed how ignorant I am of other people's mentality in general and, above all and in particular, of their opinions about myself. Our minds are sealed books only occasionally opened to the outside world.' He made a gesture that was faintly suggestive of the drawing off of a rubber band.

'It's an awful problem,' said Mary thoughtfully. 'One has to have had personal experience to realize quite how awful it is.'

'Exactly.' Denis nodded. 'One has to have had first-hand experience.' He leaned towards her and slightly lowered his voice. 'This very morning, for example . . .' he began, but his confidences were cut short. The deep voice of the gong, tempered by distance to a pleasant booming, floated down from the house. It was lunch-time. Mechanically Mary rose to her feet, and Denis, a little hurt that she should exhibit such a desperate anxiety for her food and so slight an interest in his spiritual experiences, followed her. They made their way up to the house without speaking.

## *Chapter 25*

'I HOPE you all realize,' said Henry Wimbush during dinner, 'that next Monday is Bank Holiday, and that you will all be expected to help in the Fair.'

'Heavens!' cried Anne. 'The Fair—I had forgotten all about it. What a nightmare! Couldn't you put a stop to it, Uncle Henry?'

Mr. Wimbush sighed and shook his head. 'Alas,' he said, 'I fear I cannot. I should have liked to put an end to it years ago; but the claims of Charity are strong.'

'It's not charity we want,' Anne murmured rebelliously; 'it's justice.'

'Besides,' Mr. Wimbush went on, 'the Fair has become an institution. Let me see, it must be twenty-two years since we started it. It was a modest affair then. Now . . .' he made a sweeping movement with his hand and was silent.

It spoke highly for Mr. Wimbush's public spirit that he still continued to tolerate the Fair. Beginning as a sort of glorified church bazaar, Crome's yearly Charity Fair had grown into a noisy thing of merry-go-rounds, cocoanut shies, and miscellaneous side shows—a real genuine fair on the grand scale. It was the local St. Bartholomew, and the people of all the neighbouring villages, with even a contingent from the county town, flocked into the park for their Bank Holiday amusement. The local hospital profited handsomely, and it was this fact alone which prevented Mr. Wimbush, to whom the Fair was a cause of recurrent and never-diminishing agony, from putting a stop to the nuisance which yearly desecrated his park and garden.

'I've made all the arrangements already,' Henry Wimbush went on. 'Some of the larger marquees will be put up to-morrow. The swings and the merry-go-round arrive on Sunday.'

'So there's no escape,' said Anne, turning to the rest of the party. 'You'll all have to do something. As a special favour you're allowed to choose your slavery. My job is the tea tent, as usual, Aunt Priscilla . . .'

'My dear,' said Mrs. Wimbush, interrupting her, 'I have more important things to think about than the Fair. But you need have no doubt that I shall do my best when Monday comes to encourage the villagers.'

'That's splendid,' said Anne. 'Aunt Priscilla will encourage the villagers. What will you do, Mary?'

'I won't do anything where I have to stand by and watch other people eat.'

'Then you'll look after the children's sports.'

'All right,' Mary agreed. 'I'll look after the children's sports.'

'And Mr. Scogan?'

Mr. Scogan reflected. 'May I be allowed to tell fortunes?' he asked at last. 'I think I should be good at telling fortunes.'

'But you can't tell fortunes in that costume!'

'Can't I?' Mr. Scogan surveyed himself.

'You'll have to be dressed up. Do you still persist?'

'I'm ready to suffer all indignities.'

'Good!' said Anne; and turning to Gombauld, 'You must be our lightning artist,' she said. ' "Your portrait for a shilling in five minutes." '

'It's a pity I'm not Ivor,' said Gombauld, with a laugh. 'I could throw in a picture of their Auras for an extra sixpence.'

Mary flushed. 'Nothing is to be gained,' she said severely, 'by speaking with levity of serious subjects. And, after all, whatever your personal views may be, psychical research is a perfectly serious subject.'

'And what about Denis?'

Denis made a deprecating gesture. 'I have no accomplishments,' he said. 'I'll just be one of those men who wear a thing in their buttonholes and go about telling people which is the way to tea and not to walk on the grass.'

'No, no,' said Anne. 'That won't do. You must do something more than that.'

'But what? All the good jobs are taken, and I can do nothing but lisp in numbers.'

'Well, then, you must lisp,' concluded Anne. 'You must write a poem for the occasion—an "Ode on Bank Holiday." We'll print it on Uncle Henry's press and sell it at twopence a copy.'

'Sixpence,' Denis protested. 'It'll be worth sixpence.'

Anne shook her head. 'Twopence,' she repeated firmly. 'Nobody will pay more than twopence.'

'And now there's Jenny,' said Mr. Wimbush. 'Jenny,' he said, raising his voice, 'what will you do?'

Denis thought of suggesting that she might draw caricatures at sixpence an execution, but decided it would be wiser to go on feigning ignorance of her talent. His mind reverted to the red notebook. Could it really be true that he looked like that?

'What will I do,' Jenny echoed, 'what will I do?' She frowned thoughtfully for a moment; then her face brightened and she smiled. 'When I was young,' she said, 'I learnt to play the drums.'

'The drums?'

Jenny nodded, and, in proof of her assertion, agitated her knife and fork, like a pair of drumsticks, over her plate. 'If there's any opportunity of playing the drums . . .' she began.

'But of course,' said Anne, 'there's any amount of opportunity. We'll put you down definitely for the drums. That's the lot,' she added.

'And a very good lot too,' said Gombauld. 'I look forward to my Bank Holiday. It ought to be gay.'

'It ought indeed,' Mr. Scogan assented. 'But you may rest assured that it won't be. No holiday is ever anything but a disappointment.'

'Come, come,' protested Gombauld. 'My holiday at Crome isn't being a disappointment.'

'Isn't it?' Anne turned an ingenuous mask towards him.

'No, it isn't,' he answered.

'I'm delighted to hear it.'

'It's in the very nature of things,' Mr. Scogan went on; 'our holidays can't help being disappointments. Reflect for a moment. What is a holiday? The ideal, the Platonic Holiday of Holidays is surely a complete and absolute change. You agree with me in my definition?' Mr. Scogan glanced from face to face round the table; his sharp nose moved in a series of rapid jerks through all the points of the compass. There was no sign of dissent; he continued: 'A complete and absolute change; very well. But isn't a complete and absolute change precisely the thing we can never have—never, in the very nature of things?' Mr. Scogan once more looked rapidly about him. 'Of course it is. As ourselves, as specimens of Homo Sapiens, as members of a society, how can we hope to have anything like an absolute change? We are tied down by the frightful limitation of our human faculties, by the notions which society imposes on us through our fatal suggestibility, by our own personalities. For us, a complete holiday is out of the question. Some of us struggle manfully to take one, but we never succeed, if I may be allowed to express myself metaphorically, we never succeed in getting farther than Southend.'

'You're depressing,' said Anne.

'I mean to be,' Mr. Scogan replied, and, expanding the fingers of his right hand, he went on: 'Look at me, for example. What sort of a holiday can I take? In endowing me with passions and faculties Nature has been horribly niggardly. The full range of human potentialities is in any case distressingly limited; my range is a limitation within a limitation. Out of the ten octaves that make up the human instrument, I can compass perhaps two. Thus, while I may have a certain amount of intelligence, I have no æsthetic sense; while I possess the mathematical faculty, I am wholly without the religious emotions; while I am naturally addicted to venery, I have little ambition and am not at all avaricious. Education has further limited my scope. Having been brought up in society, I am impregnated with its laws; not only should I be afraid of taking a holiday from them, I should also feel it painful to try to do so. In a word, I have a conscience as well as a fear of gaol. Yes, I know it by experience. How often have I tried to take holidays, to get away from myself, my own boring nature, my insufferable mental surroundings!' Mr. Scogan sighed. 'But always without success,' he added, 'always without success. In my youth I was always striving—how hard!—to feel religiously and æsthetically. Here, said I to myself, are two tremendously important and exciting emotions. Life would be richer, warmer, brighter, altogether more amusing, if I could feel them. I tried to feel them. I read the works of the mystics. They seemed to me nothing but the most deplorable claptrap—as indeed they always must to anyone who does not feel the same emotion as the authors felt when they were writing. For it is the emotion that matters. The written work is simply an attempt to express emotion, which is in itself inexpressible, in terms of intellect and logic. The mystic objectifies a rich feeling in the pit of the stomach into a cosmology. For other mystics that cosmology is a symbol of the rich feeling. For the unreligious it is a symbol of nothing, and so appears merely grotesque. A melancholy fact! But I divagate.' Mr. Scogan checked himself. 'So much for the religious emotion. As for the æsthetic—I was at even greater pains to cultivate that. I have looked at all the right works of art in every part of Europe. There was a time when, I venture to believe, I knew more about Taddeo da Poggibonsi, more about the cryptic Amico di Taddeo, even than Henry does. To-day, I am happy to say, I have forgotten most of the knowledge I then so laboriously acquired; but without vanity I can assert that it was prodigious. I don't pretend, of course, to know anything about nigger sculpture or the later seventeenth century in Italy; but about all the periods that were fashionable before 1900 I am, or was, omniscient. Yes, I repeat it, omniscient. But did that fact make me any more appreciative of art in general? It did not. Confronted by a picture, of which I could tell you all the known and presumed history—the date when it was painted, the character of the painter, the influences that had gone to make it what it was—I felt none of that strange excitement and exaltation which is, as I am informed by those who do feel it, the true æsthetic emotion. I felt nothing but a certain interest in the subject of the picture; or more often, when the subject was hackneyed and religious, I felt nothing but a great weariness of spirit. Nevertheless, I must have gone on looking at pictures for ten years before I would honestly admit to myself that they merely bored me. Since then I have given up all attempts to take a holiday. I go on cultivating my old stale daily self in the resigned spirit with which a bank clerk performs from ten till six his daily task. A holiday, indeed! I'm sorry for you, Gombauld, if you still look forward to having a holiday.'

Gombauld shrugged his shoulders. 'Perhaps,' he said, 'my standards aren't as elevated as yours. But personally I found the war quite as thorough a holiday from all the ordinary decencies and sanities, all the common emotions and preoccupations, as I ever want to have.'

'Yes,' Mr. Scogan thoughtfully agreed. 'Yes, the war was certainly something of a holiday. It was a step beyond Southend; it was Weston-super-Mare; it was almost Ilfracombe.'

## *Chapter 26*

A LITTLE canvas village of tents and booths had sprung up, just beyond the boundaries of the garden, in the green expanse of the park. A crowd thronged its streets, the men dressed mostly in black—holiday best, funeral best—the women in pale muslins. Here and there tricolour bunting hung inert. In the midst of the canvas town, scarlet and gold and crystal, the merry-go-round glittered in the sun. The balloon-man walked among the crowd, and above his head, like a huge, inverted bunch of many-coloured grapes, the balloons strained upwards. With a scythe-like motion the boat-swings reaped the air, and from the funnel of the engine which worked the roundabout rose a thin, scarcely wavering column of black smoke.

Denis had climbed to the top of one of Sir Ferdinando's towers, and there, standing on the sun-baked leads, his elbows resting on the parapet, he surveyed the scene. The steam-organ sent up prodigious music. The clashing of automatic cymbals beat out with inexorable precision the rhythm of piercingly sounded melodies. The harmonies were like a musical shattering of glass and brass. Far down in the bass the Last Trump was hugely blowing, and with such peristence, such resonance, that its alternate tonic and dominant detached themselves from the rest of the music and made a tune of their own, a loud, monotonous see-saw.

Denis leaned over the gulf of swirling noise. If he threw himself over the parapet, the noise would surely buoy him up, keep him suspended, bobbing, as a fountain balances a ball on its breaking crest. Another fancy came to him, this time in metrical form.

> My soul is a thin white sheet of parchment stretched
> Over a bubbling cauldron.

Bad, bad. But he liked the idea of something thin and distended being blown up from underneath.

> My soul is a thin tent of gut. . . .

or better—

> My soul is a pale, tenuous membrane. . . .

That was pleasing: a thin, tenuous membrane. It had the right anatomical quality. Tight blown, quivering in the blast of noisy life. It was time for him to descend from the serene empyrean of words into the actual vortex. He went down slowly. 'My soul is a thin, tenuous membrane. . . .'

On the terrace stood a knot of distinguished visitors. There was old Lord Moleyn, like a caricature of an English milord in a French comic paper: a long man, with a long nose and long, drooping moustaches and long teeth of old ivory, and lower down, absurdly, a short covert coat, and below that long, long legs cased in pearl-grey trousers—legs that bent unsteadily at the knee and gave a kind of sideways wobble as he walked. Beside him, short and thick-set, stood Mr. Callamay, the venerable conservative statesman, with a face like a Roman bust, and short white hair. Young girls didn't much like going for motor drives alone with Mr. Callamay; and of old Lord Moleyn one wondered why he wasn't living in gilded exile on the island of Capri among the other distinguished persons who, for one reason or another, find it impossible to live in England. They were talking to Anne, laughing, the one profoundly, the other hootingly.

A black silk balloon towing a black-and-white striped parachute proved to be old Mrs. Budge from the big house on the other side of the valley. She stood low on the ground, and the spikes of her black-and-white sun-shade menaced the eyes of Priscilla Wimbush, who towered over her—a massive figure dressed in purple and topped with a queenly toque on which the nodding black plumes recalled the splendours of a first-class Parisian funeral.

Denis peeped at them discreetly from the window of the morning-room. His eyes were suddenly become innocent, childlike, unprejudiced. They seemed, these people, inconceivably fantastic. And yet they really existed, they functioned by themselves, they were conscious, they had minds. Moreover, he was like them. Could one believe it? But the evidence of the red notebook was conclusive.

It would have been polite to go and say, 'How d'you do?' But at the moment Denis did not want to talk, could not have talked. His soul was a tenuous, tremulous, pale membrane. He would keep its sensibility intact and virgin as long as he could. Cautiously he crept out by a side door and made his way down towards the park. His soul fluttered as he approached the noise and movement of the fair. He paused for a moment on the brink, then stepped in and was engulfed.

Hundreds of people, each with his own private face and all of them real, separate, alive: the thought was disquieting. He paid twopence and saw the Tattooed Woman; twopence more, the Largest Rat in the World. From the home of the Rat he emerged just in time to see a hydrogen-filled balloon break loose for home. A child howled up after it; but calmly, a perfect sphere of flushed opal, it mounted, mounted. Denis followed it with his eyes until it became lost in the blinding sunlight. If he could but send his soul to follow it! . . .

He sighed, stuck his steward's rosette in his button-hole, and started to push his way, aimlessly but officially, through the crowd.

## *Chapter 27*

Mr. Scogan had been accommodated in a little canvas hut. Dressed in a black skirt and a red bodice, with a yellow-and-red bandana handkerchief tied round his black wig, he looked—sharp-nosed, brown, and wrinkled—like the Bohemian hag of Frith's Derby Day. A placard pinned to the curtain of the doorway announced the presence within the tent of 'Sesostris, the Sorceress of Ecbatana.' Seated at a table, Mr. Scogan received his clients in mysterious silence, indicating with a movement of the finger that they were to sit down opposite him and to extend their hands for his inspection. He then examined the palm that was presented him, using a magnifying glass and a pair of horn spectacles. He had a terrifying way of shaking his head, frowning and clicking with his tongue as he looked at the lines. Sometimes he would whisper, as though to himself, 'Terrible, terrible!' or 'God preserve us!' sketching out the sign of the cross as he uttered the words. The clients who came in laughing grew suddenly grave; they began to take the witch seriously. She was a formidable-looking woman; could it be, was it possible, that there was something in this sort of thing after all? After all, they thought, as the hag shook her head over their hands, after all . . . And they waited, with an uncomfortably beating heart, for the oracle to speak. After a long and silent inspection, Mr. Scogan would suddenly look up and ask, in a hoarse whisper, some horrifying question, such as, 'Have you ever been hit on the head with a hammer by a young man with red hair?' When the answer was in the negative, which it could hardly fail to be, Mr. Scogan would nod several times, saying, 'I was afraid so. Everything is still to come, still to come, though it can't be very far off now.' Sometimes, after a long examination, he would just whisper, 'Where ignorance is bliss, 'tis folly to be wise,' and refuse to divulge any details of a future too appalling to be envisaged without despair. Sesostris had a success of horror. People stood in a queue outside the witch's booth waiting for the privilege of hearing sentence pronounced upon them.

Denis, in the course of his round, looked with curiosity at this crowd of suppliants before the shrine of the oracle. He had a great desire to see how Mr. Scogan played his part. The canvas booth was a rickety, ill-made structure. Between its walls and its sagging roof were long gaping chinks and crannies. Denis went to the tea-tent and borrowed a wooden bench and a small Union Jack. With these he hurried back to the booth of Sesostris. Setting down the bench at the back of the booth, he climbed up, and with a great air of busy efficiency began to tie the Union Jack to the top of one of the tent-poles. Through the crannies in the canvas he could see almost the whole of the interior of the tent. Mr. Scogan's bandana-covered head was just below him; his terrifying whispers came clearly up. Denis looked and listened while the witch prophesied financial losses, death by apoplexy, destruction by air-raids in the next war.

'Is there going to be another war?' asked the old lady to whom he had predicted this end.

'Very soon,' said Mr. Scogan, with an air of quiet confidence.

The old lady was succeeded by a girl dressed in white muslin, garnished with pink ribbons, She was wearing a broad hat, so that Denis could not see her face; but from her figure and the roundness of her bare arms he judged her young and pleasing. Mr. Scogan looked at her hand then, whispered, 'You are still virtuous.'

The young lady giggled and exclaimed, 'Oh, lor'!'

'But you will not remain so for long,' added Mr. Scogan sepulchrally. The young lady giggled again. 'Destiny, which interests itself in small things no less than in great, has announced the fact upon your hand.' Mr. Scogan took up the magnifying-glass and began once more to examine the white palm. 'Very interesting,' he said, as though to himself—'very interesting. It's as clear as day.' He was silent.

'What's clear?' asked the girl.

'I don't think I ought to tell you.' Mr. Scogan shook his head; the pendulous brass ear-rings which he had screwed on to his ears tinkled.

'Please, please!' she implored.

The witch seemed to ignore her remark. 'Afterwards, it's not at all clear. The fates don't say whether you will settle down to married life and have four children or whether you will try to go on the cinema and have none. They are only specific about this one rather crucial incident.'

'What is it? What is it? Oh, do tell me!'

The white muslin figure leant eagerly forward.

Mr. Scogan sighed. 'Very well,' he said, 'if you must know, you must know. But if anything untoward happens you must blame your own curiosity. Listen. Listen.' He lifted up a sharp, claw-nailed forefinger. 'This is what the fates have written. Next Sunday afternoon at six o'clock you will be sitting on the second stile on the footpath that leads from the church to the lower road. At that moment a man will appear walking along the footpath.' Mr. Scogan looked at her hand again as though to refresh his memory of the details of the scene. 'A man,' he repeated—'a small man with a sharp nose, not exactly good looking nor precisely young, but fascinating.' He lingered hissingly over the word. 'He will ask you, "Can you tell me the way to Paradise?" and you will answer, "Yes, I'll show you," and walk with him down towards the little hazel copse. I cannot read what will happen after that.' There was a silence.

'Is it really true?' asked white muslin.

The witch gave a shrug of the shoulders. 'I merely tell you what I read in your hand. Good afternoon. That will be sixpence. Yes, I have change. Thank you. Good afternoon.'

Denis stepped down from the bench; tied insecurely and crookedly to the tent-pole, the Union Jack hung limp on the windless air. 'If only I could do things like that!' he thought, as he carried the bench back to the tea-tent.

Anne was sitting behind a long table filling thick white cups from an urn. A neat pile of printed sheets lay before her on the table. Denis took one of them and looked at it affectionately. It was his poem. They had printed five hundred copies, and very nice the quarto broadsheets looked.

'Have you sold many?' he asked in a casual tone.

Anne put her head on one side deprecatingly. 'Only three so far, I'm afraid. But I'm giving a free copy to everyone who spends more than a shilling on his tea. So in any case it's having a circulation.'

Denis made no reply, but walked slowly away. He looked at the broadsheet in his hand and read the lines to himself relishingly as he walked along:

This day of roundabouts and swings,
Struck weights, shied cocoanuts, tossed rings,
Switchbacks, Aunt Sallies, and all such small
High jinks—you call it ferial?
A holiday? But paper noses
Sniffed the artificial roses
Of round Venetian cheeks through half
Each carnival year, and masks might laugh
At things the naked face for shame
Would blush at—laugh and think no blame.
A holiday? But Galba showed
Elephants on an airy road;
Jumbo trod the tightrope then,
And in the circus armèd men
Stabbed home for sport and died to break
Those dull imperatives that make
A prison of every working day,
Where all must drudge and all obey.
Sing Holiday! You do not know
How to be free. The Russian snow
Flowered with bright blood whose roses spread
Petals of fading, fading red
That died into the snow again,
Into the virgin snow; and men
From all the ancient bonds were freed
Old law, old custom, and old creed,
Old right and wrong there bled to death:
The frozen air received their breath,
A little smoke that died away;
And round about them where they lay
The snow bloomed roses. Blood was there
A red gay flower and only fair.
Sing Holiday! Beneath the Tree
Of Innocence and Liberty,
Paper Nose and Red Cockade
Dance within the magic shade
That makes them drunken, merry, and strong
To laugh and sing their ferial song:
'Free, free . . .!'
But Echo answers
Faintly to the laughing dancers,
'Free'—and faintly laughs, and still,
Within the hollows of the hill,
Faintlier laughs and whispers, 'Free,'
Fadingly, diminishingly:
'Free,' and laughter faints away . . .
Sing Holiday! Sing Holiday!

He folded the sheet carefully and put it in his pocket. The thing had its merits. Oh, decidedly, decidedly! But how unpleasant the crowd smelt! He lit a cigarette. The smell of cows was preferable. He passed through the gate in the park wall into the garden. The swimming-pool was a centre of noise and activity.

'Second Heat in the Young Ladies' Championship.' It was the polite voice of Henry Wimbush. A crowd of sleek, seal-like figures in black bathing-dresses surrounded him. His grey bowler hat, smooth, round, and motionless in the midst of a moving sea, was an island of aristocratic calm.

Holding his tortoise-shell-rimmed pince-nez an inch or two in front of his eyes, he read out names from a list.

'Miss Dolly Miles, Miss Rebecca Balister, Miss Doris Gabell . . .'

Five young persons ranged themselves on the brink. From their seats of honour at the other end of the pool, old Lord Moleyn and Mr. Callamay looked on with eager interest.

Henry Wimbush raised his hand. There was an expectant silence. 'When I say "Go," go. Go!' he said. There was an almost simultaneous splash.

Denis pushed his way through the spectators. Somebody plucked him by the sleeve; he looked down. It was old Mrs. Budge.

'Delighted to see you again, Mr. Stone,' she said in her rich, husky voice. She panted a little as she spoke, like a short-winded lap-dog. It was Mrs. Budge who, having read in the *Daily Mirror* that the Government needed peach stones—what they needed them for she never knew—had made the collection of peach stones her peculiar 'bit' of war work. She had thirty-six peach trees in her walled garden, as well as four hot-houses in which trees could be forced, so that she was able to eat peaches practically the whole year round. In 1916 she ate 4200 peaches, and sent the stones to the Government. In 1917 the military authorities called up three of her gardeners, and what with this and the fact that it was a bad year for wall fruit, she only managed to eat 2900 peaches during that crucial period of the national destinies. In 1918 she did rather better, for between January 1st and the date of the Armistice she ate 3300 peaches. Since the Armistice she had relaxed her efforts; now she did not eat more than two or three peaches a day. Her constitution, she complained, had suffered; but it had suffered for a good cause.

Denis answered her greeting by a vague and polite noise.

'So nice to see the young people enjoying themselves,' Mrs. Budge went on. 'And the old people too, for that matter. Look at old Lord Moleyn and dear Mr. Callamay. Isn't it delightful to see the way they enjoy themselves?'

Denis looked. He wasn't sure whether it was so very delightful after all. Why didn't they go and watch the sack races? The two old gentlemen were engaged at the moment in congratulating the winner of the race; it seemed an act of supererogatory graciousness; for, after all, she had only won a heat.

'Pretty little thing, isn't she?' said Mrs. Budge huskily, and panted two or three times.

'Yes,' Denis nodded agreement. Sixteen, slender, but nubile, he said to himself, and laid up the phrase in his memory as a happy one. Old Mr. Callamay had put on his spectacles to congratulate the victor, and Lord Moleyn, leaning forward over his walking-stick, showed his long ivory teeth, hungrily smiling.

'Capital performance, capital,' Mr. Callamay was saying in his deep voice.

The victor wriggled with embarrassment. She stood with her hands behind her back, rubbing one foot nervously on the other. Her wet bathing-dress shone, a torso of black polished marble.

'Very good indeed,' said Lord Moleyn. His voice seemed to come from just behind his teeth, a toothy voice. It was as though a dog should suddenly begin to speak. He smiled again, Mr. Callamay readjusted his spectacles.

'When I say "Go," go. Go!'

Splash! The third heat had started.

'Do you know, I never could learn to swim,' said Mrs. Budge.

'Really?'

'But I used to be able to float.'

Denis imagined her floating—up and down, up and down on a great green swell. A blown black bladder; no, that wasn't good, that wasn't good at all. A new winner was being congratulated. She was atrociously stubby and fat. The last one, long and harmoniously, continuously curved from knee to breast, had been an Eve by Cranach; but this, this one was a bad Rugens.

'. . . go—go—go!' Henry Wimbush's polite level voice once more pronounced the formula. Another batch of young ladies dived in.

Grown a little weary of sustaining a conversation with Mrs. Budge, Denis conveniently remembered that his duties as a steward called him elsewhere. He pushed out through the lines of spectators and made his way along the path left clear behind them. He was thinking again that his soul was a pale, tenuous membrane, when he was startled by hearing a thin, sibilant voice, speaking apparently from just above his head, pronounce the single word 'Disgusting!'

He looked up sharply. The path along which he was walking passed under the lee of a wall of clipped yew. Behind the hedge the ground sloped steeply up towards the foot of the terrace and the house; for one standing on the higher ground it was easy to look over the dark barrier. Looking up, Denis saw two heads overtopping the hedge immediately above him. He recognized the iron mask of Mr. Bodiham and the pale, colourless face of his wife. They were looking over his head, over the heads of the spectators, at the swimmers in the pond.

'Disgusting!' Mrs. Bodiham repeated, hissing softly.

The rector turned up his iron mask towards the solid cobalt of the sky. 'How long?' he said, as though to himself; 'how long?' He lowered his eyes again, and they fell on Denis's upturned curious face. There was an abrupt movement, and Mr. and Mrs. Bodiham popped out of sight behind the hedge.

Denis continued his promenade. He wandered past the merry-go-round, through the thronged streets of the canvas village; the membrane of his soul flapped tumultuously in the noise and laughter. In a roped-off space beyond, Mary was directing the children's sports. Little creatures seethed round about her, making a shrill, tinny clamour; others clustered about the skirts and trousers of their parents. Mary's face was shining in the heat; with an immense output of energy she started a three-legged race. Denis looked on in admiration.

'You're wonderful,' he said, coming up behind her and touching her on the arm. 'I've never seen such energy.'

She turned towards him a face, round, red, and honest as the setting sun; the golden bell of her hair swung silently as she moved her head and quivered to rest.

'Do you know, Denis,' she said, in a low, serious voice, gasping a little as she spoke—'do you know that there's a woman here who has had three children in thirty-one months?'

'Really,' said Denis, making rapid mental calculations.

'It's appalling. I've been telling her about the Malthusian League. One really ought . . .'

But a sudden violent renewal of the metallic yelling announced the fact that somebody had won the race. Mary became once more the centre of a dangerous vortex. It was time, Denis thought, to move on; he might be asked to do something if he stayed too long.

He turned back towards the canvas village. The thought of tea was making itself insistent in his mind. Tea, tea, tea. But the tea-tent was horribly thronged. Anne, with an unusual expression of grimness on her flushed face, was furiously working the handle of the urn; the brown liquid spurted incessantly into the proffered cups. Portentous, in the farther corner of the tent, Priscilla, in her royal toque, was encouraging the villagers. In a momentary lull Denis could hear her deep, jovial laughter and her manly voice. Clearly, he told himself, this was no place for one who wanted tea. He stood irresolute at the entrance to the tent. A beautiful thought suddenly came to him: if he went back to the house, went unobtrusively, without being observed, if he tiptoed into the dining-room and noiselessly opened the little doors of the sideboard —ah, then! In the cool recess within he would find bottles and a siphon; a bottle of crystal gin and a quart of soda water, and then for the cups that inebriate as well as cheer. . . .

A minute later he was walking briskly up the shady yew-tree walk. Within the house it was deliciously quiet and cool. Carrying his well-filled tumbler with care, he went into the library. There, the glass on the corner of the table beside him, he settled into a chair with a volume of Sainte-Beuve. There was nothing, he found, like a Causerie du Lundi for settling and soothing the troubled spirits. That tenuous membrane of his had been too rudely buffeted by the afternoon's emotions; it required a rest.

## *Chapter 28*

TOWARDS sunset the fair itself became quiescent. It was the hour for the dancing to begin. At one side of the village of tents a space had been roped off. Acetylene lamps, hung round it on posts, cast a piercing white light. In one corner sat the band, and, obedient to its scraping and blowing, two or three hundred dancers trampled across the dry ground, wearing away the grass with their booted feet. Round this patch of all but daylight, alive with motion and noise, the night seemed preternaturally dark. Bars of light reached out into it, and every now and then a lonely figure or a couple of lovers, interlaced, would cross the bright shaft, flashing for a moment into visible existence, to disappear again as quickly and surprisingly as they had come.

Denis stood by the entrance of the enclosure, watching the swaying, shuffling crowd. The slow vortex brought the couples round and round again before him, as though he were passing them in review. There was Priscilla, still wearing her queenly toque, still encouraging the villagers—this time by dancing with one of the tenant farmers. There was Lord Moleyn, who had stayed on to the disorganized, passoverish meal that took the place of dinner on this festal day; he one-stepped shamblingly, his bent knees more precariously wobbly than ever, with a terrified village beauty. Mr. Scogan trotted round with another. Mary was in the embrace of a young farmer of heroic proportions; she was looking up at him, talking, as Denis could see, very seriously. What about? he wondered. The Malthusian League, perhaps. Seated in the corner among the band, Jenny was performing wonders of virtuosity upon the drums. Her eyes shone, she smiled to herself. A whole subterranean life seemed to be expressing itself in those loud rat-tats, those long rolls and flourishes of drumming. Looking at her, Denis ruefully remembered the red notebook; he wondered what sort of a figure he was cutting now. But the sight of Anne and Gombauld swimming past —Anne with her eyes almost shut and sleeping, as it were, on the sustaining wings of movement and music—dissipated these preoccupations. Male and female created He them. . . . There they were, Anne and Gombauld, and a hundred couples more—all stepping harmoniously together to the old tune of Male and Female created He them. But Denis sat apart; he alone lacked his complementary opposite. They were all coupled but he; all but he. . . .

Somebody touched him on the shoulder and he looked up. It was Henry Wimbush.

'I never showed you our oaken drain-pipes,' he said. 'Some of the ones we dug up are lying quite close to here. Would you like to come and see them?'

Denis got up, and they walked off together into the darkness. The music grew fainter behind them. Some of the higher notes faded out altogether. Jenny's drumming and the steady sawing of the bass throbbed on, tuneless and meaningless in their ears. Henry Wimbush halted.

'Here we are,' he said, and, taking an electric torch out of his pocket, he cast a dim beam over two or three blackened sections of tree trunk, scooped out into the semblance of pipes, which were lying forlornly in a little depression in the ground.

'Very interesting,' said Denis, with a rather tepid enthusiasm.

They sat down on the grass. A faint white glare, rising from behind a belt of trees, indicated the position of the dancing-floor. The music was nothing but a muffled rhythmic pulse.

'I shall be glad,' said Henry Wimbush, 'when this function comes at last to an end.'

'I can believe it.'

'I do not know how it is,' Mr. Wimbush continued, 'but the spectacle of numbers of my fellow-creatures in a state of agitation moves in me a certain weariness, rather than any gaiety or excitement. The fact is, they don't very much interest me. They aren't in my line. You follow me? I could never take much interest, for example, in a collection of postage stamps. Primitives or seventeenth-century books—yes. They are my line. But stamps, no. I don't know anything about them; they're not my line. They don't interest me, they give me no emotion. It's rather the same with people, I'm afraid. I'm more at home with these pipes.' He jerked his head sideways towards the hollowed logs. 'The trouble with the people and events of the present is that you never know anything about them. What do I know of contemporary politics? Nothing. What do I know of the people I see round about me? Nothing. What they think of me or of anything else in the world, what they will do in five minutes' time, are things I can't guess at. For all I know, you may suddenly jump up and try to murder me in a moment's time.'

'Come, come,' said Denis.

'True,' Mr. Wimbush continued, 'the little I know about your past is certainly reassuring. But I know nothing of your present, and neither you nor I know anything of your future. It's appalling; in living people, one is dealing with unknown and unknowable quantities. One can only hope to find out anything about them by a long series of the most disagreeable and boring human contacts, involving a terrible expense of time. It's the same with current events; how can I find out anything about them except by devoting years to the most exhausting first-hand study, involving once more an endless number of the most unpleasant contacts? No, give me the past. It doesn't change; it's all there in black and white, and you can get to know about it comfortably and decorously and, above all, privately—by reading. By reading I know a great deal of Cæsar Borgia, of St. Francis, of Dr. Johnson; a few weeks have made me thoroughly acquainted with these interesting characters, and I have been spared the tedious and revolting process of getting to know them by personal contact, which I should have to do if they were living now. How gay and delightful life would be if one could get rid of all the human contacts! Perhaps, in the future, when machines have attained to a state of perfection—for I confess that I am, like Godwin and Shelley, a believer in perfectibility, the perfectibility of machinery—then, perhaps, it will be possible for those who, like myself, desire it, to live in a dignified seclusion, surrounded by the delicate attentions of silent and graceful machines, and entirely secure from any human intrusion. It is a beautiful thought.'

'Beautiful,' Denis agreed. 'But what about the desirable human contacts, like love and friendship?'

The black silhouette against the darkness shook its head. 'The pleasures even of these contacts are much exaggerated,' said the polite level voice. 'It seems to me doubtful whether they are equal to the pleasures of private reading and contemplation. Human contacts have been so highly valued in the past only because reading was not a common accomplishment and because books were scarce and difficult to reproduce. The world, you must remember, is only just becoming literate. As reading becomes more and more habitual and widespread, an ever-increasing number of people will discover that books will give them all the pleasures of social life and none of its intolerable tedium. At present people in search of pleasure naturally tend to congregate in large herds and to make a noise; in future their natural tendency will be to seek solitude and quiet. The proper study of mankind is books.'

'I sometimes think that it may be,' said Denis; he was wondering if Anne and Gombauld were still dancing together.

'Instead of which,' said Mr. Wimbush, with a sigh, 'I must go and see if all is well on the dancing-floor.' They got up and began to walk slowly towards the white glare. 'If all these people were dead,' Henry Wimbush went on, 'this festivity would be extremely agreeable. Nothing would be pleasanter than to read in a well-written book of an open-air ball that took place a century ago. How charming! one would say; how pretty and how amusing! But when the ball takes place to-day, when one finds oneself involved in it, then one sees the thing in its true light. It turns out to be merely this.' He waved his hand in the direction of the acetylene flares. 'In my youth,' he went on after a pause, 'I found myself, quite fortuitously, involved in a series of the most phantasmagorical amorous intrigues. A novelist could have made his fortune out of them, and even if I were to tell you, in my bald style, the details of these adventures, you would be amazed at the romantic tale. But I assure you, while they were happening—these romantic adventures—they seemed to me no more and no less exciting than any other incident of actual life. To climb by night up a rope-ladder to a second-floor window in an old house in Toledo seemed to me, while I was actually performing this rather dangerous feat, an action as obvious, as much to be taken for granted, as—how shall I put it?—as quotidian as catching the 8.52 from Surbiton to go to business on a Monday morning. Adventures and romance only take on their adventurous and romantic qualities at second-hand. Live them, and they are just a slice of life like the rest. In literature they become as charming as this dismal ball would be if we were celebrating its tercentenary.' They had come to the entrance of the enclosure and stood there, blinking in the dazzling light. 'Ah, if only we were!' Henry Wimbush added.

Anne and Gombauld were still dancing together.

## *Chapter 29*

It was after ten o'clock. The dancers had already dispersed and the last lights were being put out. To-morrow the tents would be struck, the dismantled merry-go-round would be packed into waggons and carted away. An expanse of worn grass, a shabby brown patch in the wide green of the park, would be all that remained. Crome Fair was over.

By the edge of the pool two figures lingered.

'No, no, no,' Anne was saying in a breathless whisper, leaning backwards, turning her head from side to side in an effort to escape Gombauld's kisses. 'No, please. No.' Her raised voice had become imperative.

Gombauld relaxed his embrace a little. 'Why not?' he said. 'I will.'

With a sudden effort Anne freed herself. 'You won't,' she retorted. 'You've tried to take the most unfair advantage of me.'

'Unfair advantage?' echoed Gombauld in genuine surprise.

'Yes, unfair advantage. You attack me after I've been dancing for two hours, while I'm still reeling drunk with the movement, when I've lost my head, when I've got no mind left but only a rhythmical body! It's as bad as making love to someone you've drugged or intoxicated.'

Gombauld laughed angrily. 'Call me a White Slaver and have done with it.'

'Luckily,' said Anne, 'I am now completely sobered, and if you try and kiss me again I shall box your ears. Shall we take a few turns round the pool?' she added. 'The night is delicious.'

For answer Gombauld made an irritated noise. They paced off slowly, side by side.

'What I like about the painting of Degas . . .' Anne began in her most detached and conversational tone.

'Oh, damn Degas!' Gombauld was almost shouting.

From where he stood, leaning in an attitude of despair against the parapet of the terrace, Denis had seen them, the two pale figures in a patch of moonlight, far down by the pool's edge. He had seen the beginning of what promised to be an endlessly passionate embracement, and at the sight he had fled. It was too much; he couldn't stand it. In another moment, he felt, he would have burst into irrepressible tears.

Dashing blindly into the house, he almost ran into Mr. Scogan, who was walking up and down the hall smoking a final pipe.

'Hullo!' said Mr. Scogan, catching him by the arm; dazed and hardly conscious of what he was doing or where he was, Denis stood there for a moment like a somnambulist. 'What's the matter?' Mr. Scogan went on. 'You look disturbed, distressed, depressed.'

Denis shook his head without replying.

'Worried about the cosmos, eh?' Mr. Scogan patted him on the arm. 'I know the feeling,' he said. 'It's a most distressing symptom. "What's the point of it all? All is vanity. What's the good of continuing to function if one's doomed to be snuffed out at last along with everything else?" Yes, yes. I know exactly how you feel. It's most distressing if one allows oneself to be distressed. But then why allow oneself to be distressed? After all, we all know that there's no ultimate point. But what difference does that make?'

At this point the somnambulist suddenly woke up. 'What?' he said, blinking and frowning at his interlocutor. 'What?' Then breaking away he dashed up the stairs, two steps at a time.

Mr. Scogan ran to the foot of the stairs and called up after him. 'It makes no difference, none whatever. Life is gay all the same, always, under whatever circumstances—under whatever circumstances,' he added, raising his voice to a shout. But Denis was already far out of hearing, and even if he had not been, his mind to-night was proof against all the consolations of philosophy. Mr. Scogan replaced his pipe between his teeth and resumed his meditative pacing. 'Under any circumstances,' he repeated to himself. It was ungrammatical to begin with; was it true? And is life really its own reward? He wondered. When his pipe had burned itself to its stinking conclusion he took a drink of gin and went to bed. In ten minutes he was deeply, innocently asleep.

Denis had mechanically undressed and, clad in those flowered silk pyjamas of which he was so justly proud, was lying face downwards on his bed. Time passed. When at last he looked up, the candle which he had left alight at his bedside had burned down almost to the socket.

He looked at his watch; it was nearly half-past one. His head ached, his dry, sleepless eyes felt as though they had been bruised from behind, and the blood was beating within his ears a loud arterial drum. He got up, opened the door, tiptoed noiselessly along the passage, and began to mount the stairs towards the higher floors. Arrived at the servants' quarters under the roof, he hesitated, then turning to the right he opened a little door at the end of the corridor. Within was a pitch-dark cupboard-like boxroom, hot, stuffy, and smelling of dust and old leather. He advanced cautiously into the blackness, groping with his hands. It was from this den that the ladder went up to the leads of the western tower. He found the ladder, and set his feet on the rungs; noiselessly, he lifted the trapdoor above his head; the moonlit sky was over him, he breathed the fresh, cool air of the night. In a moment he was standing on the leads, gazing out over the dim, colourless landscape, looking perpendicularly down at the terrace seventy feet below.

Why had he climbed up to this high, desolate place? Was it to look at the moon? Was it to commit suicide? As yet he hardly knew. Death —the tears came into his eyes when he thought of it. His misery assumed a certain solemnity; he was lifted up on the wings of a kind of exaltation. It was a mood in which he might have done almost anything, however foolish. He advanced towards the farther parapet; the drop was sheer there and uninterrupted. A good leap, and perhaps one might clear the narrow terrace and so crash down yet another thirty feet to the sun-baked ground below. He paused at the corner of the tower, looking now down into the shadowy gulf below, now up towards the rare stars and the waning moon. He made a gesture with his hand, muttered something, he could not afterwards remember what; but the fact that he had said it aloud gave the utterance a peculiarly terrible significance. Then he looked down once more into the depths.

'What *are* you doing, Denis?' questioned a voice from somewhere very close behind him.

Denis uttered a cry of frightened surprise, and very nearly went over the parapet in good earnest. His heart was beating terribly, and he was pale when, recovering himself, he turned round in the direction from which the voice had come.

'Are you ill?'

In the profound shadow that slept under the eastern parapet of the tower, he saw something he had not previously noticed—an oblong shape. It was a mattress, and someone was lying on it. Since that first memorable night on the tower, Mary had slept out every evening; it was a sort of manifestation of fidelity.

'It gave me a fright,' she went on, 'to wake up and see you waving your arms and gibbering there. What on earth were you doing?'

Denis laughed melodramatically. 'What, indeed!' he said. If she hadn't woken up as she did, he would be lying in pieces at the bottom of the tower; he was certain of that, now.

'You hadn't got designs on me, I hope?' Mary inquired, jumping too rapidly to conclusions.

'I didn't know you were here,' said Denis, laughing more bitterly and artificially than before.

'What *is* the matter, Denis?'

He sat down on the edge of the mattress, and for all reply went on laughing in the same frightful and improbable tone.

An hour later he was reposing with his head on Mary's knees, and she, with an affectionate solicitude that was wholly maternal, was running her fingers through his tangled hair. He had told her everything, everything: his hopeless love, his jealousy, his despair, his suicide—as it were providentially averted by her interposition. He had solemnly promised never to think of self-destruction again. And now his soul was floating in a sad serenity. It was embalmed in the sympathy that Mary so generously poured. And it was not only in receiving sympathy that Denis found serenity and even a kind of happiness; it was also in giving it. For if he had told Mary everything about his miseries, Mary, reacting to these confidences, had told him in return everything, or very nearly everything, about her own.

'Poor Mary!' He was very sorry for her. Still, she might have guessed that Ivor wasn't precisely a monument of constancy.

'Well,' she concluded, 'one must put a good face on it.' She wanted to cry, but she wouldn't allow herself to be weak. There was a silence.

'Do you think,' asked Denis hesitatingly—'do you really think that she . . . that Gombauld . . .'

'I'm sure of it,' Mary answered decisively. There was another long pause.

'I don't know what to do about it,' he said at last, utterly dejected.

'You'd better go away,' advised Mary. 'It's the safest thing, and the most sensible.'

'But I've arranged to stay here three weeks more.'

'You must concoct an excuse.'

'I suppose you're right.'

'I know I am,' said Mary, who was recovering all her firm self-possession. 'You can't go on like this, can you?'

'No, I can't go on like this,' he echoed.

Immensely practical, Mary invented a plan of action. Startlingly, in the darkness, the church clock struck three.

'You must go to bed at once,' she said. 'I'd no idea it was so late.'

Denis clambered down the ladder, cautiously descended the creaking stairs. His room was dark; the candle had long ago guttered to extinction. He got into bed and fell asleep almost at once.

## *Chapter 30*

DENIS had been called, but in spite of the parted curtains he had dropped off again into that drowsy, dozy state when sleep becomes a sensual pleasure almost consciously savoured. In this condition he might have remained for another hour if he had not been disturbed by a violent rapping at the door.

'Come in,' he mumbled, without opening his eyes. The latch clicked, a hand seized him by the shoulder and he was rudely shaken.

'Get up, get up!'

His eyelids blinked painfully apart, and he saw Mary standing over him, bright-faced and earnest.

'Get up!' she repeated. 'You must go and send the telegram. Don't you remember?'

'O Lord!' He threw off the bed-clothes; his tormentor retired.

Denis dressed as quickly as he could and ran up the road to the village post office. Satisfaction glowed within him as he returned. He had sent a long telegram, which would in a few hours evoke an answer ordering him back to town at once—on urgent business. It was an act performed, a decisive step taken—and he so rarely took decisive steps; he felt pleased with himself. It was with a whetted appetite that he came in to breakfast.

'Good morning,' said Mr. Scogan. 'I hope you're better.'

'Better?'

'You were rather worried about the cosmos last night.'

Denis tried to laugh away the impeachment. 'Was I?' he lightly asked.

'I wish,' said Mr. Scogan, 'that I had nothing worse to prey on my mind. I should be a happy man.'

'One is only happy in action,' Denis enunciated, thinking of the telegram.

He looked out of the window. Great florid baroque clouds floated high in the blue heaven. A wind stirred among the trees, and their shaken foliage twinkled and glittered like metal in the sun. Everything seemed marvellously beautiful. At the thought that he would soon be leaving all this beauty he felt a momentary pang; but he comforted himself by recollecting how decisively he was acting.

'Action,' he repeated aloud, and going over to the sideboard he helped himself to an agreeable mixture of bacon and fish.

Breakfast over, Denis repaired to the terrace, and, sitting there, raised the enormous bulwark of *The Times* against the possible assaults of Mr. Scogan, who showed an unappeased desire to go on talking about the Universe. Secure behind the crackling pages, he meditated. In the light of this brilliant morning the emotions of last night seemed somehow rather remote. And what if he had seen them embracing in the moonlight? Perhaps it didn't mean much after all. And even if it did, why shouldn't he stay? He felt strong enough to stay, strong enough to be aloof, disinterested, a mere friendly acquaintance. And even if he weren't strong enough . . .

'What time do you think the telegram will arrive?' asked Mary suddenly, thrusting in upon him over the top of the paper.

Denis started guiltily. 'I don't know at all,' he said.

'I was only wondering,' said Mary, 'because there's a very good train at 3.27, and it would be nice if you could catch it, wouldn't it?'

'Awfully nice,' he agreed weakly. He felt as though he were making arrangements for his own funeral. Train leaves Waterloo 3.27. No flowers. . . . Mary was gone. No, he was blowed if he'd let himself be hurried down to the Necropolis like this. He was blowed. The sight of Mr. Scogan looking out, with a hungry expression, from the drawing-room window made him precipitately hoist *The Times* once more. For a long while he kept it hoisted. Lowering it at last to take another cautious peep at his surroundings, he found himself, with what astonishment! confronted by Anne's faint, amused, malicious smile. She was standing before him,—the woman who was a tree,—the swaying grace of her movement arrested in a pose that seemed itself a movement.

'How long have you been standing there?' he asked, when he had done gaping at her.

'Oh, about half an hour, I suppose,' she said airily. 'You were so very deep in your paper—head over ears—I didn't like to disturb you.'

'You look lovely this morning,' Denis exclaimed. It was the first time he had ever had the courage to utter a personal remark of the kind.

Anne held up her hand as though to ward off a blow. 'Don't bludgeon me, please.' She sat down on the bench beside him. He was a nice boy, she thought, quite charming; and Gombauld's violent insistences were really becoming rather tiresome. 'Why don't you wear white trousers?' she asked. 'I like you so much in white trousers.'

'They're at the wash,' Denis replied rather curtly. This white-trouser business was all in the wrong spirit. He was just preparing a scheme to manœuvre the conversation back to the proper path, when Mr. Scogan suddenly darted out of the house, crossed the terrace with clockwork rapidity, and came to a halt in front of the bench on which they were seated.

'To go on with our interesting conversation about the cosmos,' he began. 'I become more and more convinced that the various parts of the concern are fundamentally discrete. . . . But would you mind, Denis, moving a shade to your right?' He wedged himself between them on the bench. 'And if you would shift a few inches to the left, my dear Anne. . . . Thank you. Discrete, I think, was what I was saying.'

'You were, said Anne. Denis was speechless.

They were taking their after-luncheon coffee in the library when the telegram arrived. Denis blushed guiltily as he took the orange envelope from the salver and tore it open. 'Return at once. Urgent family business.' It was too ridiculous. As if he had any family business! Wouldn't it be best just to crumple the thing up and put it in his pocket without saying anything about it? He looked up; Mary's large blue china eyes were fixed upon him, seriously, penetratingly. He blushed more deeply than ever, hesitated in a horrible uncertainty.

'What's your telegram about?' Mary asked significantly.

He lost his head. 'I'm afraid,' he mumbled, 'I'm afraid this means I shall have to go back to town at once.' He frowned at the telegram ferociously.

'But that's absurd, impossible,' cried Anne. She had been standing by the window talking to Gombauld; but at Denis's words she came swaying across the room towards him.

'It's urgent,' he repeated desperately.

'But you've only been here such a short time,' Anne protested.

'I know,' he said, utterly miserable. Oh, if only she could understand! Women were supposed to have intuition.

'If he must go, he must,' put in Mary firmly.

'Yes, I must.' He looked at the telegram again for inspiration. 'You see, it's urgent family business,' he explained.

Priscilla got up from her chair in some excitement. 'I had a distinct presentiment of this last night,' she said. 'A distinct presentiment.'

'A mere coincidence, no doubt,' said Mary, brushing Mrs. Wimbush out of the conversation. 'There's a very good train at 3.27.' She looked at the clock on the mantelpiece. 'You'll have nice time to pack.'

'I'll order the motor at once.' Henry Wimbush rang the bell. The funeral was well under way. It was awful, awful.

'I'm wretched you should be going,' said Anne.

Denis turned towards her; she really did look wretched. He abandoned himself hopelessly, fatalistically to his destiny. This was what came of action, of doing something decisive. If only he'd just let things drift! If only . . .

'I shall miss your conversation,' said Mr. Scogan.

Mary looked at the clock again. 'I think perhaps you ought to go and pack,' she said.

Obediently Denis left the room. Never again, he said to himself, never again would he do anything decisive. Camlet, West Bowlby, Knipswich for Timpany, Spavin Delawarr; and then all the other stations; and then, finally, London. The thought of the journey appalled him. And what on earth was he going to do in London when he got there? He climbed wearily up the stairs. It was time for him to lay himself in his coffin.

The car was at the door—the hearse. The whole party had assembled to see him go. Good-bye, good-bye. Mechanically he tapped the barometer that hung in the porch; the needle stirred perceptibly to the left. A sudden smile lighted up his lugubrious face.

'"It sinks, and I am ready to depart,"' he said, quoting Landor with an exquisite aptness. He looked quickly round from face to face. Nobody had noticed. He climbed into the hearse.

THE END

*1921*

# HILAIRE BELLOC

## Al-Durar, or *The Pearls*

FROM 'THE MERCY OF ALLAH'

A WEEK later, at the hour of Public Executions and Beheadings, the seven boys were again assembled cross-legged at the feet of their revered uncle, who, when he had refreshed them with cold water, and himself with a curious concoction of fermented barley, addressed them as follows:

'You will remember, my lads, how I was left cut off from my dear home and from all companions, in a strange country, and with no more than 1,500 dinars with which to face the world. This sum may seem to you large, but I can assure you that to the operations of commerce' (and here the merchant yawned) 'it is but a drop in the ocean; and I had already so far advanced during one brief week in my character of Financier that I gloomily considered how small a sum that 1,500 was wherewith to meet the cunning, the gluttony, and the avarice of this great world. But a brief sleep (which I took under a Baobab tree to save the cost of lodging) refreshed at once my body and my intelligence, and with the next morning I was ready to meet the world.'

Here the merchant coughed slightly, and addressing his nephews said: 'You have doubtless been instructed at school upon the nature of the Baobab?'

'We have,' replied his nephews, and they recited in chorus the description which they had been taught by heart from the text-books of their Academy.

'I am pleased,' replied their uncle, smiling, 'to discover you thus informed. You will appreciate how ample a roof this singular vegetable affords.

'Well, I proceeded under the morning sun through a pleasantly wooded and rising country, considering by what contrivance of usury or deceit I might next increase my capital, when I saw in the distance the groves and white buildings of an unwalled town, to which (since large places, especially if they are not war-like, furnish the best field for the enterprise of a Captain of Industry) I proceeded; . . . and there, by the Mercy of Allah, there befell me as singular an adventure as perhaps ever has fallen to the lot of man.

'I had not taken up my place in the local caravanserai for more than an hour—I had met no likely fool, and my plans for the future were still vague in my head—when an old gentleman of great dignity, followed by an obsequious officer and no less than six Ethiopian slaves, approached me with deep reverence, and proffering me a leathern pouch, of a foreign kind, the like of which I had never seen before, asked me whether I were not the young man who had inadvertently left it upon a prayer-stone at a shrine outside the city.

'I seized the pouch with an eager air, held it up in transports of joy, and kissing it again and again said, "Oh! my benefactor! How can I sufficiently thank you! It is my father's last gift to me and is all my viaticum as well!" with which I fell to kissing and fondling it again, pressing it to my heart and so discovered it to be filled with coins—as indeed I had suspected it to be.

'Into so active an emotion had I roused myself that my eyes filled with tears, and the good old man himself was greatly affected. "I must warn you, young stranger," he said paternally, "against this thoughtlessness so common in youth! A great loss indeed had it been for you, if we had not had the good fortune to recover your property."

'You may imagine my confusion, my dear nephews, at finding that I had been guilty of so intolerable a fault. I blushed with confusion; I most heartily thanked the old gentleman, not for his integrity (which it would have been insulting to mention to one of his great wealth) but for the pains he had taken to seek out a careless young man and to prevent his suffering loss.

'"Nay," said that aged gentlemen to me with a low and pleasant laugh, "you must not thank me. Perhaps had I myself come upon the treasure I might have thought it too insignificant to restore. But you must know that I am the Chief Magistrate of this city and that last evening my officer noticed from some distance a young man, apparently a stranger to this city, whom he describes as of your height and features, rise from the prayer-stone, but leave behind him some object which, in the gathering dusk, he could not distinguish. On his approach he found it was this purse of yours which some boys had already found and were quarrelling over, when he took it from them. He brought it to me with some description of your person: I thought you might well be at this caravanserai and brought it with me: I had the pleasure of hearing my officer, who now accompanies me, recognize you as we approached." That functionary bowed to me and I to him most ceremoniously, and as I did so I was rapidly revolving in my head what I had better do if the real owner should appear. I was torn between two plans: whether to denounce him as a thief before he could speak, or to run off at top speed.

'This preoccupation I dismissed lest the anxiety of it should appear upon my face.

'I again thanked this good old man most warmly, and we entered into a familiar conversation. What was my delight at the close of it when he bade me without ceremony accept of his hospitality and come home to take a meal with him in his palace. I was eager for further adventures, and accompanied him with the greatest joy.

'Reclining at table, where there was served (as I need hardly inform my dear nephews) lamb stuffed with pistachio nuts, the old man asked me whence I had come, what was my trade, and whither I was proceeding.

'I answered (as I thought, prudently) that I had come from Aleppo, that I had been entrusted by my father with the sum in the purse he had so kindly restored to me, in order to purchase pearls, and that when the purchase was completed I had instructions to sell them in India in a market where my father was assured that pearls were rare and fetched the highest prices.

' "This is indeed well found!" exclaimed the old man, with enthusiasm. "I am myself seeking for some one to whom I may sell a magnificent collection of pearls inherited from my great-grandmother, an Indian Begum. The old woman," he added nonchalantly enough, "was a miser; she kept the drops higgledy-piggledy in an old cedarwood box, and I confess myself quite ignorant of their value. Moreover, as I have taken a liking to you, I shall let you fix your own price, for I should much like to remember when my time comes that I had helped a friendless man in his first step to fortune; only, I am a little ashamed to appear to be making money out of an heirloom!"

'While the old gentleman so spoke I was rapidly revolving in my mind what motive he could have for such an affectation of indifference to wealth, when I recollected that he was the Chief Magistrate of the city, and immediately concluded that these pearls, being the property of local people, and obtained by him for nothing by way of bribes and other legal channels, he would both desire to have them sold at a distance and would let them go cheap.

' "Nay," continued he, seeing that I hesitated as these thoughts occurred to me, "I will take no denial. For me it is but a mere riddance, and for you a most excellent bargain. Come, I trust your honest face and youthful candour. You shall take them at your own price! And I will even advise you of the city of India where you will find your best market."

'Put thus, the offer, I will confess, attracted me; but I had already learned the wickedness of mankind (though not as yet, I am glad to say, my dear nephews, at my own expense), and I said that I would at least so far meet him as to take the jewels to a local merchant, invent some tale, as though they were my own, and see what sum might be offered for them. Only when I thus had some measure of their value could I honourably make an offer. I continued at some length in this strain, expressing a humble inability to judge, and the fear lest my capital might not be sufficient (which he pooh-poohed). I stipulated, for a reason you will soon perceive, that a slave of his should accompany me—if only as a matter of routine—for (said I) I was very jealous of my honour. He agreed, though he was good enough to call it a pure formality.

'I left the aged magistrate with many thanks and, accompanied by the slave, proceeded with the pearls to the jewel merchants' quarter in the Bazaar. I stopped before one of the richest and most reputed booths, and spreading the pearls before the merchant told him that I was compelled to sell these under order from authority as the end of a family dispute, to pay the dowry of my sister; that I therefore was in haste to settle and would take the least price he might choose to mention within reason. I was, said I, wholly in his hands. It was urgent for me that the bargain should be quickly completed, but before I could receive his cash I must hear the lowest figure he would name.

'While I thus spoke the slave stood respectfully behind me and listened to our conversation. The jewel merchant said that no class of merchandise was more distasteful to him than pearls; there was at this moment no market for them. It was impossible to purchase them save properly set and in regular sizes; and finally it was well known that pearls were the most unlucky of gems. It was quite impossible for him to offer more than 10,000 dinars, and even so he would doubtless be the loser by the transaction.

'When I heard this I rapidly wrote upon a slip of paper the following words:

' "My Lord,—The chief merchant in this city estimates your jewels at 10,000 dinars. I cannot, alas, provide that sum, and therefore I cannot honestly make an offer myself as I had hoped; if you desire to have them sold here I will faithfully execute your commission, but if you prefer that I should return them to you send me word. Meanwhile, I will still bargain here awaiting your reply."

'I sent this note by the slave and begged him to give it to his master and to bring me an answer. The slave went off, and when I judged him to be well out of hearing I turned and said to the merchant, sighing: "Well, since you offer no more I must take what you offer; the slave whom you saw me despatch carried the news to my family; I burn when I think of how their scorn will mock my humiliation. I therefore said nothing true of the price. Indeed, I have set it down in that note as something much higher. But I submit, for, as I told you, I am pressed. Come, count me the money, and I will away."

'The merchant, after I had handed over the pearls, counted me the money into yet another large leathern bag, which I shouldered, and with rapid steps bore out of the Bazaar and soon out of the town itself, by a gate called the Bab-el-Jaffur, that is, the gate of innocence.

'Beyond the town walls was a long roll of dusty sloping land set here and there with dusty stunted bushes and having beyond it a high range of desert hills. A track led roughly rising across it, away from the town.

'I followed this track for one hour and then sat down (for my new fortune was heavy) and rested.

'As I thought it probable that my good old friend himself would return speedily with his slave to the Bazaar, and as the complication of the affair might embroil me, I hid during the remainder of the day squeezed in a jackal's earth beneath a bank. Before nightfall I ventured out and gazed about me, leaving my original pouch, my windfall and my big leathern bag of 10,000 dinars in the jackal's earth while I surveyed the track.

'It was the hour I love above all others.

'The sun had just set beyond the distant ocean towards which my face was turned, and between me and which, upon the plain below—for I had come to the rise of the mountain side—lay the beautiful city I had just left. The fragrant smoke of cedar wood rose from some of its roofs as the evening fell. There was still hanging in the air the coloured dust of evening above the roads of entry, and there came faintly through the distance the cry of the muezzin.

'I was not so entranced by the natural beauty of the scene as to neglect the duty which this sound recalled. I fell immediately upon my knees and was careful to add to the accustomed prayers of that hour my heart-felt thanks for the Guidance and the Grace which had so singularly increased my fortunes in the last few hours.

'As I rose from these devotions I heard upon my right a low wailing sound and was astonished to discover there, seated hopelessly beneath a small shrub and waving his hands in grief, a young man of much my own height and appearance: but I flatter myself that not even in my most careful assumptions of innocence have I ever worn such a booby face.

'He was swaying slowly from side to side, and as he did so moaning a ceaseless plaint, the words of which I caught and which touched me to the heart. Over and over again he recited his irreparable loss. He had but that small sum! It was his patrimony! His sole security! How should he answer for it? who should now support him? or what should he do?

'So he wailed to himself in miserable monotone till I could bear it no longer, for I saw that I had by a singular coincidence come upon that poor young man whose pouch I had been given in error by the magistrate of the city.

'I bowed before him. He noticed me listlessly enough and asked me what I would. I told him I thought I could give him comfort. Was it not he, said I, who had left a certain pouch (I carefully described it) containing sundry coins upon a prayer-stone outside the city at this very same sunset hour of the day before? His despair was succeeded by a startling eagerness. He leapt to his feet, seized my arm, rose feverishly and implored me to tell him further.

' "Alas," I said, "what I have to tell you is but little! I fear to raise your hopes too high—but at any rate I can put you upon the track of your property." '

' "Sir," said he, resuming his hopeless tone for a moment, "I have already done my best. I went to the Chief Magistrate of the city to claim it and was met by an officer of his who told me that the purse had already been delivered to its owner, suspected my claim and bade me return. But how shall I prove that it is mine, or how, indeed, receive it, since the abominable thief who took possession of it must by now be already far away?"

' "You do him an injustice," said I. "It is precisely of him whom you uncharitably call a thief that I would speak to you. You think that he is far away, whereas he is really at your hand whenever you choose to act, for this is the message that I bring you. He awaits you even now, and if you will present yourself to him he will restore your property."

' "How can you know this?" said the young man, gazing at me doubtfully. "By what coincidence have you any knowledge of the affair?"

' "It is simple enough," said I. "This person to whom your purse was given, and I, were in the same inn. We fell to talking of our adventures along the road, for he also was a stranger, and he told me the singular tale how he had recovered from the authorities a purse which he honestly thought his own, for it was very like one which he himself possessed; but that on finding his own purse later on in his wallet he was overwhelmed with regret at the thought of the loss he had occasioned; at the same time he made me his confidant, telling me that he intended to restore it this very evening at sunset to the authorities and that any one claiming it after that hour and proving it was his could recover it at the public offices. But he warned me of one thing: the officers (he told me) were convinced (from what indication I know not, perhaps from the presence of something in the purse, or perhaps from something they had heard) that the owner dealt in *pearls*."

'Here the young man interrupted me, and assured me he had never bought or sold pearls in his life, nor thought of doing so.

'I answered that no doubt this was so. But that when the authorities had a whim it was well to humour them. He would therefore do well to approach the officer who guarded the gate of the Chief Magistrate's house, with the simple words, "I am the Seller of Pearls," on hearing which his path would be made smooth for him, and he would receive his belongings.

'The young man thanked me heartily; he even warmly embraced me for the good news I had given him, and felt, I fear, that his purse and his small fortune were already restored to him. It was a gallant sight to see him in the last of the light swinging down the mountain side with a new life in him, and I sincerely regretted from my heart the necessity under which I was to imperil his liberty and life. But you will agree with me, my dear nephews, that I could not possibly afford to have him at large.

'When he had gone and when it was fully night, there being no moon and only the stars in the warm dark sky, I rapidly took my burdens from their hiding-place and proceeded, though with some difficulty, up the mountain side, staggering under such a weight, and deviating from the track so that there should be less chance of finding myself interrupted.

'I slept for a few hours. I awoke at dawn. I counted my total fortune, and found that it was just about 12,000 dinars, the most of it in silver.

'Carefully concealing it again, I left its hiding-place and glided round the mountain until I came to a place where a new track began to appear, which led to a neighbouring village. Here I bought an ass, and returning with it to my hiding-place and setting my treasure upon it I went off at random to spend the day in travelling as rapidly as I might away from the neighbourhood by the most deserted regions.

'I came, a little before sunset, upon a hermit's cave, where I was hospitably entertained and the tenant of which refused all reward, asking me only to pray for him, as he was certain that the prayers of youth and innocence would merit him a high place in Heaven.

'With this holy man I remained for some four or five days, passing my time at leisure in his retreat among the mountains, and feeding my donkey upon the dried grasses which I brought in by armfuls at dusk from the woodlands. Upon the fifth day of this concealment the hermit came in pensive and sad, and said to me:

' "My son, with every day the wickedness of this world increases, and the judgment of God will surely fall upon it in a devastating fire! I have but just heard that the Chief Magistrate of our capital city, using as a dupe an innocent stranger, sold to one of the great jewellers of the place for no less than 10,000 dinars a quantity of pearls, every one of which now turns out to be false and valueless! Nay, I am told that the largest are made of nothing but wax! And, what is worse, not content with this first wickedness, the magistrate under the plea that the young stranger had disappeared confiscated the gems again and had the poor merchant most severely beaten! But—worse and worse! the poor youth having innocently returned that very night to the city, was seized by the guard and beheaded. Ya, ya," said the good old man, throwing up his hands, "the days increase, and their evil increases with them!" '

At this moment the hoarse and discordant voice of the Public Crier croaked its first note from the neighbouring turret, and the nephews, who had sat enraptured at their uncle's tale, knew that it was time to disperse. The eldest brother therefore said:

'O uncle; before we go let me express the thanks of all of us for your enrapturing story. But let me also express our bewilderment at the absence of all plan in your singular adventures. For though we have listened minutely to all you have said, we cannot discover what art you showed in the achievement of any purpose. For instance, how could you know that the pearls were false?'

'I did not know it, my dear nephew,' replied the great Merchant with beautiful simplicity, 'and the whole was the Mercy of Allah! . . . But come, the hour of prayer is announced, and we must, following the invariable custom of the Faithful, make yet another joint in my singular tale. Come, therefore, on this day week, shortly after the last of the public executions of the vulgar, and I will tell you of my further fortunes: for you must understand that the 12,000 dinars of which my story now leaves me possessed are'—and here the honest old man yawned again and waved his hand—'but a flea-bite to a man like me.'

His seven little nephews bowed repeatedly, and, walking backwards without a trip, disappeared through the costly tapestries of their uncle's apartments.

*1922*

# MARCEL PROUST

## *REMEMBRANCE OF THINGS PAST*

TRANSLATED BY C. K. SCOTT MONCRIEFF

---

### *Madame Swann*

FROM 'SWANN'S WAY': PART TWO

I ASSIGNED the first place, in the order of aesthetic merit and of social grandeur, to simplicity, when I saw Mme. Swann on foot, in a 'polonaise' of plain cloth, a little toque on her head trimmed with a pheasant's wing, a bunch of violets in her bosom, hastening along the Allée des Acacias as if it had been merely the shortest way back to her own house, and acknowledging with a rapid glance the courtesy of the gentlemen in carriages, who, recognizing her figure at a distance, were raising their hats to her and saying to one another that there was never anyone so well turned out as she. But instead of simplicity it was to ostentation that I must assign the first place if, after I had compelled Françoise, who could hold out no longer, and complained that her legs were 'giving' beneath her, to stroll up and down with me for another hour, I saw at length, emerging from the Porte Dauphine, figuring for me a royal dignity, the passage of a sovereign, an impression such as no real Queen has ever since been able to give me, because my notion of their power has been less vague, and more founded upon experience—borne along by the flight of a pair of fiery horses, slender and shapely as one sees them in the drawings of Constantin Guys, carrying on its box an enormous coachman, furred like a cossack, and by his side a diminutive groom, like Toby, 'the late Beaudenord's tiger,' I saw—or rather I felt its outlines engraved upon my heart by a clean and killing stab—a matchless victoria, built rather high, and hinting, through the extreme modernity of its appointments, at the forms of an earlier day, deep down in which lay negligently back Mme. Swann, her hair, now quite pale with one grey lock, girt with a narrow band of flowers, usually violets, from which floated down long veils, a lilac parasol in her hand, on her lips an ambiguous smile in which I read only the benign condescension of Majesty, though it was pre-eminently the enticing smile of the courtesan, which she graciously bestowed upon the men who bowed to her. That smile was, in reality, saying to one: 'Oh yes, I do remember, quite well; it was wonderful!' to another: 'How I should have loved to! We were unfortunate!', to a third: 'Yes, if you like! I must just keep in the line for a minute, then as soon as I can I will break away.' When strangers passed she still allowed to linger about her lips a lazy smile, as though she expected or remembered some friend, which made them say: 'What a lovely woman!' And for certain men only she had a sour, strained, shy, cold smile which meant: 'Yes, you old goat, I know that you've got a tongue like a viper, that you can't keep quiet for a moment. But do you suppose that I care what you say?' Coquelin passed, talking, in a group of listening friends, and with a sweeping wave of his hand bade a theatrical good day to the people in the carriages. But I thought only of Mme. Swann, and pretended to have not yet seen her, for I knew that, when she reached the pigeon-shooting ground, she would tell her coachman to 'break away' and to stop the carriage, so that she might come back on foot. And on days when I felt that I had the courage to pass close by her I would drag Françoise off in that direction; until the moment came when I saw Mme. Swann, letting trail behind her the long train of her lilac skirt, dressed, as the populace imagine queens to be dressed, in rich attire such as no other woman might wear, lowering her eyes now and then to study the handle of her parasol, paying scant attention to the passers-by, as though the important thing for her, her one object in being there was to take exercise, without thinking that she was seen, and that every head was turned towards her. Sometimes, however, when she had looked back to call her dog to her, she would cast, almost imperceptibly, a sweeping glance round about.

*1922*

* * * * *

## *The Princesse de Guermantes*

FROM 'THE GUERMANTES WAY': PART ONE

LIKE a mighty goddess who presides from far aloft over the sports of lesser deities, the Princess had deliberately remained a little way back on a sofa placed sideways in the box, red as a reef of coral, beside a big, glassy splash of reflexion which was probably a mirror and made one think of the section cut by a ray of sunlight, vertical, clear, liquid, through the flashing crystal of the sea. At once plume and blossom, like certain subaqueous growths, a great white flower, downy as the wing of a bird, fell from the brow of the Princess along one of her cheeks, the curve of which it followed with a pliancy, coquettish, amorous, alive, and seemed almost to enfold it like a rosy egg in the softness of a halcyon's nest. Over her hair, reaching in front to her eyebrows and caught back lower down at the level of her throat, was spread a net upon which those little white shells which are gathered on some shore of the South Seas alternated with pearls, a marine mosaic barely emerging from the waves and at every moment plunged back again into a darkness in the depths of which even then a human presence was revealed by the ubiquitous flashing of the Princess's eyes. The beauty which set her far above all the other fabulous daughters of the dusk was not altogether materially and comprehensively inscribed on her neck, her shoulders, her arms, her figure. But the exquisite, unfinished line of the last was the exact starting point, the inevitable focus of invisible lines which the eye could not help prolonging, marvellous lines, springing into life round the woman like the spectrum of an ideal form projected upon the screen of darkness.

'That's the Princesse de Guermantes,' said my neighbour to the gentleman beside her, taking care to begin the word 'Princesse' with a string of P's, to shew that a title like that was absurd. 'She hasn't been sparing with her pearls. I'm sure, if I had as many as that, I wouldn't make such a display of them; it doesn't look at all well, not to my mind.'

And yet, when they caught sight of the Princess, all those who were looking round to see who was in the audience felt springing up for her in their hearts the rightful throne of beauty. Indeed, with the Duchesse de Luxembourg, with Mme. de Morienval, with Mme. de Sainte-Euverte, and any number of others, what enabled one to identify their faces would be the juxtaposition of a big red nose to a hare-lip, or of a pair of wrinkled cheeks to a faint moustache. These features were nevertheless sufficient in themselves to attract the eye, since having merely the conventional value of a written document they gave one to read a famous and impressive name; but also they gave one, cumulatively, the idea that ugliness had about it something aristocratic, and that it was unnecessary that the face of a great lady, provided it was distinguished, should be beautiful as well. But like certain artists who, instead of the letters of their names, set at the foot of their canvas a form that is beautiful in itself, a butterfly, a lizard, a flower, so it was the form of a delicious face and figure that the Princess had put in the corner of her box, thereby showing that beauty can be the noblest of signatures; for the presence there of Mme. de Guermantes-Baviere, who brought to the theatre only such persons as at other times formed part of her intimate circle, was in the eyes of specialists in aristocracy the best possible certificate of the authenticity of the picture which her box presented, a sort of evocation of a scene in the ordinary private life of the Princess in her palaces in Munich and in Paris.

* * * * *

## *The Duchesse de Guermantes*

### FROM 'THE GUERMANTES WAY': PART ONE

JUST as the curtain was rising on this second play I looked up at Mme. de Guermantes's box. The Princess was in the act—by a movement that called into being an exquisite line which my mind pursued into the void—of turning her head towards the back of the box; her party were all standing, and also turning towards the back, and between the double hedge which they thus formed, with all the assurance, the grandeur of the goddess that she was, but with a strange meekness which so late an arrival, making every one else get up in the middle of the performance, blended with the white muslin in which she was attired, just as an adroitly compounded air of simplicity, shyness and confusion tempered her triumphant smile, the Duchesse de Guermantes, who had at that moment entered the box, came towards her cousin, made a profound obeisance to a young man with fair hair who was seated in the front row, and turning again towards the amphibian monsters who were floating in the recesses of the cavern, gave to these demi-gods of the Jockey Club—who at that moment, and among them all M. de Palancy in particular, were the men who I should most have liked to be—the familiar 'good evening' of an old and intimate friend, an allusion to the daily sequence of her relations with them during the last fifteen years. I felt the mystery, but could not solve the riddle of that smiling gaze which she addressed to her friends, in the azure brilliance with which it glowed while she surrendered her hand to one and then to another, a gaze which, could I have broken up its prism, analysed its crystallisation, might perhaps have revealed to me the essential quality of the unknown form of life which became apparent in it at that moment. The Duc de Guermantes followed his wife, the flash of his monocle, the gleam of his teeth, the whiteness of his carnation or of his pleated shirt-front scattering, to make room for their light, the darkness of his eyebrows, lips and coat; with a wave of his outstretched hand which he let drop on their shoulders, vertically, without moving his head, he commanded the inferior monsters, who were making way for him, to resume their seats, and made a profound bow to the fair young man. One would have said that the Duchess had guessed that her cousin, of whom, it was rumoured, she was inclined to make fun for what she called her 'exaggerations' (a name which, from her own point of view, so typically French and restrained, would naturally be applied to the poetry and enthusiasm of the Teuton), would be wearing this evening one of those costumes in which the Duchess thought of her as 'dressed up', and that she had decided to give her a lesson in good taste. Instead of the wonderful downy plumage which, from the crown of the Princess's head, fell and swept her throat, instead of her net of shells and pearls, the Duchess wore in her hair only a simple aigrette, which, rising above her arched nose and level eyes, reminded one of the crest on the head of a bird. Her neck and shoulders emerged from a drift of snow-white muslin, against which fluttered a swansdown fan, but below this her gown, the bodice of which had for its sole ornament innumerable spangles (either little sticks and beads of metal, or possibly brilliants), moulded her figure with a precision that was positively British. But different as their two costumes were, after the Princess had given her cousin the chair in which she herself had previously been sitting, they could be seen turning to gaze at one another in mutual appreciation.

*1925*

* * * * *

## *Swann*

FROM 'THE GUERMANTES WAY': PART TWO

'VERY well, give me in one word the reason why you can't come to Italy,' the Duchess put it to Swann as she rose to say good-bye to us. 'But, my dear friend, it's because I shall then have been dead for several months. According to the doctors I consulted last winter, the thing I've got—which may, for that matter, carry me off at any moment—won't in any case leave me more than three or four months to live, and even that is a generous estimate,' replied Swann with a smile, while the footman opened the glazed door of the hall to let the Duchess out. 'What's that you say?' cried the Duchess, stopping for a moment on her way to the carriage, and raising her fine eyes, their melancholy blue clouded by uncertainty. Placed for the first time in her life between two duties as incompatible as getting into her carriage to go out to dinner and shewing pity for a man who was about to die, she could find nothing in the code of conventions that indicated the right line to follow, and, not knowing which to choose, felt it better to make a show of not believing that the latter alternative need be seriously considered, so as to follow the first, which demanded of her at the moment less effort, and thought that the best way of settling the conflict would be to deny that any existed. 'You're joking,' she said to Swann. 'It would be a joke in charming taste,' replied he ironically. 'I don't know why I am telling you this; I have never said a word to you before about my illness. But as you asked me, and as now I may die at any moment. . . . But whatever I do I mustn't make you late; you're dining out, remember,' he added, because he knew that for other people their own social obligations took precedence of the death of a friend, and could put himself in her place by dint of his instinctive politeness. But that of the Duchess enabled her also to perceive in a vague way that the dinner to which she was going must count for less to Swann than his own death. And so, while continuing on her way towards the carriage, she let her shoulders droop, saying: 'Don't worry about our dinner. It's not of any importance!' But this put the Duke in a bad humour, who exclaimed: 'Come, Oriane, don't stop there chattering like that and exchanging your jeremiads with Swann; you know very well that Mme. de Saint-Euverte insists on sitting down to table at eight o'clock sharp. We must know what you propose to do; the horses have been waiting for a good five minutes. I beg your pardon, Charles,' he went on, turning to Swann, 'but it's ten minutes to eight already. Oriane is always late, and it will take us more than five minutes to get to old Saint-Euverte's.'

Mme. de Guermantes advanced resolutely towards the carriage and uttered a last farewell to Swann. 'You know, we can talk about that another time; I don't believe a word you've been saying, but we must discuss it quietly. I expect they gave you a dreadful fright, come to luncheon, whatever day you like,' (with Mme. de Guermantes things always resolved themselves into luncheons), 'you will let me know your day and time,' and, lifting her red skirt, she set her foot on the step. She was just getting into the carriage when, seeing this foot exposed, the Duke cried in a terrifying voice: 'Oriane, what have you been thinking of, you wretch? You've kept on your black shoes! With a red dress! Go upstairs quick and put on red shoes, or rather,' he said to the footman, 'tell the lady's maid at once to bring down a pair of red shoes.' 'But, my dear,' replied the Duchess gently, annoyed to see that Swann, who was leaving the house with me but had stood back to allow the carriage to pass out in front of us, could hear, 'since we are late.' 'No, no, we have plenty of time. It is only ten to; it won't take us ten minutes to get to the Parc Monceau. And, after all, what would it matter? If we turned up at half past eight they'ld have to wait for us, but you can't possibly go there in a red dress and black shoes. Besides, we shan't be the last, I can tell you; the Sassenages are coming, and you know they never arrive before twenty to nine.' The Duchess went up to her room. 'Well,' said M. de Guermantes to Swann and myself, 'we poor, down-trodden husbands, people laugh at us, but we are of some use all the same. But for me, Oriane would have been going out to dinner in black shoes.' 'It's not unbecoming,' said Swann, 'I noticed the black shoes and they didn't offend me in the least.' 'I don't say you're wrong,' replied the Duke, 'but it looks better to have them to match the dress. Besides, you needn't worry, she would no sooner have got there than she'ld have noticed them, and I should have been obliged to come home and fetch the others. I should have had my dinner at nine o'clock. Good-bye, my children,' he said, thrusting us gently from the door, 'get away, before Oriane comes down again. It's not that she doesn't like seeing you both. On the contrary, she 's too fond of your company. If she finds you still here she will start talking again, she is tired out already, she'll reach the dinner-table quite dead. Besides, I tell you frankly, I'm dying of hunger. I had a wretched luncheon this morning when I came from the train. There was the devil of a *béarnaise* sauce, I admit, but in spite of that I shan't be at all sorry, not at all sorry to sit down to dinner. Five minutes to eight! Oh, women, women! She'll give us both indigestion before to-morrow. She is not nearly as strong as people think.' The Duke felt no compunction at speaking thus of his wife's ailments and his own to a dying man, for the former interested him more, appeared to him more important. And so it was simply from good breeding and good fellowship that, after politely shewing us out, he cried 'from off stage', in a stentorian voice from the porch to Swann, who was already in the courtyard: 'You, now, don't let yourself be taken in by the doctors' nonsense, damn them. They're donkeys. You're as strong as the Pont Neuf. You'll live to bury us all!'

*1925*

# W. J. TURNER

## *Song*

FORTUNATE are the feet of the swallow
Folded unseen past the mountain
Unmirrored in water where the willow
Undulates its wavering fountain;
In secret they sleep together
Bound by a dream in their slumber
Dream of a sailing feather
Whom only soft winds encumber.
Would you and I were thus lying
Side by side on love's pillow,
Our heart-beats the wings of love flying,
Migrating from Time's dark billow.

*1923*

# STENDHAL

## *War*

FROM 'THE CHARTERHOUSE OF PARMA'

TRANSLATED BY C. K. SCOTT MONCRIEFF

FABRIZIO soon came upon some *vivandières*, and the extreme gratitude that he felt for the gaoler's wife of B—— impelled him to address them; he asked one of them where he would find the 4th Hussar Regiment, to which he belonged.

'You would do just as well not to be in such a hurry, young soldier,' said the *cantinière*, touched by Fabrizio's pallor and glowing eyes. 'Your wrist is not strong enough yet for the sabre-thrusts they'll be giving to-day. If you had a musket, I don't say, maybe you could let off your round as well as any of them.'

This advice displeased Fabrizio; but however much he urged on his horse, he could go no faster than the *cantinière* in her cart. Every now and then the sound of the guns seemed to come nearer and prevented them from hearing each other speak, for Fabrizio was so beside himself with enthusiasm and delight that he had renewed the conversation. Every word uttered by the *cantinière* intensified his happiness by making him understand it. With the exception of his real name and his escape from prison, he ended by confiding everything to this woman who seemed such a good soul. She was greatly surprised and understood nothing at all of what this handsome young soldier was telling her.

'I see what it is,' she exclaimed at length with an air of triumph. 'You're a young gentleman who has fallen in love with the wife of some captain in the 4th Hussars. Your mistress will have made you a present of the uniform you're wearing, and you're going after her. As sure as God's in heaven, you've never been a soldier; but, like the brave boy you are, seeing your regiment's under fire, you want to be there too, and not let them think you a chicken.'

Fabrizio agreed with everything; it was his only way of procuring good advice. 'I know nothing of the ways of these French people,' he said to himself, 'and if I am not guided by someone I shall find myself being put in prison again, and they'll steal my horse.'

'First of all, my boy,' said the *cantinière*, who was becoming more and more of a friend to him, 'confess that you're not one-and-twenty: at the very most you might be seventeen.'

This was the truth, and Fabrizio admitted as much with good grace.

'Then, you aren't even a conscript; it's simply because of Madame's pretty face that you're going to get your bones broken. Plague it, she can't be particular. If you've still got some of the *yellow-boys* she sent you, you must first of all buy yourself another horse; look how your screw pricks up his ears when the guns sound at all near; that's a peasant's horse, and will be the death of you as soon as you reach the line. That white smoke you see over there above the hedge, that's the infantry firing, my boy. So prepare for a fine fright when you hear the bullets whistling over you. You'll do as well to eat a bit while there's still time.'

Fabrizio followed this advice and, presenting a napoleon to the *vivandière*, asked her to accept payment.

'It makes one weep to see him!' cried the woman; 'the poor child doesn't even know how to spend his money! It would be no more than you deserve if I pocketed your napoleon and put Cocotte into a trot; damned if your screw could catch me up. What would you do, stupid, if you saw me go off? Bear in mind, when the *brute* growls, never to show your gold. Here,' she went on, 'here's 18 francs, 50 centimes, and your breakfast costs you 30 sous. Now, we shall soon have some horses for sale. If the beast is a small one, you'll give ten francs, and, in any case, never more than twenty, not if it was the horse of the Four Sons of Aymon.'

The meal finished, the *vivandière*, who was still haranguing, was interrupted by a woman who had come across the fields and passed them on the road.

'Hallo there, hi!' this woman shouted. 'Hallo, Margot! Your 6th Light are over there on the right.'

'I must leave you, my boy,' said the *vivandière* to our hero; 'but really and truly I pity you; I've taken quite a fancy to you, upon my word I have. You don't know a thing about anything, you're going to get a wipe in the eye, as sure as God's in heaven! Come along to the 6th Light with me.'

'I quite understand that I know nothing,' Fabrizio told her, 'but I want to fight, and I'm determined to go over there towards that white smoke.'

'Look how your horse is twitching his ears! As soon as he gets over there, even if he's no strength left, he'll take the bit in his teeth and start galloping, and heaven only knows where he'll land you. Will you listen to me now? As soon as you get to the troops, pick up a musket and a cartridge pouch, get down among the men and copy what you see them do, exactly the same: But, good heavens, I'll bet you don't even know how to open a cartridge.'

Fabrizio, stung to the quick, admitted nevertheless to his new friend that she had guessed aright.

'Poor boy! He'll be killed straight away; sure as God! It won't take long. You've got to come with me, absolutely,' went on the *cantinière* in a tone of authority.

'But I want to fight.'

'You shall fight too; why, the 6th Light are famous fighters, and there's fighting enough to-day for everyone.'

'But shall we come soon to the regiment?'

'In a quarter of an hour at the most.'

'With this honest woman's recommendation,' Fabrizio told himself, 'my ignorance of everything won't make them take me for a spy, and I shall have a chance of fighting.' At this moment the noise of the guns redoubled, each explosion coming straight on top of the last. 'It's like a Rosary,' said Fabrizio.

'We're beginning to hear the infantry fire now,' said the *vivandière*, whipping up her little horse, which seemed quite excited by the firing.

The *cantinière* turned to the right and took a side road that ran through the fields; there was a foot of mud in it; the little cart seemed about to be stuck fast: Fabrizio pushed the wheel. His horse fell twice; presently the road, though with less water on it, was nothing more than a bridle path through the grass. Fabrizio had not gone five hundred yards when his nag stopped short: it was a corpse, lying across the path, which terrified horse and rider alike.

Fabrizio's face, pale enough by nature, assumed a markedly green tinge; the *cantinière*, after looking at the dead man, said, as though speaking to herself: 'That's not one of our Division.' Then, raising her eyes to our hero, she burst out laughing.

'Aha, my boy! There's a titbit for you!' Fabrizio sat frozen. What struck him most of all was the dirtiness of the feet of this corpse which had already been stripped of its shoes and left with nothing but an old pair of trousers all clotted with blood.

'Come nearer,' the *cantinière* ordered him, 'get off your horse, you'll have to get accustomed to them; look,' she cried, 'he's stopped one in the head.'

A bullet, entering on one side of the nose, had gone out at the opposite temple, and disfigured the corpse in a hideous fashion. It lay with one eye still open.

'Get off your horse then, lad,' said the *cantinière*, 'and give him a shake of the hand to see if he'll return it.'

Without hesitation, although ready to yield up his soul with disgust, Fabrizio flung himself from his horse and took the hand of the corpse which he shook vigorously; then he stood still as though paralysed. He felt that he had not the strength to mount again. What horrified him more than anything was that open eye.

'The *vivandière* will think me a coward,' he said to himself bitterly. But he felt the impossibility of making any movement; he would have fallen. It was a frightful moment; Fabrizio was on the point of being physically sick. The *vivandière* noticed this, jumped lightly down from her little carriage, and held out to him, without saying a word, a glass of brandy which he swallowed at a gulp; he was able to mount his screw, and continued on his way without speaking. The *vivandière* looked at him now and again from the corner of her eye.

'You shall fight to-morrow, my boy,' she said at length; 'to-day you're going to stop with me. You can see now that you've got to learn the business before you can become a soldier.'

'On the contrary, I want to start fighting at once,' exclaimed our hero with a sombre air which seemed to the *vivandière* to augur well. The noise of the guns grew twice as loud and seemed to be coming nearer. The explosions began to form a continuous bass; there was no interval between one and the next, and above this running bass, which suggested the roar of a torrent in the distance, they could make out quite plainly the rattle of musketry.

At this point the road dived down into a clump of trees. The *vivandière* saw three or four soldiers of our army who were coming towards her as fast as their legs would carry them; she jumped nimbly down from her cart and ran into cover fifteen or twenty paces from the road. She hid herself in a hole which had been left where a big tree had recently been uprooted. 'Now,' thought Fabrizio, 'we shall see whether I am a coward'! He stopped by the side of the little cart which the woman had abandoned, and drew his sabre. The soldiers paid no attention to him and passed at a run along the wood, to the left of the road.

'They're ours,' said the *vivandière* calmly, as she came back, quite breathless, to her little cart. . . . 'If your horse was capable of galloping, I should say: push ahead as far as the end of the wood, and see if there's anyone on the plain.' Fabrizio did not wait to be told twice, he tore off a branch from a poplar, stripped it and started to lash his horse with all his might; the animal broke into a gallop for a moment, then fell back into its regular slow trot. The *vivandière* had put her horse into a gallop. 'Stop, will you, stop!' she called after Fabrizio. Presently both were clear of the wood. Coming to the edge of the plain, they heard a terrifying din, guns and muskets thundered on every side, right, left, behind them. And as the clump of trees from which they emerged grew on a mound rising nine or ten feet above the plain, they could see fairly well a corner of the battle; but still there was no one to be seen in the meadow beyond the wood. This meadow was bordered, half a mile away, by a long row of willows, very bushy; above the willows appeared a white smoke which now and again rose eddying into the sky.

'If I only knew where the regiment was,' said the *cantinière*, in some embarrassment. 'It won't do to go straight ahead over this big field. By the way,' she said to Fabrizio, 'if you see one of the enemy, stick him with the point of your sabre, don't play about with the blade.'

At this moment, the *cantinière* caught sight of the four soldiers whom we mentioned a little way back; they were coming out of the wood on to the plain to the left of the road. One of them was on horseback.

'There you are,' she said to Fabrizio. 'Hallo there!' she called to the mounted man, 'come over here and have a glass of brandy.' The soldiers approached.

'Where are the 6th Light?' she shouted.

'Over there, five minutes away, across that canal that runs along by the willows; why, Colonel Macon has just been killed.'

'Will you take five francs for your horse, you?'

'Five francs! That's not a bad one, *ma*! An officer's horse I can sell in ten minutes for five napoleons.'

'Give me one of your napoleons,' said the *vivandière* to Fabrizio. Then going up to the mounted soldier: 'Get off, quickly,' she said to him, 'here's your napoleon.'

The soldier dismounted, Fabrizio sprang gaily on to the saddle, the *vivandière* unstrapped the little portmanteau which was on his old horse.

'Come and help me, all of you!' she said to the soldiers, 'is that the way you leave a lady to do the work?'

But no sooner had the captured horse felt the weight of the portmanteau than he began to rear, and Fabrizio, who was an excellent horseman, had to use all his strength to hold him.

'A good sign!' said the *vivandière*, 'the gentleman is not accustomed to being tickled by portmanteaus.'

'A general's horse,' cried the man who had sold it, 'a horse that's worth ten napoleons if it's worth a liard.'

'Here are twenty francs,' said Fabrizio, who could not contain himself for joy at feeling between his legs a horse that could really move.

At that moment a shot struck the line of willows, through which it passed obliquely, and Fabrizio had the curious spectacle of all those little branches flying this way and that as though mown down by a stroke of the scythe.

'Look, there's the *brute* advancing,' the soldier said to him as he took the twenty francs. It was now about two o'clock.

Fabrizio was still under the spell of this strange spectacle when a party of generals, followed by a score of hussars, passed at a gallop across one corner of the huge field on the edge of which he had halted: his horse neighed, reared several times in succession, then began violently tugging the bridle that was holding him. 'All right, then,' Fabrizio said to himself.

The horse, left to his own devices, dashed off hell for leather to join the escort that was following the generals. Fabrizio counted four gold-laced hats. A quarter of an hour later, from a few words said by one hussar to the next, Fabrizio gathered that one of these generals was the famous Marshal Ney. His happiness knew no bounds; only he had no way of telling which of the four generals was Marshal Ney; he would have given everything in the world to know, but he remembered that he had been told not to speak. The escort halted, having to cross a wide ditch left full of water by the rain overnight; it was fringed with tall trees and formed the left-hand boundary of the field at the entrance to which Fabrizio had bought the horse. Almost all the hussars had dismounted; the bank of the ditch was steep and very slippery and the water lay quite three or four feet below the level of the field. Fabrizio, distracted with joy, was thinking more of Marshal Ney and of glory than of his horse, which, being highly excited, jumped into the canal; thus splashing the water up to a considerable height. One of the generals was soaked to the skin by the sheet of water, and cried with an oath: 'Damn the f—— brute!' Fabrizio felt deeply hurt by this insult. 'Can I ask him to apologize?' he wondered. Meanwhile, to prove that he was not so clumsy after all, he set his horse to climb the opposite bank of the ditch; but it rose straight up and was five or six feet high. He had to abandon the attempt; then he rode up stream, his horse being up to its head in water, and at last found a sort of drinking-place. By this gentle slope he was easily able to reach the field on the other side of the canal. He was the first man of the escort to appear there; he started to trot proudly down the bank; below him, in the canal, the hussars were splashing about, somewhat embarrassed by their position, for in many places the water was five feet deep. Two or three horses took fright and began to swim, making an appalling mess. A serjeant noticed the manœuvre that this youngster, who looked so very unlike a soldier, had just carried out.

'Up here! There is a watering-place on the left!' he shouted, and in time they all crossed.

On reaching the farther bank, Fabrizio had found the generals there by themselves; the noise of the guns seemed to him to have doubled; and it was all he could do to hear the general whom he had given such a good soaking and who now shouted in his ear:

'Where did you get that horse?'

Fabrizio was so much upset that he answered in Italian:

'*L'ho comprato poco fa.* (I bought it just now.)'

'What's that you say?' cried the general.

But the din at that moment became so terrific that Fabrizio could not answer him. We must admit that our hero was very little of a hero at that moment. However, fear came to him only as a secondary consideration; he was principally shocked by the noise, which hurt his ears. The escort broke into a gallop; they crossed a large batch of tilled land which lay beyond the canal. And this field was strewn with dead.

'Red-coats! red-coats!' the hussars of the escort exclaimed joyfully, and at first Fabrizio did not understand; then he noticed that as a matter of fact almost all these bodies wore red uniforms. One detail made him shudder with horror; he observed that many of these unfortunate red-coats were still alive; they were calling out, evidently asking for help, and no one stopped to give it them. Our hero, being most humane, took every possible care that his horse should not tread upon any of the red-coats. The escort halted; Fabrizio, who was not paying sufficient attention to his military duty, galloped on, his eyes fixed on a wounded wretch in front of him.

'Will you halt, you young fool!' the serjeant shouted after him. Fabrizio discovered that he was twenty paces on the generals' right front, and precisely in the direction in which they were gazing through their glasses. As he came back to take his place behind the other hussars, who had halted a few paces in rear of them, he noticed the biggest of these generals who was speaking to his neighbour, a general also, in a tone of authority and almost of reprimand; he was swearing. Fabrizio could not contain his curiosity; and, in spite of the warning not to speak, given him by his friend the gaoler's wife, he composed a short sentence in good French, quite correct, and said to his neighbour:

'Who is that general who is *chewing up* the one next to him?'

'Gad, it's the Marshal!'

'What Marshal?'

'Marshal Ney, you fool! I say, where have you been serving?'

Fabrizio, although highly susceptible, had no thought of resenting this insult; he was studying, lost in childish admiration, the famous Prince de la Moskowa, the 'Bravest of the Brave'.

Suddenly they all moved off at full gallop. A few minutes later Fabrizio saw, twenty paces ahead of him, a ploughed field the surface of which was moving in a singular fashion. The furrows were full of water and the soil, very damp, which formed the ridges between these furrows kept flying off in little black lumps three or four feet into the air. Fabrizio noticed as he passed this curious effect; then his thoughts turned to dreaming of the Marshal and his glory. He heard a sharp cry close to him; two hussars fell struck by shot; and, when he looked back at them, they were already twenty paces behind the escort. What seemed to him horrible was a horse streaming with blood that was struggling on the ploughed land, its hooves caught in its own entrails; it was trying to follow the others: its blood ran down into the mire.

'Ah! So I am under fire at last!' he said to himself. 'I have seen shots fired!' he repeated with a sense of satisfaction. 'Now I am a real soldier.' At that moment, the escort began to go hell for leather, and our hero realized that it was shot from the guns that was making the earth fly up all round him. He looked vainly in the direction from which the balls were coming, he saw the white smoke of the battery at an enormous distance, and, in the thick of the steady and continuous rumble produced by the artillery fire, he seemed to hear shots discharged much closer at hand: he could not understand in the least what was happening.

At that moment, the generals and their escort dropped into a little road filled with water which ran five feet below the level of the fields.

The Marshal halted and looked again through his glasses. Fabrizio, this time, could examine him at his leisure. He found him to be very fair, with a big red face. 'We don't have any faces like that in Italy,' he said to himself. 'With my pale cheeks and chestnut hair, I shall never look like that,' he added despondently. To him these words implied: 'I shall never be a hero.' He looked at the hussars; with a solitary exception, all of them had yellow moustaches. If Fabrizio was studying the hussars of the escort, they were all studying him as well. Their stare made him blush, and, to get rid of his embarrassment, he turned his head towards the enemy. They consisted of widely extended lines of men in red, but, what greatly surprised him, these men seemed to be quite minute. Their long files, which were regiments or divisions, appeared no taller than hedges. A line of red cavalry were trotting in the direction of the sunken road along which the Marshal and his escort had begun to move at a walk, splashing through the mud. The smoke made it impossible to distinguish anything in the direction in which they were advancing; now and then one saw men moving at a gallop against this background of white smoke.

Suddenly, from the direction of the enemy, Fabrizio saw four men approaching hell for leather. 'Ah! We are attacked,' he said to himself; then he saw two of these men speak to the Marshal. One of the generals on the latter's staff set off at a gallop towards the enemy, followed by two hussars of the escort and by the four men who had just come up. After a little canal which they all crossed, Fabrizio found himself riding beside a serjeant who seemed a good-natured fellow. 'I must speak to this one,' he said to himself, 'then perhaps they'll stop staring at me.' He thought for a long time.

'Sir, this is the first time that I have been present at a battle,' he said at length to the serjeant. 'But is this a real battle?'

'Something like. But who are you?'

'I am the brother of a captain's wife.'

'And what is he called, your captain?'

Our hero was terribly embarrassed; he had never anticipated this question. Fortunately, the Marshal and his escort broke into a gallop. 'What French name shall I say?' he wondered. At last he remembered the name of the innkeeper with whom he had lodged in Paris; he brought his horse up to the serjeant's, and shouted to him at the top of his voice:

'Captain Meunier!' The other, not hearing properly in the roar of the guns, replied: 'Oh, Captain Teulier? Well, he's been killed.' 'Splendid,' thought Fabrizio. 'Captain Teulier; I must look sad.'

'Good God!' he cried; and assumed a piteous mien. They had left the sunken road and were crossing a small meadow, they were going hell for leather, shots were coming over again, the Marshal headed for a division of cavalry. The escort found themselves surrounded by dead and wounded men; but this sight had already ceased to make any impression on our hero; he had other things to think of.

While the escort was halted, he caught sight of the little cart of a *cantinière*, and his affection for this honourable corps sweeping aside every other consideration, set off at a gallop to join her.

'Stay where you are, curse you,' the serjeant shouted after him.

'What can he do to me here?' thought Fabrizio, and he continued to gallop towards the *cantinière*. When he put spurs to his horse, he had had some hope that it might be his good *cantinière* of the morning; the horse and the little cart bore a strong resemblance, but their owner was quite different, and our hero thought her appearance most forbidding. As he came up to her, Fabrizio heard her say: 'And he was such a fine looking man, too!' A very ugly sight awaited the new recruit; they were sawing off a cuirassier's leg at the thigh, a handsome young fellow of five feet ten. Fabrizio shut his eyes and drank four glasses of brandy straight off.

'How you do go for it, you boozer!' cried the *cantinière*. The brandy gave him an idea: 'I must buy the goodwill of my comrades, the hussars of the escort.'

'Give me the rest of the bottle,' he said to the *vivandière*.

'What do you mean,' was her answer, 'what's left there costs ten francs, on a day like this.'

As he rejoined the escort at a gallop:

'Ah! You're bringing us a drop of drink,' cried the serjeant. 'That was why you deserted, was it? Hand it over.'

The bottle went round, the last man to take it flung it in the air after drinking. 'Thank you, chum!' he cried to Fabrizio. All eyes were fastened on him kindly. This friendly gaze lifted a hundredweight from Fabrizio's heart; it was one of those hearts of too delicate tissue which require the friendship of those around it. So at last he had ceased to be looked at askance by his comrades, there was a bond between them! Fabrizio breathed a deep sigh of relief, then in a bold voice said to the serjeant:

'And if Captain Teulier has been killed, where shall I find my sister?' He fancied himself a little Machiavelli to be saying Teulier so naturally instead of Meunier.

'That's what you'll find out to-night,' was the serjeant's reply.

The escort moved on again and made for some divisions of infantry. Fabrizio felt quite drunk; he had taken too much brandy, he was rolling slightly in his saddle: he remembered most opportunely a favourite saying of his mother's coachman: 'When you've been lifting your elbow, look straight between your horse's ears, and do what the man next to you does.' The Marshal stopped for some time beside a number of cavalry units which he ordered to charge; but for an hour or two our hero was barely conscious of what was going on round about him. He was feeling extremely tired, and when his horse galloped he fell back on the saddle like a lump of lead.

Suddenly the serjeant called out to his men: 'Don't you see the Emperor, curse you!' Whereupon the escort shouted: '*Vive l'Empereur*'!

at the top of their voices. It may be imagined that our hero stared till his eyes started out of his head, but all he saw was some generals galloping, also followed by an escort. The long floating plumes of horsehair which the dragoons of the bodyguard wore on their helmets prevented him from distinguishing their faces. 'So I have missed seeing the Emperor on a field of battle, all because of those cursed glasses of brandy!' This reflexion brought him back to his senses.

They went down into a road filled with water, the horses wished to drink.

'So that was the Emperor who went past then?' he asked the man next to him.

'Why, surely, the one with no braid on his coat. How is it you didn't see him?' his comrade answered kindly. Fabrizio felt a strong desire to gallop after the Emperor's escort and embody himself in it. What a joy to go really to war in the train of that hero! It was for that that he had come to France. 'I am quite at liberty to do it,' he said to himself, 'for after all I have no other reason for being where I am but the will of my horse, which started galloping after these generals.'

What made Fabrizio decide to stay where he was was that the hussars, his new comrades, seemed so friendly towards him; he began to imagine himself the intimate friend of all the troopers with whom he had been galloping for the last few hours. He saw arise between them and himself that noble friendship of the heroes of Tasso and Ariosto. If he were to attach himself to the Emperor's escort, there would be fresh acquaintances to be made, perhaps they would look at him askance, for these other horsemen were dragoons, and he was wearing the hussar uniform like all the rest that were following the Marshal. The way in which they now looked at him set our hero on a pinnacle of happiness; he would have done anything in the world for his comrades; his mind and soul were in the clouds. Everything seemed to have assumed a new aspect now that he was among friends, he was dying to ask them various questions. 'But I am still a little drunk,' he said to himself, 'I must bear in mind what the gaoler's wife told me.' He noticed on leaving the sunken road that the escort was no longer with Marshal Ney; the general whom they were following was tall and thin, with a dry face and an awe-inspiring eye.

This general was none other than Comte d'A——, the Lieutenant Robert of the 15th of May, 1796. How delighted he would have been to meet Fabrizio del Dongo!

It was already some time since Fabrizio had noticed the earth flying off in black crumbs on being struck by shot; they came in rear of a regiment of cuirassiers, he could hear distinctly the rattle of the grape-shot against their breastplates, and saw several men fall.

The sun was now very low and had begun to set when the escort, emerging from a sunken road, mounted a little bank three or four feet high to enter a ploughed field. Fabrizio heard an odd little sound quite close to him: he turned his head, four men had fallen with their horses; the general himself had been unseated, but picked himself up, covered in blood. Fabrizio looked at the hussars who were lying on the ground: three of them were still making convulsive movements, the fourth cried: 'Pull me out!' The serjeant and two or three men had dismounted to assist the general who, leaning upon his aide-de-camp, was attempting to walk a few steps; he was trying to get away from his horse, which lay on the ground struggling and kicking out madly.

The serjeant came up to Fabrizio. At that moment our hero heard a voice say behind him and quite close to his ear: 'This is the only one that can still gallop.' He felt himself seized by the feet; they were taken out of the stirrups at the same time as someone caught him underneath the arms; he was lifted over his horse's tail and then allowed to slip to the ground, where he landed sitting.

The aide-de-camp took Fabrizio's horse by the bridle; the general, with the help of the serjeant, mounted and rode off at a gallop; he was quickly followed by the six men who were left of the escort. Fabrizio rose up in a fury, and began to run after them shouting: '*Ladri! Ladri!* (Thieves! Thieves!).' It was an amusing experience to run after horse-stealers across a battlefield.

The escort and the general, Comte d'A——, disappeared presently behind a row of willows. Fabrizio, blind with rage, also arrived at this line of willows; he found himself brought to a halt by a canal of considerable depth which he crossed. Then, on reaching the other side, he began swearing again as he saw once more, but far away in the distance, the general and his escort vanishing among the trees. 'Thieves! Thieves!' he cried, in French this time. In desperation, not so much at the loss of his horse as at the treachery to himself, he let himself sink down on the side of the ditch, tired out and dying of hunger. If his fine horse had been taken from him by the enemy, he would have thought no more about it; but to see himself betrayed and robbed by that serjeant whom he liked so much and by those hussars whom he regarded as brothers! That was what broke his heart. He could find no consolation for so great an infamy, and, leaning his back against a willow, began to shed hot tears. He abandoned one by one all those beautiful dreams of a chivalrous and sublime friendship, like that of the heroes of the *Gerusalemme Liberata*. To see death come to one was nothing, surrounded by heroic and tender hearts, by noble friends who clasp one by the hand as one yields one's dying breath! But to retain one's enthusiasm surrounded by a pack of vile scoundrels! Like all angry men Fabrizio exaggerated. After a quarter of an hour of this melting mood, he noticed that the guns were beginning to range on the row of trees in the shade of which he sat meditating. He rose and tried to find his bearings. He scanned those fields bounded by a wide canal and the row of pollard willows: he thought he knew where he was. He saw a body of infantry crossing the ditch and marching over the fields, a quarter of a league in front of him. 'I was just falling asleep,' he said to himself; 'I must see that I'm not taken prisoner.' And he put his best foot foremost. As he advanced, his mind was set at rest; he recognized the uniforms, the regiments by which he had been afraid of being cut off were French. He made a right incline so as to join them.

After the moral anguish of having been so shamefully betrayed and robbed, there came another which, at every moment, made itself felt more keenly; he was dying of hunger. It was therefore with infinite joy that after having walked, or rather run for ten minutes, he saw that the column of infantry, which also had been moving very rapidly, was halting to take up a position. A few minutes later, he was among the nearest of the soldiers.

'Friends, could you sell me a mouthful of bread?'

'I say, here's a fellow who thinks we're bakers!'

This harsh utterance and the general guffaw that followed it had a crushing effect on Fabrizio. So war was no longer that noble and universal uplifting of souls athirst for glory which he had imagined it to be from Napoleon's proclamations! He sat down, or rather let himself fall on the grass; he turned very pale. The soldier who had spoken to him, and who had stopped ten paces off to clean the lock of his musket with his handkerchief, came nearer and flung him a lump of bread; then, seeing that he did not pick it up, broke off a piece which he put in our hero's mouth. Fabrizio opened his eyes, and ate the bread without having the strength to speak. When at length he looked round for the soldier to pay him, he found himself alone; the men nearest to him were a hundred yards off and were marching. Mechanically he rose and followed them. He entered a wood; he was dropping with exhaustion, and already had begun to look round for a comfortable resting-place; but what was his delight on recognizing first of all the horse, then the cart, and finally the *cantinière* of that morning! She ran to him and was frightened by his appearance.

'Still going, my boy,' she said to him; 'you're wounded then? And where's your fine horse?' So saying she led him towards the cart, upon which she made him climb, supporting him under the arms. No sooner was he in the cart than our hero, utterly worn out, fell fast asleep.

*1925*

# R. H. MOTTRAM

## *Madeleine and George*

FROM 'THE SPANISH FARM'

HE was very much real Georges that day. He lay in bed until hunger forced him to rise, and then would neither dress nor shave. He was not of that type that lives on the interest of the past, nor hurriedly discounts the future. Nor can it be said that the thought of Lieutenant Skene crossed Madeleine's mind. Had it done so, she might have reflected how much more she loved this, her spoiled child, than that, her good one. But she, too, was absorbed in the present. She did not even remember the Ministry, whose service she had so peremptorily abandoned.

When the first gladness of reunion was slowing down into the assurance that she really had got him back, and had now only to devise how to keep him—a task she did not feel very difficult—she began to question him, very gently and indirectly, as to his plans. She remonstrated with him on the folly of their being there together, an object of interest to the concierge, still more on his insistence that she should stay there. But he only shouted that he would 'burst up' all the concierges, and she had to humour him and promise to stay for the present at least. Not that he threatened to leave her, but that she would not and could not threaten to leave him. At length, in the evening, as he sat in gown and slippers before the fire she had made, at the supper she had fetched and set, while she tidied the room strewn with his things, he began to think of her, asked for her father. He only asked one or two brief questions, not being the man to take deep interest in anything outside his own comfort. When she had answered, he just said: 'This sacred war!' Nothing else. But Madeleine knew what he meant. There it was, all round and over them, enveloping, threatening, thwarting. No less than he, she rebelled against it, in her decorous woman's way. But for him she rebelled against it twice over, hated it, made it responsible for his loss of health that was new, and his violence that was habitual—forgave him, on account of it, his carelessness of her—this way in which he wanted to live—the obvious fact that he had had other women in this room. She did not reflect upon her own record, then. But she coaxed him to take supper—she had bought the war-products that were nearest to the hare-paté and spicebread and confiture of old times—gave him a bowl of hot wine and water, as she had many a time that he had found her, he, glowing and triumphant, with a dog at his heels. And sure enough, under the spell of her magic, in that firelit bed-sitting room of the little flat in Paris, there came back, gradually but surely, the Georges of old days. His worn cheeks filled out, his eyes were less sunken, his hand less thin and shaky. He began to hold his head up and hum a tune. She hung near him, watching him, foreseeing not only every need, but every whim. He became almost liberal, expansive. He had fourteen days' 'convalo'—a visit every day to the hospital, which institution would not otherwise bother about him. At the end of that time he would either go back to hospital, or up to the front. He did not care which, he said, smiling. For the first time since she had rediscovered him, he did not call anything sacred, wish to 'burst' anyone, or use the expressive, untranslatable verb 'foutre'. She cleared away and tidied up and prepared herself for the night, as he sat glancing through the newspapers humming to himself, content, asking nothing. When he felt tired, he just turned out the light, and rolled into the place she had made warm for him.

* * * * *

Days so spent soon pass, nor is there anything more tragic than physical satiety, with its wiping out of what has gone before. Madeleine, not naturally apprehensive, would have gone on had not hard facts pulled her up. Georges had spent his pocket-money on paying the quarter's rent of their retreat. She had spent hers on food for him and herself. No bohemian, she began to take counsel with herself as to how to obtain fresh supplies. One source of funds she dismissed at once. She would not ask Georges for a penny. That would have seemed outrageous to her. She did not attempt it. She had a handsome sum in the Savings Bank at Hazebrouck. But how get it? She did not want to write to Monsieur Blanquart or to Marie. Even if they could have withdrawn it for her (and the difficulties of such a step she did not clearly foresee), they would both of them have found out sooner or later something about Georges. And that she would not have for all the world. Her father she could trust, but she also knew his ingrained habits regarding money, his incapacity for reading and writing. A letter would simply stupefy him. If he got some one to read it to him, he would simply be stupefied the more. His Madeleine spending her savings? Never! He would do nothing. Should she, then, go by train and get the money? There would be endless difficulties in getting authority to journey into the British Military Zone—but the great difficulty to her mind, the insurmountable one, was to leave Georges for two days. She was nonplussed.

Just then it happened that Georges, turning towards her in one of his more expansive moments, said, in his spoiled way: 'My God, how I want you!'

Occupied fully with him at the moment, her mind retained the words, her memory searching for the last occasion on which she had heard them. Georges went out to his club that morning, leaving her sewing, washing, doing a hundred and one jobs in her thorough housekeeper's way. She sat brooding, almost waiting for some stroke of luck to help her with her difficulty. Suddenly she remembered who it was that last used that phrase—Lieutenant Skene. She sat down at once and wrote to him. She had no scruples. All the English were rich. This one had no outlet for his money. She had been worth it. The reply came in three days, to the post-office address she had given. It brought a hundred francs. They lasted a week, and few people could have made them last more, save that Georges only came in to supper now. He was getting restless, smelled of drink. She wrote again to Skene. No reply came. Instead there came the end of the fortnight of Georges' 'convalo'. That day she sat alone waiting for two things, a letter bringing money, or Georges bringing fatal news. Either he was not well enough to go back to the front, so that his state must indeed be serious, or he was well enough, which was even worse. She dared not ask him; he vouchsafed nothing, seemed well enough, but restless. She, meanwhile, for the first time in her life was feeling really ill. She had never met before with this particular cruelty of Fate, resented it, but only felt worse. Perhaps the town life had sapped her vitality. Perhaps Georges had brought home from his hospital, on his clothes, in his breath, the germ of some war fever. The following day Georges was excited, and talked loud and long when he came back from the club. Her head felt so strange she did not understand.

* * * * *

Perhaps it was as well she did not. Georges had been granted another fortnight's 'convalo', but it was not that. It was the news of the battle of Vimy that excited him. The English, of whom he was good-humouredly jealous, had taken that battered ridge, disputed for years. There was talk of eleven thousand prisoners and a quantity of guns. He had missed being 'in it'. But with the news came rumour more important still. The French were preparing a great offensive in Champagne. He would not miss that one, sacred name, not he! The spirit of that period of the war, the spirit of 'On Les Aura' burned in his veins like fire. He strode and shouted about the room, cursing his 'convalo' that, a week ago, was all he desired, because now it prevented his being in the show.

Madeleine had the queerest feeling of all her life up to that day, for she was not a girl to faint—a sinking feeling, not painful, rather comforting. Then nothing. Then a reawakening, not so comfortable, dismay, weakness. Georges, who did nothing by halves, became, for the nonce, generous to the utmost limit of the nature of a man born with a silver spoon in his mouth and a cheque-book in the pocket of his first suit. Probably it never crossed his mind that she had taken infection from some carelessness of his. But he did better. He promptly called a young doctor of his set, who, having been badly wounded, was now permanently attached to the Paris garrison. Between affection for Georges and a handsome bribe—for the proceeding was thoroughly irregular—flat contrary to every by-law of the town and every order of the Medical Service—this young man took Madeleine in hand, visited her daily, did what was necessary in the way of prescribing, got a discreet sister of charity to nurse her. Being a man of the world, he further suggested to her, as soon as she was well enough to make inquiries, that she would not care for Georges to see her in her present state. That kept her quiet during the weeks of recovery. But there came a fine June day when she was well enough to walk out a little in a Paris ever more feverish and deserted. Then the young doctor, as thorough as Georges or herself, told her the truth. Georges' thoroughness had taken the form of borrowing the identity disc and pay-book of a hospital casualty whom he resembled in height and complexion. The young doctor had connived at the fraud, with the cynicism of Georges himself and all his set. Thus furnished, Georges had gone straight into the heart of that ghastly failure of the French in Champagne, during May, 1917. The hurried scrutiny of his credentials had not found him out, he was in the line and fighting when his half-recovered health broke down once more, and fatally. He was buried in a huge, ever-growing cemetery, near the Aerodrome, at Avenant-le-Petit.

* * * * *

When Madeleine realized it, she sat still, looking at nothing, gathering within her all her physical vitality to meet this blow to the spirit. On her face, refined by illness, was something of the look that horses have under heavy shell-fire, bewildered resistance to the unknown. The young doctor let her alone for twenty-four hours, and then very gently led her mind back to practical considerations. The period for which Georges had hired the flat was expiring shortly. Had she money, or the means of getting some? It did not take her long to run over the alternatives—an attempt to get back into some sort of office—or a begging letter to Skene? She avoided both, not from any sense of shame, but simply because now Paris and its life had no meaning for her. She had wanted Georges. She had said, 'If I could only see him!' She had seen him. Now she would never see him again. Why bother?

The young doctor then suggested that he could obtain her a permission to travel by train to Hazebrouck. This brought to her mind the almost certain death of her brother, Marcel, in his German prison camp, and of Marie's return to Laventie. The mere name of the market town called up at once associations so potent, so much more real than all that had happened since. The farm understaffed, the old father being swindled out of billeting money! Those were realities. Those things appealed to her more than this tragic dream-life. She accepted gladly the young doctor's offer, and left him looking after her and muttering: 'What a type, all the same!' But she had no special contempt or dislike for him.

She left Paris in the same way as she left him. The old sacred towers, the new garish restaurants, and keen bitter energy, the feminine grace, of that metropolis of the world, that had once again had the enemy at its gates, and was yet to be bombarded by such engines as had never before been turned upon city of man—she turned her back upon it all, and, for her, it was not. On a grey July day she entered the train. As she travelled homewards, the day grew greyer and wetter. She passed, unheeding, through an immense bustle between Abbeville and Calais, and down to St. Omer. Her train stopped frequently, and she glanced, uninterested, at the trains and trucks, materials and men, that choked rail and road. About her, people talked of the great offensive the English had begun, from Ypres to the sea. She looked at the crops and houses, thought of her father, whose very double, tall, old, dark-clothed, and bent, she saw in almost every teeming field of flax or hops, grain or roots, of that rich valley. Perhaps she had occasional bitter spasms of anger against this war, that had enslaved, and then destroyed Georges. But to her, facts were facts, and she did not deny them.

* * * * *

Outside Hazebrouck the train stopped interminably. The guns had been audible, loud and angry for some time, but the long roll of them was punctuated now by a sharper nearer sound, that clubbed one about the ears at regular intervals—artillery practising, no doubt, she thought. After waiting in the motionless train as long as she considered reasonable, she got out, finding a perverse satisfaction in the use of her limbs, swinging down the steep side of the second-class carriage of the Nord Railway, and asking for her box and 'cardboard' (containing hats) to be handed down to her. Shouldering these, she marched along the asphalt with which the prodigal English had reinforced the embankment, showing no concern at the cries of 'They bombard!' shouted to her by her fellow-passengers. She passed the engine, from which the driver and fireman were peering ahead. The fields were very deserted, but she was hardly the sort to be frightened in daylight, or dark either. She passed the points where the Dunkirk line joined that from St. Omer. Near by, stood a row of cottages, known as the 'Seven Chimneys', the first houses of Hazebrouck, on the station side. Her idea was to leave her trunk at the estaminet, for her father to fetch in the morning. To her astonishment, the whole row appeared deserted, empty, doors open, fires burning, food cooking. Somewhat nonplussed, she stopped a moment to get her breath, pushed her box behind the counter of the estaminet, where she was known, and then passed on, with her 'cardboard', keeping the path that separates the St. Omer road from the railway. Where this reached its highest point, just at the entry to the town, she happened to glance across the rich, lonely, hedgeless fields towards the Aire road, and saw, on that side, every wall and alley black with people. She had no time to reflect on this peculiarity before she was deafened by such a roaring upheaval of earth as she had certainly never imagined. It took away her breath, wrenched her 'cardboard' out of her hands. For some seconds she could hear nothing, see nothing, but when her senses returned, the first thing she noticed was the patter of falling debris. The shell had fallen in the ditch of the railway embankment, and made a hole the size of the midden at home, and three times as deep. She picked herself up from her knees, dusted herself, recaptured her 'cardboard', and passed on, greeted by a long 'Ah—a—ah!' from scores of throats of the spectators, a quarter of a mile away. The incident annoyed her. They were bombarding, and no mistake. But it would take worse than that to prevent her from crossing the railway under the arch, and taking the Calais road. The rue de St. Omer was empty, but undamaged. They were a jumpy lot, she thought; it revolted her to see all those good houses, left unlocked and open to all the ills that attack abandoned property. There was not even another shell-hole nearer than the station, so far as she could see. She would have liked a cup of coffee and a slice of bread, but the town was empty as an eggshell. She heard another explosion behind her as she reached the Calais pavé. The persistence of those Bosches! But she was persistent too, and gathered her damp clothes and battered 'cardboard' to her, as she strode vigorously home. She was not sentimental—no one less so, but it may well have been that her blood quickened, and her rooted strength returned, as she found herself, once more, facing that salt wind, under those low grey skies, among which she had been bred and born.

At length she came to the earth road, the signpost, and the turning, and saw the farm, the fringe of dead wallflower stalks on the ridge of the thatch, the old 'shot' tower by the bridge over the moat. It was between six and seven when she passed the brick-pillared gate, noted a new bomb-hole, and signs of military occupation. Entering by the door, she found her father in the passage.

'It's our Madeleine,' he said quietly.

Madeleine kissed him and told him to fetch her box in the morning, from 'Seven Chimneys'.

He said, 'Thy room is empty', and went into the kitchen, while she said a word to Berthe. It was true, her little room was just as she had left it a year before. She noted the fact with quiet satisfaction, but did not bother over the significance of it—over the fact that her father, who usually paid so little heed to anything that went on in the house, had kept her room untouched and empty for her. She quietly accepted the fact, conscious that he felt that neither the God to whom he muttered prayers on Sunday, nor the various temporal powers whom he obeyed, when he had to, on weekdays, really understood him or cared for him as his younger daughter did. She sat down with him, in the dim kitchen, to the evening meal, by the light of the day that was dying in thin drizzle and incessant mutter of guns. Once some fearful counter-barrage made the old panes of the oriel window rattle, and the old man said:

'It's a swine of a war, all the same!'

Madeleine replied: 'It's something new for them to be bombarded in Hazebrouck!'

'I'm going to take the money out of the Savings Bank,' he commented. In his mind, unused to the facilities of book-keeping, and cradled in the cult of the worsted stocking for savings, he probably thought of his money as being held in notes or coin in the stoutly-barred vault behind the Mairie. After a long pause, during which he surveyed her hands, busy with household mending, somewhat neglected since Marie had relinquished it to Berthe, he spoke again:

'You are quite a fine lady of the town!'

'That will soon pass,' she answered, without ceasing to ply her needle.

Later he said: 'You know Marie has returned to Laventie?'

Madeleine nodded. The remark was not so stupid as it sounded. He knew she knew the fact. It was his way of appealing to her.

'Now you have come back, you will be just the Madeleine you used to be, and all will go on as before, won't it?'

Her nod was all the answer he asked.

Once again he spoke: 'You know Marcel is dead?'

Again she nodded. Again it was only his way of saying, 'Come what may, you will see me through, we shall not be worse off for the cruelties of Fate!' She understood and acquiesced. Nothing else passed until with 'Good night, father,' and 'Good night, my girl,' they parted.

Of her life during the past twelve months and all it had contained, not a word.

*1926*

# RICHARD HUGHES

## *A Moment of Time*

'*THAT* was the end of the world,' he said, and sighed. 'It's all gone—finished.'

'I had not noticed it,' said I.

The eyes that regarded me were flecked with brown in the iris.

'No? No; perhaps some wouldn't. But there is no more Space, no Time, no Matter.'

'But there is,' said I. 'I can see a sunset in the sky, and there is a smoky mist in the hollows.'

'There is not,' said he.

'And I can hear that lame mare nicker.'

'You cannot,' said he.

'And the bank soaks through my breeches.'

'It does not,' said he.

'But to-day is Friday.'

'It is not,' said he.

'Yet you are still biting your black finger-nails.'

'I am not,' said he.

'And talking to me.'

'I am not,' said he. 'How could I be talking to you? The world is ended.'

'Then what is it I am seeing? Am I like a man struck blind who carries under his lids what he last set eyes on?'

'All your senses are clean cut off you like limbs, and you have only the illusion of them, as men do who have lost a leg or an arm.'

At that I was dismayed, because I have always taken a great delight in my senses. Then a little, melancholy, wandering smell wisped down the road: partly bitter, from the scent of a horse in it and some new whitewash.

'I don't believe you!' I cried suddenly.

'You do not,' said he, 'for you are destroyed too.'

'Will! Ynysfor!' I cried, in sudden panic, using his Bardic name. 'Ynysfor! If it's all Illusion, are you also destroyed? What are you, Will?'

'I AM *not*.'

'You deny that you exist, then?'

'I do not deny it: for if I do not exist, how can I deny?'

Then that many-coloured goat from Hafod Uchaf got up-wind from me. I could see him, and the wind brought him, and his small feet clicked on the rock. Somewhere very high up the lambs were yelling because of the frost between their two toes. Steadily the tide of mist rose, while the sun went down in a glory of cloudlets like little green fish-scales.

'I don't believe you!' I cried again. 'It's real, I tell you; *real.*'

'Have you never said to yourself in a dream, "Now I really am awake"?'

'Yes. But why should I dream all this?'

'Why are dreams ever dreamt?'

'They say, to save the mind from some shock too terrible for it.'

'And what shock could be more terrible than the ending of all things? The heavens are rolled up as a scroll: in the twinkling of an eye the earth, and all that in it is, consumed as with fire. What shock could be more violent than that?'

My hair tingled on to its ends with horror. 'I will not dream!' I cried. 'If I am a naked soul lost in the Absolute, at least I will know it! I dare not love Dream with the love I have given to the real world; I will count three, and wake! One—two——'

'You cannot,' said Ynysfor.

'Three!' So I opened my eyes. Darkness was quietly settling down among the hills, where the voices of plovers floated. Then I lay down on my face, and rubbed it in the wet grit of the road.

'I *will* wake up!' I cried.

'You will dream that your forehead is all bloody,' said Will. 'But how will that wake you? If there is no more Time, there is no Future: therefore you can never wake.'

I wiped the misty glass of my watch with my thumb.

'It is ten minutes since you told me that the world was ended.'

'The action of a dream may cover many weeks, and yet the dream itself only last a few seconds.'

'How long am I, then, dreaming this?'

'One moment of time—the moment of the world's ending.'

'And how long will the action of the dream last?'

'For ever. If there is no time, Eternity coincides with a moment. You can never cease dreaming.'

'But if I suffer Illusion, I exist: if I dream, I am. I cannot be cheated into a belief that I exist.'

'Suppose that you exist. . . .'

'Then *you*: have you no existence outside my dream?'

'If I have, it is in utter isolation. There is no more Space, therefore there can be no proximity, no communication, only utter isolation. For no soul can any other soul exist. If I do exist, in this isolation, how can I say "yes"? The communicative *me* you only dream.'

The moisture from the mist collected on my hair, and two drops rolled over the dried blood on my cheek.

'What you have been saying is a pack of paradox,' said I. 'Nothing can both be and not-be.'

'On the contrary, it is on the exact balance of Being and Not-being that existence depends. I will show it. All things—all Time, all Space, all Mind—*perish.* If Time could survive the destruction of Mind, then it would be possible for the act of destruction to become complete, then would Mind *have perished*: but because Time cannot survive it, the existence of all minds must hang for ever poised on a moment, the moment of their destruction, dreaming that Time and Space still are, exactly balanced in an eternal dead-lock between Being and Not-being. That is the infinite Dead-lock, causing the infinite, convincing Dream of men: and so an Illusion of Time, of Space, of Self, as still existent, arises.'

'In fact, the end of the world has made no difference whatever to anything,' said I. 'Since it is impossible to know that it has ended, everything goes on exactly as before. I might prove conclusively in some paper that the world had ended, and myself and that paper with it three issues before.'

'It makes absolutely no difference to you,' said Ynysfor, 'since you can't believe it.'

'Man! Man!' I cried, suddenly raging. 'What do you want to *make* me believe it for? If you know it is ended, why can't you keep silent?'

'It is the truth.'

'But you will never convince anyone.'

'Never.'

'But if we shall never know, it makes very little difference whether it be true or false.'

'No, no: perhaps not; to you.'

The scratches on my face were smarting. 'Not *now*,' I said.

'Now?' He played with the word, as if to remind me that it was meaningless.

Then a young girl trotted by on a grey mare, nervous of the lurking night. I stood up, and fitted my pipe to my teeth.

'I must get on with my dream,' I said; and left him.

*1926*

## PETER QUENNELL

### *Procne*

SO she became a bird and bird-like danced
On a long sloe-bough, treading the silver blossom
With a bird's lovely feet,
And shaken blossoms fell into the hands
Of sunlight, and he held them for a moment
And let them drop.
And in the autumn Procne came again
And leapt upon the crooked sloe-bough singing
And the dark berries winked like earth-dimmed beads,
As the branch swung beneath her dancing feet.

*1926*

## C. E. MONTAGUE

### *Man Afraid*

'May he dream of the Devil and wak in a fright.'

*Old Curse*

I

AS I walked to our village to-day, after breakfast, a big and handsome tramp was lying asleep on the strip of hot grass by the road. The high midsummer sun shone benedictively down on the man's up-turned face. But the face was troubled. Neither beer nor skittles could possibly have been the theme of that fellow's dreams. An hour later I came back that way. The wanderer still slept. But he had rolled over on to his front. His face was buried in the grass as a child buries his in a cushion, to shut out the sight of some frightful object.

I had to go down to the village again after luncheon. The tramp was sitting up now, with his back to a low wall of stones. He looked a degree more professional, too: he gave me good-day in the coming-on manner of competent tramps; nor did he hide a pipe which needed only tobacco and a match in order to achieve the highest purpose of its being. To render it easy for others to do what you wish is the essence of all diplomacy. This practitioner of the business made it perfectly easy for me to produce my pouch, followed by my matches, to hand them to him and then to fill my own pipe and to take a seat on the wall, not far from his head. But all this he did in a half-absent way, like a man who is waiting for some momentous hour to strike while he gives perfunctory chat to people round him.

Somebody in Homer says that all tramps come from God. I am not quite so sure. But some of them still talk the good English that tastes like a nut, though the schools and the press are scouring it so swiftly off the face of this island. Besides, I was piqued by the odd way Black Care had eaten into this fellow's face. It was a face quite remarkably virile in shape. Indeed it was the face that sculptors, in all ages, seem to have agreed to give to Roman private soldiers. And it was burnt a very deep, rich, even brown. He only needed a helmet, of the right make, to resemble a classic warrior done in bronze—except that his countenance had acquired one of the completest sets of taut, minute and circumstantial wrinkles that I had ever seen, bar photographs of aged Cardinals and portraits by Rembrandt.

II

From the grand weather our talk shifted round to the vagabond's past. It was I made it shift. He showed no itch to be gabbing or bucking, like most of us middle-aged men, about the uncommonness of his youth—and that though most of his forty-eight years had clearly been active; these lives that are given to action in their spring are apt to be given, in their autumn, still more plenteously to words. I had to draw from him forcibly, as with a corkscrew, that he was born in the County Kildare, where all the talk is of horses; that his mother had died at his birth; and that his father had taken him out, at the age of some two years, to New South Wales.

There, at the ripe age of ten, my new friend's first adventure had matured. As he recalled it, a little animation came into his voice. He was to ride a rogue horse which his father's employer had entered for an up-country handicap on the flat. This malignant was given the minimum weight—5st. 6 lb.—in justice to an inveterate hobby it had of stopping, half-way through a race, in order to savage its jockey at leisure in that quiet part of the course. My man's eye began to take light now, as he revived the state of expectation in which he had thrown his infant leg across this carnivorous animal. His voice quickened.

' "What you got to do, Gnat O'Brine," says the master to me, "is jus' get 'im off, if you can, and then sit on 'im, sly-like an' secret. Let 'im think you ain't there. 'Ide from 'im, that 's a good boy, so 's 'e won't bite your knees off."

'I kep' myself out of his thoughts so successf'ly that we were left at the post for a consid'rable time. Then that tiger percaived that the others were gone, an' off he went beltin' after, wishful to kick them. You don't know Australian racin'—no? Well, it 's little ye lose. An

Australian course is nothin' at all, only dust. Be the time we were movin', there wasn't a horse to be seen in the world; only a fat cloud of dust—it hid all. We lep' into the back of that cloud, like a boy leppin' over a fire of weeds in a field, and it smoking sulky. From that out I saw nothin' at all for a very long while, savin' one pair of heels that gev a fling up at us out of the fog of the dust an' flicked me kind Angel of Death on the nose. That med him madder than ever to butcher the whole of the field. Now, if only he had a low motive to show ut, that horse was a flyer. He flew an' he flew, seekin' prey, till, be cripes, the fog thinned to our front, an' out we came into the light of day, with the crowd on th' off side of us screamin' "The cannibal wins," an' the red winning-post slidin' past on me left, before that divvil discovered his error an offered to ait me. Hurt, do ye say? Is ut frikened? Not a tittle. Ye know where ye are with a horse.'

While he recalled the old race I could almost see the fumes of a happy intoxicant rise to his brain. Before he began he had been like a man who suspects that the crust of the earth may be only a trap-door, to let him down into a pit underneath. Then, when he warmed to his story, you might suppose he had quite forgotten the pit. But at the end of the story the cheerful glow seemed to fade from him quickly. He was the man on the trap-door again. 'The time ye'd be frikened,' he said with conviction, not to say gloom, 'is the time ye'd not know where ye are, an' the time there 's nothin' at all to do in the world, only think of the power of things do be waiting to hurt you.' He puffed his pipe with an air of the darkest determination. A man looks like that when he wants tobacco to help him to drive away care, but is not at all sure that the enemy won't down the two of them.

III

I had to say something or other. I asked, did O'Brine strike it rich, after that, on the plan of letting them run their own race?

'For three years an' a bit,' he said, quite dully now, 'I was a jockey be trade—first on the flat, an' then over the sticks, me weight growing excissive.'

I could believe it. Lean as he is to-day, he must still weigh thirteen stone good.

O'Brine viewed me and my vain curiosity with melancholy eyes, like Age watching sadly the blundering capers of blindfolded Youth. 'A gran', stirrin' life, would ye think ut? Ye'd be astounded to feel the tejiousness of ut the time ye were that aisy in doin' the work that your mind 'd be free to bedivvil itself with worryin' over the turrible things that are loose in the world—aye an' you in the act, it mebbe, of takin' a very enjoyable lep.'

To my poor plain mind this seemed a hard saying. I asked did he mean that his nerve would give way at a jump?

The notion evidently struck him as absurd. 'Ach! not at all. Ye'd know where ye were with a hurdle. The divvil and all of ut was that the leppin' itself got to be no distraction at all from the state I was in. I'd have the fear on me, an' me goin' over a fence an' a brook, as voilent as if I were walkin' about in the fields with nothin' to take me mind off.'

Ah! I began to see now. 'The end of ut was,' he went on, 'that I ran away to sea in desprit hopes of routin' the tim'rousness out of me. For a year an' a half I folla'd the sea; an' mebbe ye'll think me an ijjut, an' mebbe ye'll see what I mean, when I say there was only a week of that time when me mind had seren'ty an' rest, an' that was a foul-weather week we were roundin' the Horn wid a very fair share of the cargo on fire. It 's not that I've ever been one o' the fools do be askin' for dangers—God knows it 's safety I'm chasin', the whole of me life. An' yet those were the good days, the Divvil knows why.'

His large eyes were regaining their lustre. 'That fire was deep away down in the hold; no way to reach it at all; an' there it stayed, burnin' and burnin' away till a good fourth part o' the ship was a match for a kettle—only kep' from bein' perished and all of red-hotness be havin' water one side of itself though the fire 's the other. A grand wind was blowing; it kep' the tub well on the roll, the way her port plates would no sooner be gettin' as red as a horse's shoe in a forge than th' cntirc port side of her'd dip pretty nigh gunwale-under so 's the sea'd be hissin' with steam, an' the ship's dhrunken colour quickly rejuced. It was work, work, work, for the pack of us, bestin' the fire an' bestin' the sea; but all the time ye were at it ye knew where ye were an' your life was singin' itself like a chune. But what 's a week in a year an' a half? Nothin' at all.'

O'Brine's face had fallen again. As I saw it I pictured the glow dying off the ship's side when the cold water rose to it. Lifelessly he continued. 'For anny man who'd be apt to take fright at the world, the sea is no place to be on. Hours an' hours there'll be at a time, an' you waitin' there for an order to come, an' your mind lyin' out unprotected for anny ol' dread that would rush at it out of nowhere at all. In me terror I quitted the sea an' went back to me fawther, the way of the Prodigal Son, to take the beltin' I knew I should get, an' look after the pigs an' the poulthry.

'For a year I enjured ut. An' then—ye know the way that it is with a boy. Annywhere else in the worl', excep' just where he is! Everywhere else is the place where the great doin's are an' the dragons are waitin' for him to put ut all over them an' to obtain the peace that the worl' cannot give. An' then Ballon's Circus came round.

'Ach! that was the circus! Lions an' bears an' an el'phant itself, an' Ballon giving ut out he was seeking a steady apprentus to managing lions an' bears. Then I knew in the wink of an eye it was this I'd been wanting, the whole of a year. Sick I had been with the fear of the Divvil knows what at the pit of me stomach. When that is the case the wan thing that'll give you your aise is having ut out with a beast or a sea or a fire or anny ol' thing that'll keep you busy an' happy endeav'rin' not to be killed. An' that's how I couldn't resist having thruck with the lions.'

I asked how the cure had answered.

'Cure? There's no cure in ut,' he said discontentedly. 'Lions are not what ye read in the papers at all. Ye'd think, by the way people talk, every lion ye'd meet would be raging to eat ye. He is not. It's mere van'ty. Why, what in the name o' good sinse, is a man to a lion? A middlin' piece of beef, done up in a sthringy ould bundle of clothes. Put yourself in his place. Would ye rush at a good chop itself, an' it smothered in flannels an' tweeds would wring the teeth out of your head? No more would a lion, with good naked meat to be had, an' he used to captiv'ty an' quit of the foolish ambish'n the wild lions do have to do their own killing always. Lions! Nothing *to* them. An' so I schemed an' contrived till they shifted me pitch from tamin' lions to walking a rope of the Blondin or out-door vari'ty—walking an' cap'ring an' wheeling a barrow, that has a great groove to its wheel, along a monsthrous cable forty feet up in the air, or a hundhred itself, to suit the surroundin's.'

'Well?' I inquired, with sympathy. Could there be nothing risky enough to quench the thirst of this 'timorous' man for perils to outface?

'Only the ould, ould story,' he avowed ruefully. 'Danger, is ut? No, but a fraud on the public. Anny time that ye're out in the street the sthrip of pavement ye'd use would not be the width of a rope-walkin' rope. An' what good would ye get from the rest of the street? An' what's more, d'y' ever hear of a man, or a woman itself, bein' killed be walkin' a rope—aye or swallowin' fire or swords? No, an' nobody has, in th' entire histhory of the world, though there's men droppin' dead on the flat of the road every day, or falling under the cars. An' the reason is plain. A hundhred feet up in the air is a hundhred good reasons for givin' your mind to what ye're about an' not leaving it go tormintin' itself about the precar'sness of human affairs. The soul of you 's filled an' at peace, instid of the poor way it's in when there's nothin' at all has got to be done an' your inside is empty an' swep' an' invitin' every terr'fyin' divvil that's loose in the world to come in an' desthroy. So I was in Hivvin the time I was learning me stunts on the rope, an' li'ble to slip. But the instiant I had the trade learned, so 's I couldn't fall off if I tried, all the good of ut came to an end an' me sense of secur'ty was ruined.'

Neither I nor my printer possesses the means of emphasis needed to give you any measure of the bitter earnestness that rasped in the urgently logical voice of O'Brine. He then paused for a while and viewed with a profound uneasiness the pastoral tranquillity of western Oxfordshire. The man's immense virility of body, his Roman legionary face, his look of lifelong converse with astringent winds and cheerful suns, and then his stricken sense of some infinite, unfixable and unaccountable unfriendliness hemming him in like an atmosphere—all these together formed a tragi-comic contrast that kept me piqued and curious. Somehow I knew that if an armed madman, eager to kill, had come down the road at that moment, O'Brine would have got up and stopped him while I should have tried to look as if I had not observed the phenomenon. And yet I had a quiet mind, as minds go, while fear gnawed O'Brine. 'Very apt I'd ha' been,' he resumed, 'to go mad if the War hadn't come, to bring me a little disthraction.'

## IV

Yes, I had just been wondering what the big smash might have brought to a being like this—imperturbable while any actual danger gave him its tiger jaws to look into, and yet so perturbed when that strong pick-me-up was not to be had. I asked him.

He answered sombrely at first. The War? Be all I've heard, there was great excitement in Europe—men bein' hayroes an' every sort of gran' hullabaloo. But we were out and away at the back of beyant, in German East Africa. All the plain stuff that there was in the War must ha' been dumped in East Africa. Every year we bet the Germans: some diff'rent gen'ral went back every year to the great worl' an' said that he'd won. An' then another came out. Schultz said it loudest, so he got the glory. But divvil a German could anyone see, an' no fightin' at all. So I wangled me way to a hospital ordherly's job where promotion was good because most of the lot were weak creatures would not last a fortnight, but if ye did that ye might live the duration.'

As he spoke a faint spark was kindling again in O'Brine's joyless eye. He went on, the spark brightening a little. 'Four grand huts there were to that hospital, an' they were spesh'lised intinsely. Each disease went into the hut that became it. All the chol'ra an' dysenthry cases in one. They had Epsom salts. All the shiv'rers were put in another. Theirs was quinine. The ones that were tied up in knots had a hut to themselves because they were going surely to die, for they had sleeping sickness. Cases couldn't be asked how they felt, because they had thirty-five diff'rent languages, every one of them diff'cult, an' me an' the Med'cal Off'cer had English only. I'd go round in the morning an' count what had died in the night, an' then we'd go after the beasts an' the butterflies in the bush—ye see, the M.O. was a great man of sci'nce—an' then I'd go round the wards in the evening again.

'There was nobody lived very long in that place. It was right up agin the Equator. A donkey would die in three weeks. There were four hundred beds in me hospital an', on an average, twenty would die in a night. Me first commandant died in five weeks. He was the butterfly man. Me second stuck it out a full six weeks before we buried him. I was the only Eur'pean that didn' peg out in one way or another.'

The eyes of O'Brine were growing almost brilliant. He was no longer peering at the sun-filled landscape as if it might bite him. He went on with increasing gusto. 'The fact is, ye had to be careful. Wheriver the temp'rachure in the sun is a hundhred an' forty, there 's this, that an' th' other attimptin' to play little games wi' you. Flies come an' lay their eggs under your skin. There 's a bean has a pollen will irr'tate your face till I've seen a man lep into water was crawlin' with crocodiles, just to be quit of the itch of ut. Then there 's puff adders will lie on the groun' in the shadows be moonlight an' offer to bite at your leg the way you're due to die in the nex' fifty seconds. But all ye'd need to do is just to be careful.'

For the first time O'Brine was talking with absolute relish. He went on expanding. 'F'rinstance, far too much is made of the pythons they have in those parts. Divvil a python will hurt ye as long as he hasn't a sizeable branch of a tree to belay himself to, with a bend of his tail, the way he can lever the whole of his stren'th out to squash ye. That 's how a man knows where he is with a python. Hol' down his tail an' ye have him perplexed, for want of the lev'rage. Besides, he 's a mod'rate eater, desirin' a meal not above twice or three times in a twelvemonth—about a goat at a time—an' then he'll swallow ut whole and the horns of the goat do be stickin' out far, through the skin of the python, till the digestive proceedin's inside will dhraw the flesh off from all roun' the roots of the horns, an' the horns dhrop away from th' outside of the python's abdomen, an' so he 's all right. With an an'mal like that, one that 's not rushin' up an' down daily, ragin' for victuals, there 's no insecur'ty to speak of.'

For the moment O'Brine was rattling away with the whole-hearted delight of any good Irishman in a good course of adventure. He even went on, without pressing, to a new chapter of his experiences. 'Some o' the natives were lads, an' no questhion. One day I was sitting alone in the hospital yard an' a mob o' them came rushin' in. Ravin' they were, an' foamin', fit to wear bibs. No off'cer bein' on duty, they did the whilla-balooin' at me that knew sorra a word of the five-an'-thirty lingoes they swore in. However, I'd heard from me infancy out, how dimmocracy was the plan of lettin' everyone talk at the top of his voice before doin' the thing that came into your head. So I dimmocratised them. I had them shoutin' the odds for a space of two hours, an' me given' the shindy a very fair hearin', as if I were takin' it in, an' then I gev out, be the language of signs, they must dig me a hell of a trench to bury the dead we had in the place. That set them off roarin' with laughter, the Divvil knows why, an' they went off an' did ut. 'Twas manny days later I heard they'd come up to destroy ev'ry soul because some black quarthermaster was thievin' their rations. I was surprised. There hadn't been annythin' terr'ble about them at all. Th' absurdity was that they gev me a medal'—I saw that he wore, almost out of sight on his waistcoat, the treasurable ribbon of the D.C.M., which always means stout work—'for "quellin' at th' outset a dang'rous native risin'." It was the greatest mistake.'

His voice had filled out while he spoke of the riot. It was a wondrous fine voice, indescribably manly, like those of some great tenor singers and some wind instruments. And then, when he spoke again, the voice's round fulness had sagged into something argumentative and almost pettish. 'As if annyone didn't know where he was with a nigger! The time ye've a right to be given a medal for livin' at all is the time ye're up agin nothing on earth, but the fear 's in yourself, the way a man would have thirst in himself though porter an' beer an' every partic'lar drink that there is had never been made—only the thirst of him achin' out into space, an' fear is the same.'

The kindly fumes that had risen to gladden his brain while his recollections of sun-stroke and pestilence, murderous reptiles and murderous men, possessed him, had passed away utterly now.

## V

From the place where we sat I could see nothing to scare any man. Beyond the very low wall on the other side of the road, the ground fell away in a long easy slope. At the foot of the slope, unseen among trees, I knew the infant Thames to be playing quietly in his nursery, nine miles away. Far beyond that, and the sylvan Vale of White Horse, one's eyes came to rest on the dim blue that blurred Lambourn Down. Rest, rest—everything had rest. No air was stirring. Half-way down the sky the sun himself seemed to have turned as lazy as everything else: he paused for a while on his way. Warm, pensive and indolent, all the visible landscape lay outstretched and basking. Quite unsuspiciously it accepted the golden day's benediction. 'Well, it feels pretty safe here,' I said, very sincerely.

He turned his head quickly. I found his eyes curiously searching. 'Are ye sure?' he said shrewdly. 'Wouldn't ye think it would be jus' the time that the will of God would be sloshin's down at the two of us out of the sky, an' it the blue that it is?'

In the sabbatical peace of the hour I heard the familiar voice of one of my own hens, far, far away, rejoicing sleepily that unto her an egg was born. 'Why bother about the off chance of a knock?' I said. 'What can we do?'

'An' isn't that jus' the bother?' he argued tormentedly. 'If there was even the teeniest whiff of a smell of anny partic'lar danger, ye'd know where ye were, an' what to mind out for. The dreadfullest danger there is, an' the one that ye can never be quit of, is not knowin' what to mind out for.'

I brooded on that. In the course of my brooding there came to my mind a beautiful road, lined with trees, that runs into the town of Arras. During part of the War it was looked down upon by many invisible enemies' eyes. So it lay out in the sun for at least a whole summer, shunned like something accursed, all its excellent surface touched by no feet except those of the terror that walketh by noon-day. Well, this goodly frame the earth, I mused, must have become like that road for this luckless O'Brine. No: much worse. For at Arras the peril that could not be seen had at least an easily imaginable form: O'Brine would probably have exulted in bluffing the hidden Fritz snipers. Only here, in the deep peace of an idyllic countryside, could the malign infestation of space reach its dread maximum of ungraspable vagueness. Wherever his uncommon sensibility to fear found any solid object of apprehension to deal with, he was already well on the way to relief; the need for instant action set him free and made him tranquil. A lion, a python, a foundering ship or a race in the dark on a man-eating horse—any of these would let loose the passion and power to fight the thing through. The trouble only returned when every palpable object of terror was gone. Then the man's power of fearing would 'race' like the screw of a ship when it has no water against which to put forth its strength.

O'Brine was positively haggard by this time. I never saw a man further away from the blest state of those devotees who can say with the uttermost force of belief 'The Lord is my keeper' and go about honestly feeling that they are looked after in their goings out and in their comings in. O'Brine had become like a man who at any moment might cry out 'Help! Help!' The fear staring out of his eyes was so real that—well, it almost seemed to compromise all the pleasant things round us, since this was the best they could do for a great healthy Hercules of a man who had given his proofs by land and sea, fire and air. Even I, stolid lump as I am, felt that the fair scene was becoming a little unnerved under the intense suspicion of his gaze: his fear breathed so hard as to tarnish the mirroring candour of day. I had to shiver a little, for all the mothering warmth of that afternoon sun.

The tormented O'Brine must have come to the end of his power of taking rest. He gave a half roll-over from his seat, to lever up his stiff body. 'I must be leggin' it on,' he said, 'into Lechlade.'

I offered the farewell gifts of a friend. These he received with the courtesy of his nation. But what could I give? Only a short-lived command of the bread, the beer and the 'baccy that perish—not liberation, even for a moment, from the curiously compounded self which is one's fate. However, he gave handsome thanks: 'May the blessing of God stay with ye always an' keep the fear from ye.'

I watched him slouching down the white road rather hurriedly, with his great shoulders much bent. He looked far more than forty-eight, from behind. Black Care must weigh a lot, I thought. And no hope of relief for the poor devil, either, unless a bull with a temper should break loose on the road, or fire or small-pox visit some casual ward where he lay.

*1928*

# T. F. POWYS

## *I Came as a Bride*

A MUDDY lane led from the Maidenbridge Road to Walberton. Upon either side of the lane there were wide ditches that, even in summer time, were never dry. The lane went along for a mile and then Walberton was reached.

If the lane was muddy the village was more so, for all the cottages seemed to be splashed by the dirt, and even Walberton Hall, though now owned by good Mr. Cobb, who endeavoured to enjoy the mud as well as he could, was built in the mire. In Walberton it was best to believe that all the world is dirt and each man and woman but a walking part of it, for so each seemed to be when out of doors.

Mr. Cobb had come to Walberton to be alone, and he certainly succeeded, for the mud of the lane kept all his friends away, and, with the exception of his housekeeper, Mrs. Williams—for Mr. Cobb had no wife to care for him—and Wicks the gardener, he saw scarcely anyone—though once he saw the bride.

Mr. Cobb had come to Walberton an old man, and he did but wait, in no unfriendly manner, an event that would at least place him beyond all ugliness and release him for ever from a very muddy world, and yet he felt strangely startled when he saw the bride.

It was a night in winter when a cloud that resembled, both in colour and in kind, the mud of the lanes and fields of the village, as cold as the frozen air could make it, hung down over Walberton, out of which was squeezed by the black hands of the night great drops of rain. As there was a moon, though the night was so gloomy, it was not altogether dark and, before going to bed, Mr. Cobb extinguished the dining-room lamp, stayed for a moment by the window and looked out.

Mr. Cobb was too good to be afraid, but he certainly felt a little strangely when he saw a young girl, dressed in a wedding frock and wearing white shoes and stockings, step quickly along the drive and knock at the door.

A sensation that approached excitement hurried Mr. Cobb to the door, which he threw widely open, for he knew well enough the honour and consideration that is due to a bride. He saw no one.

Although during the night the rain had changed to snow, the clean white dress that it had given to the village was gone again by the morning and Walberton had returned to its old state of mud and slush.

Mr. Cobb could not forget the look of his ghostly visitor. He took up a book and read:

Her face too dazzling for the sight,
Her winning coyness fires my soul,
I feel a strange delight.

He sat in his study after breakfast and, ringing the bell for his housekeeper, he asked to see Mr. Wicks.

Mr. Wicks came in a hurry, holding a blacking-brush that he had just been using upon his master's boots.

'Wicks,' said Mr. Cobb, 'last night, when I looked out of the window, I saw——'

'Ah,' said Wicks, 'I know very well what you are going to say. You saw the bride of Walberton, sir.'

'Tell me about her, Wicks,' said Mr. Cobb, 'and I must say to you that, old as I am, I would have laid my heart at her feet, had she come as a live bride, instead of a ghostly presence, to Walberton.'

'I would to God you had, sir,' replied Wicks, feeling for his handkerchief, but finding none he wiped his eyes with the blacking-brush.

'Ah,' said Mr. Wicks, 'most of we have seen the bride about this time of the year, and 'tis said she won't never rest quiet until someone be willing to husband her and to lie beside her in the bed where she be.'

'The grave,' said Mr. Cobb.

Wicks nodded.

'The bride came to Walberton,' said Wicks, 'when Squire Goddy was owner here, and he were a man who liked a young maid.'

'I have heard of him,' said Mr. Cobb, 'for I purchased the estate from his heirs.'

'I mind the bride coming well,' said Wicks. ' 'Twas a cold snowy day when she did come, but though the snow fell it turned to mud and water in Walberton. I do mind the night well. Mr. Goddy had been staying at Maidenbridge, and it chanced that the pretty maid was a servant in his friend's house, and Mr. Goddy had a mind to her and said, jokingly maybe, "Come as my bride to Walberton."

'The bride were a poor girl, and she had only her black servant's frock to walk in, and 'tis twenty miles from Maidenbridge to Walberton. She were a pretty meek thing, same as some be who dream of weddings.

' 'Twas her afternoon out, and so she did start walking, saying to sheself, to make the way seem shorter, "I be going as a bride to Walberton."

' 'Twas a cold day for she to walk so far, but she went along well enough, telling her story in the villages that she passed, and though some didn't believe her there were some who did.

'At Norbury one old wife, Mrs. Balliboy, cried, when she heard the bride's tale.

' "But where be thee's frock?" Mrs. Balliboy asked of the bride, "where be thee's wedding clothes?"

' "I have none," the maid answered, "but I did hope that someone upon the road might give me a dress."

'Mrs. Balliboy took her own wedding-dress—'twas old and belonged to forgotten times, but 'twas white and clean.

' "Take it and welcome," she said, "for 'tis another kind of clothes that I'd best be thinking of."—Mrs. Balliboy kissed the bride.

'At Dodder the bride knocked at another door and old Potten who was standing near did listen to her tale. Potten did nod at she and look at her dress.

' " 'Tis white stockings thee do want," he said. Potten stepped into the doorway and called. "Here, wold 'oman," he shouted, "a maid be going as a bride to Walberton, so do 'ee give she they white stockings that thee do hoard and save for thee's own burial." '

'And did Mrs. Potten give them to her?' asked Mr. Cobb.

'She did,' replied Wicks, 'and 'tweren't long before the bride were in Madder and a girl did say, when she heard where she was going, "I will give thee a pair of white shoes, for I do only cry over them every night time, for they bain't needed now."

'The bride walked on, trying to keep they white shoes clean. She walked gaily and thought of all the happiness that was to come when she was a wedded woman. She stopped once more at me brother's house, that be upon the main road before the turn to Walberton, and I were told what she looked like then.

'She were a little thing with a small cherry mouth and eyes as soft as any heifer's be. She were womanly too, wi' the body of a pretty breeder, and she held herself up proudly as any bride should do. She did ask her way to Walberton, and brother John, who do buy and sell straw and hay, did invite her into front room.

' "Thee be a walking bride," said John, 'but where be thee going?'

' "I am going to wed Mr. Goddy," she said boldly.

'Brother John did look foolish when she named the Squire, and the little children did creep into corners, for there weren't one of them that hadn't felt the lash of Mr. Goddy's riding-whip one time or another. Brother John's wife be a woman——'

'I do not doubt you,' said Mr. Cobb, smiling.

' "Mr. Goddy has a wife already," she said, "and so thee best take and go home, for I do fancy thee be nothing only a street-walker."

' "I don't believe you," answered the bride. 'No gentleman would ask a young maid to come as his bride if he were married already. I will not stay to be mocked."

'Brother John opened the door to her.

' " 'Tis the first muddy turn on the left," he said, "and some folks' true lies be meant for kindness."

'The bride took the lane, and however much she tried to keep her shoes clean they were soon soaked and spoiled, and though the rain hadn't yet begun there was a thick low-hanging mist ahead.'

Mr. Wicks gently rubbed his knee with the blacking-brush.

'I was groom at the Hall then, and I mind the night well, for Squire had his friends there and I did bide late to tend their horses. I think it were Farmer Pardy who had just driven away, and I did stand and look, for someone was coming.

' 'Twas a young girl, and when she came to me she said quietly, "I be come as a bride."

'I did stand back a little when she said that, for I thought the maid mid be mad. But there was no madness in her eyes, only excitement and hope. And then 'twas that I thought Squire had beguiled her there with his wicked ways.

' "Do 'ee go home quick, young maid," I said, "for Squire be worse than any Bluebeard."

'The bride held her head high and went by me and rang the bell that hung beside the great open door. I do mind the clatter of 'en now. An old witch woman who did serve Squire did come to her, and I did go to the great window and peeped in.

'The fire roared in the hearth. Farmer Mew and James Andrews were drinking wine, and Squire were leaning back wi' his glass filled before him. The door opened then and the bride entered.

'The Squire leaned back and laughed. But she wasn't abashed; she went and knelt to him.

' "I am come as your bride," she said. . . .

'The bride was given a cotttage to live in, that no one else didn't want, and she were made to work on the home farm, for Mrs. Goddy wouldn't let she bide in house after what happened that night.

' 'Twas mud upon the bride then, mud and mire, but she would work hard and did still say to folk that she came as a bride.

' 'Twas as much as we all did expect that when her dead child were born she had no strength to live, and 'twas heard about from one to another that "the bride be a-dying".

' 'Tis strange,' said Mr. Wicks thoughtfully, 'how religious me wold 'oman be.'

'I am glad to hear it,' said Mr. Cobb.

'She did tend the bride when her mind did wander,' continued the gardener, 'and the bride were too far gone to notice that her baby was dead.

' "I be going as a bride," she said, but did forget the name of village.

'Me woman leant over she.

' "Thee be going as a bride," she did say. "The bridegroom awaits you and in woon moment thee'll be saying in Paradise, 'I came as a bride'." '

*1928*

# HAROLD MONRO

## *The Terrible Door*

TOO long outside your door I have shivered.
You open it? I will not stay.
I'm haunted by your ashen beauty.
Take back your hand. I have gone away.

Don't talk, but move to that near corner.
I loathe the long cold shadow here.
We will stand a moment in the lamplight,
Until I watch you hard and near.

Happy release! Good-bye for ever!
Here at the corner we say good-bye.
But if you want me, if you do need me,
Who waits, at the terrible door, but I?

*1928*

Drawing by Gilbert Spencer, 1929, for the title-page of T. F. Powys's *Kindness in a Corner*

# H. J. C. GRIERSON

## *The Renaissance*

FROM 'CROSS CURRENTS IN ENGLISH LITERATURE OF THE XVIIth CENTURY'

IN speaking of the Renaissance I shall not take as typical such extreme manifestations as the Italian tyrants, or even such characters as Benvenuto Cellini or Machiavelli or Aretino. What I wish to consider is rather the saner spirit of a secularism which no longer feels it necessary to apologise for itself, but has awakened to a curious and serious interest in nature, and especially in human nature. For this purpose I will take Montaigne as representative. He, with perhaps Erasmus and, in his own sphere and manner, Shakespeare, seems to me an ideal representative of the new humanism, nurtured by the thought and literature of antiquity. He is untouched by the pedantry of his age. Like Erasmus he has only contempt for the Ciceronian cult of style of the Italian scholars. His own style is at the opposite pole from that of the Italians as described by Bacon in *The Advancement of Learning*. Nor is Montaigne a devout disciple of any revived school of philosophy —Platonism or Stoicism or Epicureanism. What Montaigne learned from the ancients was not a dogmatic, philosophical scepticism, but a new interest in and understanding of human nature. The scepticism of the *Apology for Raymond Sebond* is a scepticism about human nature rather than concerning dogmatic Christianity. Indeed Montaigne accepts Catholic Christianity on trust, seeing that ultimate things transcend human reason. He studied human nature by introspection, for, before Coleridge,[1] Montaigne emphasised the fact that we under-

[1] 'Now I appeal confidently to my hearers whether the closest observation of the manners of one or two old nurses would have enabled Shakespeare to draw this character of admirable generalisations? Surely not. Let any man conjure up in his mind all the qualities and peculiarities that can possibly belong to a nurse, and he will find them in Shakespeare's picture of the old woman: nothing is omitted. This effect is not produced by mere observation. The great prerogative of genius (and Shakespeare felt and availed himself of it) is now to swell itself to the dignity of a God and now to subdue and keep dormant some part of that lofty nature and to descend even to the lowest characters—to become everything in fact but the vicious.' 'Where from observation could he have learned such lines as these which are put into the mouth of Othello when he is talking to Iago of Brabantio?

> Let him do his spite:
> My services which I have done the signiory
> Shall out-tongue his complaints. 'Tis yet to know,—
> Which, when I know that boasting is an honour,
> I shall promulgate—I fetch my life and being

stand others only in so far as they are revealed in ourselves, in what we feel we might ourselves be. The better a man knows himself, the more he knows of human nature. 'Chacque homme porte la forme entière de l'humaine condition.' 'Ce n'est pas dans Montaigne', says Pascal, 'mais dans moi que je trouve tout ce que j'y vois.' This is what Montaigne learned, not so much from the ancient philosophers, as from the moralists, biographers, historians, and poets—Seneca, Plutarch, Livy, Tacitus, Lucretius, Virgil. These it was that quickened his interest in that 'sujet merveilleusement vain, divers et ondoyant, que l'homme'; and he learned to check their comments by his own introspection. Montaigne was the first of modern psychologists. The field of physical inquiry was not for him; but in his own field he had no rival. He anticipated much on which we dilate to-day—the small part played by reason in the life of most men, the enormous potency of the imagination.

The significance of all this, as Pascal saw, was that in Montaigne the natural man reasserted, rediscovered himself, in all his weakness and variableness, but capable also of amazing *élans* of endurance and of achievement, prone to *paresse* (the sin of *paresse*, sloth, is what Pascal lays to the charge of Montaigne, *orgueil*, pride, to that of Epictetus, for both have reckoned without the Fall and its consequences) and demanding pleasure as an essential element of the Good.[1] 'For my part I love life and cultivate it as it has pleased God to grant it to me . . . I accept cheerfully and gratefully what nature has done for me, and am pleased with it and proud of it. . . . Of philosophical opinions I more willingly embrace those which are the more solid, that is to say, the most human and the most our own. . . . Nature is a gentle guide, yet not more gentle than she is prudent and just. I hunt everywhere for her trail. . . . These transcendental humours terrify me, like lofty and inaccessible places, and nothing I find so hard to digest in the life of Socrates as his ecstasies and his intercourse with daemons. . . . The fairest lives, to my mind, are those which are regulated after the ordinary human pattern, without miracle, without extravagance.'[2] Thus sanely and luminously Montaigne expresses one thing which the revival of learning was bringing back, a fairer estimate of man's nature,

From men or royal siege, and my demerits
May speak unbonneted to as proud a fortune
As this that I have reached: for know, Iago,
But that I love the gentle Desdemona,
I would not my unhoused, free condition
Put into circumscription and confine
For the sea's worth.

I ask where was Shakespeare to observe such language as this? If he did not observe it, it was with the inward eye of meditation upon his own nature: for the time he became Othello and spoke as Othello in such circumstances must have spoken.'—*Lectures on Shakespeare*.

[1] 'Poetry which produces delight, the parent of so many virtues.'—COLERIDGE.

[2] *Les Essais*, III. 13, *De l'Expérience*.

his natural capacities and virtues, the legitimate instinct of enjoyment. 'You will never convince me that the marriage of pleasure with necessity is not a most suitable one, with which, saith an ancient writer, the gods even conspire.' In the Middle Ages—ages of great saints, great sinners, and great penitents—average human nature had been distorted under the sense of sin and judgement, and overstrained by the ideals of asceticism. 'Man at that time', says Huizinga, 'was convinced that right is absolutely fixed and certain. Justice should prosecute the unjust everywhere and to the end. Reparation and retribution have to be extreme, and assume the character of revenge. In this exaggerated need of justice primitive barbarism, pagan at bottom, blends with the Christian conception of society. The Church, on the one hand, had inculcated gentleness and clemency, and tried in that way to soften judicial morals. On the other hand, in adding to the primitive need of retribution the horror of sin, it had to a certain extent stimulated the sense of justice. . . . The barbarous idea of retaliation was reinforced by fanaticism . . . crime came to be regarded as a menace to order and society, an insult to divine majesty. Thus it was natural that the late Middle Ages should become the period of special cruelty.'[1] To one who has come to think of human nature as less wicked than 'divers et ondoyant' such rigour is repellent; and there is no vice against which Montaigne protests more warmly than cruelty: 'Cowardice is the mother of cruelty. . . . All that goes beyond simple death seems to me pure cruelty; our justice cannot hope that he whom the fear of death and of being beheaded or hanged will not keep from wrong-doing will be deterred therefrom by the apprehension of a slow fire, or of pincers, or of the wheel. And it may be that we thus drive them to despair; for what can be the state of a man's mind awaiting death for twenty-four hours broken on the wheel, or, after the old manner, nailed to a cross.' . . . 'Even the execution of the law, however just it be, I cannot view with steadiness.'[2]

So speaks the spirit of humanism in Montaigne, and not in Montaigne alone, but in Rabelais and Erasmus and others. It was Erasmus' dream to unite the spirit of humanism with that of Christianity, and to substitute for a scholastic, dogmatic, monastic, ascetic Christianity what he called the philosophy of Christ. But the temper of the age was too warlike for compromise or philosophy. Luther and Calvin and Ignatius Loyola were more to its taste than Erasmus or Montaigne, Milton than Shakespeare. But of that later. What I wish for the moment to emphasise is that humanism was not a reawakening of man's interest in his own life on earth. *That* he never has lost and never will lose, by whatever means he may attempt to reconcile his interest in love and war and the game of life with the more transcendent claims to

[1] Huizinga: *The Waning of the Middle Ages.*
[2] *Les Essais*, II. xi, *De la Cruauté.*

which he does obeisance. In the ages of faith men played that game passionately and fantastically enough,

> Le Donne, i Cavaliér,' l'arme, gli amori,
> Le cortesie, l' audaci imprese . . .

—these were the interests of life and poetry in the centuries of romance, shaping the ideals and dreams of men and women. The difficulty was to justify them on Christian grounds. To slay Saracens was doubtless always a Christian's duty, and to defend women and succour the helpless a humane task. But life and romance were filled with many other things, and these, if more exciting, less easy to sanctify, and accordingly life and literature abound in great conversions and repentances. For warrior and lover alike the hour comes when one must repent in sackcloth and ashes, or run the risk of losing one's way, like the Templars, in perversions of passion and unbelief. Humanism was an acceptance of human life and values as right and reasonable, and, if controlled by a sense of measure, needing not in themselves to be repented of, a revival of values and ideals on which the best thought of antiquity had set the seal of its approval; and among these values is pleasure, the enjoyment of life and its good things, and chief among them the arts—the great decorators of man's life, the fullest and finest expression of his sense of the joy of life, the beauty inherent in all that is.

*1929*

# WILLIAM EMPSON

## *Ambiguity*

FROM 'SEVEN TYPES OF AMBIGUITY'

AN ambiguity, then, is not satisfying in itself, nor is it, considered as a device on its own, a thing to be attempted; it must in each case arise from, and be justified by, the peculiar requirements of the situation. On the other hand, it is a thing which the more interesting and valuable situations are more likely to justify. Thus the practice of 'trying not to be ambiguous' has a great deal to be said for it, and I suppose was followed by most of the poets I have considered. It is likely to lead to results more direct, more communicable, and hence more durable; it is a necessary safeguard against being ambiguous without proper occasion, and it leads to more serious ambiguities when such occasions arise. But, of course, the phrase 'trying not to be ambiguous' is itself very indefinite and treacherous; it involves problems of all kinds as to what a poet can try to do, how much of his activity he is conscious of, and how much of his activity he could become conscious of if he tried. I believe that the methods I have been describing are very useful to critics, but certainly they leave a poet in a difficult position. Even in prose the belief in them is liable to produce a sort of doctrinaire sluttishness; one is tempted to set down a muddle in the hope that it will convey the meaning more immediately.

As for the immediate importance of the study of ambiguity, it would be easy enough to take up an alarmist attitude, and say that the English language needs nursing by the analyst very badly indeed. Always rich and dishevelled, it is fast becoming very rich and dishevelled; always without adequate devices for showing the syntax intended, it is fast throwing away the few devices it had; it is growing liable to mean more things, and less willing to stop and exclude the other possible meanings. A brief study of novels will show that English, as spoken by educated people, has simplified its grammar during the last century to an extraordinary degree. People sometimes say that words are now used as flat counters, in a way which ignores their delicacy; that English is coming to use fewer of its words, and those more crudely. But this journalist flatness does not mean that the words have simple meanings, only that the word is used, as at a distance, to stand for a vague and complicated mass of ideas and systems which the journalist has no time to apprehend. The sciences might be expected to diminish the ambiguity of the language, both because of their tradition of clarity and because much of their jargon has, if not only one meaning, at any rate only one setting and point of view. But such words are not in general use; they only act as a further disturbing influence on the words used already. English is becoming an aggregate of vocabularies only loosely in connection with one another, which yet have many words in common, so that there is much danger of accidental ambiguity, and you have to bear firmly in mind the small clique for whom the author is writing. It is to combat this that so much recent writing has been determinedly unintelligible from any but the precise point of view intended.

Of the increasing vagueness, compactness, and lack of logical distinctions in English, the most obvious example is the newspaper headline. I remember a very fine one that went

ITALIAN ASSASSIN BOMB PLOT DISASTER

Here we have the English language used as a Chinese system of flat key-words, given particular meaning by noun-adjectives in apposition, or perhaps rather as an agglutinative system, one word one sentence, like Esquimo. I am told that American headlines, however mysterious, are usually sentences; the English method is more complete. *Bomb* and *plot*, you notice, can be either nouns or verbs, and would take kindly to being adjectives, not that they are anything so definite here. One thinks at first that there are two words or sentences, and a semicolon has been left out as in telegrams: 'I will tell you for your penny about the Italian Assassin and the well-known Bomb Plot Disaster'; but the *assassin*, as far as I remember, was actually not an *Italian*; *Italian* refers to the whole aggregate, and its noun, if any, is *disaster*. Perhaps, by being so far separated from its noun, it gives the impression that the other words, too, are somehow connected with *Italy*; that *bombs*, *plots*, and *disasters* belong both to government and rebel in those parts; perhaps *Italian Assassin* is not wholly separate in one's mind from the injured Mussolini. This extended use of the adjective acts as a sort of syncopation, which gives energy and excitement to the rhythm, rather like the effect of putting two caesuras into a line; but, of course, the main rhythm conveys: 'This is a particularly exciting sort of disaster, the assassin-bomb-plot type they have in Italy,' and there is a single chief stress on *bomb*.

Evidently this is a very effective piece of writing, quite apart from the fact that it conveys its point in a form short enough for large type. It conveys it with a compactness which gives the mind several notions at one glance of the eye, with a unity like that of metaphor, with a force like that of its own favourite *bombs*. Nor can I feel that it will be a *disaster* if other forms of English literature adopt this fundamental mode of statement, so interesting to the logician; it is possible that a clear analysis of the possible modes of statement, and a fluid use of grammar which sets out to combine them as sharply as possible into the effect intended, may yet give back something of the Elizabethan energy to what is at present a rather exhausted language. The grammatical sentence is not the only form of statement in modern English, and I want to suggest that the machinery I have been using upon poetry is going to become increasingly necessary if we are to keep the language under control.

*1930*

### *Arachne*

TWIXT devil and deep sea, man hacks his caves;
Birth, death; one, many; what is true, and seems;
Earth's vast hot iron, cold space's empty waves:

King spider, walks the velvet roof of streams:
Must bird and fish, must god and beast avoid:
Dance, like nine angels, on pin-point extremes.

His gleaming bubble between void and void,
Tribe-membrane, that by mutual tension stands,
Earth's surface film, is at a breath destroyed.

Bubbles gleam brightest with least depth of lands
But two is least can with full tension strain,
Two molecules; one, and the film disbands.

We two suffice. But oh beware, whose vain
Hydroptic soap my meagre water saves.
Male spiders must not be too early slain.

*1935*

## AUGUST STRINDBERG

### *The Big Gravel-Sifter*

TRANSLATED BY L. J. POTTS

THERE was once an eel-pout who lay with her son at the bottom of the sea by the steamboat jetty, watching a boy fixing his rod for fishing.

'Look at him,' said the eel-pout, 'and you will learn the wickedness and deceit of the world. . . . Look at him now; he has a whip in his hand: he throws out the line: there it is! Then, sinking down, comes the weight: there it is: and *then* comes the hook with a snake on it. You mustn't take *that* in your mouth, or you will be caught. It's only silly perches and roaches that are taken in. So now you know.'

But the forest of sea-weed, with its mussels and winkles, began to sway: there was a sound of splashing and drumming, and a big red whale darted past over their heads: he had a caudal fin like a corkscrew to work himself along with.

'It's the steamer,' said the old eel-pout. 'Mind yourself.'

Then came a fearful din overhead, stamping and rumbling, as they made a bridge in two seconds between the boat and the land. But it was difficult to see; they were letting out soot and oil overhead.

There was something very heavy on the bridge, for it creaked under the weight; and some men joined in, singing:

'Hea-ve!—Hoi-ee! Let her go!—Together hea-ve!—Hoi-ee!—Hey, ease her up!—Hoi-ee! Let her go!'

Then something quite indescribable happened. First there was a sound like sixty dalesmen splitting wood; then a hole opened, reaching right to the bottom of the sea, and between three stones stood a black cupboard, singing and playing and jingling and ringing right up against the eel-pout and her son, who made for deep water.

Then there came a voice overhead, shouting:

'Three fathom of water. It's no good. Let her lie; it isn't worth while getting up the old vamp—it'd cost more to mend it than it's worth.' It was the Inspector of Mines, whose piano had fallen into the sea.

All was now quiet again; the big red fish swam out with its screw-fin, and it was quieter still. But when the sun had set, it began to blow; the black cupboard down in the forest of sea-weed swayed and bumped against the stones; and at every knock it played, so that all the fishes in the neighbourhood came swimming up to see and hear.

The eel-pout was the first to come and look; and as she could see her reflection in the cupboard, she said, 'It's a wardrobe with a mirror.'

That was logical, so they all said, 'It's a wardrobe with a mirror.'

Up came a goby and smelt out the candlesticks, which had kept their place; and there were still candle-ends, burnt down in the sockets. 'This is eatable,' he said, 'if it wasn't for the string.'

Up came a big cod and settled down on the pedal; then there was a booming inside the cupboard, and all the fishes fled.

They got no further that day.

That night there was a half-gale, and the musical-box bumped on like a navvy's beetle till the sun came up. Then, when the eel-pout came back with the rest of the company, the cupboard had changed.

The lid had opened like the jaws of a shark, showing a row of teeth so big that they had never seen its like; and every other tooth was black. And the whole machine had swollen out sideways like a spawner; the boards described circles, the pedals pointed up into the air like a kicking foot, and the arms of the candlesticks were clenched like fists. It was an awful sight.

'It's coming apart,' cried the cod, and put out a fin, ready to turn.

'It's coming apart,' they all cried.

And now the boards broke up, the box opened, and they could see what it looked like inside; that was the greatest fun of all.

'It's a trap! Don't go near it!' said the eel-pout.

'A hand-loom, that's what it is,' said the stickleback, who crochets his nest and understands that sort of thing.

'A gravel-sifter,' said the perch, who used to put up under the lime-works.

Yes, a gravel-sifter, that was what it was. But there were all sorts of tricks and catches that made it different from the sieve they sift gravel with. There were little gadgets like toes with white woollen socks, and when they moved, a foot with a hundred skeleton fingers started working; it worked and worked, but never got any further.

It was a queer body. But there was no more playing; for the skeleton couldn't get at the strings any longer; it flourished in the water, as if it was knocking with its knuckles to be let in.

There was no more playing! But a shoal of sticklebacks came and swam right through the cupboard. And when they drew their spikes over the strings it played again, but in a new way; for the strings were tuned differently now.

One rosy evening just afterwards, two children sat on the steamboat jetty, a boy and a girl. They were thinking of nothing in particular, perhaps some mischief or other, when suddenly they heard soft music from the bottom of the sea and became serious.

'Can you hear?'

'Yes. What is it? They're playing scales.'

'No, it's the gnats singing.'

'It isn't. It's the mermaid.'

'There isn't such a thing as a mermaid, my master at school says.'

'He doesn't know.'

'Well, anyhow, listen.'

They listened for a long time and then went away.

Two newly arrived visitors sat down on the jetty; he looked into her eyes, which reflected the whole of the rosy sunset and the green shores. Then they heard music, like the musical-glasses only in a new key, such as they alone had dreamt, they who wanted to create something new on earth. But it never occurred to them to look outside themselves; they thought the song was in their own hearts.

Then came two old visitors, who knew the trick; and they amused themselves by saying in a loud voice:

'It's the piano of the Inspector of Mines—the one that fell overboard.'

But whenever new visitors came, who did not know the trick, they sat and wondered and revelled in the unknown music, till older visitors came and explained the trick to them. Then they no longer revelled in it.

But the musical-box lay there the whole summer through; and the sticklebacks taught their art to the perches, who were better at it. The piano became a perch-bed for the visitors, the pilots put nets round it, and one day a waiter tried to fish cod in it. When he had let down his line with the old clock-weight on it and was going to pull it up, he heard a roulade in X flat, and the hook stuck fast. He coaxed and jerked and at last got up five finger-bones with wool on the end; and the bones crackled like a skeleton. Then he was frightened and flung his catch into the sea, though he knew what it was.

Then came the dog-days, when the water got hot, and all the fishes went off into the deeps in search of cool. The music was silent again. But the August moon came, and the visitors held a regatta. The Inspector of Mines and his wife were there, sitting in a white boat, which was rowed gently to and fro by their boys. As they rowed over the black water, silvered on the top, with a touch of dull gilding added, they heard music under the boat.

'Ha ha!' said the Inspector of Mines; 'that's our old vamp of a piano. Ha ha!' But there he stopped, seeing his wifc bend her head low on her breast like the pelicans you see in pictures, as if she wanted to bite her bosom and hide her face.

The old piano and its long history had wakened memories from the depths of her soul, memories of the first dining-room they had fitted out, of the first of her children who had learnt to play, of the long evenings whose weariness could only be driven away by the tempestuous rush of notes which made the whole flat shake off its apathy, which braced their hearts and set a new lustre on the very furniture. . . . But that is another story.

With the first storm of autumn the pilchards came in their thousand thousands and swam through the musical-box. It was a farewell concert with a vengeance; terns and sea-gulls gathered to hear it. And that night the musical-box went out to sea; and there was an end of the whole business.

*1930*

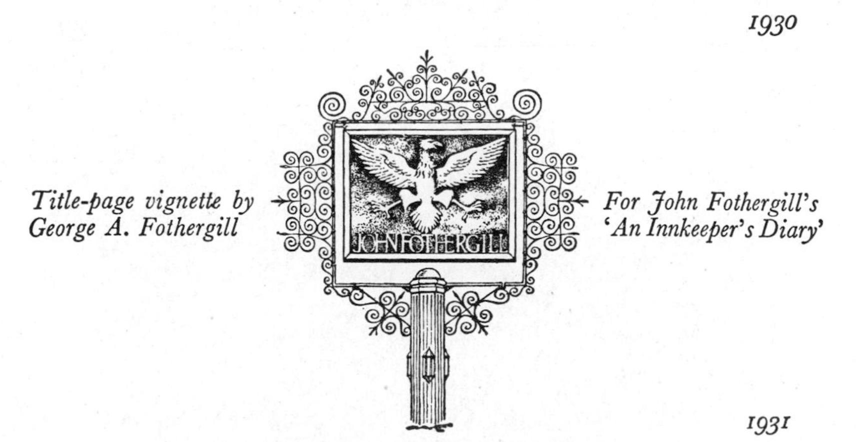


*Title-page vignette by George A. Fothergill*

*For John Fothergill's 'An Innkeeper's Diary'*

*1931*

## H. D.

### *Songs from Cyprus*

IV

WHERE is the nightingale,
in what myrrh-wood and dim?
ah, let the night come back,
for we would conjure back
all that enchanted him,
*all that enchanted him.*

Where is the bird of fire?
in what packed hedge or rose?
in what roofed ledge of flower?
no other creature knows
what magic lurks within,
*what magic lurks within.*

Bird, bird, bird, bird, we cry,
hear, pity us in pain:
hearts break in the sunlight,
hearts break in daylight rain,
only night heals again,
*only night heals again.*

*1931*

# LYTTON STRACHEY

## *Sir John Harington*

An old miniature shows a young man's face, whimsically Elizabethan, with tossed-back curly hair, a tip-tilted nose, a tiny point of a beard, and a long single earring, falling in sparkling drops over a ruff of magnificent proportions. Such was John Harington, as he appeared in the happy fifteen-eighties, at Greenwich, or at Nonesuch—a courtier, a wit, a scholar, a poet, and a great favourite with the ladies. Even Gloriana herself usually unbent when he approached her. She liked the foolish fellow. She had known him since he was a child; he was her godson—almost, indeed, a family connection, for his father's first wife had been a natural daughter of her own indefatigable sire. Through this lady the young man had inherited his fine Italian house at Kelston, in Somersetshire, where one day Elizabeth, on her way to Bath, paid him the honour of an extremely expensive visit. He had felt himself obliged to rebuild half the house to lodge his great guest fittingly; but he cared little for that—he wrote a rhyming epigram about it all, which amused the ladies of the bedchamber. He wrote, he found, with extraordinary ease and pleasure; the words came positively running off the end of his pen; and so—to amuse the ladies again, or to tease them—he translated the twenty-eighth book of Ariosto's *Orlando Furioso*, in which the far from decorous history of the fair Fiammetta is told. The Queen soon got wind of this. She read the manuscript and sent for the poet. She was shocked, she said, by this attempt to demoralise her household; and she banished the offender from Court until—could there be a more proper punishment?—he should have completed the translation of the whole poem. Harington hurried off to Kelston, worked away for a month or two, and returned with a fine folio containing the entire *Orlando* in English, together with notes, a life of Ariosto, 'a general allegory of the whole,' and 'apologie of Poetrie,' an 'epistle dedicatorie to the Queenes Majestie,' and an engraved title-page with the portrait of himself and his dog Bungay. The book was printed in 1591. The exquisite elegance and mature serenity of the original are nowhere to be found in it; but Harington himself, bringing with him the natural abundance, the charming ingenuousness, the early morning freshness of his wonderful generation, comes to us delightfully on every page.

The translation was well received, and the gay young man looked about for new worlds to conquer. Not to be talked of was his only fear. A curious notion struck him. His nose was sensitive as well as impudent, and he had been made to suffer agonies by the sanitary arrangements in the houses of the great. Suddenly inspired, he invented the water-closet. Then, seizing his pen, he concocted a pamphlet after the manner of Rabelais—or, as he preferred to call him 'the reverent Rabbles'—in which extravagant spirits, intolerable puns, improper stories, and sly satirical digs at eminent personages were blended together into a preposterous rhapsody, followed by an appendix—written, of course, by his servant—could a gentleman be expected to discuss such details?—containing a minute account, with measurements, diagrams and prices, of the new invention. *The Metamorphosis of Ajax*—for so the book, with a crowningly deplorable pun, was entitled—created some sensation. Queen Elizabeth was amused. But then some malicious courtier told her that one of the satirical digs was aimed at the memory of Leicester, whereupon her smiles changed to frowns, the Star Chamber was talked of, and Harington made a strategic retreat to Somersetshire. 'The merry poet, my godson,' the Queen declared, 'must not come to Greenwich, till he hath grown sober and leaveth the ladies' sports and frolics.' But before very long she relented. With her supreme sense of the practical, she saw that, as she put it, 'the marrow of the book' was not entirely ludicrous; she sent down word to the poet that she approved of his invention; and eventually she set the fashion for the new contrivances by installing one of them in Richmond Palace, with a copy of the *Ajax* hanging from the wall.

Harington's next adventure was more serious. He was summoned by Essex to join his ill-fated expedition to Ireland, in command of a troop of horse. In Ireland, with a stretch of authority which was bitterly resented by the Queen, Harington was knighted by the rash Lord Deputy, and afterwards, when disaster came thick upon disaster, he followed his patron back to London. In fear and trembling, he presented himself before the enraged Elizabeth. 'What!' she cried, 'did the fool bring you too?' The terrified poet fell upon his knees, while the Queen, as he afterwards described it, 'chafed much, walked fastly to and fro, and looked with discomposure in her visage.' Then, suddenly rushing towards him, she caught hold of his girdle. 'By God's Son,' she shouted, 'I am no Queen, and that man is above me!' His stammering excuses were cut short with a 'Go back to your business!' uttered in such a tone that Sir John, not staying to be bidden twice, fled out of the room, and fled down to Kelston, 'as if all the Irish rebels had been at his heels.'

It is clear that poor Harington never quite recovered from the shock of that terrific scene. The remainder of his life passed in ineffectiveness and disillusionment. In the bosom of his family he did his best to forget the storms and shipwrecks of 'the Essex coast'; he wrote incessantly; he cracked scandalous jokes with his mother-in-law, old Lady Rogers; he busied himself over the construction of a curious lantern for King James of Scotland. But his happy vein had deserted him. His *Discourse shewing that Elyas must personally come before the Day of Judgment* could never get finished, and he threw aside his *Treatise on Playe* as a failure.

His epigrams, no doubt, were more successful; he scribbled them down on every possible occasion, and the most scurrilous he invariably despatched to old Lady Rogers. She roared with laughter, but omitted to leave him a legacy. He dashed into her house as she was dying, broke open the chests, tried to get possession of everything, and was at last ignominiously ejected by his brother-in-law. King James was equally disappointing. Even the curious lantern, even a learned, elaborate, and fantastic dissertation *On the Succession to the Crown*, failed to win him. After he had been a year in London, the new King granted Sir John an interview, but, though his Majesty was polite, he was not impressed. 'Sir John,' he said, with much gravity, 'do you truly understand why the Devil works more with ancient women than others?' And, unluckily, on that, Sir John 'could not refrain from a scurvy jest.' Nevertheless, though he felt that he had made no headway, he would not despair; a little later, the Lord Chancellorship of Ireland and the Archbishopric of Dublin fell vacant, and the author of *Ajax* bravely requested that he should be appointed to both offices. Oddly enough, his application received no answer. He solaced himself with an endeavour to win the good graces of the young Prince Henry, to whom he addressed a discourse, full of pleasant anecdotes, concerning all the bishops of his acquaintance, followed by a letter describing 'the good deedes and straunge feats' of his 'rare Dogge,' Bungay—how he used to carry messages from London to Kelston, and how, on one occasion, he took a pheasant from a dish at the Spanish Ambassador's table, and then returned it to the very same dish, at a secret sign from his master.

But in truth the days of Bungay were over, and the new times were uncomfortable and strange. 'I ne'er did see such lack of good order, discretion, and sobriety.' There had been jollities and junketings, no doubt, in his youth, but surely, they were different. He remembered the 'heroicall dames,' the 'stately heroyns' whom he had celebrated aforetime—

These entertayn great Princes; these have learned
The tongues, toys, tricks of Rome, of Spayn, of Fraunce;
These can correntos and lavoltas daunce,
And though they foote it false 'tis ne'er discerned.

More and more his thoughts reverted to his old mistress. 'When she smiled, it was a pure sunshine, that everyone did choose to bask in, if they could; but anon came a storm from a sudden gathering of clouds, and the thunder fell in wondrous manner on all alike.' Yes! Those were great times indeed! And now . . . he was 'olde and infirme'; he was forty-five; he must seek a quiet harbour and lay up his barque. He lingered at Kelston, impoverished, racked by various diseases; he vainly took the Bath waters; he became 'stricken of a dead palsy'; until, in 1612, at the age of fifty-one, he passed into oblivion. And in oblivion he has remained. Nobody reads his *Orlando*; his letters are known to none but a few learned historians; his little books of epigrams lie concealed in the grim recesses of vast libraries; and Englishmen to-day, reflecting on many things, as they enjoy the benefits of a sanitary system unknown to the less fortunate inhabitants of other countries, give never a thought to Sir John Harington.

*1931*

E. McKnight Kauffer's celebrated design for the jacket of *Queen Victoria*. The original was printed by lithography in three colours.

# WILFRED OWEN

## *Insensibility*

I

HAPPY are men who yet before they are killed
Can let their veins run cold.
Whom no compassion fleers
Or makes their feet
Sore on the alleys cobbled with their brothers.
The front line withers,
But they are troops who fade, not flowers,
For poets' tearful fooling:
Men, gaps for filling:
Losses who might have fought
Longer; but no one bothers.

II

And some cease feeling
Even themselves or for themselves.
Dullness best solves
The tease and doubt of shelling,
And Chance's strange arithmetic
Comes simpler than the reckoning of their shilling.
They keep no check on armies' decimation.

III

Happy are these who lose imagination:
They have enough to carry with ammunition.
Their spirit drags no pack,
Their old wounds save with cold can not more ache.
Having seen all things red,
Their eyes are rid
Of the hurt of the colour of blood for ever.
And terror's first constriction over,
Their hearts remain small-drawn.
Their senses in some scorching cautery of battle
Now long since ironed,
Can laugh among the dying, unconcerned.

IV

Happy the soldier home, with not a notion
How somewhere, every dawn, some men attack,
And many sighs are drained.
Happy the lad whose mind was never trained:
His days are worth forgetting more than not.
He sings along the march
Which we march taciturn, because of dusk,
The long, forlorn, relentless trend
From larger day to huger night.

V

We wise, who with a thought besmirch
Blood over all our soul,
How should we see our task
But through his blunt and lashless eyes?
Alive, he is not vital overmuch;
Dying, not mortal overmuch;
Nor sad, nor proud,
Nor curious at all.
He cannot tell
Old men's placidity from his.

VI

But cursed are dullards whom no cannon stuns,
That they should be as stones;
Wretched are they, and mean
With paucity that never was simplicity.
By choice they made themselves immune
To pity and whatever mourns in man
Before the last sea and the hapless stars;
Whatever mourns when many leave these shores;
Whatever shares
The eternal reciprocity of tears.

*1931*

# J. R. ACKERLEY

## *His Highness the Maharajah*

FROM 'HINDOO HOLIDAY'

CHHOKRAPUR has no railway station. The nearest is at Dipra, thirty-five miles away, and there the Maharajah's car was awaiting me. It was manned by a very fat chauffeur and a small boy. With me was a black-bearded Mohammedan, servant to His Highness, who had met me at an earlier stage in my journey with a letter of instructions.

We drove off, passing about midway through Rajgarh, the nearest British Cantonment to Chhokrapur, and residence of the Political Agent.

A sudden turn from the main road, which seemed to skirt the town, brought us through white gates up a long red-gravel drive on to this small conical hill. The hill is flattened at the top to form a plateau, and is appended, like the full-stop in an exclamation mark, to a long rocky ridge which rises in a gradual incline to the south. There are two houses on the plateau, one big and one small, and I was set down in front of the latter. This was to be my abode for some months, so as soon as I arrived I made a tour of inspection. It did not take long. I found an oblong, one-storeyed building, with thick walls whitewashed inside and out. There were two communicating rooms, two verandahs, one in front and the other behind, and an outhouse bathroom in a corner of the back porch, from which stone steps led down to a small walled courtyard at the foot of the stony ridge. There were no windows, but five doorways, one from each room to each verandah, and one between the two rooms. The house was simply furnished. Canvas carpets, striped blue and red, covered both the floors, and across the thresholds of the open doorways long linen curtains of a rose pattern floated in the breeze. A round table and three chairs completed the sitting-room; in the other was a gigantic iron bedstead and a small table with a mirror on it. The outhouse contained a bath-tub on a wooden platform, some large earthenware water-vessels, a po, a close-stool, and a washstand. The washstand contained a little water and a drowned mouse.

When I had inspected my house I returned through the bedroom to my sitting-room and found the Mohammedan, the chauffeur, and the boy facing me in a grave semicircle behind my luggage, apparently awaiting further instructions.

I glanced at them nervously. They all salaamed with one movement and became erect again. I had already tried English on them and failed; so now I gave a 'That'll do' nod which was also without effect. Feeling quite at a loss I sat down at the table and opened my notebook to write, hoping that they would eventually fade away for lack of attention; but when I looked up again they were still there, gravely watching me, and they began at once to talk and make signals, at first separately and then together.

'Maharajah Sahib', I said hopefully.

They nodded agreeably.

Through the open doorway I could see the other house about one hundred and fifty yards away—a massive, square, white building, on the farther side of the plateau.

'Palace Maharajah Sahib?' I asked, pointing to it.

They all nodded agreeably again. Then appeared an imposing figure, very old, with a patriarchal grey beard and a network of wrinkles on his handsome brown face. He was barefoot, and clad in airy white draperies, and a bunch of keys dangling from his waist identified him among the Apostles.

He, too, seemed to have something urgent to impart, but was also unable to speak English. After considerable cogitation, however, he produced the word 'Ticket'; I played a visiting-card, and with exclamations of satisfaction St. Peter departed with it, followed by the chauffeur and the boy.

I had already noticed, in the mirror in the bedroom, that my face was spectral with dust, so I introduced the Mohammedan to the drowned mouse, and conveyed by gesture that besides some clean water I would like a cup of tea, for it was now about four o'clock. He went off on these errands, and while I was rolling up my shirt sleeves, an ancient man with bare, skinny legs and a straggling beard crept slowly and soundlessly in, carrying what looked at first like bag-pipes, but turned out to be a swollen dripping goatskin of water slung under one arm. The weight of his burden bowed him down, and he did not raise his eyes to me in passing, but sketched a salaam with an unsteady, wandering hand. He looked very like a goat himself. Left to myself, I began to wonder what my first meeting with the Maharajah would be like. I had heard that he possessed a pronounced sense of the theatre, and used to send on ahead of him, to herald his approach, a naked warrior armed with a spear. Something as melodramatic, I hoped, was in store for me; but even as I speculated and slung water over my face and neck, I heard a pattering behind me, and perceived, through soapsuds, St. Peter hurriedly returning.

'Maharajah Sahib! Maharajah Sahib!' he whispered excitedly, pointing behind him to my sitting-room.

This was very upsetting. I had spent several months in corresponding and arranging this meeting with His Highness; I had travelled over six thousand miles to accomplish it; he might at least have managed better than to catch me in this state of unreadiness. He wasn't playing up.

'Ask him wait,' I said, with economy of words and effect; and hurrying into the bedroom, I had just time to dry my face and restore my collar and tie when a shadow fell across the threshold of the sitting-room, and a stout Indian of unpleasing aspect, in a black frock-coat, entered and drew aside the curtains for His Highness to pass.

I had been given a detailed description of the Maharajah, but found myself unprepared nevertheless for the curious figure which now hobbled into the room. His face with its bridgeless nose, sunken lips, prominent chin and protuberant brown eyes, over which a faint bluish film had formed, bore a strong resemblance to a pekingese dog; half-way down the collapsed bridge of his nose, from the centre of his forehead, trickled some spots of yellow paint; a diamond shone in the lobe of each ear, and from beneath the front of his little round hat, which was made of green velvet and gold brocade, a wisp of dark grey hair upcurled. He was small and very slight, and his stiff-jointed body was neatly sheathed in a long-skirted coat of violet and grey tweed with a high military collar of grey velveteen and cuffs of the same material; his trousers were of white cotton, wrinkling tightly down the lower half of his leg, but expanding above the knee; his socks were bright purple, and upon his long thin feet he wore a pair of patent-leather dancing-pumps. I took in these details slowly.

'His Highness the Maharajah Sahib!' announced the stout person pompously.

Carrying my coat with me, I hastened forward and shook hands, apologising for my condition; but he took no notice of this.

'But you are so early!' he said. 'I did not expect you for another hour, for I intended to come part of the way to meet you; but just as I was thinking of starting they brought me your card!'

He seemed quite vexed about it, and, turning to his companion, uttered some brief remarks in Hindi which caused the other to pass a nervous hand over his jaw and mouth; but immediately he returned to me with—

'Welcome to India!'

—and introduced his companion as Mr. Babaji Rao, his private secretary.

I placed a chair for him, and, leaning on his stick, he hobbled round the table and sat down.

'Have you had your tea?' he asked. I said I had ordered it, and he told his Secretary to hurry it up; but at that moment it arrived, borne by a tall, handsome waiter in a long, blue uniform coat with a sash round his waist.

He shuffled off his shoes outside the door, and entered with bare feet.

'Won't you join me?' I asked His Highness, for there was only one cup; 'or have you had your tea already?'

This amused them both, and the Maharajah explained that, although it was all very silly and nothing to do with him, Hindoos were not permitted to eat with Europeans. I apologized for my blunder; but he waved it aside with a small jewelled hand, saying that, as a matter of fact, he didn't conform strictly to the rule, and sometimes took a cup of tea with his guests, but that he didn't feel inclined for one just now.

'Now take your tea,' he said, 'and I will keep my questions for when you have finished.'

So, rather self-consciously, I chewed leathery buttered toast, while they sat and watched me and exchanged remarks in Hindi—His Highness smoking a cigarette with a purple tip; Babaji Rao with his legs wide apart, his elbows out, and his hands planted firmly upon his knees. He was not much better to look at than his master, I thought. Smallpox had ravaged his face; a ragged moustache drooped untidily over his big, loose mouth, and behind large spectacles his small brown eyes seemed evasive and sly. His costume was much the same as the Maharajah's, but dingy and of coarse material; he wore neither socks nor collar, and a brass stud shone beneath his unshaven chin. When he took off his round black hat I saw that the top of his head was bald, and that the thick untidy fringe round the sides and back was turning grey.

His Highness did not manage however to keep all his questions for when I had finished.

'How do you say your name?' he asked.

I told him, and he repeated it after me until he got it right, and then glanced at his secretary as much as to say, 'Remember that.'

'Do you like this?' He indicated the walls. 'Is it comfortable? If there is anything you want you must tell Babaji Rao. I thought you would like to stay here instead of in the Guest House with my other guests.'

'Is that the Guest House?' I asked, looking at the square building outside. 'I thought it was your Palace.'

'No, no, no,' he said, subsiding into wheezy laughter, and I was astonished to see that his tongue was bright orange—almost the colour of nasturtium.

I put the last piece of toast into my mouth, and no sooner had I done so than he asked—

'Have you finished your tea?'

—and called the waiter to clear it away before I could manœuvre the toast into a position that would enable me to reply.

Then began a very bewildering examination of my history. It jumped from one thing to another without pause, and was too long and confusing to reproduce.

How old was I? So old? He had been under the impression that I was only twenty-two. Did I come from London? Of whom did my family consist? Could I speak Latin and Greek? Did I know Rider Haggard? Had I read his books? Was I religious? Did I believe that the tragedy of Jesus Christ was the greatest tragedy that ever happened?

Was I a pragmatist? Had I read Hall Caine? Had I read Darwin, Huxley, and Marie Corelli? . . .

His Highness seemed very disappointed. I didn't know what 'Pragmatism' meant, and had read practically none of the authors he named. I must read them at once, he said, for they were all very good authors indeed, and he wished me to explain them to him. He had them all in his library in the Palace; I must get them out and read them. He was practically toothless, I noticed, and his brown lips sank in and blew out tremulously as he mumbled his questions.

'Have you read Spencer's *First Principles*, and *Problems of Life and Mind* by Lewes?' he asked.

'No, Maharajah Sahib, I'm afraid I haven't.'

His face took on a very grave expression.

'But you must do so. It is very important. You must do so at once. It is the first thing I wish you to do.'

'Very well, Maharajah Sahib.'

'Babaji Rao will give them to you. You must give them to him tonight, Babaji Rao. Lewes refutes Spencer. Spencer says . . . What does he say, Babaji Rao? Explain it.'

The Secretary cleared his throat, and passed a nervous hand over his bald head.

'Spencer says that there is a reality behind appearances, and Lewes. . . .'

'Is there a God or is there no God?' rapped out His Highness impatiently. 'That is the question. That is what I want to know. Spencer says there *is* a God, Lewes says no. So you must read them, Mr. Ackerley, and tell me which of them is right.'

He got up to go. I felt I had not made at all a good impression and that he was disappointed in me. Before leaving he asked me about the expenses I had incurred during my journey, and told me to give an account of them to the Secretary, for he wished to refund them at once.

When he reached the doorway he turned:

'At last we are face to face!' he said, and then shuffled out, very stiffly, on splayed feet, to his car.

*1932*

# ROSAMOND LEHMANN

## *Getting Ready for the Ball*

### FROM 'INVITATION TO THE WALTZ'

TIME crawling by at length delivered up the evening of the dance.

That morning Mrs. Curtis said:

'Nannie, you'll help the girls to dress, won't you?' And they felt the first thrill of preparation. It sounded so important and correct, as if they were authentic debutantes with a maid, like Marigold, to lay out, to fold up after them.

Upon their beds lay the dresses. Olivia's had come home that morning from Miss Robinson with a note pinned to it. *Have a nice time. E. Robinson.* The underclothes were prepared, the new satin slippers, the long kid gloves borrowed from their mother; and Nannie, rising supcrbly to thc occasion, had crowned all by running the bath for them and spreading their towels over the chair; so that all they had to do, after Kate had shaken in a packet of Heart of a Rose bath-salts, was to step in and lie back one at each end. Even the nursery bathroom, with its scarred white paint and old red blind, its enamel mug bristling with the family toothbrushes, its well-worn paraphernalia of sponges, face-cloths, nail-brush and pumice-stone, its cake of plain Castile soap, its faded eighteen-year-old bath-mat stencilled with animals—even the nursery bathroom seemed somehow glorified and new; seemed to lose its true character of straightforward scrubbing place, and, veiled in unwonted clouds of scented steam, to take on an air of luxury and refinement, suitably enshrining the ritual of young ladies at their toilet.

'All this extra regard for detail,' said Kate, 'and we shall look just the same in the end.'

'And smell the same. After a bit.'

After a silence Kate said, squeezing the sponge over her shoulders:

'I shouldn't think *he'd* notice if we came down in our knickers and stank of onions. I didn't see him look at us once—did you? He must be a woman-hater.'

'I expect he's awfully shy. He hasn't got any sisters. Did you see what long eyelashes he's got? Only they're so fair you don't notice them. He isn't really bad looking—is he?—except for the pince-nez. . . . Miss Robinson calls them pinch-knees.'

Kate smiled, but mournfully. The glasses had been a cruel blow; exactly what she had foretold in her gloomiest prognostications.

Olivia added:

'Perhaps he'll leave them off for the dance.'

Kate checked the retort which rose to her lips, 'And go falling over everybody's feet . . .,' and, willing for once to be seduced by Olivia's insensate optimism, merely said in a meek and yearning voice:

'Do you think he might?'

She tried to dismiss from her mind the discouraging scene of his arrival at five o'clock, in a dripping wet burberry, soaked suit-case in hand, having walked the mile from the station after missing the village taxi painstakingly sent by Mrs. Curtis to meet him. The first glimpse had revealed him standing in the hall, wiping his glasses, dabbing at his neck, at his dank burberry-coloured hair, repeating in a loud flat voice that it was nothing, it didn't matter, he didn't mind a bit—stressing his plight instead of laughing at it, or even enjoying it as a proper young man should (as Tony Heriot would have). After that, how passionately one had wished to return him at once, marked Not Suitable. Perhaps, he'd said, he'd better get out of his wet things at once, as he was liable to colds: might he borrow some dry clothes? So tea had been put off half an hour while he bathed and changed into a flannel shirt and a pair of grey flannels from his host's wardrobe. Then at tea, after asking him if he went to many dances and hearing he didn't, after saying did he like dancing and hearing he liked it in moderation—after that there seemed nothing to do but sit and watch him take greedy helps of butter and honey, and listen while he told Mrs. Curtis about the necessity for an operation for cataract upon his mother.

Kate and Olivia had had the melancholy satisfaction of studying his appearance without once being obliged to avert their eyes out of modesty or politeness; for he neither looked at them nor seemed aware of their scrutiny by so much as a twitch. He sat with his head poking forward on a short neck between high round shoulders. His skin was smooth, pinkish, rather shiny—not a healthy rough shine, but a sort of surface glisten, very unappetizing. His mouth shut like the two halves of a muffin. It too was shiny, rather full and pale. His eyes were opaque, the same colour as the hair on his flat broad head. He was not exactly ugly, they thought: but one might be alone with him on a desert island for ten years without ever being able to bear to kiss him.

After tea, Mrs. Curtis, with a look which said, Now, girls, you must look after your guest, went away to write letters. They took him into the drawing-room and put a ukulele solo on the gramophone. But he didn't seem to listen. Then they put on *Rustle of Spring*, in case his tastes were classical. But still he didn't seem to listen. He sat in the best armchair with his legs crossed, looking at the toe of his stubby black shoe and pulling rhythmically at his forelock. He appeared quite at home.

'Do you like music?' said Kate.

'I beg your pardon?'

She repeated very loudly:

'Do you like music?'

'Oh. Well, as a matter of fact I don't particularly care for the gramophone. But do go on if you like it.'

'Oh no, I wouldn't dream of it. We know every record by heart. We were doing it entirely for you.'

She shut down the gramophone lid with a bang and shot him one of her witherers. But he didn't notice it. Then she opened the new box of Abdullas bought in his honour.

'Cigarette?'

'Thanks, no. I don't smoke.'

Then it was six-thirty, and they gave him a bound volume of *Punch* to look at, and left him and went upstairs to dress a good half-hour earlier than necessary.

'Perhaps we ought to have suggested ludo or demon,' said Olivia on the stairs.

'It wouldn't have been any use. "Thanks, no. I don't particularly care for games." Can't you hear him?'

Olivia giggled.

'You were naughty to say that about the gramophone.'

'Well, did you ever—? I can't stand those priggish sort of idiots. . . . What price your clean-limbed footballer?'

But now, after an hour's absence from him, she felt inclined to be more hopeful. At least he was a partner. Unprepossessing but not unpresentable. Perhaps he would warm up and prove a good dancer. At least he was taller than either of them; and at least he hadn't said he'd never tried, but supposed he could walk round the room like anybody else.

They sighed, stirred idly, setting the water rippling. It was not a big bath and it looked overcrowded with their limbs. They had long well-turned arms and legs and small shapely breasts.

'Turn on the hot,' said Olivia. 'It's chilly up my end. You didn't mix it properly.'

'No. I'm getting out. So ought you. You were in before me. Look at your legs, you've simply boiled them. If you don't look out you'll come down to dinner with a lobster face again.'

She sprang up and out lightly and landed on the bath-mat. Olivia turned on the hot and lay back again.

Kate shook out talc powder (sweet geranium) all over herself in patches and rubbed it in. A cloud of it rose up and veiled her.

'Lend us a spot,' murmured Olivia.

'Why can't you buy some of your own? You are so lazy, you never will think for yourself. You don't want to go through life copy-catting me, do you? Didn't you read that article in the *Daily Mirror* about choosing scents and colours to suit your personality?'

Olivia said meekly:

'Yes. But I hadn't a bean in the wide after going that bust over the decoration.'

'Hmm. You'd better let me arrange that for you.'

'No thanks, bossy. I'm quite capable of sticking a flower in my own belt.'

'Hmm. Are you?'

Kate drew the cami-knickers over her slender thighs and hips. She had finished off the garment with *diamanté* shoulder straps and a couple of pale blue butterflies *appliqué* on the legs.

'Oh! You look exactly like some one in that French paper Etty brought—what was it?—*La Vie Parisienne*. What a pity you can't go like that. You really look your best.'

Kate surveyed herself placidly.

'Wouldn't you love to see his face?' She held out her arms and tripped forward, entreating in a tender languishing voice: 'Dance with me, Reggie. . . .'

Olivia giggled.

Kate squeezed out a double allowance of toothpaste and vigorously attacked her teeth.

'I say, you are going it,' said Olivia, still prostrate in the water.

'A young girl should be spotlessly pure both within and without.'

A sudden resolve to do likewise spurred Olivia to heave herself out and wrap herself in a towel. Then she sat down on the edge of the bath.

Kate studied her face in the mirror-front of the little medicine cupboard on the wall.

'I'm glad I washed my hair when I did. The wave's just right.' She examined her eyelashes and sighed. 'That Lashalene's a swindle. They haven't grown a millionth of an inch. None of these hush-hush things you send a postal order for ever work. Etty knew a girl afflicted with chronic red nose, and she saw an advertisement saying a lady well known in society guaranteed a cure on receipt of five bob. So she sent off the five bob, and what do you think she got? A typewritten slip of paper saying *Drink till it's blue*. . . . Livia, do pull yourself together. It's fearfully bad for your skin to sit and soak like that, and then not dry properly.'

She whisked on her dressing-gown and vanished.

Left alone, Olivia started suddenly to life, dried, powdered, brushed her teeth. She looked at her nails: they were clean, but that was all. Kate had spent an hour manicuring hers. All these dainty devices, so natural to Kate, seemed when she performed them to become unreal, like a lesson learnt by heart, but not properly understood. Something in her fumbled, felt inharmonious, wanted almost to resist.

She experienced a sudden distress of spirit, thinking in a half-conscious way that she hadn't—hadn't yet found herself . . . couldn't—*could* not put herself together, all of a piece. During a period of insanity she had accepted, with alacrity, with excitement, an invitation to a dance. Now, this moment having recovered her wits, she saw what she was in for.

Why go? It was unthinkable. Why suffer so much? Wrenched from one's foundations; neglected, ignored, curiously stared at; partnerless, watching Kate move serenely from partner to partner, pretending not to watch; pretending not to see one's hostess wondering: must she do something about one again?—(but really one couldn't go on and on introducing these people); pretending not to care; slipping off to the ladies' cloakroom, fiddling with unnecessary pins and powder, ears strained for the music to stop; wandering forth again to stand by oneself against the wall, hope struggling with despair beneath a mask of smiling indifference. . . . The band strikes up again, the first couple link and glide away. Kate sails past once more. . . . Back to the cloakroom, the pins, the cold scrutiny or (worse) the pitying small talk of the attendant maid.

Oh, horrible images! Solitude in the midst of crowds! Feast from which, sole non-participator, one would return empty!

She thought of a children's party at the Spencers', years ago; of falling in love at first sight with a most beautiful boy of ten called Archie, a cousin of the house. Dancing the baby polka with him, she had gazed enraptured at his profuse yellow locks and angelic pale-blue eyes. Between each dance he took a large broom from the corner of the room where he kept it, and swept the floor. (Why had he done that?) The fourth time she asked him to dance, he replied in a ringing treble, most gaily, most politely, rushing with his broom down the middle of the floor: 'Another? oh, right you are! We've had quite a lot of dances together, haven't we?' And all the grown-ups sitting round the room had burst out laughing; and the sound was like houses falling. That had been the beginning of self-consciousness, of failure of confidence. Some day I'll write a story about it.

She put on her stockings, regretting their cotton tops. With care they wouldn't show. All the same, lisle-thread knees made absolute poise impossible. How did Kate manage always to have in reserve an all-silk pair? Kate said it was a good maxim never to go out without making sure one would be, in the event of accident, the body of a well-dressed woman.

Now, how much, how little in the way of underclothes. . . . She put on three layers, then took off one. Even so there seemed a lack of suppleness, a thick look. Oh, for Kate's skill to fashion a featherweight trifle, her courage to wear it.

'What's that?' Mother had held it up between finger and thumb. 'A handkerchief?'

'No.' Kate snatched it back, smiling a little. 'Guess again.'

Mother had guessed long ago. From the ensuing scene Kate emerged unshaken—though she whistled for a bit afterwards—flouting the categorical *I forbid* and amused at the charge of indecency.

She gathered up her discarded clothes and went back to her room. There on the bed lay the red frock, smooth, inviting, brilliant; pressed out by Nannie, not yet tried on.

Now for the hair. She had practised nightly for the past week: this was its public debut. Part it in the middle, bring the two lots forward, plait them, coil one round each ear, like a German girl. Kate's idea. To-night the divided strands obeyed her, weaving themselves swiftly, smoothly. Round went the coils, exactly symmetrical, the ends tucked themselves neatly in. Now clamp them to the head with dozens and dozens of pins, fortify them with prongs. It was done. It was firm as a rock. Not even lancers could prevail against it. She dropped her hands and stared into the mirror.

Yes, it suits me. Head a good shape from the side; and it looked nice in the place just below the ear, where jawbone swept up in a soft clear curve and met the neck. One single hair was pulling somewhere out of reach. It must just be borne. Mademoiselle, jabbing at tangles with the comb, used to say, *Il faut souffrir pour être belle.*

Now for the dress.

After all, I shall probably enjoy the dance frightfully.

Quarter of an hour passed.

Kate put her head round the door.

'Ready?'

Olivia was standing still, with leaden stillness, before the glass. One glance, and Kate had spotted disaster.

'Here. You've got it twisted.' She gave a few sharp twitches to the waist and skirt. After a pause she said with restraint:

'It looks all right. Very nice.'

But it was not so. In the silence the truth weighed, became a stone that could not be rolled away.

Uneven hem; armholes too tight; and the draping—when Olivia looked at the clumsy lumpish pointless draping a terrible boiling-up, a painful constriction from chest to forehead started to scorch and suffocate her.

'It simply doesn't fit anywhere. . . .' The words burst from her chokingly. 'It's the most ghastly—— It's no good. I won't go looking like a freak. I must simply *rip* it off and burn it and not go to the dance, that's all.' She clutched wildly at the bodice, as if to wrench it from her.

Kate cried suddenly:

'You've got it on back to front!'

Olivia's hands dropped.

'Have I?' she said meekly.

'You would.' With the asperity of relief Kate seized and reversed her hurriedly, plunged her once more through the armholes. 'Now let's see you. Hm. It drops at the back now, of course.'

Olivia turned away from the glass while Kate hooked, tweaked, patted her into shape. It was a comfort to look into space for a little while before having to face once more the now irrevocable and perhaps scarcely improved image.

'The arms seem to catch a bit.' She crooked her elbows, strained at the seams and heard them crack with satisfaction.

'You're *not* to do that, Livia. You'll just have to bear it. Why on earth couldn't you *force* her to cut them properly? It's always the same with your clothes. You never could control her.'

'I know. I seem to make her feel so cheerful.'

Olivia sighed, thinking how at each fitting Miss Robinson had become increasingly volatile—her scissors more profuse and inconsequent, her piano-playing more frequent.

'She's loopy,' said Kate vigorously; adding, as she gave the skirt a final tweak: 'And I really believe you are too. Not to know your back from your front. How'll you ever get on in the world? Mm? . . . There.'

Now I must look.

She looked.

It was not so bad. It dipped at the back; and there was a queer place in the waist where, owing to a mistake in the cutting, Miss Robinson had had, in her own words, to contrive it. But still, but still . . . if one didn't look too closely, it was all right. Certainly the colour was becoming.

Delivered from despair, once more a young girl dressed for her first dance—not a caricature of one—able again to compete with and appreciate others, she saw Kate suddenly with seeing eyes and cried enthusiastically:

'Oh! You look simply topping!'

The airy apple-green frock which Kate had made for herself flared out below her hips and clung lightly to waist and breast. A little floating cape was attached just over each flat delicately-moulded shoulder-blade by a band of minute flowers, buds, leaves of all colours. She wore green stockings and silver shoes. Against the green, her skin looked white as coral, and her hair had a green-blonde gleam.

'You look like the girl on the cover of a Special Spring Number.'

Twisting to look at her cape, Kate said placidly:

'I just took it straight from *Vogue*.'

Side by side they stood and looked at their reflections. After a bit Kate said:

'Thank heaven, anyway, we don't look alike.'

Olivia ventured:

'We set each other off really rather well, don't you think?' She thought: The younger girl, with her gypsy colouring, afforded a rich foil to her sister's fair beauty.

'Your hair's gone up all right,' murmured Kate dreamily.

'It makes me rather deaf, though.'

Kate roused herself, said briskly, 'I must go and hook up Mother,' and disappeared.

Olivia took from a drawer a silver tinsel spray—a water-lily with some leaves—and stuck it in her belt, just where Miss Robinson's graceful bow overlooped itself. From the back of the same drawer she extracted a box of powder and, breaking into its crumbling virgin surface with a swansdown puff, dabbed at her chin. The powder was pink. It took off the shine nicely, but seemed scarcely to blend with her skin. She wiped some of it off again. Would Mother notice; and, if so, attack in public?

Now for the crowning touch: a little scent on the hair, for one's partners to sniff up rapturously. The idea came from the *Daily Mirror* serial, whose heroine had hair smelling naturally of violets. This was one better: lily of the valley. She opened the tiny flask—a birthday present from Nannie—and shook it into her parting. Immediately she was drenched in a thick sweetish yet acrid odour. It didn't seem to smell quite like lilies of the valley, particularly blent, as it now was, with the smell of hair. Well, well. . . . Two hours yet in which to become faint yet delicious. Still, perhaps . . .

She opened the window and hung her head out into the breeze for some minutes.

*1932*

# ANN BRIDGE

## *Chieh T'ai Ssu*

FROM 'PEKING PICNIC'

CHIEH T'AI SSU, the Monastery of the Platform of Vows, stands on a sort of natural terrace just below the crest of one of the ridges running down from the Western Hills towards the Peking plain, flanking the valley of the Hun-ho on the south. Its innumerable courts, pavilions, shrines and terraces stretch up the hill-side, one above another, connected by paved walks and broad flights of marble steps, scattered irregularly in all directions at all sorts of levels; diversified by trees springing from the stone pavements, by rocky landscapes and grottoes in corners, by little pagodas, by Drum Towers and Bell Towers, and by vast bronze incense-burners—the whole beautiful confusion, covering several acres and containing as many souls as an English village, enclosed within a high wall which follows its irregular outline over the contours of the steep stony slopes. Men in bright flower-blue cassocks, with blue trousers tucked into high white gaiter boots, wander about its shade-splashed walks and disappear through its unexpected doorways; grey-robed priests tend its latticed shrines, filling the courts with the perfume of incense, beat its vast resonant drums and its musical gongs; or stand in dreamy meditation, rosary in hand, beside its carved marble balustrades. It is a great religious foundation in being, in full and serene activity. Here the monastic life of a thousand years ago, painstakingly dug up and described by travellers like Hédin and Stein in the ruined temples of the Central Asian wastes, is unrolled before the Western eyes of the week-end visitor from Peking, breathing, actual, undecaying—the past wells up into the present in a timeless continuity, unchanging, quiet, with the still perfection of the figures on some Greek vase.

Nothing is stranger to the newcomer to China than this custom of Temple authorities of throwing open their sacred precincts to European visitors. A courtyard, or two, or three, according to their needs, is let off to each party, and there with their beds, food, chairs and servants they establish themselves for a day or two. But they are not confined to their hired apartments—freely they stroll about the terraces, among the shrines and pavilions, where the wealth and tribute of centuries is accumulated in buildings, in treasures, of a stylised beauty and a formal grace peculiarly Chinese, saluted with grave courtesy as they go by the black-robed monks. And in and around the whole temple, in spring, the fruit-blossom flows like a tide, surging up in waves of exquisite pale colour against the ancient walls, springing like flowery fountains in the paved courtyards. More than one of the party, that night, was to fall asleep with the sprays of peach-blossom shadowed between him and the stars, and to wake with fallen petals on his face. Strange magic of the blossoming tree—ancient wisdom that brings in the spring to worship within its holy places! It is not easy to escape these wholly; all did not wholly escape. There is no cause for wonder if in that place, and then, some bonds of thought and custom were loosened, some curtains of the soul drawn back—if eyes were opened, if vision for a moment gleamed, and ardour sprang in pursuit.

Chieh T'ai Ssu is approached from below by a paved road, winding up and round the curves and hollows of the hill, crossing the beds of torrents on beautifully-arched bridges, and protected always on the valley side by a plastered parapet. On leaving the smallpox village the General's little party turned to the left, crossed a stream near a broken high-backed bridge, and began the ascent of this road. For the first time for nearly eight miles they walked in shade, for they were close in under the hill now, and the ridge cut off the sun. And immediately the fruit-blossom was about them. All over the brown hill-side, on narrow stone-built terraces and wherever the slope would hold a little soil, stood the trees, so irregularly and in such profusion as to suggest a natural growth—the pink of almond-flower, the deeper pink of apricot, the phlox-like greenish white of pear-blossom. But with no green carpet, pied with daisies, below them; straight from the brown soil, an incredible flowering from the still naked earth. North China, with its rainless snowless winter, knows no spring as Europe knows it—only the deeply-rooted plants and trees can come to life. Later the thunderstorms of early summer revive the parched world, covering the hills with a rank un-nourishing verdure, but in spring the flowering trees carry the torch of rebirth alone. Unbelievable, the shock of this beauty—the delicately-shaped perfection of flower of rose and paler rose and white, against the unrelieved fawn-coloured background. It is easy, here, to see why the Chinese have painted their masterpieces of flowers on backgrounds of brown silk—even Nature, in China, is a consummate artist, and with a sure hand has shown the way in which that race of consummate artists has followed, to produce a beauty unknown to the Western world. If you want to get some idea of the road to Chieh T'ai Ssu, go to the British Museum and look at the Chinese paintings—above all at the 'Earthly Paradise.' But fill its air with a delicate scent, hardly more than a freshness, and yet more; and break its silence with the loud sweet notes of hidden babblers among bare wayside bushes, and with the tapping and scraping of the small feet of donkeys on steep cobbles. And because that picture is one of the supreme masterpieces of the world, and because Art carries truth like an arrow or a pang, you shall perhaps come to some knowledge of a Chinese spring, one of the rarest perfections ever permitted itself by the rejoicing spirit of creation.

*1932*

# NORMAN DOUGLAS

## *Mr. Frank Harris*

### FROM 'LOOKING BACK'

FRANKIE could have passed for a Balkan conspirator. I liked him: perhaps because I never saw too much of him.

He wrote some admirable short stories, and those he could tell by word of mouth, in that carefully modulated bass voice of his, were as good as any of the written ones He was different from many notable raconteurs in that he never played variations on the theme, never gave his hero a new hat or stick, never altered his tales by a hair. They must have been elaborated and brought to their final state of perfection in his mind, and then memorized for public utterance; I can imagine no other process. I have heard him tell the same story, of a white man's adventure in the African bush, at an interval of two or three years. If one could have counted the number of words used on those two occasions, if one could have measured the length of his dramatic pauses, recorded the intonation of his voice and the force of emphases employed for this or that phrase, it would have been difficult to detect a shade of difference between the two versions. His stories were stereotyped; and how good!

Frankie thought he could ram himself down everybody's throat. He was a swashbuckler, and one of the last exponents of the art of living—of the art of living well, no matter at whose expense; at his own, if possible. Owing to a fateful flaw in his alloy he lost all that his rare combination of gifts should have gained for him. Would he have suffered this eclipse, I wonder, if he had lived in the days of Aretino, when an unscrupulous and accomplished writer could say what he liked in print, and squeeze with impunity the last drops of blood out of his prey?

These two men had much in common; curiously much. Both were of lowly origin, both journalists, lavish with money, charitable to the poor, dabblers in politics, collectors of paintings, of pretty women and conspicuous men; both were free-lances thriving on their wits, realists with a freshness of outlook which despised tradition and went straight to life for its themes; both were masters in the art of knowing everybody worth knowing, and choosing the right moment and the right method for extracting what they wanted out of them. Now the likeness ends. Harris could not count kings and emperors among his victims, nor men like Titian among his friends. Harris could not inspire an enduring passion such as Giovanni delle Bande Nere, the greatest warrior in Italy, felt for Aretino. It was not only that social customs and legal usage had changed since the sixteenth century. Frankie had a flaw. He died snarling; embittered and discredited. The other was a harmonious monster; a phenomenon. He raked in money and gifts and honours to his last breath, and died, they say, in a fit of laughter. . . .

Harris possessed one noble quality which is becoming extinct in England—a heartfelt and outspoken reverence for all that is admirable in art or literature. You heard no suburban chuckle and no sniggering reservations when he spoke of the great men of the past, and what they have done to make our own life worth living. On such occasions this boastful and thick-skinned adventurer was transformed into a humble disciple. In other words, he was a man. To appraise these giants frankly, at their full worth, calls for manliness of spirit—a quality which is likewise dying out.

He once got into trouble over something which he had printed in his paper called, I think, *Vanity Fair*—a libel suit, possibly, ending in a short sentence. The day after he came out of prison he said to me:

'They treated me badly, very badly. I'm a pretty old man, you know; older than I look. Now for any number of years back I've been accustomed to wearing bed-socks. I can't go to sleep without them. Would you believe it? They didn't allow me to wear my bed-socks in prison. They took them away from me. Fancy doing that to an old fellow like me! It's the sort of indignity you can be made to suffer only in England. The torturing brutes. . . .'

Yes; I liked Harris, though he once did victimize me in a small way. He had a powerful new car; wouldn't it be good fun to run down, both of us, to see his friend Joseph Conrad at Orlestone in Kent? That was in 1914 or 1915. I thought it strange that Frankie, with his reputation of a perfect immoralist, should be on terms of intimacy with Conrad who was the greatest stickler for uprightness I have ever known; little I dreamed that he was simply using me to get another sight (with a view to future 'copy') of Conrad whom, as I afterwards heard, he had met just once before, when he ran down to Kent with Austin Harrison on some other pretext. On the way there he told me of his past life in Japan, as a rivetter on Brooklyn bridge, as a cowboy, and I cannot remember what else. The moment we set foot in the house I saw that something was wrong.

Conrad managed to scrape up a polite greeting and then, after three minutes, went upstairs to sulk in his room and not to emerge again till Harris was off the premises. He did this on the usual and only too justifiable plea of gout, saying to me, as I accompanied him up the stairs:

'I should like to know why you bring this brigand into my house. Am I never to see the last of him?'

That earlier impression, apparently, had not been favourable. Whether Harris got any 'copy' out of the family I cannot say, but so far as Conrad was concerned it was a misspent afternoon—doubly misspent, because on the way home we ran into a police trap, and Frankie was afterwards fined for exceeding the speed limit.

*1933*

# WILLIAM FAULKNER

## *A Rose for Emily*

### I

WHEN Miss Emily Grierson died, our whole town went to her funeral: the men through a sort of respectful affection for a fallen monument, the women mostly out of curiosity to see the inside of her house, which no one save an old manservant—a combined gardener and cook—had seen in at least ten years.

It was a big, squarish frame house that had once been white, decorated with cupolas and spires and scrolled balconies in the heavily lightsome style of the seventies, set on what had once been our most select street. But garages and cotton gins had encroached and obliterated even the august names of that neighbourhood; only Miss Emily's house was left, lifting its stubborn and coquettish decay above the cotton wagons and the gasoline pumps—an eyesore among eyesores. And now Miss Emily had gone to join the representatives of those august names where they lay in the cedar-bemused cemetery among the ranked and anonymous graves of Union and Confederate soldiers who fell at the battle of Jefferson.

Alive, Miss Emily had been a tradition, a duty, and a care; a sort of hereditary obligation upon the town, dating from that day in 1894 when Colonel Sartoris, the mayor—he who fathered the edict that no Negro woman should appear on the streets without an apron—remitted her taxes, the dispensation dating from the death of her father on into perpetuity. Not that Miss Emily would have accepted charity. Colonel Sartoris invented an involved tale to the effect that Miss Emily's father had loaned money to the town, which the town, as a matter of business, preferred this way of repaying. Only a man of Colonel Sartoris' generation and thought could have invented it, and only a woman could have believed it.

When the next generation, with its more modern ideas, became mayors and aldermen, this arrangement created some little dissatisfaction. On the first of the year they mailed her a tax notice. February came, and there was no reply. They wrote her a formal letter, asking her to call at the sheriff's office at her convenience. A week later the mayor wrote her himself, offering to call or to send his car for her, and received in reply a note on paper of an archaic shape, in a thin, flowing calligraphy in faded ink, to the effect that she no longer went out at all. The tax notice was also enclosed, without comment.

They called a special meeting of the Board of Aldermen. A deputation waited upon her, knocked at the door through which no visitor had passed since she ceased giving china-painting lessons eight or ten years earlier. They were admitted by the old Negro into a dim hall from which a stairway mounted into still more shadow. It smelled of dust and disuse—a close, dank smell. The Negro led them into the parlour. It was furnished in heavy, leather-covered furniture. When the Negro opened the blinds of one window, they could see that the leather was cracked; and when they sat down, a faint dust rose sluggishly about their thighs, spinning with slow motes in the single sun-ray. On a tarnished gilt easel before the fireplace stood a crayon portrait of Miss Emily's father.

They rose when she entered—a small, fat woman in black, with a thin gold chain descending to her waist and vanishing into her belt, leaning on an ebony cane with a tarnished gold head. Her skeleton was small and spare; perhaps that was why what would have been merely plumpness in another was obesity in her. She looked bloated, like a body long submerged in motionless water, and of that pallid hue. Her eyes, lost in the fatty ridges of her face, looked like two small pieces of coal pressed into a lump of dough as they moved from one face to another while the visitors stated their errand.

She did not ask them to sit. She just stood in the door and listened quietly until the spokesman came to a stumbling halt. Then they could hear the invisible watch ticking at the end of the gold chain.

Her voice was dry and cold. 'I have no taxes in Jefferson. Colonel Sartoris explained it to me. Perhaps one of you can gain access to the city records and satisfy yourselves.'

'But we have. We are the city authorities, Miss Emily. Didn't you get a notice from the sheriff, signed by him?'

'I received a paper, yes,' Miss Emily said. 'Perhaps he considers himself the sheriff . . . I have no taxes in Jefferson.'

'But there is nothing on the books to show that, you see. We must go by the—'

'See Colonel Sartoris. I have no taxes in Jefferson.'

'But, Miss Emily—'

'See Colonel Sartoris.' (Colonel Sartoris had been dead almost ten years.) 'I have no taxes in Jefferson. Tobe!' The Negro appeared. 'Show these gentlemen out.'

II

So she vanquished them, horse and foot, just as she had vanquished their fathers thirty years before about the smell. That was two years after her father's death and a short time after her sweetheart—the one we believed would marry her—had deserted her. After her father's death she went out very little; after her sweetheart went away, people hardly saw her at all. A few of the ladies had the temerity to call, but were not received, and the only sign of life about the place was the Negro man—a young man then—going in and out with a market basket.

'Just as if a man—any man—could keep a kitchen properly,' the ladies said; so they were not surprised when the smell developed. It was another link between the gross, teeming world and the high and mighty Griersons.

A neighbour, a woman, complained to the mayor, Judge Stevens, eighty years old.

'But what will you have me do about it, madam?' he said.

'Why, send her word to stop it,' the woman said. 'Isn't there a law?'

'I'm sure that won't be necessary,' Judge Stevens said. 'It's probably just a snake or a rat that nigger of hers killed in the yard. I'll speak to him about it.'

The next day he received two more complaints, one from a man who came in diffident deprecation. 'We really must do something about it, Judge. I'd be the last one in the world to bother Miss Emily, but we've got to do something.' That night the Board of Aldermen met—three greybeards and one younger man, a member of the rising generation.

'It's simple enough,' he said. 'Send her word to have her place cleaned up. Give her a certain time to do it in, and if she don't . . .'

'Dammit, sir,' Judge Stevens said, 'will you accuse a lady to her face of smelling bad?'

So the next night, after midnight, four men crossed Miss Emily's lawn and slunk about the house like burglars, sniffing along the base of the brickwork and at the cellar openings while one of them performed a regular sowing motion with his hand out of a sack slung from his shoulder. They broke open the cellar door and sprinkled lime there, and in all the outbuildings. As they recrossed the lawn, a window that had been dark was lighted and Miss Emily sat in it, the light behind her, and her upright torso motionless as that of an idol. They crept quietly across the lawn and into the shadow of the locusts that lined the street. After a week or two the smell went away.

That was when people had begun to feel really sorry for her. People in our town, remembering how old lady Wyatt, her great-aunt, had gone completely crazy at last, believed that the Griersons held themselves a little too high for what they really were. None of the young men were quite good enough to Miss Emily and such. We had long thought of them as a tableau; Miss Emily a slender figure in white in the background, her father a spraddled silhouette in the foreground, his back to her and clutching a horse-whip, the two of them framed by the back-flung front door. So when she got to be thirty and was still single, we were not pleased exactly, but vindicated; even with insanity in the family she wouldn't have turned down all of her chances if they had really materialized.

When her father died, it got about that the house was all that was left to her; and in a way, people were glad. At last they could pity Miss Emily. Being left alone, and a pauper, she had become humanized. Now she too would know the old thrill and the old despair of a penny more or less.

The day after his death all the ladies prepared to call at the house and offer condolence and aid, as is our custom. Miss Emily met them at the door, dressed as usual and with no trace of grief on her face. She told them that her father was not dead. She did that for three days, with the ministers calling on her, and the doctors, trying to persuade her to let them dispose of the body. Just as they were about to resort to law and force, she broke down, and they buried her father quickly.

We did not say she was crazy then. We believed she had to do that. We remembered all the young men her father had driven away, and we knew that with nothing left, she would have to cling to that which had robbed her, as people will.

## III

She was sick for a long time. When we saw her again, her hair was cut short, making her look like a girl, with a vague resemblance to those angels in coloured church windows—sort of tragic and serene.

The town had just let the contracts for paving the sidewalks, and in the summer after her father's death they began the work. The construction company came with niggers and mules and machinery, and a foreman named Homer Barron, a Yankee—a big, dark, ready man, with a big voice and eyes lighter than his face. The little boys would follow in groups to hear him cuss the niggers, and the niggers singing in time to the rise and fall of picks. Pretty soon he knew everybody in town. Whenever you heard a lot of laughing anywhere about the square, Homer Barron would be in the centre of the group. Presently we began to see him and Miss Emily on Sunday afternoons driving in the yellow-wheeled buggy and the matched team of bays from the livery stable.

At first we were glad that Miss Emily would have an interest, because the ladies all said, 'Of course a Grierson would not think seriously of a Northerner, a day labourer.' But there were still others, older people, who said that even grief could not cause a real lady to forget *noblesse oblige*—without calling it *noblesse oblige*. They just said, 'Poor Emily.

Her kinsfolk should come to her.' She had some kin in Alabama; but years ago her father had fallen out with them over the estate of old lady Wyatt, the crazy woman, and there was no communication between the two families. They had not even been represented at the funeral.

And as soon as the old people said, 'Poor Emily,' the whispering began. 'Do you suppose it's really so?' they said to one another. 'Of course it is. What else could . . .' This behind their hands; rustling of craned silk and satin behind jalousies closed upon the sun of Sunday afternoon as the thin, swift clop-clop-clop of the matched team passed: 'Poor Emily.'

She carried her head high enough—even when we believed that she was fallen. It was as if she demanded more than ever the recognition of her dignity as the last Grierson; as if it had wanted that touch of earthiness to reaffirm her imperviousness. Like when she bought the rat poison, the arsenic. That was over a year after they had begun to say 'Poor Emily', and while the two female cousins were visiting her.

'I want some poison,' she said to the druggist. She was over thirty then, still a slight woman, though thinner than usual, with cold, haughty black eyes in a face the flesh of which was strained across the temples and about the eye-sockets as you imagine a lighthouse-keeper's face ought to look. 'I want some poison,' she said.

'Yes, Miss Emily. What kind? For rats and such? I'd recom—'

'I want the best you have. I don't care what kind.'

The druggist named several. 'They'll kill anything up to an elephant. But what you want is—'

'Arsenic,' Miss Emily said. 'Is that a good one?'

'Is . . . arsenic? Yes, ma'am. But what you want—'

'I want arsenic.'

The druggist looked down at her. She looked back at him, erect, her face like a strained flag. 'Why, of course,' the druggist said. 'If that's what you want. But the law requires you to tell what you are going to use it for.'

Miss Emily just stared at him, her head tilted back in order to look him eye for eye, until he looked away and went and got the arsenic and wrapped it up. The Negro delivery boy brought her the package; the druggist didn't come back. When she opened the package at home there was written on the box, under the skull and bones: 'For rats.'

## IV

So the next day we all said, 'She will kill herself'; and we said it would be the best thing. When she had first begun to be seen with Homer Barron, we had said, 'She will marry him.' Then we said, 'She will persuade him yet,' because Homer himself had remarked—he liked men, and it was known that he drank with the younger men in the Elks' Club—that he was not a marrying man. Later we said, 'Poor

Emily' behind the jalousies as they passed on Sunday afternoon in the glittering buggy, Miss Emily with her head high and Homer Barron with his hat cocked and a cigar in his teeth, reins and whip in a yellow glove.

Then some of the ladies began to say that it was a disgrace to the town and a bad example to the young people. The men did not want to interfere, but at last the ladies forced the Baptist minister—Miss Emily's people were Episcopal—to call upon her. He would never divulge what happened during that interview, but he refused to go back again. The next Sunday they again drove about the streets, and the following day the minister's wife wrote to Miss Emily's relations in Alabama.

So she had blood-kin under her roof again and we sat back to watch developments. At first nothing happened. Then we were sure that they were to be married. We learned that Miss Emily had been to the jeweller's and ordered a man's toilet set in silver, with the letters H. B. on each piece. Two days later we learned that she had bought a complete outfit of men's clothing, including a nightshirt, and we said, 'They are married.' We were really glad. We were glad because the two female cousins were even more Grierson than Miss Emily had ever been.

So we were not surprised when Homer Barron—the streets had been finished some time since—was gone. We were a little disappointed that there was not a public blowing-off, but we believed that he had gone on to prepare for Miss Emily's coming, or to give her a chance to get rid of the cousins. (By that time it was a cabal, and we were all Miss Emily's allies to help circumvent the cousins.) Sure enough, after another week they departed. And, as we had expected all along, within three days Homer Barron was back in town. A neighbour saw the Negro man admit him at the kitchen door at dusk one evening.

And that was the last we saw of Homer Barron. And of Miss Emily for some time. The Negro man went in and out with the market basket, but the front door remained closed. Now and then we would see her at a window for a moment, as the men did that night when they sprinkled the lime, but for almost six months she did not appear on the streets. Then we knew that this was to be expected too; as if that quality of her father which had thwarted her woman's life so many times had been too virulent and too furious to die.

When we next saw Miss Emily, she had grown fat and her hair was turning grey. During the next few years it grew greyer and greyer until it attained an even pepper-and-salt iron-grey, when it ceased turning. Up to the day of her death at seventy-four it was still that vigorous iron-grey, like the hair of an active man.

From that time on her front door remained closed, save for a period of six or seven years, when she was about forty, during which she gave lessons in china-painting. She fitted up a studio in one of the downstairs rooms, where the daughters and granddaughters of Colonel Sartoris' contemporaries were sent to her with the same regularity and in the same spirit that they were sent to church on Sundays with a twenty-five cent piece for the collection plate. Meanwhile her taxes had been remitted.

Then the newer generation became the backbone and the spirit of the town, and the painting pupils grew up and fell away and did not send their children to her with boxes of colour and tedious brushes and pictures cut from the ladies' magazines. The front door closed upon the last one and remained closed for good. When the town got free postal delivery, Miss Emily alone refused to let them fasten the metal numbers above her door and attach a mailbox to it. She would not listen to them.

Daily, monthly, yearly we watched the Negro grow greyer and more stooped, going in and out with the market basket. Each December we sent her a tax notice, which would be returned by the post office a week later, unclaimed. Now and then we would see her in one of the downstairs windows—she had evidently shut up the top floor of the house—like the carven torso of an idol in a niche, looking or not looking at us, we could never tell which. Thus she passed from generation to generation—dear, inescapable, impervious, tranquil and perverse.

And so she died. Fell ill in the house filled with dust and shadows, with only a doddering Negro man to wait on her. We did not even know she was sick; we had long since given up trying to get any information from the Negro. He talked to no one, probably not even to her, for his voice had grown harsh and rusty, as if from disuse.

She died in one of the downstairs rooms, in a heavy walnut bed with a curtain, her grey headpropped on a pillow yellow and mouldy with age and lack of sunlight.

## V

The Negro met the first of the ladies at the front door and let them in, with their hushed, sibilant voices and their quick, curious glances, and then he disappeared. He walked right through the house and out the back and was not seen again.

The two female cousins came at once. They held the funeral on the second day, with the town coming to look at Miss Emily beneath a mass of bought flowers, with the crayon face of her father musing profoundly above the bier and the ladies sibilant and macabre; and the very old men—some in their brushed Confederate uniforms—on the porch and the lawn, talking of Miss Emily as if she had been a contemporary of theirs, believing that they had danced with her and courted her perhaps, confusing time with its mathematical progression, as the old do, to whom all the past is not a diminishing road but, instead, a huge meadow which no winter ever quite touches, divided from them now by the narrow bottle-neck of the most recent decade of years.

Already we knew that there was one room in that region above stairs which no one had seen in forty years, and which would have to be forced. They waited until Miss Emily was decently in the ground before they opened it.

The violence of breaking down the door seemed to fill this room with pervading dust. A thin, acrid pall as of the tomb seemed to lie everywhere upon this room decked and furnished as for a bridal: upon the valence curtains of faded rose colour, upon the rose-shaded lights, upon the dressing table, upon the delicate array of crystal and the man's toilet things backed with tarnished silver, silver so tarnished that the monogram was obscured. Among them lay a collar and tie, as if they had just been removed, which, lifted, left upon the surface a pale crescent in the dust. Upon a chair hung the suit, carefully folded; beneath it the two mute shoes and the discarded socks.

The man himself lay in the bed.

For a long while we just stood there, looking down at the profound and fleshless grin. The body had apparently once lain in the attitude of an embrace, but now the long sleep that outlasts love, that conquers even the grimace of love, had cuckolded him. What was left of him, rotted beneath what was left of the nightshirt, had become inextricable from the bed in which he lay; and upon him and upon the pillow beside him lay that even coating of the patient and biding dust.

Then we noticed that in the second pillow was the indentation of a head. One of us lifted something from it, and leaning forward, that faint and invisible dust dry and acrid in the nostrils, we saw a long strand of iron-grey hair.

*1933*

# DAVID GARNETT

## FROM *Beany-Eye*

ONE morning while I was standing watching him at work with my hands in my overcoat pockets, our dogs roused a rabbit in the wood above us which bolted through our shaw across the top of our garden and into the next field. I was already becoming a keen rabbiter, but Beany-eye's excitement was far greater than mine. Both of us raced as fast as we could after the dogs, I slipped through and Beany-eye burst by main force through the hedge and vaulted the post and rail fence beyond and dashed across the old pasture and found the dogs at the mouth of a burrow on a very precipitous bank, or shaw, which divided the meadow and which we always called the ravine. It is at the bottom of this ravine that I always visualise the scene so beautifully described by Turgenev in 'Byezhin Prairie' though I cannot have read the 'Sportsman' Sketches before I was ten years old—two years after the events that I am describing.

There were two dogs: Nietzsche, a little short-haired red mongrel with a bushy tail like a fox, and Puppsie, a collie of imbecile disposition afflicted with a spasmodic twitch of the left forepaw. I was brought up to gentle treatment of these animals and was horrified when Beany-eye, who seemed to have been transformed into a wild beast himself, flung Puppsie from the mouth of the rabbit-bury down the almost sheer face of the ravine and, dropping in front of the hole, seized Nietzsche by the tail, dragged him out with terrific force, and sent him also flying backwards, with all four legs asprawl, down the scree of Kentish ragstone. Then he flung himself as far down the hole as he could reach, but, of course, he could come nowhere near the rabbit. By the time that he had withdrawn his head and shoulders, the dogs were limping back and I very heatedly told him that he must never dare to treat them like that again. Beany-eye was in a very odd state just then; his head was full of sand and his face smeared with it; his whole expression was almost apoplectic with frenzied excitement, his lips twitching with passion. But I also was very angry; Nietzsche was slipping between his knees down the hole and Nietzsche was my dog. So I spoke up fiercely and threatened Beany-eye that if he laid a hand on the dogs it would be the worse for him. I would tell. I don't know quite why I didn't go the way of the dogs; I was balanced on a tiny ledge beside Beany-eye at the mouth of the bury, and the slightest push would have sent me flying to the bottom of the ravine. But Beany-eye only stared as though he didn't see me, whilst his mouth twisted, and my words, though not having an immediate effect, had some. Slowly he calmed down and then he went off to fetch a spade and a pick. But by the time he had returned with them from the stable he was cool enough to see that the rabbit-hole ran through the roots of an old pollard ash and that it would be a labour of hours to dig the rabbit out. So, after a little while, the hunt was abandoned and we climbed up out of the ravine, while Nietzsche stared with a look of questioning disillusion at our backs before plunging into the hole to do his digging for himself single-handed. For Puppsie was useless.

We were not always uninterrupted since my mother had reasons of her own for disliking my being too much in Beany-eye's company and would call me down to the house if she thought I was up in the stable. She was, however, a very busy woman and for several hours a day the affairs of Vronsky, Levin, and Dolly were perforce as real to her as those of her own household. Thus it would happen that, if, after looking up a difficult word in the dictionary, she chanced to notice my absence, she would go to the door with the book in her hand and call me down from the stable. But that did not always mean that the evening was over, since once her nib began to scrape faster and faster across the sheets of foolscap, there was always a fair chance that I could slip quietly out of the back door and return to hear what Beany-eye still had to say. And if it was hard to keep me away from him in the evening, it was impossible during the day. My mother was glad to think that very soon I should be going back to my little day-school, attendance at which had been interrupted by a neighbouring case of measles.

My mother's instinctive fear of Beany-eye was tempered by exasperation at the way in which he had been doing his work and with my father for employing him. And she was also exasperated with herself for feeling afraid of the man, and for being unable to argue fairly about him with my father. When she explained how much she disliked having him round the house, my father would listen patiently and say:

'It is just because everyone has this instinctive feeling about the poor fellow that he is an outcast in this pitiable condition. What on earth is the good of setting out to help a man if you are going to give way at once to the same unreasoning prejudices as everybody else?'

My mother recognised that this argument was unanswerable and she knew that my father would think it unworthy of her to ask: 'But why must *we* help this man? Why shouldn't someone else do it for a change?'

The morning after this conversation my father decided to work with Beany-eye in cutting up the trunk of a large pine tree which, standing in the corner of our copse, had been violently uprooted by a south-westerly gale and had crashed through the fence into the wood. It was one of those bright January mornings when there is not a breath of wind and the hoar frost sparkles along the edges of every fallen leaf, when the redbreast perches close by for company and when, in spite of the frost, one soon takes off one's waistcoat as well as one's coat if one is working out of doors.

My father and Beany-eye carried out the crosscut saw and soon set to work, but though Beany-eye took the lower ground, they found some difficulty in settling down. Then directly they had got going, my father was out of breath and they took a rest.

'You don't need to push the Saw, sir. You are trying to do my work as well as your own. If you just pull and I just pull it will cut like butter,' said Beany-eye.

When they began again, my father acted on his advice and pulled, then, letting his arm go slack, waited for Beany-eye to pull the blade back and then pulled again himself. As soon as he mastered the trick of letting his arm go quite slack and caught the right rhythm, the work went of itself, and the saw-blade sank deeper rapidly until its back was below the burnt-sienna, crocodile-skin bark and a strong scent of resin filled the still air. A moment later they had finished the first cut that severed the whole head of the pine tree and, before they began again, the postman came down the steep path through the wood from the little hamlet of Shirley Gate and, seeing my father, stopped and handed the letters and newspaper out of his bag.

'You've heard the news, Sir, I suppose? The Queen is dead.'

It was Tuesday, January 22, and although since the previous Friday it had been announced that the Queen was very ill, my father was tremendously surprised and could hardly believe the fact. Queen Victoria had been such a landmark for so many years, she was so much taken for granted as part of the permanent condition of the world, that her subjects could hardly imagine it without her.

'Do you hear, Joe, that the Queen is dead?' he said as they took up the crosscut again.

'Yes, master. And you may lay that it's the war what's killed her. She hasn't been able to sleep at night thinking of the Boers creeping up and killing our poor fellows. She kept seeing our young chaps going off and thinking of them lying out in the moonlight dead and murdered by them Boers. That's what killed her, poor soul, depend upon it.'

'Well, she was a good age you know, Joe, anyhow.'

When they had finished the next cut my father took the newspaper down to the house for my mother and, when he came back, Beany-eye said:

'I saw the Prince of Wales at Epsom once, fat as a turkey, a real sportsman by the look of him. That's what we want. A king what loves a bit of sport.'

They went on working happily in unison, their faces dewy with sweat and the grains of sawdust caught in the unshaven stubble of Beany-eye's beard. When they had cut the trunk into five or six lengths, my father went down again to the house and brought back two bottles of beer.

It was a peaceful and delightful moment, and I remember coming up to them and looking at the foam standing up above the rim of the glass and watching Beany-eye's face as my father handed it to him, and he took it in his trembling fingers and drank it off rather unsteadily and a trickle of beer went running down from the corner of his mouth among the grains of sawdust on his chin. The robin that had been hopping near them, perched on the fence and began to sing.

'Let's see if we can split up one of these short lengths,' said my father, and fetched the axe from the stable.

'Let me have it,' cried Joe, suddenly excited, and, taking it, whirled it over his head, almost shouting out as he did so: 'Stand clear, Sir, stand clear. Don't come too near me,' in such an earnest voice that we felt quite amazed by him.

The blow, however, that Beany-eye delivered did not split the log and the axe had to be wrenched out again and again before at length he was successful.

'That will do for now, Joe,' said my father. 'You can split up the rest with the wedges and beetle later on and clear up the pine branches this afternoon and stack them by the woodpile.'

And at lunch my father told us that Beany-eye had been working quite well.

'The after-effects of prison are working off. He's not nearly so wild and talked quite well about the Queen's death and the Prince of Wales.'

Sometimes when it was getting dark or was raining, I would go up to the stable and Beany-eye would tell me stories while he chopped and whittled at a short ash stake. He collected lengths of old iron and formed an armoury of rusty old knives, broken shears, ancient scythe-blades, bill-hooks and hatchets, and among them, I remember, there was the iron bar and coulter of a plough. But he also had a partiality for a wooden weapon, and it is this which I remember that he was shaping. It was a short truncheon of ash-plant, with a smoothed handle and a heavy head which terminated in a sharp conical point. Except that it was short, so that one man might use it single-handed, it was like the pointed olive-wood stake that Odysseus fashioned to put out the eye of Polyphemus. Beany-eye made two of these, and while he was hacking at them with his jack-knife or scraping them with a piece of broken glass, he told me many strange stories, all but one of which have now vanished, leaving nothing behind but a memory of my childish wonder and incredulity. I suppose the reason why I remember this one story is because I absolutely and unquestioningly believed it. It was impossible not to do so, for he related it with the intense horror and conviction of a man describing a personal experience. It was about rats.

According to Beany-eye, there were not only the ordinary rats such as I had seen, which lived in their twos and threes and half-dozens about the house and the dust-heap and after which men went ratting, but at certain times and places there were other rats which gathered into armies, recruited from all the garbage heaps of the country, and these armies soon became hungry and travelled about in lonely places eating up everything they came across. When one of these great rat-armies found a man sleeping out of doors in a ditch, they ate him alive. Nothing of him was ever seen again, not one trace, because there was such a vast army that when a thousand rats had eaten all the flesh off his bones, there were still thousands more of the starving behind them that gnawed up and devoured every fragment of the skeleton.

Beany-eye had seen this happen with his own eyes and he himelf had escaped from the rat-army almost by a miracle. It had been a brilliant moonlight night and Beany-eye had been lying in the loft of a big barn in Kent when he woke up at the sound of a terrible screaming, and looking out through a loose board he had seen a figure jump up, run a little way and fall down. It was a man completely covered in rats that were tearing at his throat, his ears, his nose, and that had bitten out his eyes already.

'They'd blinded 'im, mate. They'd gone for his eyes while he was on the ground, while he was asleep. As soon as he opened 'is eyes, they 'ad nailed him.'

The ground on which this figure ran was thickly packed with rats, and as fast as he tore one off his body another took its place, while the screaming blinded man ran over the bodies of his enemies into their thickest ranks, until at last he tumbled over a ditch and never rose again. And all night Beany-eye lay watching the black ranks of the rat-army scurrying about in the brilliant moonlit yard; knowing that if he made an incautious movement, or drew a deep breath, that they would hear him and that he would suffer the same terrible fate as the man whom he had seen eaten alive.

For hours there had been a thick cluster of rats all round the ditch where the man had fallen, but at last the whole army got on the move and before dawn the last ranks had disappeared. Not till the sun had risen did Beany-eye come down from his hiding-place and he saw that not a spot of blood, not a morsel of the man's bones nor of his clothing had been left. That day Beany-eye travelled as far as possible.

I knew that he was telling the truth while I listened to this story. It was not vaguely horrible like the dreadful fears that I had experienced myself when the wind in the chimney would turn into the laugh of a hyena, or my mother's dressing-gown become animated by some blood-curdling spirit of evil. It was not like the rhinoceros in our cellar, a creature I had invented and was rather proud of, but which sometimes got out of hand and revenged himself on his creator for keeping him in such a narrow prison. What Beany-eye was speaking of was an experience, it was not hearsay, and it had been so terrible that even the bravest man could hardly face the thought of encountering it again. Moreover the story did not strike me as at all extraordinary; it was just what I should have expected of such creatures and bore out what I had always heard of them. Someone had read the 'Pied Piper of Hamelin' to me and well I knew that:

> Rats!
> They fought the dogs and killed the cats
> And bit the babies in the cradles.

And as for eating the man up, down to his bones and boots, had not the rats at Froghole eaten a whole set of ash cricket-stumps which my father had oiled before he put them away for the winter? That they had, and some of the scarred stumps still existed to prove what famished rats will do. Thus I stood listening with nothing but respect and horror, watching the wooden face of my new friend while his broken-nailed fingers kept turning the ash truncheon round and round and scraping it smoother and smoother.

For all the while the rats were mustering their legions and Beany-eye busied himself more and more in preparing his armaments so as to be ready for whatever was in store for him. He was a brave and very simple man; there was a dreadful nemesis awaiting him; he felt it coming and he prepared for it simply and prudently. The powers of evil were vast and irresistible but they should not catch him unarmed. And while he sat scraping and whittling by the light of a candle, stuck in the neck of a bottle, it was a comfort to him to have my companionship, to speak knowing that someone was listening, to know that my eight-year-old heart beat in my breathless breast as he told the horrors that he had known.

*1935*

One of the wood engravings by R. A. Garnett for the original edition of David Garnett's *Lady into Fox*, 1922

# CLARENCE DAY

## *Mother and the Armenian*

### FROM 'LIFE WITH FATHER'

MOTHER used to take us boys to a summer resort in our vacations. In all such places there was usually an Armenian, prowling around the hotel piazza. Blue-black hair, dark skin, gleaming eyes, a hooked nose, perfect teeth. Mother said that there wasn't a lady on the piazza who didn't envy those teeth. The Armenian was always trying to catch the eye of one of them to see if he couldn't persuade her to look at his rugs or his silks. 'Not buy, Madam! Just look!' She would say no; but he would tell her they were 'Oh, so beautiful,' and offer to give her some perfume, till perhaps if it were a dull afternoon she would roll up her knitting, and saunter down to the end of the hall where his dark little room was.

Since Mother had both a kind heart and a weakness for rugs, she was occasionally snared in this fashion and shown some bargain, some rug that was intrinsically priceless and could never be duplicated, but which could be had for a few hundred dollars, as it happened, that morning. The crisis that made such a price possible would to-morrow be gone, but to-day it was here, and a wise and clever woman would seize it. Whoever did would be helping a most grateful young man get through college. He was no dealer; he was just a poor student with a few priceless rugs, and if the lady would only make him an offer she could buy at her own figure. She could make him an offer, surely, *some* offer, let it be what it might.

It began to seem unreasonable to Mother not to make him some offer, especially as he was trying to get through college, and it might be a bargain. So she silently tried to figure how much she'd have had to pay at places like Sloane's; and then she took a lot off; and then she felt a little ashamed at taking so much off—she didn't wish to cheat the young man. He seemed to mean well, poor creature. So she worked her price up a little, in her mind, and then got a bit frightened because, after all, it was a good deal of money—though it did seem perfectly safe to pay that much, since Lord & Taylor's or Arnold Constable's would have charged more. Still, you never could tell about a rug, because it might not be genuine, and she wished the young man had let her alone and could get through college without her, though he didn't much look as though he would manage it; he could hardly speak English—and how could the poor thing talk to the professors, or the professors to him, when even on the subject of rugs he had to use a sort of sign language which consisted of hunching his shoulders till she feared he would dislocate them, and picking out sums on his fingers in the most confusing manner. However, she had better make him an offer, she felt, and then perhaps he'd stop smiling, which no doubt he intended as pleasant, but his breath was so bad.

So she finally said, fingering the rug in a dissatisfied way, that she supposed she could give him a hundred for it. The Armenian's smile instantly disappeared. He walked off in gloom. Then he rushed back, excited and jerky, and began a long, rapid expostulation that threatened to deafen us. Mother reluctantly raised her bid to a hundred and twenty to stop him, whereupon it suddenly appeared that he had misunderstood her first offer. He had supposed it to be two hundred, not one. She meant *two* hundred and twenty? Mother said, No, one hundred and twenty was all she had offered. The Armenian then tottered around, sank into a chair, and sort of hissed through his teeth, with such a ghastly look that it made Mother fear he might be having a fit. It began to seem advisable to her to do anything she could to get out of it, and then never buy anything again for the rest of her life. So she miserably and angrily said she would make it one-fifty. She had to say it several times, however, before he seemed to hear her, and even then he received it only with low shrieks and groans in Armenian. He said that now he would have to give up college, because he could not bear such losses. All he had ever hoped of America, he said, was that he wouldn't lose too much money here, but he had found that no one cared how badly he ruined himself, nor did they understand rugs. Poor Mother, half dismayed, half indignant, said she did not want the rug; she had only made him an offer because he had asked her to, and she would now like to go. This brought on a frightful collapse, so full of despair it seemed mortal. He was heard, however, to murmur what she took to be a dying request that she would take the rug with her and split the difference and leave him alone in his agony. On the way out, she had to tell the hotel-clerk to pay him and have it charged on the bill.

At the end of the week, when Father came to visit us and stay over Sunday, Mother had to explain to him that he was now the owner of a rare Eastern rug. Her attempts to announce this to him as a triumph somehow fell very flat. He began by not believing his ears, no matter how many times she repeated it. 'Rug? Rug? You say you've bought a *rug*? Nonsense! Pooh! Don't be ridiculous!' And when he found that the story seemed true, and that he couldn't thrust it away, his face turned a dark unhealthy red and he burst into roars of resentment. He shouted that he had only just arrived from hard toil in the city, in search of 'a little damned peace,' that was all that he asked, instead of which, before he had had time to smoke one cigar, he was harried and tortured and victimized by a pack of low swindlers, with whom his own family had leagued themselves, to render him penniless. He urgently demanded to see the rug so that he could throw it straight out of the window, and the Armenian after it. He swore he'd break every bone in his body. All reports as to the rarity and value of the rug he discredited, declaring he could buy better for fifty cents a barrel on Front Street. He then marched to the Armenian's parlour, with vague but violent intentions, only to find that that astute sufferer had closed his place up. The door was shut and locked and a sign was on it:

BAK
NEKS
WEK

'What's this gibberish?' Father demanded. 'You said his name was Dourbabian.'

Poor old fawning Dourbabian! His things were not good value at the time; but they at least have become so. That rug and the sofa-cushion covers and great squares of silk which Mother picked up in the eighties would cost a lot more to-day. She had to keep them out of Father's sight though, until he had forgotten their origin.

Years afterwards, one day, when the newspapers printed some clergyman's denunciations of Turkey for its cruel Armenian massacres, I thought of how Father had longed to massacre Dourbabian, and reminded him of it. Though older and calmer on some subjects he was still resentful on this. 'That's just like a parson,' he said, 'to sympathize with those fellows, without even asking first what they have done to the Turks.'

*1936*

# ISAAC ROSENBERG

## *Wedded*

I

THEY leave their love-lorn haunts,
Their sigh-warm floating Eden;
And they are mute at once;
Mortals by God unheeden;
By their past kisses chidden.

But they have kist and known
Clear things we dim by guesses—
Spirit to spirit grown—
Heaven, born in hand caresses—
Love, fall from sheltering tresses.

And they are dumb and strange:
Bared trees bowed from each other.
Their last green interchange
What lost dreams shall discover?
Dead, strayed, to love-strange lover.

## *Song*

A silver rose to show
Is your sweet face,
And like the heavens' white brow,
Sometime God's battle-place,
Your blood is quiet now.

Your body is a star
Unto my thought.
But stars are not too far
And can be caught—
Small pools their prisons are.

*1937*

# L. C. KNIGHTS

## *Seventeenth-Century Melancholy*

### FROM 'DRAMA AND SOCIETY IN THE AGE OF JONSON'

THE persistence of the plague and the consequent realization of man's impotence by a generation hitherto impressed by man's powers was undoubtedly one cause of early seventeenth-century melancholy; but it was not the sole or even the main cause. Man can adjust himself to the fact of death, he cannot adjust himself to a life disorganized and thwarted, and the root cause of melancholy and discontent is to be found in the social and economic conditions of the time. A study of these conditions suggests why melancholy entered on a new phase about the year 1600. Even under Elizabeth the factors already noticed had helped to produce symptoms of melancholy in literature. By the 'nineties it had become an affectation:

> Young gentlemen would be as sad as night
> Only for wantonness.

But in the seventeenth century the note of melancholy suddenly deepened; and the reason for this, I believe, was that those social and economic factors then took their full effect.

Under James I, in each rank of society, there were men who by character and education were fitted, or considered themselves fitted, for a higher position than they were able to obtain. Under Elizabeth there had been a considerable increase of educational activity, with a consequent heightening of men's expectations. Even before the close of the sixteenth century there were more than a few who could find no definite place in the existing organization of the state, and with the coming of the Stuarts, and the ending of the war with Spain, many more felt themselves capable of undertaking tasks which they saw in the hands of favourites and jobbers.

In 1611 Bacon wrote to the King:

> Concerning the advancement of learning, I do subscribe to the opinion of one of the wisest and greatest of your Kingdom, that, for grammar schools, there are already too many, and therefore no providence to add where there is excess. For the great number of schools which are in your Highness's realm, doth cause a want, and likewise an overthrow: both of them inconvenient, and one of them dangerous; for by means thereof, they find want in the country and towns, both of servants for husbandry and apprentices for trade; and on the other side, *there being more scholars bred than the State can prefer and employ, and the active part of that life not bearing a proportion to the preparative, it must needs fall out*

*that many persons will be bred unfit for other vocations, and unprofitable for that in which they were bred up, which fill the realm full of indigent, idle and wanton people, who are but* materia rerum novarum.

There is no need to stress the hardships of university men and the difficulty that they had in obtaining suitable employment. Apart from the fairly lucrative professions of medicine and the law, they might take orders and seek a benefice, become schoolmasters or private tutors, or become professional writers; if all else failed or if drawn by natural inclination they might remain at the university. None of these courses offered many opportunities of obtaining fame or riches. Headmasters of provincial schools rarely obtained more than £20 a year, and the normal salary for undermasters or ushers was £10. Private tutors fared even worse; Studioso in *The Return from Parnassus*, who is engaged to teach the son of a rich farmer, is treated as a menial and forced to wait at table and work in the fields all harvest time, besides having to endure the tyranny of a stupid pupil. Preferment in the church was hard to obtain and was often dependent on the favour of a mercenary patron. In Elizabeth's reign Harrison had complained that men preferred to study physic and the law rather than the Scriptures, 'for fear lest they should in time not get their bread by the same', and in 1621 Burton echoed the complaint against the ignorance and avarice of patrons. The profession of letters offered no better opportunities. The days of generous patronage were over (if they ever existed), and not until the eighteenth century was it possible for a writer to expect a regular livelihood from his pen. From the time of the University Wits, dramatists had led a precarious existence, and Jonson's poverty and Dekker's long imprisonment for debt show how little was to be expected from the stage. Poets of any social standing were not expected to sell their verses, and poets lower in the social scale—minor satirists, ballad makers, pamphleteers and hacks—were at the mercy of publishers and plagiarists. As for the scholar's last resource, the university, says Academico, 'The university is a melancholic life . . . but the point is, I know not how to better myself, and so I am fain to take it.' The general conclusion was

> Let scholars be as thrifty as they may
> They will be poor ere their last dying day;
> Learning and poverty will ever kiss.
> Mechanic arts may smile, their followers laugh,
> But liberal arts bewail their destiny,

for, 'The world is bad, and scholars are ordained to be beggars'. These quotations are from the pen of a satirist, but it does not appear that in bewailing the lot of scholars he was unduly exaggerating their fate. In consequence disappointed scholars turned malcontents and satirists. 'Most other trades and professions, after some seven years' prenticeship, are enabled by their craft to live of themselves. . . . Only scholars are most uncertain, unrespected, subject to all casualities, and hazard', so, 'Their Rhetoric only serves them to curse their bad fortunes'.

Scholars and writers were not the only discontented members of the commonwealth. Those who sought a public career were just as likely to have their hopes thwarted, or if they achieved success it was only after long years of disappointment and delay. 'The reign of Queen Elizabeth', says Sir Egerton Brydges, soberly, 'was a period of difficulty for the individuals whom it excited to fame and distinction, in which was cherished an emulation of great things with insufficient means'. The remark applies equally to the reign of James I, except that the standard of luxury expected from courtiers and public men was raised, and there was less chance than formerly of merit obtaining its reward. It was a frequent complaint of satirists that at court desert went unrewarded, and that wealth and a flattering tongue were the first requisites of a courtier, and the 'advancement of unworthy persons' by James I is well known.

Apart from the army and the learned professions an administrative career was the only one open to men of education and social standing, and there was a far greater number of aspirants than there were places for them to fill. Sir John Harington was a godson of Queen Elizabeth, a wit, a poet, and a man of considerable ability, yet he spent his life in looking for the preferment which he considered his due and which never came. In his 'Brief Notes and Remembrances' (1594–1603) he writes, 'I have spent my time, my fortune, and almost my honesty, to buy false hopes, false friends and shallow praise'. He tried all ways to obtain advancement, paraded his wit for Queen Elizabeth, flattered King James, and at the age of forty-five was prepared to take orders if the vacant archbishopric of Dublin could be obtained for him, but all was in vain. 'Now what findeth he who loveth the pride of life, the Court's vanity, ambition's puffball? In sooth, no more than empty words, grinning scoff, watching nights and fawning days'.

The first forty years of Bacon's life show the same succession of promises and disappointments accompanied by poverty. It is impossible to read Bacon's letters during the period when he was seeking advancement without realizing that the small measure of success which followed the highest aspirations was a fundamental cause of melancholy and discontent. Indeed Bacon himself is explicit. When he was beginning to give up hope of the Solicitorship he wrote to Essex, 'I humbly pray your lordship to pardon me for troubling you with my melancholy'; and some time later, when the appointment was still unbestowed, he declared, 'This is a course to quench all good spirits, and to corrupt every man's nature'. Political discontent was common; from the Earl of Essex downwards there were many who knew that their natural abilities were not being used as they might be by the state; unexercised they became restless, and unrewarded, melancholy. Donne's letters in the period between his marriage and his ordination show how mere poverty can distort the outlook and depress the spirit. There is no need to-day to emphasize the miseries of unemployment.

Although the economic cause of seventeenth-century melancholy is rarely mentioned in modern accounts of the subject, contemporaries were well aware of the danger of over-education and thwarted ambition. In chapter xxxvi of his *Positions* (1581) Mulcaster declared that it was dangerous for a commonwealth to have either too few learned or too many:

> Too many burdens any state too far, for want of provision. For the rooms which are to be supplied by learning being within number, if they that are to supply them grow on beyond number, how can it be but too great a burden for any state to bear? To have so many gaping for preferment, as no gulf hath store enough to suffice, and to let them roam helpless whom nothing else can help, how can it be but that such shifters must needs shake the very strongest pillar in that state where they live, and loiter without living?

The danger was not confined to any one rank of society. If tradesmen's sons are allowed to learn Latin they will not be willing to follow their fathers' occupations:

> For all the fear is, though it be more than fear where it still falleth out so, lest having such benefits of school they will not be content with the state which is for them, but because they have some petty smack of their book, they will think any state, be it never so high, low enough for them.

Thereupon they become dangerous members of the commonwealth: 'For youth being let go forward upon hope, and checked with despair while it roameth without purveyance, makes marvellous ado before it will die'. Bacon's opinion has been quoted, and the *Essays* utter the same warning as the letter to the King. It is dangerous for the State 'when more are bred scholars than preferments can take off'. 'Ambitious men, if they find the way open for their rising, and still get forward, they are rather busy than dangerous; but if they be checked in their desires, they become secretly discontent, and look upon men and matters with an evil eye'. Similarly Harington wrote concerning Essex, 'It resteth with me in opinion, that ambition thwarted in its career doth speedily lead to madness'. Discontent with one's fortunes was generally regarded as a cause of melancholy or madness; the occasion, said Earle, is 'commonly one of these three, a hard father, a peevish wench, or ambition thwarted'. The malcontents of the drama frequently owed their melancholy to the same causes. In *The White Devil* Flamineo is disgusted by his own poverty and dependence: 'O, 'tis a brave thing for a man to sit by himself (in the saddle)! he may stretch himself in the stirrups, look about, and see the whole compass of the hemisphere'. In *The Revenger's Tragedy* Vendice speaks of 'discontent, the noble man's consumption'; and Jonson describes Macilente as, 'A man well parted, a sufficient scholar, and travelled; who, wanting that place in the world which he thinks his merit capable of, falls into an envious apoplexy'.

This section may be closed by a quotation from *The Worth of a Penny, or a Caution to keep Money*, by Henry Peacham the Younger, which forms an interesting addition to the gallery of seventeenth-century 'Characters':

> He that wanteth money is for the most part extremely melancholy in every company or alone by himself, especially if the weather be foul, rainy or cloudy. Talk to him of what you will, he will hardly give you the hearing; ask him any questions, he answers you in monosyllables. . . . He walks with his arms folded, his belt without a sword or rapier, that perhaps being somewhere in trouble, hat without a band, hanging over his eyes, only it wears a weather-beaten fancy for fashion's sake. He cannot stand still, but like one of the Tower wild beasts is still walking from one end of his room to another, humming out some new Northern tune or other. If he meets with five or ten pieces, happily conferred upon him by the beneficence of some noble friend or other, he is become a new man, and so overjoyed with his fortune that not one drop of small drink will down with him all that day.

By 1647 when this was written the connexion between poverty and the melancholic mood had become proverbial,—a sort of music-hall joke. Indeed the connexion is so obvious that it is difficult to understand why it has been so constantly overlooked. '*Augent animos fortunae* saith the Mimist, and very truly, for nothing pulleth down a man's heart so much as adversity and lack.'

In the economic and social organization of the state the early seventeenth century was a period of transition. The relatively stable medieval society had decayed, and the new economy was not yet understood. Throughout the sixteenth century the Tudors had followed a policy of encouraging the middle classes, but by 1600 neither the new aristocracy nor the new commercial classes had altogether adjusted themselves to the changed conditions. The beginnings of the Industrial Revolution can be traced to this period, but commerce and industry were not yet sufficiently developed (nor always sufficiently reputable) to provide attractive careers. 'They are happy men', said Bacon, 'whose natures sort with their vocations.' Inevitably at this time there were many whose occupations were uncongenial, who were dependent upon precarious and ill-paid professions, or who were unemployed. And under James I non-material causes increased the general unrest. Until about 1599 there had been a constant threat of a Spanish invasion. Under Charles I constitutional issues became important and once more, on one side or the other, men found occupation and—many of them—ideals. But between these periods no great national question focused the attention of all, and the court of James I was not an inspiring centre of the national life. The literary expression of melancholy was in part the result of this combination of circumstances.

*1937*

# D. M. LOW

## *The Luminous Historian*

FROM 'EDWARD GIBBON'

BY universal assent *The Decline and Fall* had set Gibbon 'at the very head of the whole literary tribe at present existing in Europe'. Robertson voluntarily renounced any claims to primacy. 'Before you began your historic career, I used to pride myself in being at least the most industrious historian of the age; but now, alas! I can pretend no longer even to that praise.'

The deliberate ambition of Gibbon's youth had been surpassed. He had once looked up to Robertson and Hume as almost inaccessible peaks. Now he stood above them and had been acclaimed by both. There was certainly some excuse for being vain.

It was said that Gibbon came to believe at last that he was the Roman Empire. The jest veils a true compliment, so completely was he immersed, yet not lost, in his subject. Moreover, and it is the triumph of imaginative art, he carries his reader into it with him. It may not be easy to fix the sources of such an impression. It depends in part on simple devices. Gibbon always speaks from Rome or Constantinople and defines 'beyond the Alps, the Rhine, the Danube, etc.', accordingly. He makes no exceptions. The British in India are described as 'a company of Christian merchants of a remote island in the Northern ocean'. The reader insensibly surrenders; he surrenders still more to the pervading dream of antiquity in which the author moves.

'Our early studies', Gibbon says, 'allow us to sympathise in the feelings of a Roman.' The most sceptical of men has no doubt either of the supremacy of the classical authors or of his own complete intimacy with their spirit. It was no sentimental enthusiasm.

Nor could it have been merely vanity that sent him with undefeated energy down what Bywater, I think, calls the dusty corridors of learning. They were very dusty and encumbered in those days. This knowledge he reconstructed in a solid world of space and time, in which he moves to and fro at his ease, but always with a sense of inexorable progress towards its end. By numberless touches the whole story seems to be his intimate concern. He tells us the limits of his personal acquaintance with the Bishop of Hippo. He takes a courteous leave of Ammianus, 'the last subject of Rome who composed a profane history in the Latin language', and warns us that henceforward he must advance amid fragmentary and prejudiced authorities, 'with doubtful and timorous steps'.

The calamities of human affairs may recur, though not always with a Tacitus to depict them. A feature indeed of such times is the inconceivability of a Tacitus existing in them at all. The peaks of civilisation, on the other hand, are those ages in which political freedom, all the manly virtues and literary excellence occur together as though with some essential connexion. The periods which Gibbon chose had in the main for him only the negative value of contrast with that ideal. Whenever he pauses to survey the road he has traversed, there is only one method of valuation. After the growth of superstition in the fourth century has called forth all his wit, he adds:

'If it be possible to measure the interval between the philosophic writings of Cicero and the sacred legend of Theodoret, between the character of Cato and that of Simeon, we may appreciate the memorable revolution which was accomplished in the Roman empire within a period of five hundred years.

By pinning his faith to one standard, Gibbon becomes at times as much involved in the consequent notion of degeneration as some modern optimists have been in the idea of progress. He sometimes forgets that brave men have lived since Agamemnon, and his picture of the decay of military virtue in the provinces does not explain the success of the barbarians. Sometimes he tries to have it both ways, as when he accuses Christianity of inculcating pusillanimity, and at the same time never fails to record a fighting bishop. Nevertheless his claim to have recounted the triumph of barbarism and religion is not to be denied. He showed that they were inseparably connected with each other and with the passing of the ancient world, and he opened a debate which shows no sign of terminating.

A disregard for Gibbon's values has led to an unfair severity towards some parts of his work. It is true that he treats the Byzantine period summarily and at times unjustly. Nevertheless it is improbable that he would find any reason to revise his judgment or alter his proportions. In his view, the decline of Constantinople was almost coeval with her foundation. He was well aware of the city's function as 'the most important barrier of the West'. He does not dispute 'the long prosperity of the Byzantine Caesars', and in his 53rd chapter he gives an admirable sketch of Byzantine civilisation, especially in its contrast with the contemporary condition of Europe. It was a stagnant pool, however. The value of an age lies with Gibbon in what it bequeaths, and the greatest legacy must be literature, art and science. But the later historians who have done such immensely important work on the Byzantine world do not pretend to induce us to read the literature. Even the modern interest in Byzantine art is lukewarm. We gaze at the mosaics, but 'there is no speculation in those eyes'.

But the Roman Empire in its turn is Gibbon. Everything is subdued to his thought and style. Even the vicious Tertullian appears in an English dress indistinguishable from his introducer's. Walpole perceived this truth when he compared the homogeneous texture of *The Decline and Fall* to the smoothness of a Flemish picture. Later critics have been more concerned to complain that Gibbon reduces all ages and varieties of humanity to a periwigged uniformity. I do not know whether this criticism is improved or not by the reflexion that Hellenism in our day has been made to run about in house colours and shorts.

Gibbon was in fact well aware of the predicament which no historian can escape:

> Tout homme de génie qui écrit l'histoire y répand, peut-être sans s'en apercevoir, le caractère de son esprit. À travers leur variété infinie de passion et situation, ses personnages semblent n'avoir qu'une façon de penser et de sentir; et cette façon est celle de l'auteur.

The historian who is conscious of this inevitability will be the more guarded against earning a place among those many historians who put us in mind of the admirable saying of the great Condé to Cardinal de Retz: 'Ces coquins nous font parler et agir comme ils auroient fait eux-mêmes à notre place.'

But opposite to the whirlpools of imaginative reconstruction stands the barren wall of self-stultification which arises out of too much knowledge. The more minutely the historian of our day examines the past, the more aware must he be of other worlds than his own; and the more diffident he becomes of committing himself. Froude has eloquently described the impassable barrier which stands between us and even our fellow countrymen of the Middle Ages.

Gibbon avoided these dangers by keeping to fundamental probabilities. He believed in the stability of human nature and in 'the sure operation of its fierce and unrestrained passions'. Such guides could not retrieve a story whose records were lost, but they could destroy one the evidence of which was inconsistent with themselves. Of the eulogistic records of a Persian dynasty he writes with a force that anticipates so much of the burden of *The Decline and Fall*:

> Je pense bien que ces rois ne sont pas uniquement occupés des lois, des sciences, et des beaux-arts . . . si cette histoire s'étoit conservée, on y liroit comme dans toutes les autres, les vices des grands, et les malheurs des peuples; on y verroit ce triomphe perpétuel de la violence et de l'intrigue sur la justice, qu'elles outragent en la violant, et qu'elles outragent cent fois davantage en se servant impunément de son nom sacré.

This broad psychology is part of the strength of Gibbon's work. If it is unadventurous it is unassailable. It has the merit of design. Gibbon assuredly was not incapable of the fine analysis of character. His Journal proves as much; but in the long journey of his History he could not linger over subtleties of that kind.

Those who know the old engravings of dramatic scenes and of actors (the upturned eyes and streaming hair) will be insensibly reminded of them as they read *The Decline and Fall*. The characters rush on and off stage tumultuously. They intercede and upbraid, they tremble, they blush—even Baronius blushes in a footnote—and they weep. Akin to this are the epithets which Gibbon uses so summarily to praise or to damn. One after another the personages are artful, credulous, intrepid, timorous, equitable or haughty, etc. Here it is the epic rather than the dramatic manner, and Gibbon has received it from Homer through Pope. These methods have their weaknesses as well as their merits. A great amount of learning and thought may be staked on a single word. There can be no reservations or redress, and the vivacity of the narrative may sometimes appear specious.

But history was in Gibbon's view essentially personal and dramatic. He believed in the man and the hour. When in the flight from Mecca to Medina, Mahomet encountered the emissaries of the Koreish, 'the lance of an Arab might have changed the history of the world'. 'In human life the most important scenes will depend on the character of a single actor', and 'an acrimonious humour falling on a single fibre of one man may prevent or suspend the misery of nations'. This is rather high-flown, but it bears a lesson for an age which deals overmuch in impersonal inevitabilities, and has even seen an attempt to reduce history to a graph. It is an outlook which will always win human attention.

'Some tincture of philosophy and criticism', Gibbon remarks, 'is demanded of a work that is to i nstruct or amuse an enlightened age'. It is no contradiction of this to say that another and still greater element of durability in *The Decline and Fall* is the author's abstention from theorising. He has nothing to prove. The detachment which was the politician's weakness is the historian's strength. With the exception of the 15th and 16th chapters his analysis of causes is perfunctory. When at the close of his third volume he has brought the Western Empire to an end, he feels obliged to reflect upon the causes. But he is content to remark that the extraordinary thing is not that the Roman Empire fell, but that it stood for so long. The last three volumes, moving so surely over a vast scene, propound and answer no questions explicitly, but their power of suggestion is inexhaustible. The structure of the narrative stands by itself. An architect builds a house; he is not called upon to say why it does not fall down. Gibbon's criticism is absorbed in his creation, which is a picture of human destiny.

This destiny is no external force. 'Man has much more to fear from the passions of his fellow creatures than from the convulsion of the elements.' In this wider generalisation religion falls into its own place. There are many other superstitions and impostures to be denounced; the sentimentalities that cling about the almost divine quality of kings, the follies of militarism, and the mystifications of the law; a very personal grievance here. No ruse of modern dictatorship, no political strategem is absent from his pages. The History is charged with reflexions that anticipate the most progressive thought of our own day and earn the judgment of 'the ultimate modern morality of his work'. It is modern because, like *The Decline and Fall* itself, it is firmly planted on this earth and does not look beyond the life on it.

But Gibbon was neither a propagandist nor a preacher. Hence we still read him.

> History which undertakes to record the transactions of the past, for the instruction of future ages, would ill deserve that honourable office, if it condescended to plead the cause of tyrants, or to justify the maxims of persecution.

But its lessons are negative. It does not propose what is to be done. The final conclusion seems to be that though individuals may learn from experience, 'it is seldom profitable to the successive generations of mankind'.

With this reflexion, he accepted, as most of his advanced contemporaries did, the existing order of society. He chastises the vices of the great. But his banners were not likely to be found on the side of the people. Still, 'all that is human must retrograde if it do not advance'. On the whole he felt it to be advancing in his day. Reason was keeping her head up. The competition of the European nations was productive of good. Even war was conducted in a gentlemanly fashion. The barbarian invasions could not recur. Gibbon did not reckon with the barbarism that might arise from within. He had witnessed a surprising increase in England's prosperity, and reflects that luxury never hurt a vigorous people. In one at least of his political judgments he had been triumphantly right; he prophesied that the loss of the American colonies would not ruin England's trade. There is much to smile at here. But even we have our optimisms.

As early as 1763 Gibbon had set his ideal of a historical writer in an appreciation of Herodotus. He must be 'un observateur dont le coup d'œil pénétrant et juste ne voit que les grands objets, qui les voit de sang-froid et qui les peint avec chaleur'. One of the best of Gibbon's modern critics sums up his achievement in very similar words: 'His picture is drawn with the integrity of a scholar, and coloured with the intention of an artist.'

The extent and accuracy of Gibbon's scholarship have been weighed and accepted by the few men who have been his equals or even superiors. The merits and defects of his style have been similarly canvassed. Here the verdict is more subjective. It has been increasingly favourable in recent years with the passing of the grand manner from contemporary letters. We admire the bow which we do not presume to draw, and which is no longer made contemptible in the hands of vulgar suitors. Mr. G. M. Young has laid a sure finger on the oratorical quality of Gibbon's prose. He achieved here what he never dared to attempt in Parliament, and seems often at the end of a period to be waiting for the applause which should break out. A complementary criticism may not be out of place, if the notes are said to be Gibbon's table talk. Here he is conversing familiarly in the library and filling in the miscellaneous information which the dignity of Clio's House would not allow.

For Gibbon's style was based on the Latin Orators; but both the architecture and the decoration of his History owe much to Herodotus. Like Herodotus he chose a great and moving theme of human destiny, and like him too moved slowly towards his goal, marshalling a still more complex army of events with deliberation, and surveying at the same time the whole field of human knowledge on his way, and not disdaining to entertain his audience in many a learned and witty by-way. Like Herodotus also, he was under Homer's spell. Homer, after Voltaire, and with the exception of the immediate authorities, is more often referred to than any other writer. But Homer's real influence was exerted not only in his early reading, in the close study recorded in the Journal, but also in that preoccupation with details of epic construction, common to Gibbon and his contemporaries, which are to us of so remote interest.

Gibbon's art never attains to that pitch where it conceals itself. Every movement is conscious and he has been accused more than once of displaying himself rather than his subject. Yet, 'Julian discovers his own character with that naïveté, that unconscious simplicity, which always constitutes genuine humour'. So does Gibbon. This trait has the singular effect of putting the several parts of a variegated world in their place. They are valued impartially in the scale of the historian's favourite epithets. Le Nain de Tillemont's accuracy is 'incomparable'; what of the cherry trees which 'produce our incomparable marasquin'? One of the most musical sentences of the whole work is devoted to a fish, a very important fish:

> The endless exportation of salt fish and caviar is annually renewed by the enormous sturgeons that are caught at the mouth of the Don or Tanais, in their last station of the rich mud and shallow water of the Maeotis.

Moreover, they earn a note on their length, weight and yield, ending with an irrelevant reminder that the Bosphorus had supplied the Athenians with corn in the time of Demosthenes. This is the very spirit of Herodotus and the essence of Gibbon's leisurely and irresponsible procedure. There is something very salutary about this tribute to a fish. Julian himself could receive no more.

Attempts are made to place Gibbon in honourable retirement. If he is read, it is as literature, or as a typical figure of the eighteenth century. Some ulterior motives are to be suspected in this kind of criticism. Its weakness should be apparent. To be a typical man of the age is a poor guarantee of being read, and those whose literary qualities predominate over their subject generally do cease to be read except by the dilettante.

It may be enough to ask such critics if they think that Gibbon would still be read if he had not written with the substantial accuracy with which he did. Amid the enormous accessions of knowledge and the widening of the curiosity about the past which goes with the expansion of modern life, Gibbon's bridge between the ancient and modern worlds remains remarkably safe. Moreover, the journey is unfailingly entertaining. No more masterly skill in holding the reader's attention over so vast a theme has ever been known. At the heart of it is the informing spirit of the creator with his conception of the unity of history, his suggestive judgments and unsleeping scepticism and his truly humane outlook. This expresses itself partly in his roguish wit and his unflagging gusto, no less also in his sober recognition that mankind goes its way never much better and never much worse. What changes there may be, must be evolved by ourselves. There is no other help.

Nothing is extolled more often by Gibbon than freedom. But freedom, either political or personal, is beset with equivocations. Nevertheless his most insistent lesson—for in the end there is a lesson—is that the freedom of the mind is 'the source of every generous and rational sentiment'. His still timely warning is that it may be destroyed by 'habits of credulity and submission'.

*1937*

# RICHARD EBERHART

## *Two Loves*

THAT her serene influence should spread
An afternoon of soft autumnal light
Is to my heart not unaccountable
For she was young, and is not dead.
And still her cheek is red and white.

But that this stealthy still insistent power
Pervades my mind and will not slumber me
Is delicate woe and glory hard to bear;
Her life lives in a ghost-wrought hour,
From whose chill spirit I am not free.

The one was willow to an ardent touch
And she was mood that had a right to die.
But she, the other, the passion of my mind
Long-living still, does overmuch
Come from the dead, and from the sky.

## *The Child*

Five years of cringing child small,
Bewildered by the barren wall.
Laughed Atlantic its heated summer,
This I do not remember.
O the fearful cliff wall,
And the fearful sapling nigh.
And the dove that will hurt me,
And the great hand of the sky.

*1940*

# F. SPENCER CHAPMAN

## *The First Ascent of the Fluted Peak*

FROM 'LIVING DANGEROUSLY'

I THINK most mountaineers will agree that, except for the feeling of satisfaction afterwards, there is no pleasure at all in trying to climb the higher peaks in the Himalaya. I once heard a veteran of several Everest expeditions remark: 'If only someone would get to the top of the —— mountain, then we could get on with some serious climbing'.

There is no doubt that at some point around 20,000 feet—depending, of course, on the individual's power of adapting himself to the height—the atmosphere becomes so rarefied that existence for a human being becomes increasingly unbearable, until somewhere round about 29,000 feet, the height of the summit of Everest, it becomes impossible. That is really the attraction of Everest, that nobody knows whether, without the aid of oxygen, a human being can retain sufficient control of his mind and body to overcome the undoubted technical difficulties of the last 800 feet of the ascent.

Personally I have never been higher than 24,000 feet, and for several thousand feet below that height I begin to feel that life is simply not worth living. I have a continual headache, the skin is all burnt off my face by the terrific glare of the sun reflected off the snow, I cannot sleep, I have no desire to eat and find myself wondering why on earth anybody every tried to reach the top of a mountain. I only want somebody in the party, it does not matter who, to reach the summit, so that I can get off the mountain as soon as possible and descend to the truly delectable existence of life in the upper Himalayan valleys—the cheerful Tibetan nomads with their great herds of yaks and sheep; the birds, the butterflies, and above all the sun-steeped banks starred with wild flowers.

No, the ideal mountain, in the Himalaya at any rate, is the 20,000 footer, for with the snow-line at round about 18,000 feet or even higher, as it is in many parts of the Himalaya, you have only about 2,000 feet of rock or snow climbing to reach the summit. Which means, of course, that you can get to the top of the mountain and back from a comfortable camp below the snow-line, and that you do not have the added responsibility of taking porters on to the dangerous part of the mountain.

The most enjoyable climb I have ever done was an ascent, the first ascent as a matter of fact, of the Fluted Peak, which is exactly 20,000 feet high. It lies about ten miles due east of Kanchenjunga, on the borders of Sikkim and Tibet and within sight of Nepal. The three of us who made this ascent appreciated it all the more as we had just spent a very unpleasant week making the first ascent of a 23,000 foot peak called the Sphinx, and failing to get to the top of the Pyramid, a twenty-four thousander. We knew that the weather was breaking and this would probably be our last climb together before the arrival of the monsoon.

It was on 11th June 1936 that Cooke (who, alas, was killed in the war) and Harrison (who lost all his toes from frost-bite on a climb a few years later) and I left our base camp at 16,000 feet in the beautiful Lhonak valley and, carrying light rucksacks, meandered up a peaceful side valley, the Langpo Chu, to the foot of the Fluted Peak. The level ground in the foot of the valley was carpeted with azaleas, at this height not more than a foot tall, with aromatic leathery leaves and sparse waxy cream and plum-coloured flowers. The grassy banks of the valley, fed by the melting snows above, were carpeted with Alpine flowers—little blue irises and primulas of every colour from the deep purple of *Primula royalii* to the pendant cream-coloured blooms of *Primula sikkimensis*. Apollo and swallow-tail butterflies chased each other in the warm sunshine, and mousehares and marmots popped into their burrows as we approached. Once we surprised a great herd of *burrhal* (a kind of wild sheep with huge curling horns), which bounded away and then turned to gaze at us.

In the afternoon we camped at about 18,000 feet on a patch of sand beside a shallow lake fed by one of the glaciers flowing down the south-east side of the Fluted Peak. We had intended to camp even higher, but it came on to snow and the visibility was poor. The three porters soon arrived with their loads and, while two returned to the base camp, one, Ang Nima, an old Everest 'tiger', stayed on to help us with the camp chores and to carry the gear back to the base camp.

After tea the snow stopped, and putting on our gym. shoes we set off to find a way on to the rocky ridge which we intended to climb next day, for we had seen that this ridge led up to the final cap of snow and ice. The difficulty of getting on to a Himalayan peak is sometimes as severe as the climbing itself; but we were lucky and found a fairly easy route up a rocky gully between the two glaciers which flowed down towards our camp.

That night a very remarkable thing happened. We had had supper—pea-soup and fried bully-beef, and were just going to sleep when outside the tent we heard a noise as of tins being knocked together and sounds of heavy breathing and grunting. I said I thought it was a snow-leopard, an animal I was always hoping to see, but we agreed it was more likely to be Ang Nima washing up the supper things in a fit of enthusiasm. So we went to sleep; but next morning, when we emerged from our tent at half-past four, we saw a line of large pad-marks in the soft sand beside the lake, and the tin plate in which we had fried the bully-beef was lying some distance from the tent and had been licked clean. Not only had a snow-leopard been within a yard of our tent but, judging by the size of his pad-marks, he was an exceptionally large one too.

We set off at 5 a.m. As there was no need to take more than a single rucksack with some lunch, we left Ang Nima behind, telling him to start making tea as soon as he saw us coming down the ridge.

It was an uncertain sort of day: sometimes snow clouds swept up the Lhonak valley and great violet shadows passed across the dun-coloured plateau where we could just make out the little dots that were the yakherds' tents, and the still smaller black spots that were hundreds of grazing yaks.

The climbing on the ridge was spectacular but not unduly difficult, over fairly firm rock which afforded good belays for the rope. Occasional descents were needed to avoid the rock gendarmes which guarded the ridge. At one place we were held up for some time by an awkward pitch which we tried to turn by traversing out to the right, but the slabs here were steep and holdless and at last we found a steep chimney on the left, and a little back-and-knee work soon got us to the top of it. About here, when I was last on the rope, one of the others dislodged a boulder the size of a football, but luckily I was looking up at the time and was able to dodge it. The boulder struck the mountainside a few times as it fell, then buried itself in the snow a thousand feet below us.

At ten o'clock we stopped for a hurried lunch of sardines, cheese, biscuits and chocolate. Clouds were occasionally blowing across the ridge above us and we were afraid we might not reach the summit before the weather broke; in any case we should only just have time to get there and back to our camp before dark.

Now the rock stopped and gave way to a horizontal snow *arête* of such sharpness that, as we worked our way along it, we could look down on either side into the snow-fields and open crevasses of the glaciers below. After the warm sunshine of the morning the ridge was so rotten that the leader had to sit astride it and demolish the top two or three feet with his ice-axe so that we could stand upright and push our ice-axes into the firm snow and ice beneath. As the clouds swept over us the temperature fell and the loose snow picked up by the rope froze solid so that it became most unwieldy, like a wire hawser.

This was slow work, and at two o'clock we held a council of war. We had previously agreed that at two o'clock we must turn in order to get back to our camp by daylight, and we knew that the snow- and ice-ridge got much steeper before the summit. On the other hand, it could not be more than a few hundred feet above us.

Harrison thought we ought to return. The weather was turning nasty and we still had some way to go to reach the summit. We might not be able to get off the mountain even if the weather held. Cooke thought we could get off the ridge by nightfall even if we had to rope down the more difficult pitches, and we could do the last and easier part even in the dark. I had to give the casting vote. I thought it was a fair risk, and decided to go on.

The clouds soon descended over us, and Cooke, who was leading, continued his work of demolition. The angle of the ridge was much steeper now and he seemed to be in difficulties. I could not see him but I could hear the snow and ice rattling down on either side of the ridge to be lost in the mist. Then there was a long halt and, when at last I moved on, I found he had excavated a twelve-foot tunnel to avoid an awkward over-hang of rotten snow. After crawling through this we reached an unpleasant spot where the angle of the *arête* became unduly steep. Cooke hacked away the looser surface snow and ice and then cut foot- and hand-holds for a perilous ten feet. Harrison kept on saying we were crazy and would have to spend the night on the mountain, but now our luck changed and a final fifty feet of steep but not unduly difficult snow brought us at last to the blunt, cloud-covered summit.

By then it was half-past three. The ascent had taken ten and a half hours. In three hours it would be dark and now it was snowing steadily.

Cooke lowered the two of us bodily over the steep pitches, and we steadied him in turn as he came down. Then all three moved together, concentrating in grim silence on the small details that go to make a safe descent. To lean out on steep snow so that the steps do not crumble beneath you; to keep on pulling in the slack of the rope so that it does not get in the way of the others; and above all to hold your ice-axe in such a way that at a moment's notice you can both stop yourself by digging it into the snow, and hold the others if need be by hastily throwing a turn of the rope over the head of the axe.

As we got off the snow on to the rock the mist cleared, but even more concentration was needed on the difficult pitches, and our speed slackened. We could no longer all move together; each of us in turn had to be ready with a loop of the rope round a belay in case one of us lost his footing in our hurried descent.

In traversing across a rock face to reach a snow-filled gully, where the descent would be easier and faster, I was edging past an enormous flake of rock a yard wide when it suddenly came away. I was just able to jump to one side and catch hold of a projecting rock as the flake rebounded over the rocks below, and there was an acrid gunpowdery smell.

At last we got off the ridge and unroped quickly to make progress faster. The rope was frozen stiff and could only just be coiled. Then we were off again, clambering over the final slabs and at last running down the loose stones of the gully towards our tents, one of which glowed like a Chinese lantern with the light inside it. Soon Ang Nima, who had been alarmed by the noise of the rock flake crashing down the mountain, appeared, and by half-past six, just as darkness closed in, we were back in camp feeling so deliriously happy that our weariness, sore finger-tips and burnt faces were forgotten.

That night we slept for ten hours, and if the snow-leopard visited us again we were not aware of it.

*1940*

# COMPTON MACKENZIE

## *The Scuffle in the Heather*

FROM 'THE MONARCH OF THE GLEN'

WHILE Mrs Chester Royde Jr. was asleep on that green knoll in Glenbristle the members of the house party together with two or three of the neighbouring shots the Chieftain of Ben Nevis considered worthy of his best moor were enjoying their lunch after the most satisfactory bag registered on any morning of the Twelfth for six years.

'If we do as well this afternoon on Drumcockie, Hugh, we might lower the '22 record.'

This remark was addressed by the Chieftain to Hugh Cameron of Kilwhillie, a small button-headed man with long thin drooping moustaches, a faded kilt and a faded eye. Although some ten years junior to Ben Nevis, he was his prime favourite among the Inverness-shire lairds. Their land nowhere marched together. Kilwhillie was a better fisherman; but Ben Nevis preferred the gun, and Kilwhillie was no match for him with a gun. Both were fond of whisky and both flattered themselves they could carry as much of it without a slip of the tongue or a trip of the toe as any two lairds on either side of the Great Glen. You could not call them boon companions, for there was a touch of Celtic melancholy about Kilwhillie, attributed by some to liver, which forbade the epithet; but their intimacy was as close as men in their class can achieve. It was beautifully expressed once by Mrs MacDonald when she said that Donald never slept so soundly and so peacefully as when Hughie Cameron had dined at Glenbogle. The laird of Kilwhillie was unmarried, not from misogyny but because he had failed to persuade either of the two young women to whom he had proposed to accept him.

'And I don't intend to try again,' he used to assure Ben Nevis. 'I don't think this Bruce and the spider business has any bearing on marriage.'

And Ben Nevis, who always called it a pity when a good fellow got married, used to agree warmly with his friend, though sometimes he would remind him about the succession.

'There's not so much to succeed to now,' Kilwhillie would say, swallowing a dram recklessly. 'Let the Department of Agriculture take over what's left.'

But this was the kind of talk which suited a dying fire and an empty decanter. Up here in the heather on a fine Twelfth of August the mood was different.

'Splendid view, isn't it?' Ben Nevis exclaimed to his guests, with a justifiable touch of Highland pride, for indeed it was a splendid view over the wide level of Strathdun away to where flashed the silver of Loch Hoch, whose farthest bank marked the boundaries of Mac'ic Eachainn's land.

Chester Royde eyed the chieftain thoughtfully as he chewed slowly on a mouthful of chicken and ham. Then he turned to Kilwhillie, who was reclining next him on the heather.

'What exactly lets anybody in on wearing kilts?' he asked. 'I mean to say, suppose I took a fancy to wearing kilts, would that strike a low note in Scotland?'

Kilwhillie, who was also chewing on a mouthful of chicken and ham, gulped it down and murmured, 'Kilt not kilts,' with a hint of reproachful pedantry.

'Are you only allowed one then?' the young financier asked. He did not like this kind of restriction.

'Only one at a time.'

'I get you. But what would happen if I were to wear one of these kilts? Would I be run out of the country on a rail or lynched or anything like that?'

'There's no objection to anybody's wearing the kilt,' said Kilwhillie. 'But there's always the question of the tartan. Some people who haven't themselves the right to a tartan wear their mother's tartan. But I'm against that. I believe it to be contrary to the best tradition. There's a tendency nowadays to introduce alien notions of female descent into the clan system, so that you actually get women claiming a chiefship, which is preposterous.'

'I suppose now we have women lawyers and preachers and doctors they don't see why they shouldn't be Highland Chiefs. So you'd be against me wearing my wife's tartan, which by the way is the same as our host's. I tell you I was tickled to death when I found that out.'

'Personally I am strongly against wearing the tartan of one's wife. Some people without a tartan of their own who want to wear a tartan wear the Stewart tartan as subjects of King George.'

'But I'm not a subject of King George. And I guess George Washington never had a tartan.'

'The solution for you is to wear a kilt of hodden grey.'

'Grey? Is that the best you can do for me?' Royde exclaimed indignantly. 'I guess I'm better off as I am.' He contemplated his own polychromatic tweediness with frank admiration.

'Boswell in his account of his trip with Johnson through the Hebrides describes Malcolm Macleod as wearing a purple kilt.'

'Purple? Say, that's an idea.'

'But I've never seen a purple kilt in these days,' Kilwhillie added hastily.

'You will,' the young financier promised with fervour. 'But see here, this purple kilt is a secret between you and me. I want to give Carrie a surprise.'

'I shan't say a word about it,' Kilwhillie vowed.

And he meant it. A fine subject for Inverness-shire gossip if it leaked out that he was responsible for an American financier in a purple kilt! Why, it would be conspicuous even at the Oban Gathering.

'That's bully,' said Chester Royde in a tone of the deepest satisfaction. 'I'm crazy about the Highlands, Kilwhillie. I used to laugh at Carrie, but I tell you I've been bitten by this Highland bug myself. Now, see here, let me get this right, old man. Provided I stick to plain colours I'm O.K.? I mean to say purple, blue, green, anything I like so long as I keep off lines and checks and any kind of pattern?'

'It's unusual, of course, but . . .'

'I don't give a darn about it being unusual provided I'm not muscling in on somebody else's property.'

'You certainly wouldn't be doing that.'

'That's all I wanted to know. I mean to say, when I was in Canada I was adopted into the Carroway tribe of Indians with the name of Butting Moose. That's Chester Royde Jr. among the Carroways, and that's the way I want to feel in the Highlands. The romance of the whole business has gotten a hold of me, Kilwhillie. I aim to buy a place up here.'

Kilwhillie's faded eyes were lighted up with that strange light which never was on sea or land, but is only to be seen in the eyes of a landed proprietor in the Highlands who hopes he has found a buyer for an overtaxed forest of twelve heads and a shooting-lodge that looks like a bunch of tarnished pepper-pots.

'I could probably help you with my advice over that,' he murmured. 'I think I know the kind of place you want. When you've definitely made up your mind let me know. And if I may venture to offer a word of advice, don't talk about it till you have. Otherwise you'll be pestered with all sorts of shooting-properties you don't want to waste time looking at. I think Miss Royde's enjoying it up here with us.'

'Oh, Myrtle's enjoying herself fine.'

Myrtle Royde was seated between the two beefy sons of Ben Nevis—Murdoch the sailor and Iain the undergraduate. They, like their sisters Mary and Catriona, had inherited size and weight from their mother; they could indeed be called massive, particularly Iain, who was the heaviest Five that ever rowed in the Trinity Hall boat. It had been the impressive showing they made in the kilt which had prompted Chester Royde's emulation more than the superb appearance of Ben Nevis himself upon his native heath, with which he would probably never dream of competing.

Myrtle undoubtedly was enjoying herself, but an observer would have been right in dissociating her enjoyment from the company of the two young men, whose conversation indeed was hardly more enlivening than a couple of megaliths. Ben Nevis had noticed optimistically the opportunities a two-seater sports car offered to develop an understanding between two young people. He forgot his second son's lack of conversation and was also unaware of the American point of view which makes dumbness and stupidity synonymous. Iain had more to say than Murdoch, but Myrtle Royde was twenty, and a month or two past the final stage when College boys are interesting to the majority of the female sex.

'Well, I envy you your lovely country,' she had exclaimed when Kilwhillie had commented to her brother on the enjoyment he had fancied in the brightness of her dark brown eyes and the rosy flush upon her cheeks.

'It's not bad,' the sailor agreed.

'Not bad, indeed? Why, Lieutenant MacDonald, it's divine.'

Murdoch knitted his brows. He wished she would not call him Lieutenant MacDonald, and that if she must she would not pronounce it 'Lootenant!'

'I used to think my sister-in-law Carrie crazy when she was always on at Chester to take her to Scotland, but I understand it now. I wish I had Scotch ancestors myself. Look at that lovely lake shining away down here. We used sometimes to spend the summer in Vermont when we were children, and that's lovely, too. But I think it's the romance here that gets me. Look at your father now. What a wonderful figure of a man he is! You can fancy him leading his clan to battle, can't you? Oh, I tell you I'm just in a sort of dream state. And so's Carrie. And I think Chester's pretty taken with it. I noticed a look in his eye I've never seen before when the pipers came in at dinner last night.'

'I think they're rather boring as a matter of fact,' said Iain.

'Mr MacDonald, how can you say that? Why, I was getting thrills all down my back every time they passed behind my chair.'

But Myrtle was spared further disillusionment by the voice of Ben Nevis asking if the guns were ready to move off.

'Drumcockie this afternoon, eh, Ben Nevis?' asked a thin elderly man in plus fours, with a white toothbrush moustache, his countenance dyed an indelible brownish yellow by the Indian sun.

'Yes, and if we do as well as we did this morning, we ought to make a record.'

'Hope we do,' said the thin man.

Chester Royde asked Kilwhillie who the thin man was. He had not caught his name when they were introduced.

'Colonel Lindsay-Wolseley of Tummie.'

'Say, I don't have to call him Tummie, do I?' the young financier enquired anxiously.

'You can if you like, but he only bought Tummie after the war. I should call him "Colonel" if I were you.'

Chester Royde sighed his relief as he threw a leg across the hill pony that was to bear him to the grouse-teeming moor of Drumcockie.

Alas, for the high hopes of Ben Nevis! His dearest moor failed him. There were some birds. There could not fail to be some birds on Drumcockie. But compared with the number of birds there ought to have been the few that whirred towards the butts and death were nothing.

'What the devil are the beaters playing at, Duncan?' he demanded wrathfully, his eagle's beak darkening to the tint of an Anglican prelate's evening apron.

Big Duncan MacDonald, who looked like a major prophet in tweeds, shook his head.

'I'm thinking it's some of these hikers, Ben Nevis.'

'You think it's what?' the chieftain gasped.

'Hikers.'

'Hikers? Hikers on Drumcockie?'

'They're after frightening every bird in the neighbourhood,' he declared, with a muttered imprecation in Gaelic.

'You're not seriously telling me, Duncan, that some of these abominable hikers have dared to defile Drumcockie on the Twelfth of August?'

'There were a party of sixteen of them camping in Strathdiddle last night.'

'In defiance of these notice-boards I've just had freshly painted?'

'My grandson Willie says they were camping right round the notice-board on the north bank of the loch.'

Mac'ic Eachainn glared across Drumcockie Moor away to where the fair expanse of Loch Hoo crowned the head of Strathdiddle with gleaming silver.

'Why wasn't I told of this outrage before, Duncan?'

'Because I was not so anxious to spoil your eye, Ben Nevis. You would not have hit a bird this morning if you were after hearing about those hikers in Strathdiddle. I was hoping no harm would have been done, but there you are. While we were shooting Clacknaclock these hikers were at their devilment on Drumcockie.'

'Duncan,' his chief asked, 'how long have you been in my service?'

'Thirty-two years last June, Ben Nevis.'

'In the whole of that time have you ever known me go back on my word?'

'No, I don't believe you ever went back on your word, Ben Nevis.'

'Then when I tell you that whatever it costs me I am determined to rid my land of hikers you know I mean what I say.'

'You said the very same thing about rabbits, Ben Nevis, three years back,' his old henchman reminded him.

'Hikers don't breed like rabbits.'

'But you cannot trap hikers, Ben Nevis.'

'No, I can't trap them, thanks to the grandmotherly laws under which we suffer, but I can clear them off my land, and I will too. They're a fouler pest than rabbits. They're worse than bracken. Are hikers going to be able to do what the Macintoshes were never able to do? Am I or am I not the twenty-third MacDonald of Ben Nevis?'

'Gently now, gently, Ben Nevis. You're getting very red in the face. You mustn't excite yourself too much. It's very annoying, right enough. Och, it's terrible. But you mustn't let it boil your blood too much. If I call in the beaters we might move along to the Derrybeg. It's not too late at all.'

'I'm not going to shoot another bird to-day. The morning bag was the best for six years. I'm not going to spoil it. I want to find these hikers. Go and get hold of my two boys and Kilwhillie. I can't ask my other guests . . . no, stay where you are and I'll speak to them myself.'

The Chieftain strode across the moor, his kilt swinging, his sporran jigging, his amaranthine nose cleaving the air. He came to the butt at which Colonel Lindsay-Wolseley was standing.

'Look here, Wolseley, you had a lot of experience on the North-West Frontier. I want your help. There's a band of filthy hikers loose in Strathdiddle.'

Colonel Wolseley looked a little apprehensive. He did not immediately perceive the link between Inverness-shire and Waziristan.

'What action exactly were you proposing to take, Ben Nevis?'

'I'm going to round the brutes up. They've ruined any hope of good sport on Drumcockie for to-day. And I *don't* see why they should get away with it.'

'You mean you're going to turn them off your land?'

'I'm going to lock them up in Glenbogle for a couple of nights and see if that'll give them the lesson they deserve.'

'You're proposing to use force?' the Colonel asked, amazement only kept in check by the traditions of his caste and calling.

'When these savages see themselves covered by half a dozen guns I don't assume they'll offer any resistance,' the Chieftain barked.

'But you can't threaten to shoot trespassers, Ben Nevis. You really can't.'

'I can and I will,' he declared.

'Well, I'm sorry, but I'm afraid I cannot take any part in such a proceeding. You must remember that I am Convener of the Police Committee of the County Council. It would put me in an impossible position. And if you'll take the advice of a friend, Ben Nevis, you'll avoid putting yourself in an impossible position by taking any such action as you contemplate. The proper course is to ask for their names and addresses and institute legal proceedings. If you take the law into your own hands you'll expose yourself to an action for assault and false imprisonment. You may get heavy damages against you.'

'Look here, Lindsay-Wolseley, I don't want you to take what I'm going to say personally. I've no desire to be offensive. But I'm not in the mood to be lectured about my actions. This band of miscreants camped last night on the banks of Loch Hoo, actually right round one of my freshly-painted No Camping notice-boards. Not content with that they've evidently been careering about all over Drumcockie this morning, and our Twelfth has been wrecked.'

'My dear Ben Nevis, do not misunderstand me. I sympathize profoundly over this beastly business. But when you ask me to take part with you in what amounts to a punitive expedition I should be no true friend of yours if I didn't try to dissuade you from such an action. I suppose you'll call me a cold-blooded Lowlander, but I do beg you to think twice before you embark upon a course of action the consequences of which may be . . . I mean to say, Ben Nevis, we landed proprietors cannot afford to stir up popular feeling in these democratic days.'

'Clap-trap!'

'What?'

'I said clap-trap, Lindsay-Wolseley. You're talking Bolshie clap-trap.'

'You are allowing your feelings to get the better of you, Ben Nevis,' the Colonel observed, a dull flush asserting itself beneath the brownish-yellow dye of the Indian sun.

'I have no desire to quarrel with you, Lindsay-Wolseley.'

'I accept that, Ben Nevis. So let us say no more about it,' the Colonel replied, with a gesture of old-world courtliness. 'I'm very sorry that the splendid sport you've been giving us has been interfered with by uninvited guests.'

'I suppose Bottley won't be any more anxious than you to round up these filthy hikers,' Ben Nevis growled, with a glance in the direction of Sir Hubert Bottley, the owner of the famous forest of Cloy which had been bought by his father, the first baronet, out of Bottley's Bottled Beans.

'I won't answer for him,' said the Colonel hurriedly. 'Bottley must decide for himself.'

'I shan't try to involve him or Rawstorne or Jack Fraser,' Ben Nevis said proudly. 'I think I can manage with my own people. We've managed for a good many years now. I only asked you, Wolseley, because I thought you might enjoy the kind of sport you must often have enjoyed at Peshawar. Well, I'm sorry to break up our day like this, but I must get my forces together.'

The Colonel saw it was useless to argue further with his friend. At any rate, he was glad to hear himself addressed again as 'Wolseley.' It indicated that his refusal to take part in the punitive expedition against the hikers was no longer resented. Lindsay-Wolseley was what Ben Nevis always called him when they found themselves in disagreement at a meeting of the County Council.

'That was the kind of thing which wrecked the 'Forty-five, Hugh,' the Chieftain observed to the laird of Kilwhillie when the ponies with the four recreant guns were lost to sight in a dip of the moor on the way back to the Pass of Ballochy and the waiting cars. 'However, thank God, the old loyalties haven't entirely disappeared!'

'You can't expect newcomers to feel as we do, Donald.' Then Hugh Cameron remembered his plan to sell Knocknacolly and its dilapidated lodge to Chester Royde Jr.

'Not *all* newcomers, that is.'

'Well, I'll say I'm enjoying myself,' the young financier declared. 'But what do we do if these hoodlums won't put their hands up, Ben Nevis?'

'I'm sending the beaters round to cut off their retreat. I don't think they'll resist. They're a weedy type. And there are some women with them. Extraordinary class of people altogether. I'm relying on you, Mary, and you, Catriona, to deal with these women. And what about you, Miss Royde?'

'Oh, please don't call me that, Ben Nevis. I don't feel a little bit like a daughter of the clan when you call me Miss Royde.'

'Very nice of you. Appreciate it very much. Well, what are you going to do, Myrtle? I think Murdoch had better look after you.'

'No, I know just what I'm going to do,' said Myrtle firmly. 'I'm going to stay right by you, Ben Nevis. I'm going to be your vivandière.'

The imaginative observer capable of rejecting the materialistic explanation that it was a sporting party walking up any game that was about would have derived from the spectacle of Mac'ic Eachainn's line of battle the deepest romantic gratification. On the right as befitted MacDonald was the Chieftain himself, a hefty son on either side of him, a daughter not less hefty on either side of their brothers, the tartan of the kilts and skirts in which red predominated recalling a dozen poems of battles fought by the MacDonalds of Ben Nevis. A few yards behind this line of red and immediately behind Mac'ic Eachainn himself marched Myrtle Royde carrying a flask of whisky.

A pity Hector was out with his regiment in India, his father reflected. This was the very girl for him. Murdoch was too much of a slowcoach. He ought to have done better with the chances he had already had. And after all this jolly little girl with so much money in prospect would want an eldest son. She'd be sure to cotton on to Hector. He had a good mind to send an urgent cable telling Hector to apply for leave at once and fly home. It would cost a bit, but nothing venture nothing win. Ben Nevis looked round and smiled benignly at his vivandière, and the answering smile dimpling those cheeks decided him. He would cable Hector to obtain leave for urgent family reasons and come by plane.

The centre of Mac'ic Eachainn's line of battle consisted of Chester Royde, whose fat face had taken on the severe lines of an Arizona sheriff riding after a gang of rustlers in the timeless air of Wild West romance, and his head-keeper, Duncan Macdonald, who looked like Elijah hot upon the trail of the priests of Baal. The left was commanded by Hugh Cameron of Kilwhillie, who had a couple of gillies with him.

For a quarter of an hour the line advanced steadily across Drumcockie's heather. Then as the moorland began to slope towards the braes of Strathdiddle Mac'ic Eachainn uttered a shout.

'There they are!'

Yes, there they were in green corduroy shorts and brown corduroy shorts, in pink shirts and pale green shirts and coffee-coloured shirts, hatless, towzled, with long sticks and crêpe-soled shoes and knapsacks, there they were sitting round a fire they had just lighted to make tea and listening to a portable wireless, female hikers and male hikers to the number of sixteen.

Ben Nevis charged ahead of the others, and five of the hikers dived for their cameras to get snapshots of this magnificent specimen of the native fauna striding through the heather in the sun's eye. One young woman with smoked glasses and very short green corduroy shorts whose fat flaming thighs looked as if they were melting at the knees held up her hand when the Chieftain was almost on top of the party and asked him to stand still for a moment while she altered the focus of her Kodak.

'Who is in command of this party?' Ben Nevis bellowed.

The hikers looked at one another. The spirit of comradeship which had animated them ever since they had got out of the train from London at Perth and hiked their way to the bonny banks of Loch Hoo had made a leader superfluous.

'Who is in command of this party?' Ben Nevis bellowed again.

The loudness of his voice had by now convinced the hikers that the first specimen of the native fauna they had seen between Perth and Inverness was angry about something. They turned to the only member of the party over twenty-four. This was a dark desiccated little man of anything between forty and fifty with legs as thin and hairy as a spider's and the eyes of a kindly old maid, the sort of eyes one so often sees in confirmed scoutmasters.

'I am the Secretary of the N.U.H., sir,' he told Ben Nevis in a prim voice. 'Were you wanting information about anything?'

'I don't know what the N.U.H. is, but you must be aware that you are . . .'

'Excuse me, sir, the initials N.U.H. stand for National Union of Hikers. We are now a very large organization with branches in every one of our great cities. My name is Prew, Sydney Prew. I'm afraid I haven't a card with me. One disembarrasses oneself of such urban paraphernalia, does one not, when one takes to the open road?'

The combination of some peculiarly irritating quality in the timbre of Mr. Prew's spinsterish voice, of the sight of his own armed forces closing in upon the hikers and a dozen beaters advancing upon them from the rear, and of the recollection of his ruined Twelfth of August was too much for Donald MacDonald, the Twenty-third of Ben Nevis. He was suddenly seized with an access of rage that must have been similar to the convulsion which had seized his ancestor Hector of the Great Jaw when in the year 1482 he speared eleven Macintoshes beside Loch na Craosnaich and drowned them in it one after another. Grasping the Secretary of the N.U.H. by the collar of his khaki shirt, he shook him as a conscientious housemaid shakes a mat.

'This is assault and battery,' protested Mr. Prew. 'I call on all you boys and girls to observe what this gentleman is doing. He is assaulting me. And please note I am making no resistance whatever. May I ask what is the meaning of this outrage?'

The sight of Mr. Prew's enquiring face turned round with some difficulty owing to the grip upon his shirt-collar seemed to rouse Ben Nevis to fresh fury, and he shook him more violently than ever.

'I'll teach you to run amok among my birds. I'll teach you to camp out round one of my notice-boards forbidding camping. I'll teach you to light fires in the heather.'

By this time the shaker and the shaken were both so much out of breath that neither could speak, and the only sound that broke the heathery silence of the braes of Strathdiddle was the voice of a crooner coming from the portable wireless. Even those who disapprove of Mac'ic Eachainn's assault upon Mr Prew will not blame him for dropping Mr Prew and giving the crooner the contents of his gun's two barrels.

'Look here, that's my portable,' a tall pink-faced young man expostulated. Whereupon Ben Nevis seized him by the front of his mauve shirt and shook him as violently as he had shaken Mr Prew. The young woman with the melting knees screamed in a rage and banged away at Ben Nevis with her hiker's staff. Catriona MacDonald caught hold of her by the back of her shorts and put a hefty arm round her neck. There was a general mêlée, but the male hikers, severely handicapped by the attempts of the female hikers to help them, were no match for Clan Donald.

'What will we do with them, Ben Nevis?' Duncan asked when the invaders were disarmed and surrounded.

'Bring them along to Ballochy, and I'll send the lorry for them when we get back to the Castle. You want to camp on my land, do you?' he snarled at Mr Prew. 'Very well, then you shall camp in the dungeons of Glenbogle Castle and see how you like that.'

'This is going to be a serious matter for you, Mr MacDonald,' said the Secretary of the N.U.H., his prim voice trembling with indignation, 'for I presume you are the Mr MacDonald who owns this land.'

Mac'ic Eachainn turned away with a look of utter disgust. A gardener would as soon think of arguing with a slug as he would with Sydney Prew.

*1941*

One of Mervyn Peake's illustrations for
*The Ancient Mariner*

# MARGARET IRWIN

## *The King's Christmas*

FROM 'YOUNG BESS'

THE King sat in his great chair with the new seat embroidered by his daughter Mary for his Christmas present. The seats of Henry's chairs were apt to wear out; this one was so ample that the materials had cost Mary £20. He was spread over every stitch of that labour of filial love as he sat staring at all those glittering young figures prancing, dancing, running here and there. Usually he chuckled and cheered them on, but now he stared without seeming to notice them; only, once or twice, his pouched eyes rolled round between the folds of his cheeks to follow the antics of the pretty young widow of his old friend Charles Brandon who ran with tittering shricks to escape the blindfolded pursuer.

Would she be his seventh wife? It had been whispered. But there was another whisper that said the King would never have a seventh wife.

Now came the real importance of the evening, and his flat eyes opened with the gleam of a hawk's as a host of silver-clad pages carried in long tables and set them up on trestles in the hall; roasted peacocks in their pride with spread tails and swans re-invested in their snowy plumage were perched on them, waiting to be carved, and a few of the lately discovered turkeys brought to breed in Europe from the New World by a Spanish adventurer, Pedro Nino. 'But it will take more than Nine Pedros to make us English take to such poultry, tasteless as wood,' proclaimed King Henry, who, however, liked to show these novelties among the old Christmas dishes; mince pies in the form of the Christ Child's manger, boars' heads whose jellied eyes glared between their tusks as fierce as in life, shepherds and their flocks made of sweetmeats, and flagons of cock ale, a mixture of ale and sack in which an old cock braised with raisins and cloves had been steeped for nine days and the liquid then strained and matured.

Henry was hoisted by four men out of his chair and into one that fitted his stomach more accommodatingly against the table.

The buzz of talking and guzzling rose higher and higher as the wine circulated; when it had soared almost an octave, music took up the note, and the voices of choristers clear and piercing sweet. They sang a song that Henry himself had composed, words and music, when he had just come to the throne, a youth of eighteen, in the full flush of his cherubic beauty and athletic vigour, 'rejoicing as a giant to run his course.'

Pastime with good company
I love, and shall, until I die.

The little eyes blinked and closed; the vast padded figure in the chair sat like a dummy, apparently insensible, as he listened to what he once had sung. It was still true, he told himself, it always would be, —pastime—good company—none had had better. Odd that of all that brilliant company it was only those that he had enjoyed long ago who now stood out vividly in his mind, so much more vividly than all these scattering, chattering young apes he had just been watching, even that brisk young widow of Charles Brandon's—the half-Spanish girl—what was her name? He could not trouble himself to remember. The notes that he had once plucked out for the first time on his lute were teasing him with older memories.

Charles Brandon himself seemed nearer now than his widow, so did all those other vigorous young men with whom he had once played games and practical jokes and exchanged low stories with roars of laughter and thumps on the back: that young rascal Bryan whom he had nicknamed the Vicar of Hell—Buckingham—Compton—Bullen—all dead; some, it is true, by his orders, but that didn't make it the less pitiful for him that there were now so few of the old faces round him, so few to remember him as he once had been.

There was that tough old ruffian Norfolk, of course, he'd always been there from the beginning of time,—where *was* Norfolk? He stared at all these new young upstart whipper-snappers, seeking Norfolk's grizzled peaked beard and wiry hair, still black, somewhere among them. 'Where—' he began aloud, then checked; he had remembered, just in time, that Norfolk was in the Tower, awaiting sentence of death. He had already signed the death-warrant for Norfolk's son, the Earl of Surrey; in a day or two now the insolent conceited lad would lay on the block the handsome head that had dared compose verses against his King.

Whose glutted cheeks sloth feeds so fat
That scant their eyes be seen.

Was it possible young Surrey had intended that for his Dread Sovereign? But anything was possible with these Howards. Two nieces Norfolk had wedded to him, and both had to be beheaded. Now Cranmer and Ned Seymour said that he had conspired to put his son on the throne. He denied it, of course. 'When I deserve to be in the Tower,' he had exclaimed, 'Tottenham will turn French!'

Just like old Norfolk! Told George Lawson once that he was as good a knight as ever spurred a cow! Useful fellow, Norfolk, always ready to run and pull down whoever he was set on;—how he'd chased Wolsey from town, swearing he'd 'tear the butcher's cur with his teeth if he didn't shog off!' Pity you couldn't tell with the best wolf-hound when it mightn't turn and bite its master.

He took a deep drink, with a glance at his watchful physician. 'Let every man have his own doctor,' he wheezed. 'This is mine.'

This was a good song of his. Surrey, the lazy cub, was writing verse without rhyme and calling it a new invention, blank verse. Blank it was. His own was the real thing.

Youth will needs have dalliance,

sang the choristers.

His youth had had all that youth ever dreamed of, once his dreary lonely boyhood had passed, and his stingy old father in the shabby fur cloak had died, and young Prince Hal found himself one of the richest kings in Europe. He had turned everything to gold with his Midas touch; the foreign visitors could not believe their eyes, they had to finger all the tassels and cups and jugs and horses' bits, to bc convinced that they were solid gold. He had been the most splendidly dressed king in Europe. What feasting there had been, unequalled by Cleopatra or Caligula, the ambassadors said; what spiced game and vension cooked in sour cream, what flowing of fulsome wines.

It was the same now, but it had tasted better then, after his father's diet of porridge and small beer; and with the zest of youth, an appetite as voracious for fun as for food, that pie he had carved, full of live frogs that leaped out over the table and floor, making the girls scream and jump on the benches, lifting their skirts above their knees—what a roar of laughter from him and all the other young fellows had volleyed and tumbled round the hall, echoing back to him now after all these years.

The lids of those lowered eyes just lifted; the grey lips moved. 'Another cup of wine,' they mumbled.

Every man hath his free will,

sang the choristers from Henry's early song.

What masquerades there had been then, what pranks and dressing-up as Muscovites or Saracen robbers, surprising the Queen and her ladies into delicious alarm and then laughter! What dancing, he himself leaping higher than any, and long, long into the night, and that after he had played a hard game of tennis, wrestled in bout after bout, run races and leaped with the long pole, or been in the saddle all day riding at the gallop after hounds, riding in the lists and unhorsing all his opponents. There was no one could beat 'Sir Loyal Heart,' the name he always took in those tournaments of his youth when he cantered up on his great war-horse with his wife's Spanish colours on his sleeve in defiance of the fashion (for a knight should wear some other lady's), into the pavilion that was all spangled with gold Tudor roses and the pomegranates of Aragon, and H.K. intertwined.

H.K. everywhere for Henry and Katherine.

As the holly groweth green and never changeth hue,
So I am—ever have been—unto my lady true.

For whoso loveth should love but one,
Change whoso will, I will be none.

That was another song of his, but he never cared to hear it sung after the 'H.K.' was all changed everywhere to 'H.A.' for Henry and Anne. 'HA HA!' shouted the rude Cockney boys, and they were right—the common people always were in the long run—right to mock and distrust that accursed whore who bewitched Sir Loyal Heart and led him into captivity, unrewarded for six long years. What torture of desire he had undergone for her, what abject letters he had written her—and then the reward, good God, another girl!

He blinked down the table at the girl, as lithe and whippy as a greyhound puppy, and the light glinting on her red-gold hair. 'Nan Bullen's brat!' he muttered to himself, 'a whey-faced scrap of a thing like her mother, a green apple, a codling,' he drooled on, regarding her with a fixed and menacing eye.

She looked back at him; for one instant he saw himself reflected in the dreadfully dispassionate eyes of a very young girl. But the image was quickly blurred; the light seemed oddly dim tonight, as it had been in his father's day when they cut down the number of candles and saved the candle-ends.

What did that girl matter—or all the other girls either?—though it was enraging the way the Tudor stock had run to seed in a crop of females: first his own two daughters; and then the only grandchildren of his two fine strapping sisters were those three diminutive Grey brats, and the baby [Queen Mary] in Scotland who might well become the most dangerous person in Europe.

But he had the boy, his son Edward, yes, he had got a legitimate son at last. He turned his great stiff head slowly and stared at the pale child beside him; nothing like as big and strong as he himself had been at his age; he was much more like what Henry's elder brother Prince Arthur had been, but that Henry could not bear to recognize; for the slight boy whom he could scarcely remember had died at fifteen of a consumption. No, Henry would see no likeness to Arthur in Edward; for one thing, Edward was far cleverer, already he knew more than lads twice his age. 'I wish I had more learning' Henry had sighed when a youth, as greedy for the beauty of great minds as for rich food and drink, for pleasure and sport and glory and conquest.

He had welcomed Erasmus to his Court, he had been proud to count him as a friend; and witty ironic Thomas More too, with whom he had walked so often in More's garden at Chelsea, watching the river flow past and the seagulls swoop and swirl, while they discussed everything under heaven and in it too as they walked up and down, his arm round his friend's neck. But his friend had betrayed him, defied him, tacitly refused to recognize the righteousness of his divorce with Katherine of Aragon, turned stiff-necked in resistance to his will, until there was nothing for it but to cut off his learned and witty head. Tom Cromwell had urged him to it. 'More must go,' he had said; and then in his turn Crum had to go. Crum was a knave if ever there was one: when Henry held a knave in his hands at cards he used to say 'I hold a Cromwell!' But he was a witty devil and a good servant.

The best of friends, the best of his servants, the best of women, how was it that all had failed him? He needed friendship, he needed love, he needed a wise, tender, infinitely understanding companion who, while giving him all the glowing admiration that was his due, would also know just where to throw out a hint in guidance of his judgment, where to encourage and where to still the doubts that often stirred deep down within himself, so deep that even he did not always recognize them until too late.

But he had never had such a companion; never since— Was there a strong draught that made the candles gutter and sway, and the smoke swirl in wreaths from their flickering flames? Through the blue and shifting mist he was seeing pictures he had not seen for over forty years —a fair Spanish princess of sixteen, all in white, with long hair down her back, seated in a litter hung with cloth of gold, and himself riding beside her, a cavalier of ten, entrusted to escort his brother Arthur's bride through the roaring cheering flower-strewn streets of London. He, who was never allowed all his boyhood to be with any girl except his sisters, had then his first taste of the pageantry of chivalry that he adored in the romances; and was so intoxicated by it that, that evening, to show off to Katherine, he danced so hard that he had to tear off his hot coat and caper in his small-clothes. And after Arthur had died a few months later, and Henry had married his widow a few years later, he went on showing off to Katherine, finding her the perfect audience, through twenty years of marriage,—until he found to his rage that she too claimed to take a part in the play herself.

Muttering something to himself, he reached forward to take another helping of sugared marchpane, felt the marble edge of the table pressing into his belly, and squinted down at it resentfully. How long had he been in labour with this huge paunch? Tonight it seemed so short a time had turned that splendid young athlete, with fit hard stomach and limbs clean as a whistle, into this mountain of pain and disease, in labour with—was it death? The choristers sang:

> To hunt, sing, dance
> My heart is set.
> All goodly sport
> To my comfort
> Who shall me let?

There was no one to offer let or hindrance to his pleasures; except himself. '*Every man hath his free will,*' but what use was that? since a vast aching body told one, as sternly as any gaoler come to arrest a quaking girl, that 'it is no more the time to dance.'

There was no pleasure now left to that body except to cram it further with food, with deep stupefying draughts of wine, cloying the palate, mercifully dulling the senses. He reached forward for his cup. '*Who shall me let?*' Neither his anxious-eyed physician nor his fearfully watching wife dared offer let or hindrance.

And suddenly he began to talk. His great voice swayed gustily to and fro, a storm wind rising and falling in the hall that a moment since had been full of music and pattering chatter, and now was paralysed into silence with the resurgence into life of the figure-head, monstrous and moribund at head of the table.

He talked of the French and how he had so lately beaten them; he had made the Narrow Seas English for all time; no other foreign invaders would ever dare come sailing up the Channel. Oncc indeed he might havc turned the tables the other way and conquered the whole country of France after winning a yet more glorious Agincourt; he had in fact conquered and now held Boulogne. When only twenty-two he had taken the Chevalier Bayard prisoner and shown them that an Englishman could be every bit as much a 'very perfect gentle knight' as any bowing Frenchman. ('Now,' thought Bess, playing with the nutshells on her plate, 'now he will say, "Stout fellow, Bayard, a very fine fellow."') Sure enough he said it, and with episcopal authority—'Old Gardiner showed sense, for a bishop, when he said Bayard is a stout fellow.' He always had to say that when he mentioned Bayard, to remind himself that he did not really bear the noblest man in Europe a grudge for knighting François on the terrible battlefield of Marignano when the young French King and his armies had fought 'like infuriated bears.' Henry had never been in a battle like that; even now, when François too had grown old and cautious, it irked him to think how the Foxnose had once fought his own battles, where Henry had only paid the Emperor to fight them.

Well, it was something to have had an Emperor in his pay. And once he had planned to make himself Emperor when his servant Wolsey had aimed to be Pope—Wolsey the butcher's son, a fellow that had once been put in the stocks for a brawl at a fair, but whom he had raised to be the greatest priest and statesman in England, and, almost, in Europe. Yes, he had brought England back into the Continent, he had made her a power to be feared and courted.

'Look at the Field of the Cloth of Gold!' he shouted suddenly. *That* showed Europe was at his feet—and with what a show! The English had outvied the French at every point; François, alarmed at the competition, had sent anxiously to him beforehand to ask him to forbear making so many rich tents and pavilions. François had shown him with great pride a portrait of a woman called Mona Lisa that he had bought from the old painter Leonardo da Vinci who had died the year before; he had paid four thousand florins for it, a ridiculous sum for a picture, and of a rather plain woman too.

Henry could retaliate with Holbein, whom he had honoured with his patronage and an income of £30 a year (less £3 for taxes) apart from the sale of his pictures. The new Dutch School was coming far more into fashion than those old Italians.

They said François was as tall as Henry, but it was only because the Frenchman's wretchedly thin legs made him seem taller than he really was. If only he could have matched his knightly prowess against François in the tourney, which cautious royal etiquette forbade, he would have proved himself the victor, he was sure of it. He had overcome all his opponents in it, and killed one of his mounts from sheer exhaustion (François had overcome all his too, but they had probably thought it wise to let him win). Henry had excelled even his crack English archers at the long bow; the French had gasped with admiration of his aim and strength. Certainly he would have been more than a match for François.

'Remember how I threw him in the wrestling bout?' he chuckled. 'What a to-do there was! Kings mustn't be thrown! Why, Kate, you and the French Queen had to pull us apart, d'you remember, hanging on to our shirt-tails like a couple of fishwives parting their husbands in a brawl!'

The hall seemed to rock to the sound of that mighty guffaw, and echoed it back in a frozen silence. No one knew where to look, what to say. The King heard and saw the emptiness all round him, a herd of sheep staring, but not at him, not at anyone, a wavering cloud of white foolish faces, scared and averted, and among them a very young red-headed girl playing with the nutshells on her plate. Who *was* that girl? She was always cropping up, baffling, frustrating, charged with some hideous memory.

The scene grew thicker, more confused. 'Kate!' he called in sudden terror, '*Kate!*' A woman was hanging on to his arm, imploring him something. She seemed to think it was her that he had called—why, he did not even know who she was! Some fellow was loosening his collar, the woman put water to his lips.

He stared at the red-headed girl and knew now she was his daughter—but not by Kate. There had been other Kates, Annes, Jane,—but the Kate who could remember him at the Field of the Cloth of Gold, as King and bridegroom at eighteen, as a child of ten riding beside her, that Kate had gone for ever, and would never come back.

Not Katherine of Aragon hung on his arm, but Catherine Parr, who knew him only as an obese, sick old man.

He made a mighty effort and guffawed again. 'Why, how I've scared the lot of you!' he gasped out. 'Who do you think I took you for,

Kate? I was asking only if you remembered hearing the tale. You were only a little girl when it happened.'

But he spoke with difficulty and his lips had gone blue, and his twitching hands where the great jewelled rings were sunk in fat.

Bess, holding on to her nutshells so tight that they cut into her hands, stole a glance at him under her down-dropped eyelids and thought his face looked like a glistening suet pudding. Then, even as she glanced, it sagged, a deflated bag, turned a greyish purple, and a tight smile twisted it as though trying to hold it together; the eyes opened for one instant in a puzzled, frightened stare,—and then the crash came. He fell forward over the table, into clattering plates and knives and cups, and a great red pool of spilt wine pouring over and drip-dripping on to the floor like drops of blood.

*1944*

# ROBERT HARLING

## *Early Years*

FROM 'AMATEUR SAILOR'

I BECAME early acquainted with the sea, for when I was three my mother died, and, my father having been killed in a motoring accident three months before I was born, I was taken to live with an uncle and aunt, my mother's cousin, in a large holiday town on the South Coast.

My Uncle Taff was a Welshman about fifty; a dairyman with an extensive connection along the coast. He was a short, wiry man with a brown wizened face; he had unusually intense, staring blue eyes and a long, grey, drooping moustache which gave him always an expression of extreme dourness; but actually he was the most humorous and lively of men, and this seeming paradox has caused me to grow up with no desire to take people at their face value. From the first, my uncle's clothes aroused my keenest admiration and envy. He wore riding breeches which were invariably unlaced, and those laces are amongst my earliest recollections of him, for they were continuously whipping against his socks and sometimes, if very slack, against his brightly polished brown boots. These lackadaisical laces were the only blemish in what was otherwise a most carefully considered wardrobe. His long hacking jackets in subfusc whipcords were always beautifully cut, with magnificent flares to the skirts, and his suede waistcoats were never wrinkled, however arduous his day's work. He wore strangely old-fashioned, deeply cut, rounded stiff collars, and always the same dark brown tie; and I remember thinking quite early in my life that these collars seemed incongruous items in the total sum of his magnificence. That he was an original, there could be no doubt. In the blaring, South-Coast originality of the town he stood out as an eccentric, but that eccentricity, as I soon discovered, was connected only with the sartorial façade he presented. In his business life he was successful in the most conventional manner; and was, indeed, very comfortably off.

My Aunt Ruth was a complete contrast to my uncle; she was slow-moving, slow-thinking and slow of speech, yet in no way was she overshadowed by the vivid personality of her husband. She was big, and already white-haired, although not much over thirty. She was extremely gentle and kind. I thought that she was beautiful. In retrospect I see that it was the strength of character which she possessed in so pronounced a degree which gave this impression of beauty to my young mind. Her features, which I see now in period photographs, are firm and regular, but heavy for conventional beauty. This quiet yet strong character made her a perfect foil for my uncle's nervous energy and irritability. When he was in his cups, which was often, she never nagged, but gently manœuvred him into silence or slumber. Many years later I was to see the same type of woman in Scandinavia, but in those early days she seemed to me strange and unique amongst all the women I ever saw. It was Aunt Ruth's innate dignity which dominated my new home and not my Uncle Taff's restless spirit.

With this widely differing pair I began my new life. I began, indeed, the only life of which I have any true recollection, for I remember no home before the busy life of my Uncle Taff's establishment, a maelstrom for a somewhat bewildered small boy. It was a spacious shop, as clean and white as the milk itself, and all day long it held an unceasing stream of women and children passing through, their heels hard and clear on the black and white chequered tiled floor; and with these sounds was mingled the continuous ring of metal measure against china jug. There was much gossip, too, for the three young Welsh serving-girls in the dairy were garrulous throughout the day. Little wonder that I was fascinated by the unbelievable activity of this new world and stood for hours at the door of the shop parlour watching the life of the shop. Yet even more thrilling experiences were to come, for within a week or so of my arrival my uncle decided to take me out with him on his mid-morning journey along the coast in the pony and trap.

There are certain experiences in life which are so clear-cut in their sensation, whether of pain or joy, hatred or love, that they remain always sharply chiselled within our memory, never fading. Such a sensation was that journey. The pony was nervous and kicked its heels outside the shop as I clambered into the trap. I was surrounded by what seemed to be literally hundreds of cans. In front of me was a gigantic churn. My uncle leapt up, seized the reins, hissed some magic word, and we were off. The cans evoked a discordant pattern of sounds in the street, a pattern of great beauty in my ears. People turned to stare at the lively equipage. One or two waved and my uncle waved back with his short whip, sometimes calling a cheery salutation, for this was his daily indulgence. There was no need for him to have made this journey. After many years of hard work he had made himself one of the most successful of the independent dairymen on the South Coast. He employed more than twenty roundsmen, but this daily jaunt he still reserved for his own pleasure. I think it gave him the satisfaction that he was still as good as any of his men at the actual job, in exactly the same way that a master mariner will occasionally lay off a course, quickly and accurately, to show his navigating officer that he hasn't lost his touch.

This was the first of these mid-morning excursions, and they immediately became for me experiences of pure pleasure. There were movement, colour, noise, and the great sweep of the sea at the foot of each street we passed on our way out of the town, to the suburbs to the east. My uncle had cheery words for mistresses, cooks and maids. To them he was obviously rather a character, and it pleased their vanity to be attended by my uncle himself, the proprietor of the thriving dairy. For me the journey was a passage through a magic land. This was not a story of another boy, read from a book or told to me in halting words; this was *now* and this was *me*; and beyond all this, giving the excursion an even more magical colour, was the sea, and on the sea were ships, some with sails, others moving slowly beneath thin trails of smoke. The vista was like a story-book come true, and for a small boy taken from a London suburb it was indeed an enchanted and exciting world.

A day or so later I was taken down to the front by Jenny, one of the serving-girls. She was very patient with the scores of questions I shot at her. Many of them made her laugh. I cannot remember what these questions were, but I remember her quick laughter. She was amused by my continuing delight in the sea, especially by my preoccupation with the recurring rhythm of the waves, which intrigued me beyond all telling. Thus in the early days of that summer, with these excursions, equestrian and pedestrian, my lasting interest in the shapes of sailing vessels was born, for there at the water's edge or drawn up on the millions of pebbles were fishing boats and pleasure craft; some large, some very small; some carrying great brown sails, others with blindingly white sails; some drab and dirty, yet still beautiful despite their dirt; others painted in bold and startling primary effects; and gathered by the sides of these boats were usually groups of men wearing blue jerseys, old trousers and sea-boats, talking amongst themselves or watching with speculative eyes the crowds of holiday-makers.

*1944*

# E. M. W. TILLYARD

## *The Two Village-Greens*

FROM 'POETRY DIRECT AND OBLIQUE'

A FAMILIAR contrast, directed usually to illustrating some differences between Augustan and Romantic styles of poetry, is that between Goldsmith's picture of Auburn in *The Deserted Village* and Blake's *Echoing Green* in *Songs of Innocence*. And these two pieces will serve neatly enough as text for the quite different contrast I have to explain. Here is Goldsmith's village-green with the pleasures that enlivened it:

> How often have I loitered o'er thy green,
> Where humble happiness endeared each scene!
> How often have I paused on every charm,
> The sheltered cot, the cultivated farm,
> The never-failing brook, the busy mill,
> The decent church that topt the neighbouring hill,
> The hawthorn bush, with seats beneath the shade,
> For talking age and whispering lovers made!
> How often have I blest the coming day,
> When toil remitting lent its turn to play,
> And all the village train from labour free
> Led up their sports beneath the spreading tree,
> While many a pastime circled in the shade,
> The young contending as the old surveyed;
> And many a gambol frolicked o'er the ground,
> And slights of art and feats of strength went round;
> And still as each repeated pleasure tired,
> Succeeding sports the mirthful band inspired.

This is a fair example of the poetry of direct statement: it is to some degree concerned with what the words state as well as with what they imply. Had Goldsmith been describing one actual village, were it certain that he were describing an actual remembered scene at Lissoy, the element of statement would be solider than it is; and in that he is imagining his village on the analogy of a number of villages he has known, he is the less direct. But at least he wants the reader to think primarily of villages when he talks of Auburn; not of the Social Contract or of heavenly beatitude. We believe this because the formal parts of the poetry reinforce the statement rather than suggest thoughts alien to it. The couplets evolve in a simple explicatory sequence; they unfold the scene with no hint of ulterior meaning; their freshness and unobstructedness are those of the clear sunny day they describe. The vocabulary is as close to simple statement as Goldsmith's epoch allowed to anyone but a rebel; and when he is not simple, it is for convention's sake and not with any view to obliquity. Thus by 'humble happiness' he probably means 'humble, happy people,' and by 'talking age' he certainly means 'garrulous old folk': but these phrases are no more than the poetic idiom of his day.

True, some obliquity cannot be denied. Goldsmith wants to say that he likes villagers to be hard-working and sober and to enjoy simple pleasures, and in that he says so, not by a general statement but through describing an imagined single occasion when the villagers enjoy these pleasures, he is being slightly oblique. And there is another, much more important example of obliquity. Goldsmith idealises his Auburn not only because this is how he would like villages to be, but because, feeling homesick for some place other than the one he is in, he must imagine his perfect refuge. Thus, when he says,

> And still as each repeated pleasure tired,
> Succeeding sports the mirthful band inspired,

he reveals himself day-dreaming of perpetually unexhausted pleasure, forgetful of the cruel actual law of diminishing returns.

For all this, Goldsmith's lines mainly concern their professed subject, village-life, and therefore exemplify the poetry of statement.

Here is Blake's village-green:

> The Sun does arise,
> And make happy the skies;
> The merry bells ring
> To welcome the Spring;
> The skylark and thrush,
> The birds of the bush,
> Sing louder around
> To the bells' cheerful sound,
> While our sports shall be seen
> On the Echoing Green.
>
> Old John, with white hair,
> Does laugh away care,
> Sitting under the oak,
> Among the old folk.
> They laugh at our play,
> And soon they all say:
> 'Such, such were the joys
> When we all, girls and boys,
> In our youth time were seen
> On the Echoing Green.'
>
> Till the little ones, weary,
> No more can be merry;
> The sun does descend,
> And our sports have an end.

Round the laps of their mothers
Many sisters and brothers,
Like birds in their nest,
Are ready for rest,
And sport no more seen
On the darkening Green.

It is very easy to allow to Blake's lines just about the same amount of directness and obliquity as to Goldsmith's. Blake's is the greater mind, and of course he uses a different language; but he has every appearance of describing as real a village as Goldsmith's and of knowing quite as much about village games. The sunshine has got into Blake's verse no less than into Goldsmith's. Blake, too, is using his village to express approval of a way of life. He finds in the traditional village sports and pieties a type of his world of innocence, a wider notion perhaps than Goldsmith's more didactic approval. All this is true as far as it goes, and did it respond to our feelings about *The Echoing Green* we might be content with criticising the poem by standards of no profounder obliquity than satisfied *The Deserted Village*.

Now the statements that confront us in *The Echoing Green* have so solid an appearance, present so winningly confident a front, that it seems initially ridiculous not to take them as the poem's major concern. It is the structure that should first put us on our guard. Blake's three verses contrast emphatically with the leisurely roll-out of Goldsmith's couplets. Dawn in the first stanza. Why in the second does Old John sit under the oak? To keep off the noonday sun. Evening in the third. The form is a stylised day-cycle; and if we heed this form, some element of abstraction is set up against the concrete activities of the villagers. There is a careful balance of idea between opening and close: the echoing green becomes the darkening green to balance (though not for this reason only) the rising sun of the first line; the awakening birds in the first stanza are balanced by the simile 'like birds in their nest' in the last. Congruently with the full noonday heat and light the old unfreeze and join their mirth to make up a full chorus with the children. Why all this ingenuity? Does it merely add a pleasing regularity to the statement, or is it a symptom of something else? The truth is that Blake is expressing an idea, an idea that has nothing in itself to do with birds, old and young folk, or village-greens, and one of those most common in Blake's poetical works. It is the idea that there is a virtue in desire satisfied. Though desire is not mentioned, yet the keynote of the poem is fruition. Nature fulfils itself in the cycle of a perfect day. Old John gets a perfect vicarious satisfaction, the little ones are utterly played out and ready for rest. And at the end the 'echoing green' is the 'darkening green' because its function is fulfilled. The very completeness of formal balance points the same way. The poem gives the sense of the perfectly grown apple that comes off at a touch of the hand. It expresses the profound peace of utterly gratified desire.

Thus explained, *The Echoing Green* is as nearly perfect an example of poetical obliquity as can be found. The main sense is stated in no particular whatever, but is diffused through every part of the poem and can be apprehended as a whole only through the synthesis of all those parts. The abstract idea, far from being stated, has been translated into completely concrete form; it has disappeared into apparently alien facts. Through its major obliquity *The Echoing Green* is in a different category from Goldsmith's lines and must be judged by different standards.

Even if this interpretation of *The Echoing Green* be wrong (and such bold guesses at obliquity are likely to please oneself better than others), the *principle* illustrated is not thereby invalidated. Those who reject this instance may find a better and agree that directness and obliquity must vary widely from poem to poem and that to judge an oblique poem as if it were direct, and the other way round, can only lead to disaster.

*1945*

# V. S. PRITCHETT

## *The Saint*

WHEN I was seventeen years old I lost my religious faith. It had been unsteady for some time and then, very suddenly, it went as the result of an incident in a punt on the river outside the town where we lived. My uncle, with whom I was obliged to stay for long periods of my life, had started a small furniture-making business in the town. He was always in difficulties about money, but he was convinced that in some way God would help him. And this happened. An investor arrived who belonged to a sect called the Church of the Last Purification, of Toronto, Canada. Could we imagine, this man asked, a good and omnipotent God allowing his children to be short of money? We had to admit we could not imagine this. The man paid some capital into my uncle's business and we were converted. Our family were the first Purifiers—as they were called—in the town. Soon a congregation of fifty or more were meeting every Sunday in a room at the Corn Exchange.

At once we found ourselves isolated and hated people. Everyone made jokes about us. We had to stand together because we were sometimes dragged into the courts. What the unconverted could not forgive in us was first that we believed in successful prayer and, secondly, that our revelation came from Toronto. The success of our prayers had a simple foundation. We regarded it as 'Error'—our name for Evil—to believe the evidence of our senses and if we had influenza or consumption, or had lost our money or were unemployed, we denied the reality of these things, saying that since God could not have made them they therefore did not exist. It was exhilarating to look at our congregation and to know that what the vulgar would call miracles were performed among us, almost as a matter of routine, every day. Not very big miracles, perhaps; but up in London and out in Toronto, we knew that deafness and blindness, cancer and insanity, the great scourges, were constantly vanishing before the prayers of the more advanced Purifiers.

'What!' said my schoolmaster, an Irishman with eyes like broken glass and a sniff of irritability in the bristles of his nose. 'What! Do you have the impudence to tell me that if you fell off the top floor of this building and smashed your head in, you would say you hadn't fallen and were not injured?'

I was a small boy and very afraid of everybody, but not when it was a question of my religion. I was used to the kind of conundrum the Irishman had set. It was useless to argue, though our religion had already developed an interesting casuistry.

'I *would* say so,' I replied with coldness and some vanity. 'And my head would not be smashed.'

'You would not say so,' answered the Irishman. 'You would not say so.' His eyes sparkled with pure pleasure. 'You'd be dead.'

The boys laughed, but they looked at me with admiration.

Then, I do not know how or why, I began to see a difficulty. Without warning and as if I had gone into my bedroom at night and had found a gross ape seated in my bed and thereafter following me about with his grunts and his fleas and a look, relentless and ancient, scored on his brown face, I was faced with the problem which prowls at the centre of all religious faith. I was faced by the difficulty of the origin of evil. Evil was an illusion, we were taught. But even illusions have an origin. The Purifiers denied this.

I consulted my uncle. Trade was bad at the time and this made his faith abrupt. He frowned as I spoke.

'When did you brush your coat last?' he said. 'You're getting slovenly about your appearance. If you spent more time studying books'—that is to say, the Purification literature—'and less with your hands in your pockets and playing about with boats on the river, you wouldn't be letting Error in.'

All dogmas have their jargon; my uncle as a business man loved the trade terms of the Purification. 'Don't let Error in,' was a favourite one. The whole point about the Purification, he said, was that it was scientific and therefore exact; in consequence it was sheer weakness to admit discussion. Indeed, betrayal. He unpinched his pince-nez, stirred his tea and indicated I must submit or change the subject. Preferably the latter. I saw, to my alarm, that my arguments had defeated my uncle. Faith and doubt pulled like strings round my throat.

'You don't mean to say you don't believe that what our Lord said was true?' my Aunt asked nervously, following me out of the room. 'Your uncle does, dear.'

I could not answer. I went out of the house and down the main street to the river where the punts were stuck like insects in the summery flash of the reach. Life was a dream, I thought; no, a nightmare, for the ape was beside me.

I was still in this state, half sulking and half exalted, when Mr. Hubert Timberlake came to the town. He was one of the important people from the headquarters of our Church and he had come to give an address on the Purification at the Corn Exchange. Posters announcing this were everywhere. Mr. Timberlake was to spend Sunday afternoon with us. It was unbelievable that a man so eminent would actually sit in our dining-room, use our knives and forks, and eat our food. Every imperfection in our home and our characters would jump out at him. The Truth had been revealed to man with scientific accuracy—an accuracy we could all test by experiment—and the future course of human development on earth was laid down, finally. And here in Mr. Timberlake was a man who had not merely performed many miracles —even, it was said with proper reserve, having twice raised the dead—but who had actually been to Toronto, our headquarters, where this great and revolutionary revelation had first been given.

'This is my nephew,' my uncle said, introducing me. 'He lives with us. He thinks he thinks, Mr. Timberlake, but I tell him he only thinks he does. Ha, ha.' My uncle was a humorous man when he was with the great. 'He's always on the river,' my uncle continued. 'I tell him he's got water on the brain. I've been telling Mr. Timberlake about you, my boy.'

A hand as soft as the best quality chamois leather took mine. I saw a wide upright man in a double-breasted navy blue suit. He had a pink square head with very small ears and one of those torpid, enamelled smiles which were said by our enemies to be too common in our sect.

'Why, isn't that just fine?' said Mr. Timberlake who, owing to his contacts with Toronto, spoke with an American accent. 'What say we tell your uncle it's funny he thinks he's funny.'

The eyes of Mr. Timberlake were direct and colourless. He had the look of a retired merchant captain who had become decontaminated from the sea and had reformed and made money. His defence of me had made me his at once. My doubts vanished. Whatever Mr. Timberlake believed must be true and as I listened to him at lunch, I thought there could be no finer life than his.

'I expect Mr. Timberlake's tired after his address,' said my aunt.

'Tired?' exclaimed my uncle, brilliant with indignation. 'How can Mr. Timberlake be tired? Don't let Error in!'

For in our faith the merely inconvenient was just as illusory as a great catastrophe would have been, if you wished to be strict, and Mr. Timberlake's presence made us very strict.

I noticed then that, after their broad smiles, Mr. Timberlake's lips had the habit of setting into a long depressed sarcastic curve.

'I guess,' he drawled, 'I guess the Al-mighty must have been tired sometimes, for it says He re-laxed on the seventh day. Say, do you know what I'd like to do this afternoon,' he said turning to me. 'While your uncle and aunt are sleeping off this meal let's you and me go on the river and get water on the brain. I'll show you how to punt.'

Mr. Timberlake, I saw to my disappointment, was out to show he understood the young. I saw he was planning a 'quiet talk' with me about my problems.

'There are too many people on the river on Sundays,' said my uncle uneasily.

'Oh, I like a crowd,' said Mr. Timberlake, giving my uncle a tough look. 'This is the day of rest, you know.' He had had my uncle gobbling up every bit of gossip from the sacred city of Toronto all the morning.

My uncle and aunt were incredulous that a man like Mr. Timberlake should go out among the blazers and gramophones of the river on a Sunday afternoon. In any other member of our Church they would have thought this sinful.

'Waal, what say?' said Mr. Timberlake. I could only murmur.

'That's fixed,' said Mr. Timberlake. And on came the smile as simple, vivid and unanswerable as the smile on an advertisement. 'Isn't that just fine!'

Mr. Timberlake went upstairs to wash his hands. My uncle was deeply offended and shocked, but he could say nothing. He unpinched his glasses.

'A very wonderful man,' he said. 'So human,' he apologized.

'My boy,' my uncle said. 'This is going to be an experience for you. Hubert Timberlake was making a thousand a year in the insurance business ten years ago. Then he heard of the Purification. He threw everything up, just like that. He gave up his job and took up the work. It was a struggle, he told me so himself this morning. "Many's the time," he said to me this morning, "when I wondered where my next meal was coming from." But the way was shown. He came down from Worcester to London and in two years he was making fifteen hundred a year out of his practice.'

To heal the sick by prayer according to the tenets of the Church of the Last Purification was Mr. Timberlake's profession.

My uncle lowered his eyes. With his glasses off the lids were small and uneasy. He lowered his voice too.

'I have told him about your little trouble,' my uncle said quietly with emotion. I was burned with shame. My uncle looked up and stuck out his chin confidently.

'He just smiled,' my uncle said. 'That's all.'

Then we waited for Mr. Timberlake to come down.

I put on white flannels and soon I was walking down to the river with Mr. Timberlake. I felt that I was going with him under false pretences; for he would begin explaining to me the origin of evil and I would have to pretend politely that he was converting me when, already, at the first sight of him, I had believed. A stone bridge, whose two arches were like an owlish pair of eyes gazing up the reach, was close to the landing-stage. I thought what a pity it was the flannelled men and the sunburned girls there did not know I was getting a ticket for *the* Mr. Timberlake who had been speaking in the town that very morning. I looked round for him and when I saw him I was a little startled. He was standing at the edge of the water looking at it with an expression of empty incomprehension. Among the white crowds his air of brisk efficiency had dulled. He looked middle-aged, out of place and insignificant. But the smile switched on when he saw me.

'Ready?' he called. 'Fine!'

I had the feeling that inside him there must be a gramophone record going round and round, stopping at that word.

He stepped into the punt and took charge.

'Now I just want you to paddle us over to the far bank,' he said, 'and then I'll show you how to punt.'

Everything Mr. Timberlake said still seemed unreal to me. The fact that he was sitting in a punt, of all commonplace material things, was incredible. That he should propose to pole us up the river was terrifying. Suppose he fell into the river? At once I checked the thought. A leader of our Church under the direct guidance of God could not possibly fall into a river.

The stream is wide and deep in this reach, but on the southern bank there is a manageable depth and a hard bottom. Over the clay banks the willows hang, making their basket-work print of sun and shadow on the water, while under the gliding boats lie cloudy, chloride caverns. The hoop-like branches of the trees bend down until their tips touch the water like fingers making musical sounds. Ahead in midstream, on a day sunny as this one was, there is a path of strong light which is hard to look at unless you half close your eyes, and down this path on the crowded Sundays go the launches with their parasols and their pennants; and also the rowing boats with their beetle-leg oars, which seem to dig the sunlight out of the water as they rise. Upstream one goes, on and on between the gardens and then between fields kept for grazing. On the afternoon when Mr. Timberlake and I went out to settle the question of the origin of evil, the meadows were packed densely with buttercups.

'Now,' said Mr. Timberlake decisively when I had paddled to the other side. 'Now I'll take her.'

He got over the seat into the well at the stern.

'I'll just get you clear of the trees,' I said.

'Give me the pole,' said Mr. Timberlake standing up on the little platform and making a squeak with his boots as he did so. 'Thank you, sir. I haven't done this for eighteen years but I can tell you, brother, in those days I was considered some poler.'

He looked around and let the pole slide down through his hands. Then he gave the first difficult push. The punt rocked pleasantly and we moved forward. I sat facing him, paddle in hand, to check any inward drift of the punt.

'How's that, you guys?' said Mr. Timberlake looking round at our eddies and drawing in the pole. The delightful water sished down it.

'Fine,' I said. Deferentially I had caught the word.

He went on to his second and his third strokes, taking too much water on his sleeve, perhaps, and uncertain in his steering, which I corrected, but he was doing well.

'It comes back to me,' he said. 'How am I doing?'

'Just keep her out from the trees,' I said.

'The trees?' he said.

'The willows,' I said.

'I'll do it now,' he said. 'How's that? Not quite enough? Well, how's this?'

'Another one,' I said. 'The current runs strong this side.'

'What? More trees?' he said. He was getting hot.

'We can shoot out past them,' I said. 'I'll ease us over with the paddle.'

Mr. Timberlake did not like this suggestion.

'No, don't do that. I can manage it,' he said. I did not want to offend one of the leaders of our Church, so I put the paddle down; but I felt I ought to have taken him farther along away from the irritation of the trees.

'Of course,' I said. 'We could go under them. It might be nice.'

'I think,' said Mr. Timberlake, 'that would be a very good idea.'

He lunged hard on the pole and took us towards the next archway of willow branches.

'We may have to duck a bit, that's all,' I said.

'Oh, I can push the branches up,' said Mr. Timberlake.

'It is better to duck,' I said.

We were gliding now quickly towards the arch, in fact I was already under it.

'I think I should duck,' I said. 'Just bend down for this one.'

'What makes the trees lean over the water like this?' asked Mr. Timberlake. 'Weeping willows—I'll give you a thought there. How

Error likes to make us dwell on sorrow. Why not call them *laughing* willows?' discoursed Mr. Timberlake as the branch passed over my head.

'Duck,' I said.

'Where? I don't see them,' said Mr. Timberlake turning round.

'No, your head,' I said. 'The branch,' I called.

'Oh, the branch. This one?' said Mr. Timberlake finding a branch just against his chest, and he put out a hand to lift it. It is not easy to lift a willow branch and Mr. Timberlake was surprised. He stepped back as it gently and firmly leaned against him. He leaned back and pushed from his feet. And he pushed too far. The boat went on, I saw Mr. Timberlake's boots leave the stern as he took an unthoughtful step backwards. He made a last-minute grasp at a stronger and higher branch, and then, there he hung a yard above the water, round as a blue damson that is ripe and ready, waiting only for a touch to make it fall. Too late with the paddle and shot ahead by the force of his thrust, I could not save him.

For a full minute I did not believe what I saw; indeed our religion taught us never to believe what we saw. Unbelieving, I could not move. I gaped. The impossible had happened. Only a miracle, I found myself saying, could save him.

What was most striking was the silence of Mr. Timberlake as he hung from the tree. I was lost between gazing at him and trying to get the punt out of the small branches of the tree. By the time I had got the punt out there were several yards of water between us and the soles of his boots were very near the water as the branch bent under his weight. Boats were passing at the time but no one seemed to notice us. I was glad about this. This was a private agony. A double chin had appeared on the face of Mr. Timberlake and his head was squeezed between his shoulders and his hanging arms. I saw him blink and look up at the sky. His eyelids were pale like a chicken's. He was tidy and dignified as he hung there, the hat was not displaced and the top button of his coat was done up. He had a blue silk handkerchief in his breast pocket. So unperturbed and genteel he seemed that as the tips of his shoes came nearer and nearer to the water, I became alarmed. He could perform what are called miracles. He would be thinking at this moment that only in an erroneous and illusory sense was he hanging from the branch of the tree over six feet of water. He was probably praying one of the closely reasoned prayers of our faith which were more like conversations with Euclid than appeals to God. The calm of his face suggested this. Was he, I asked myself, within sight of the main road, the town Recreation Ground and the landing-stage crowded with people, was he about to re-enact a well-known miracle? I hoped that he was not. I prayed that he was not. I prayed with all my will that Mr. Timberlake would not walk upon the water. It was my prayer and not his that was answered.

I saw the shoes dip, the water rise above his ankles and up his socks.

He tried to move his grip now to a yet higher branch—he did not succeed—and in making this effort his coat and waistcoat rose and parted from his trousers. One seam of shirt with its pant-loops and brace-tabs broke like a crack across the middle of Mr. Timberlake. It was like a fatal flaw in a statue, an earthquake crack which made the monument mortal. The last Greeks must have felt as I felt then, when they saw a crack across the middle of some statue of Apollo. It was at this moment I realized that the final revelation about man and society on earth had come to nobody and that Mr. Timberlake knew nothing at all about the origin of evil.

All this takes long to describe, but it happened in a few seconds as I paddled towards him. I was too late to get his feet on the boat and the only thing to do was to let him sink until his hands were nearer the level of the punt and then to get him to change hand-holds. Then I would paddle him ashore. I did this. Amputated by the water, first a torso, then a bust, then a mere head and shoulders, Mr. Timberlake, I noticed, looked sad and lonely as he sank. He was a declining dogma. As the water lapped his collar—for he hesitated to let go of the branch to hold the punt—I saw a small triangle of deprecation and pathos between his nose and the corners of his mouth. The head resting on the platter of water had the sneer of calamity on it, such as one sees in the pictures of a beheaded saint.

'Hold on to the punt, Mr. Timberlake,' I said urgently. 'Hold on to the punt.'

He did so.

'Push from behind,' he directed in a dry businesslike voice. They were his first words. I obeyed him. Carefully I paddled him towards the bank. He turned and, with a splash, climbed ashore. There he stood, raising his arms and looking at the water running down his swollen suit and making a puddle at his feet.

'Say,' said Mr. Timberlake coldly, 'we let some Error in that time.'

How much he must have hated our family.

'I am sorry, Mr. Timberlake,' I said. 'I am most awfully sorry. I should have paddled. It was my fault. I'll get you home at once. Let me wring out your coat and waistcoat. You'll catch your death . . .'

I stopped. I had nearly blasphemed. I had nearly suggested that Mr. Timberlake had fallen into the water and that to a man of his age this might be dangerous.

Mr. Timberlake corrected me. His voice was impersonal, addressing the laws of human existence, rather than myself.

'If God made water it would be ridiculous to suggest He made it capable of harming his creatures. Wouldn't it?'

'Yes,' I murmured hypocritically.

'O.K.,' said Mr. Timberlake. 'Let's go.'

'I'll soon get you across,' I said.

'No,' he said. 'I mean let's go on. We're not going to let a little thing like this spoil a beautiful afternoon. Where were we going? You spoke of a pretty landing-place farther on. Let's go there.'

'But I must take you home. You can't sit there soaked to the skin. It will spoil your clothes.'

'Now, now,' said Mr. Timberlake. 'Do as I say. Go on.'

There was nothing to be done with him. I held the punt into the bank and he stepped in. He sat like a bursting and sodden bolster in front of me while I paddled. We had lost the pole of course.

For a long time I could hardly look at Mr. Timberlake. He was taking the line that nothing had happened and this put me at a disadvantage. I knew something considerable had happened. That glaze, which so many of the members of our sect had on their faces and persons, their minds and manners, had been washed off. There was no gleam for me from Mr. Timberlake.

'What's the house over there?' he asked. He was making conversation. I had steered into the middle of the river to get him into the strong sun. I saw steam rise from him.

I took courage and studied him. He was a man I realized, in poor physical condition, unexercised and sedentary. Now the gleam had left him one saw the veined empurpled skin of the stoutish man with a poor heart. I remembered he had said at lunch:

'A young woman I know said, "Isn't it wonderful. I can walk thirty miles in a day without being in the least tired." I said, "I don't see that bodily indulgence is anything a member of the Church of the Last Purification should boast about."'

Yes, there was something flaccid, passive and slack about Mr. Timberlake. Bunched in swollen clothes, he refused to take them off. It occurred to me, as he looked with boredom at the water, the passing boats and the country, that he had not been in the country before. That it was something he had agreed to do but wanted to get over quickly. He was totally uninterested. By his questions—what is that church? Are there any fish in this river? Is that a wireless or a gramophone?—I understood that Mr. Timberlake was formally acknowledging a world he did not live in. It was too interesting, too eventful a world. His spirit, inert and preoccupied, was elsewhere in an eventless and immaterial habitation. He was a dull man, duller than any man I have ever known; but his dullness was a sort of earthly deposit left by a being whose diluted mind was far away in the effervescence of metaphysical matters. There was a slightly pettish look on his face as (to himself, of course) he declared he was not wet and that he would not have a heart attack or catch pneumonia.

Mr. Timberlake spoke little. Sometimes he squeezed water out of his sleeve. He shivered a little. He watched his steam. I had planned when we set out to go up as far as the lock, but now the thought of another two miles of this responsibility was too much. I pretended I wanted to go only as far as the bend which we were approaching, where one of the richest buttercup meadows was. I mentioned this to him. He turned and looked with boredom at the field. Slowly we came to the bank.

We tied up the punt and we landed.

'Fine,' said Mr. Timberlake. He stood at the edge of the meadow just as he had stood at the landing-stage—lost, stupefied, uncomprehending.

'Nice to stretch our legs,' I said. I led the way into the deep flowers. So dense were the buttercups there was hardly any green. Presently I sat down. Mr. Timberlake looked at me and sat down also. Then I turned to him with a last try at persuasion. Respectability, I was sure, was his trouble.

'No one will see us,' I said. 'This is out of sight of the river. Take off your coat and trousers and wring them out.'

Mr. Timberlake replied firmly:

'I am satisfied to remain as I am.'

'What is this flower?' he asked to change the subject.

'Buttercup,' I said.

'Of course,' he replied.

I could do nothing with him. I lay down full length in the sun; and, observing this and thinking to please me, Mr. Timberlake did the same. He must have supposed that this was what I had come out in the boat to do. It was only human. He had come out with me, I saw, to show me that he was only human.

But as we lay there I saw the steam still rising. I had had enough.

'A bit hot,' I said getting up.

He got up at once.

'Do you want to sit in the shade?' he asked politely.

'No,' I said. 'Would you like to?'

'No,' he said. 'I was thinking of you.'

'Let's go back,' I said. We both stood up and I let him pass in front of me. When I looked at him again I stopped dead. Mr. Timberlake was no longer a man in a navy blue suit. He was blue no longer. He was transfigured. He was yellow. He was covered with buttercup pollen, a fine yellow paste of it made by the damp, from head to foot.

'Your suit,' I said.

He looked at it. He raised his thin eyebrows a little, but he did not smile or make any comment.

The man is a saint, I thought. As saintly as any of those gold-leaf figures in the churches of Sicily. Golden he sat in the punt; golden he sat for the next hour as I paddled him down the river. Golden and bored. Golden as we landed at the town and as we walked up the street back to my uncle's house. There he refused to change his clothes or to sit by a fire. He kept an eye on the time for his train back to London. By no word did he acknowledge the disasters or the beauties of the world. If they were printed upon him, they were printed upon a husk.

Sixteen years have passed since I dropped Mr. Timberlake in the river and since the sight of his pant loops destroyed my faith. I have not seen him since, and to-day I heard that he was dead. He was fifty-seven. His mother, a very old lady with whom he had lived all his life, went into his bedroom when he was getting ready for church and found him lying on the floor in his shirt-sleeves. A stiff collar with the tie half inserted was in one hand. Five minutes before, she told the doctor, she had been speaking to him.

The doctor who looked at the heavy body lying on the single bed saw a middle-aged man, wide rather than stout and with an extraordinarily box-like thick-jawed face. He had got fat, my uncle told me, in later years. The heavy liver-coloured cheeks were like the chaps of a hound. Heart disease, it was plain, was the cause of the death of Mr. Timberlake. In death the face was lax, even coarse and degenerate. It was a miracle, the doctor said, that he had lived as long. Any time during the last twenty years the smallest shock might have killed him.

I thought of our afternoon on the river. I thought of him hanging from the tree. I thought of him, indifferent and golden in the meadow. I understood why he had made for himself a protective, sedentary blandness, an automatic smile, a collection of phrases. He kept them on like the coat after his ducking. And I understood why—though I had feared it all the time we were on the river—I understood why he did not talk to me about the origin of evil. He was honest. The ape was with us. The ape that merely followed me was already inside Mr. Timberlake eating out his heart.

*1945*

Title-page vignette by George Plank for
*Chosen Poems* by Frederic Prokosch, 1944

# JACQUETTA HAWKES

## *Skara Brae*

FROM 'PREHISTORIC BRITAIN'

THE ignorance of domestic life in the Early Bronze Age which we have regretted in the case of the nomadic Beaker Folk is to some extent made good by the happy survival of an entire hamlet of the same age in the Orkneys. Its inhabitants were not themselves of true Beaker stock, but had probably been forced to quit the Continent to make way before the Beaker expansion. Kinsfolk of theirs were settled in many parts of Britain, particularly on the east coast, where they probably first landed, and in Wessex, but it so happens that it is only in the remote Orkneys that we can get any clear idea of their way of life. Here the most complete and best known of their settlements is Skara Brae, a village whose final fate it was to be overwhelmed with drifting sand—sand which has preserved it from decay for thousands of years. In the teeth of a harsh and inhospitable climate, a hardy group of colonists found it possible to form a settled community supported by herds of cows and sheep pastured on the open grassland, and by an abundant supply of shell-fish. Together these provided a staple diet which they could vary with venison, sea-birds and fish, although no trouble was taken to devise specialized implements for hunting or fishing.

Agriculture was not practised at all. They used no metal or foreign raw materials of any kind, and were as entirely self-supporting as any Neolithic community: an independent, intimate society, often cut off from the world by gales and rough seas, and concerned with little beyond the struggle for its own existence. As in such conditions there was no need for warfare, Skara Brae economy was quite free from the burden of armaments, and if life was hard, it was peaceful. The half-dozen houses and communal workshop were huddled together for mutual warmth and shelter, the narrow alley-ways between being roofed, and the whole cluster served by an efficient sewerage system of slab-lined drains.

A house consisted of a single, well-sized living-room and one or more side cells that probably served as store-rooms and privies. It is astonishingly good fortune to find in Britain houses largely intact after some 3,500 years, but yet more fortunate that they should still contain much of their original furnishings. Wood being almost unobtainable on these windswept islands, the villagers instead used the local flagstone to build furniture that was not only convenient but imperishable. So it is that we can reconstruct complete domestic interiors and feel something of their atmosphere. And they must have been pleasant enough homes. Imagine with what relief a woman returning in the early dusk of a northern winter afternoon, perhaps with hands cold and aching after collecting shell-fish, would have turned into the comparative shelter of the village alleys. Exchanging a word with a neighbour, she would duck through the low entrance of her hut until she could stand upright below her own roof and enjoy the warmth and familiar fragrance of the peat. Putting her limpets in a richly decorated pot on the stone dresser, she could sit on the edge of one of the two box-beds, with their mattresses of heather and skins, and warm her hands at the central fire. Above the bed behind her head a small recess in the wall would contain her special possessions, while opposite, the store-room was readily accessible through a low doorway. Altogether nearly as well-equipped and comfortable a dwelling as many inhabited in such remote regions up to the last century. But the element of savagery was there, and one instance would not be far to seek: hidden in the foundations were the crouched bodies of two old women, buried that their spirits might hold up the walls of the house.

*1947*

## M. C. BRADBROOK

### *The Making of an Artist*

FROM 'IBSEN THE NORWEGIAN'

'HE who would know me fully must know Norway.' So said Ibsen to a German who could not understand *Rosmersholm*. Yet no great writer of that age has been more cut off from his background and his own early history than Ibsen. Singleminded devotion to his art fashioned a life that, because it is largely uneventful, has been thought without significance. His command of the theatrical[1] has given him an international fame which is partly independent of the language of

[1] Purely as a *theatrical*, as distinct from a *dramatic*, artist Ibsen offers the actors more than Shakespeare. Hjalmer Ekdal or Hedda Gabler as parts are more fully within the scope of a great actor than Falstaff or Cleopatra, where the interpretation must always be partial. And though an actor may prefer that his reach should exceed his grasp, and attack Hamlet rather than achieve Rosmer, the theatregoer will derive a satisfaction from having absorbed Ibsen in a performance which no performance of Shakespeare can give.

the plays, and this has made for wide recognition, but imperfect knowledge. The feeblest translation could not disguise that *A Doll's House* is structurally well built and as good theatre as *Charley's Aunt*; this is not altogether a happy thing for Ibsen. A knowledge of his country, his background, above all of his writings in the original, brings up as many unsuspected colours as the cleaning of an Old Master. The work is not only seen more clearly, but it is seen to be different.

After the age of Ibsenism, which in England was the 'nineties, came the reaction. 'The drama, like the symphony, does not teach or prove anything,' wrote Synge. 'Analysts with their problems and teachers with their systems, are soon as old-fashioned as the pharmacopœia of Galen—look at Ibsen and the Germans . . .' and, with Huxley and Tindall and Bastien-Lepage, Ibsen's name was anathema among 'companions of the Cheshire Cheese'.

This reaction is long since dead, but it is still too common to think of Ibsen as the Restoration thought of Shakespeare—indubitably a genius but how deplorably outmoded! To see Ibsen merely as the precursor of Shaw and Brieux when he was also the precursor of Strindberg and Tchekov is to retain at this late date the false perspective of his contemporary critics and admirers. His contemporaries found the true Ibsen in the plays of his middle period, and slurred or depreciated his other work. Hence a generation which abandoned naturalism most unwisely abandoned Ibsen, forgetting that his early reputation was based on a very small proportion of his work, although the conflicts which he provoked made it the duty of all true Ibsenites to cherish, modify, and utilize even his least doctrinaire productions.

In so far as Ibsen has a constant theme, it is the destructive power of genius. The biological determinism of *Ghosts* and *The Wild Duck*, the social preoccupations of *A Doll's House* and *Rosmersholm* do not mean that Ibsen's true place is in the army headed by John Stuart Mill and brought up by H. G. Wells. Of course, Ibsen had twinges of the hopes and fears which were common to his age, but his more constant preoccupation was the spiritual conflict which is born of the vitality of Brand, Nora or Solness, which brings dislocation and ruin on the life of their nearest. The troll in all of them gives them power, and denies them peace. All, like Emily Brontë's Heathcliff, are born to dominate and blindly to destroy even where they most love, as much by their own superabundant power as by untoward circumstance. If Ibsen saw mankind as the victim of fate, it was not merely as the potential victim of syphilis, like Osvald, but as the inheritor of 'the thousand natural shocks that flesh is heir to'.

> What a towering mount of sin
> Rises from one small word: To be

Original sin has seldom had a more Calvinistic interpretation than it received in Brand.

Ibsen's most naturalistic studies transcend the science of his day. Dr. Wangel's treatment of his wife's neurosis might have been learnt from a psycho-analyst but would have been somewhat in advance of the textbook therapy of the time. Gunhild Borkman would fit into a case book that should also include D. H. Lawrence's Mrs. Morel. Nor was Ibsen averse from drawing from the life. But the root of his greatest plays remains a poetic unity, a single vision, even when they are not written in verse. *Bygmester Solness* was crystallized out in eight lines of verse; a vision of 'the burnt-out pair', Solness and Aline, sitting in the rubble of his 'burnt-out faith' and her 'burnt-out joy' cannot be reduced to a tract on the New Woman with some observations on the power of natural hypnosis.

Two facts need not only to be accepted but to be grasped before Ibsen can be fully known: that he was, all his life, a poet and a Norwegian, that he wrote in a language not generally known or easy to translate and set his plays in the least known country of Western Europe. Professor Halvdan Koht, the greatest living student of Ibsen, opens his *Life* with these words:

> This would seem self-evident; yet it may be useful and even necessary to establish the fact definitely from the beginning. Too many have attempted to make him a thinker or a philosopher, a social critic or social reformer. He himself was fully conscious that his genius was that of the creative artist and he desired to be not merely an artist first and foremost, but wholly and in all things an artist. He once expressed in a single word the meaning of poetic art. To a young man who himself dreamed of becoming a poet, he said: 'To be a poet is to *see*.'

Koht goes on to describe Ibsen's struggle to *see*, to embody in images, and how it necessarily involved a measure of self-dissection. The experience which is embodied must have been directly 'lived through', and creation was not easy for Ibsen. He was acutely, 'even morbidly', sensitive to the movement of life about him. 'Almost unconsciously he sensed the thoughts that were in the air.' But he did not build his plays spontaneously upon this sensitive appreciation. He struggled to transmute it. There was distinct separation of the man who suffered and the mind which created.

The legendary picture of Ibsen does not suggest delicate and vulnerable sensibility. Formidable, irascible Herr Doktor Ibsen in his frock coat and silk hat, keeping even his family shut out from his writing, regulating his life by clockwork, jealously collecting decorations and orders, protecting his copyright and balancing his investments, is not a poetic figure. And yet his latest works most clearly of all

> were born of spiritual need and principally bear witness to the drama within his own soul. . . . Many things which at that time seemed involved and enigmatic find a direct and natural explanation when one sees them in relation to the spiritual life of Ibsen himself.

His early life supplies the clue. The cruel struggle of his first thirty-eight years, embittered by poverty, contempt and crossed friendship, had hardened the stony mask upon him. Not even Kierkegaard masked himself more completely than Ibsen. The thoughts that still in old age 'went through him like a spear' were of his early failures; and in that early story, far more important than his relations to any individual were his relations to his country. He had longed to speak for Norway, he had thought in terms of Norway's freedom, and hoped to become a great national poet. His rejection by his own people led to a kind of spiritual excision, and yet always, and most distinctively in the last plays, the tone and temper are Norwegian.

*1947*

# AUBREY MENEN

## *Gangabai*

FROM 'THE PREVALENCE OF WITCHES'

THE Durbar Hall had been built overnight of bamboo and matting. The aboriginals squatted, a thousand of them, all around it and on half of the floor inside. In front of them was a raised platform made up of tables. On that was yet another table and a swivel chair such as is used at office desks. To bring a touch of state to this chair somebody had thrown across it a tablecloth of Victorian red plush, with rows of small pendulous balls around its edges. The occupant of the throne had been provided with two bottles of ink, one red and one black, both as they came from the makers and still with their labels, a gavel in the shape of an iron-headed jack-hammer, a rocker such as is used for blotting signatures, and an empty gin bottle with water and no glass. From end to end of the bamboo hut hung paper chains of various colours, diversified with the small silver bells that are hung on Christmas trees. At one end of the hall these paper chains ended in a bunch around a poster that must have been put up during the war which had been finished a year and a half before. It showed a British soldier facing up to an enormous and shadowy German, with the legend 'It won't be long now.' At the other end the streamers made loyal loops around full-length portraits of the King and Queen, flanking a coloured centre-piece of Prince Albert and Queen Victoria boating on the Lake of

Windsor, the small craft filled to the point of danger with young Princes and Princesses of the Blood, the whole illustrating the legend underneath 'A Happy Family.' Underneath this and behind the throne was a row of seats for officials, each bearing a neatly printed label of the names of officials who had held office five years ago.

I was conducted to my seat by a servant dressed in white and scarlet. He saluted and showed me a chair marked *Miss Thelma Macey* on which I sat. I turned to the man sitting next to me and said, 'I hope Miss Thelma Macey will not turn up at the last moment.' He turned a pale grey face to me glittering with a pair of rather skittish American spectacles.

'You're the new Education Officer.'

'Yes. You must be the American missionary.' I had heard that there was one, from Virginia, and this man's accent fitted.

'I am.'

'I was saying, I hope Miss Thelma Macey does not turn up now.'

'I agree with you,' he said. 'She has been dead ten years.'

'Oh! I'm sorry,' I said rather foolishly.

'Not that there aren't quite a few people out there who wouldn't be in the least surprised if she *did* come back,' said the missionary, nodding his head at the squatting Limbodians. 'Dead witches do.'

'Was Miss Macey a witch?'

'She *said* she was.'

'Really? Tell me, Mr. . . . er . . .'

'Small is the name,' he said, shaking hands with me. It was a diffident handshake, part of his whole nervous manner. But his expression was pleasant; he seemed willing to be friendly but almost certain that nobody would like him.

'Have you seen a witch yet?' he asked me.

'No. I should like to.'

'Don't do anything in a hurry about witches. Things go wrong. Things get back at you.'

'You take witches very seriously, Mr. Small?'

'One does, in Limbo. Limbo's witch-country.

'How can I see one?'

'Just ask. Say to any village headman "I want to see a witch." But be careful to add "any time at your convenience." The Limbodians are polite people and if they think you're in a hurry they'll just put up any old witch so as not to disappoint you. Maybe just a witch-trainee.'

'So they train them?'

'There's a regular five-year course, with examinations every so often. For the final examination she has to kill a member of her own family by saying spells.'

'Who holds the examination?'

'A sort of board of other witches.'

'At midnight, I suppose, on a bare mountain?' I said.

'Dear me, no. In broad daylight. Everybody knows who's a witch and who isn't. The thing is to discover *which* witch is doing them dirt. That is done by the witch-doctor.'

'How very interesting. Can I also see a witch-doctor?'

'Why, surely,' said the Reverend Small obligingly, 'there's one standing over there.' He pointed to a Limbodian who was leaning against one of the small tree-trunks that held up the roof of the Durbar Hall. He was well over five feet, tall for an aboriginal, and he wore no clothes save a turban and a bag in his crotch. He was an old man: just now he had his chin sunk on his bare chest and he seemed to be watching his belly with interest. As he breathed in, it grew round and smooth, and became an even, polished dark brown. As he breathed out it collapsed suddenly into a network of grey wrinkles.

'He's down here at the central village on a professional visit. There's been sickness and witch-trouble and he's here to pick out the witch.'

'When he does I shall ask to see her.'

'Yes, but do be careful. Well, of course, you being an official of the Administration you will naturally be careful, but when I did it I was only a silly missionary, and I caused a lot of trouble.'

'I should very much like to hear about it.'

'Would you?' said Small gratefully. 'Well, it was this way. I asked the headman to bring me a witch and he said "Yes; when?" So me being fresh out from home I said "Right now." And about ten hours later they brought one.'

'Very prompt,' I said.

'Well,' said Small, 'the word "now" in Limbo is a pretty large word. When one Limbodian says to another he wants a thing done "now," he means he wants it done while the thing is still in his mind. What he's really saying is "Do it before I get drunk and forget all about it." It's quite a good measure of time, really, since every Limbodian gets drunk every evening. So they brought me a witch just about sundown, which they took to be just before my heavy drinking time.'

The witch had done her best, Small explained, but they hadn't been able to get hold of a fully trained one, not at that short notice. She had said some spells for blasting crops, and then some more that they use when digging up dead bodies. She was rather shy about saying the digging-dead-body spell, but the headman insisted on it. Small had said that he didn't want to embarrass the woman and she need not say anything she would rather not.

'But the headman wouldn't hear of it,' said Small. 'He pointed out that as a missionary I had certain spells which I always said when burying people. He thought that no doubt they were very good spells so far as they went, but since I had the chance I may as well complete my training and learn the spells for digging them up again. So he made her say them, which she did in a sing-song voice. That got us on to the topic of killing people, and the headman told the witch to show me how she did that. Well, this led to quite a little scene, because she said she didn't know the spell, and the headman said she did, and she said if she did she wouldn't say it. Then the headman got really annoyed and said that she was letting down the village and if he'd have known she was going to behave so badly he'd never have brought her to see the missionary. She said she was right down sorry to be rude but it was a professional secret; so there it was. The headman told her not to be a silly woman and that missionaries were as much in the business as she was, if not more so since I'd probably been longer at it. He was an obstinate man when he was crossed. She saw his point after a while and agreed to say the killer-spell if he, as a layman, would cover up his ears. Well, he did, and she reeled off a lot of names and then gave a happy little chuckle. That was the end of the performance and they both went home.'

That night it had been very hot and Small had been struggling with the bad dreams that always come when you first sleep inside a mosquito-net. One of them was filled with horrible shrieks and cries of pain, coming from nowhere. Small woke up sweating, still hearing the shrieks. Then he was out of bed and scrambling into his clothes because he had realized the shrieks were real ones, and coming from the village. When he got there he found the witch hanging by her heels from a tree branch and two villagers beating her with bamboo sticks.

'You can imagine how I felt,' said Small. 'Here was I getting a poor woman a beating just because of my curiosity. I was entirely in the wrong, so of course, being human, I made out it was everybody else's fault. They told me that the headman had gone down with some sickness as soon as he left me, but I said that was no excuse for beating a poor old woman. So I told them to take her down. They said they wouldn't, because she was a wicked witch. I went up to her, and upside down as she was, I asked her, "Are you a witch?" She was crying, and do you know, just to show you how heartless one can be—at least I can—all I could think about was how funny it was to see her crying upside down with the tears running into her hair. I said, "Look, are you a witch?" She said "No." I asked her three times, to make it sound ritualistic and each time she said "No." I made them cut her down, and I took her home and made some tea. She drank it out of the saucer and asked for more.'

What with the heat, his bad dreams and the worse things he saw on waking, Small was in low spirits. He kept on apologizing to the woman for getting her into trouble. She neither blamed him nor consoled him but merely went on drinking tea out of her saucer. In the end Small was so contrite that he offered her houseroom so that she could live in safety from the villagers. She stopped her tea-drinking long enough to say that it was a good idea. Small told her that the very next day he would call the villagers together and speak sternly to them. He would tell them that all the spells that she had told him were just a lot of childish nonsense.

'They know that already,' she told him.

Small asked her what she meant.

'They know it's nonsense because they fixed it all up themselves. They couldn't get a witch, not a real one. The only real witch they could get is Gangabai, who has been dead two years, and she only comes back in wet weather. So they asked me, seeing that I was a friend of Gangabai's when we were girls. I didn't know any spells, but they didn't want me to disappoint you. So I made them up. It was all nonsense.'

Small was relieved and delighted, and his heart warmed toward the unfortunate woman. He said that it was most unfair for the villagers to make her pretend to be a witch and then beat her as though she were a real one.

She thought that it *was* most unfair.

Small said that if he ever heard any man in the village accuse her of witchcraft, why, missionary or not, he'd give him a beating just to see how he liked it.

She thought that it would be a good lesson to them if he did.

Small by this time thought she was one of the most friendly souls he had ever met, and he found it so easy talking to her that he was even telling her about Christianity. 'A thing,' added Small to me in extenuation, 'I hardly ever talk about in private conversation.' She still remained agreeable. Small told her that he thought she had a Christian soul, particularly since she had seen that witchcraft was all nonsense. She crowned his happiness by raising no objection when Small suggested she should become a convert.

'It was my first job as a missionary and I was very moved,' said Small to me. 'She was not only the first heathen I had convinced of Christianity, but I really think she was the first person I had ever convinced of anything in my life. I never was a very persuasive man. I felt I had to do something to mark the occasion. I might have gone down on my knees and prayed, of course, but it might have looked a bit vainglorious, and in any case I was shy. So I made some more tea. I think it was a good choice. Praying would have been a bit one-sided anyway, and tea sort of brought her into the celebration.'

He had poured out two cups, then, remembering his manners, poured the tea into the saucers. They sat sipping for a while, until Small thought of the sick headman who was the cause of the beating. Small said that first thing in the morning he would go down and see him. Perhaps he could give him something to make him better.

'Oh, don't worry about that fool,' said the woman. 'He'll be all right by to-morrow evening.'

Small asked how she could be so sure.

'It was one of Gangabai's curses that I used,' she said simply. 'One

I remembered her telling me. She said they always got better by next evening.'

Small put down his saucer very carefully, without spilling a drop, he remembers, and waited for the woman to go on.

'Yes,' she said, 'after all I was doing my best. Then that big good-for-nothing headman started insulting me and making me look silly in front of you, thinking he could talk to me as he pleased because I wasn't a witch, so I thought I would teach him a lesson, just like you said all of them ought to be taught a lesson to treat one with respect. So I tried hard to remember what Gangabai had told me, and all of a sudden I remembered that spell. It isn't a very bad one but,' she said, screwing up her face with glee at the thought, 'Ooooo! What a horrible belly-ache I gave him!'

He looked thoughtfully round the Durbar Hall and then again at me.

'I've never made another convert,' he said. 'I don't really think I've got the courage. So you have to be careful.' He glanced towards the door. 'Anyway, I think it's almost time for the ceremony to begin and it's certainly time I stopped chattering. But you know you shouldn't listen to me. I'm only a missionary. What you want to do is to get to know the Chiefs. Those people out there in front,' he said, pointing.

*1947*

# SYLVIA TOWNSEND WARNER

## *Triste Loysir*

FROM 'THE CORNER THAT HELD THEM'

RECEIVING the bishop's order to go to Esselby, Henry Yellowlees felt wings break from his shoulders. To travel into a new county, to see strange towns and the unwinding of strange roads and the glitter of unforeseen rivers, to hear people talking in a different dialect about things he had no concern with, to be overtaken by dusk in an unfamiliar place: all this made his blood quicken. Yet routine and its slow mildewing of the mind had so far decayed him that to break with his work even for a week or so seemed like a break in the earth's surface, and a minute later he was asking what would become of his scholars—for he now taught in a school for pious poor boys which had been founded by Bishop Walter; and an uncommonly dull set they were, being chosen on merits of piety and poverty without regard to intellectual promise.

That, and everything else, had been arranged for. His route was planned, his expenses reckoned: so much for lodgings, so much for stabling, so much for tolls, and a small sum for gratuities and incidental expenses.

'Please count it,' said the treasurer's clerk, pouring out small money from a bag, 'and sign the receipt. You will start on the day after the feast of Saint Pancras. We shall recover the money, of course, from the convent of Oby.'

The convent of Oby had been lightly taxed. Everything was planned with the greatest economy. For the first night he must lodge with the chaplain of a leper-house, and on the morrow he must ride several miles out of his direct route in order to avail himself of a midday dole at Killdew Priory.

'You will need to ride hard on the last day in order to reach Esselby by nightfall. See that they give your horse a good feed and a good rub down, he will need it. And as these debtors are blacksmiths, they might very well re-shoe the beast.'

'What sort of place is Esselby?'

The clerk shrugged his shoulders.

The weather turned wet. All through Saint Pancras' day the rain dripped through the schoolroom roof. The patter of raindrops mixed with the clatter of his pupils' abacuses, and random peals of thunder rumbled in the cold air. But he did not think so much of what a detestable journey lay before him as of the certainty that the school's warden was too much devoted to Bishop Walter to ask for the roof to be mended.

When he set out the sky was still a heavy slate grey, darkening to purple where the sun slashed through the clouds. The night's rain still dripped from the house-eaves, young leaves and immature fruits floated in puddles. Before he had left the bounds of the city he was splashed to the thighs.

* * * * *

At the summit of a long rise he drew rein and stared out over the landscape. The clouds were gone, only a few shadows were left, hastening to the northward. Brilliant, senseless, irresponsible, the landscape stretched before him. What soul was there, what trace of praise to its Maker? What trace of reason, what trace of purpose, except where man's sad hand had etched it? Alongside the river water-scars like old burns showed where the winter floods had run. Now it was spring. Everything was new, was remade. The night's rain glittered in every runnel, flashed from bush and bramble, lay pearled in the clasp of daisies and liverwort leaves. Rain had washed the face of the earth like the waters of baptism. And the young leaves on the oak tree were not more bright than those which the storm had torn off and cast on the ground, and in the furrows the weeds were growing up with the corn. How can this praise God? he said sternly to the ghost beside him; all this beauty and promise is barely a month old, and already it is full of ruin and has not the sense to know good from evil.

His horse tossed its head, jerking away the flies. Having despatched Francis he rode on till he found an elder bush, and broke off a handful of twigs and fastened them in the headband. He was beginning to feel pleasure in his journey. It was pleasant to sit with his back against a thorn tree eating cold bacon while the horse cropped the young grass. Though a cuckoo sat in the branches it did not irk him. Before vespers, he said to himself, I shall be in country I have never seen before. So it was; though he could not be certain where the familiar changed to the unknown, the change had taken place. Presently he began to meet groups of labourers, their tired legs moving in time to the gait of their oxen, and when he asked them if he were going right for the leper-house their accents were strange to him.

The chaplain of the leper-house, a burly man with tow-coloured hair and a mincing manner of speech quite out of keeping with his looks, welcomed him warmly enough: that is to say, he continued to repeat that he was delighted, though at the same time he yawned and stared at the horse as if it resembled something he knew of by hearsay. Supper was scarcely on the table before he asked if his guest could read music at sight.

'What sort of music? I can read church-note, of course.'

'No, no! Music in measure. Do you understand the prolations? Well, I can soon teach you.'

He laid out a music-book among the mutton bones and the bread-crumbs, and began to explain.

'See, these red notes are to be sung in the triple prolation. And these red minims, following the black breve, show that the breve is imperfect. Bear that in mind, and the rest will be simple. You have only to get the knack of it. Let us begin with an easy one. This is charming: *Triste loysir*. Suppose I just run through your part to give you an idea of it? When it comes to *mors de moy* the longs are perfect, and you will be enraptured.'

His voice was slender as a reed, but accomplished. As he sang he thumped the measure on Henry's shoulder. Though written out with such complications, the music itself seemed simple, almost like a ballad-tune, and before long Henry interrupted, and rather scornfully at that, saying that he was ready to take his part.

He began loudly and steadily; but after half a dozen notes it seemed to him that he must have gone wrong, and he broke off.

'Go on, go on! You were doing excellently.'

'But surely there was something wrong? It sounded very odd.'

'No, there was nothing wrong. Perhaps the interval unsettled you.

You expected a fourth, no doubt. This is composed in the style of the *Ars nova*, it is disconcerting at times. Let us begin again. And hold on: you will soon become accustomed to it.'

This time he held on, though he felt himself astray, bewildered by the unexpected progressions, concords so sweet that they seemed to melt the flesh off his bones. Coming to *mors de moy*, where the chaplain's voice twittered in floriations high above his tolling longs, he could hardly contain himself for excitement.

'But this is astonishing,' he said. 'Are there others like this?' He began to turn the pages of the book.

'Yes, most of the things in this book are in *Ars nova* style. This Kyrie by Machault, for instance. . . . Unfortunately, it is for three voices. Of course, we could sing it without the middle voice, but you would not get a true idea of it. The bishop's message did not tell me to expect a musician.'

Henry Yellowlees realized with certainty how strongly Bishop Walter would dislike *Ars nova*; and if anything could deepen his dislike of the bishop, this did.

'Out here, one has so few chances of meeting a competent musician. It is a stroke of good fortune for me that you should come. That is why I wish you could hear the Machault. Of course. . . .' The chaplain paused, staring at his hand as it lay on the music-book. 'One of my lepers here has an extremely fine voice and is a skilled singer. He used to be in the Duke of Burgundy's chapel. I don't know if you would object—he is not an advanced case of leprosy. He and I often sing together. To him, too, a third voice would be a godsend.'

Not knowing whether he turned hot or cold Henry Yellowlees answered: 'No, of course not. I should like to hear the Kyrie.'

The chaplain slid back a panel in the wall and called: 'John! Will you come and sing?'

Shuffling footsteps approached. The leper came in. In the dusk of the doorway he seemed to glimmer like bad fish. He stank, too. He stationed himself at the further end of the room; it was clear that he knew his place as a dog does. There he stood, rubbing his scaly hands together, drawing preparatory breaths. His expression was professionally calm.

'Now John! The Machault Kyrie.'

The three voices sprang into the air.

If *Triste loysir* had seemed a foretaste of paradise, the Kyrie was paradise itself. This was how the blessed might sing, singing in a duple measure that ran as nimbly on its four feet as a weasel running through a meadow, with each voice in turn enkindling the others, so that the music flowed on and was continually renewed. And as paradise is made for man, this music seemed made for man's singing; not for edification, or the working-out of an argument, or the display of skill, but only for ease and pleasure, as in paradise where the abolition of sin begets a pagan carelessness, where the certainty of Christ's countenance frees men's souls from the obligations of christian behaviour, the creaking counterpoint of God's law and man's obedience.

It ended. Henry Yellowlees raised his eyes from the music-book. The rays of the levelling sun had shifted while they sang and now shone full on the leper. His face, his high bald head, were scarlet. He seemed to be on fire.

'Again! Let us sing it again!'

'I told you so,' said the chaplain. 'I tell you, there has never been such music in the world before.'

All through the evening they sang, the leper standing apart and singing by rote. And Henry thought how many an hour these two must have spent together, the leper at one end of the room, the chaplain at the other; or perhaps they bent over the same music-book, their love of music overcoming the barrier between life and death-in-life. What did the other lepers think of it, those who could not sing, sitting in their straw, mumbling their sour bread (for if the food given to a guest were so bad the food given to the lepers must be worse), and hearing the music go on and on? Most of the night Henry lay awake, recalling the music, humming it over again to the burden of the chaplain's snores, with half of his mind in a rapture and the other half wishing that there were not so many and such ferocious bugs. It struck him that every bug in the place must have heard the good news and forsaken the lepers for flesh that was a novelty.

'You will come again?'

'Yes, indeed. In a week's time, perhaps.'

'I hope you slept well?'

'Excellently, thank you.'

The morning mist was just floating off the meadows. It would be a hot day, and he had started late. But the heat of the day was as yet only a theory, and he huddled his cloak round him, chilled by lack of sleep even when the mist had cleared and the sun filled the long narrow valley. Singing and whistling he rode on, and presently came to the valley's head and a hillside where the track showed out clearly in the poorer grass.

*1948*

# HOPE MUNTZ

## *The Battle of Hastings*

### FROM 'THE GOLDEN WARRIOR'

### OF THE BATTLE-ORDER

THERE was a little chapel in the Weald hard by the English camp. It was named for Our Lady, St. Mary-in-the-Wood. Abbot Elfwy sang Mass there before the King and his captains, setting at naught the Roman ban. The Mass was but begun when an alarm was sounded. Harold sprang up in dread, calling his men.

The King drew up his array in haste. His battle-order made the fyrd murmur. He bade the men stand close, many ranks deep, the Danes and English heavy-armed before them. The fyrd had expected to charge down from the whole length of the ridge in line of battle, but now they heard that they must hold their ground till nightfall and fight on the defence. Harold bent back the wings as far as the steep northward slopes, making a great shield-burgh, a fortress of armed men. Within it he left open ground, that men might carry word from the commanders and have space for the wounded. The road led back thence towards Caldbec. In the midst of the shield-burgh he set up the Golden Dragon and the Fighting Man, banners and pennons grouped around them.

The Wessex levies and their Thegnhood were upon the right; upon the left those of East Anglia and Huntingdon, and in the centre the men drawn from London and the shires adjoining. The picked Men of Kent had their place where the slope was easiest, for theirs was the right of the first blow in battle. Well forward also were the Men of York, who had come South with Harold, not tarrying for their Earl. These men alone came from beyond the Humber. The Housecarles of London had the right to guard their King in battle. They stood under Ansgar's banner by the Standard where the ground was highest, the good fyrd of Middlesex and Essex backing them. Elsewhere thralls fought beside the levies, but here were none but trained men.

Duke William's spies saw how the English poured out of the forest. They watched the King's array, and spoke together fearfully, gazing on the glittering ranks, the many banners.

'There is a captain yonder,' they said. 'See how he marshals them.'

They drew near as they dared. They saw the towering stature of the Housecarles, their gilded mail, their inlaid bills and axes, their gold-hilted swords, their shields, locked like a wall.

'God help our men,' they said, 'these giants must be his Knights who fight on foot. These are the victors of Stamford Bridge. What shall avail us?'

They saw archers and slingers set within the shield-burgh and in the woods on either flank. They saw no cross-bow men or horse and yet their hearts misgave them. A host on foot seemed to them no longer a thing of scorn. They turned and bore word to the Duke, and told their comrades what they had seen. Duke William heard their words unmoved, but many of his soldiers quaked. No great pitched battle had been fought in Normandy for twenty years. William had won his fights by stratagems and by surprise. This new manner of warfare filled their minds with dread.

When Harold had made all ready, he perceived that the alarm had been a false one. He bade his men take food. The empty ale-casks were set within the shield-burgh filled with water, basins and cups and pails beside them.

They ate and were sufficed, and there was still no sight of William. The King spoke. His words were for thralls and the fyrd. The Thegns and Housecarles knew his thoughts, as he knew theirs. He told the levies of Duke William's archers and his cross-bow men, who opened a way for the horse. He told them that for the first time they must meet the charge of mounted men, but that naught could prevail against them, if they stood fast.

The fyrd-men shouted: 'When do we charge, lord King?'

At his answer, their faces fell. They took to muttering.

'Men,' said Harold, 'the Duke comes hither to seize our land. It is his part then to attack, mine to defend. Count the place where you stand as your hearth-stone. Mark your captains' banners. Do not stir from them. To you I give the highest trust. It is the hardest trial for brave warriors to stand and to endure while others fight. That trial is yours this day. You must not fail. The battle rests with you.'

Then the fyrd murmured, saying: 'He packs us here with thralls, like herring in a barrel. He sets Danes before us. Are we to get no fighting and no spoil? What of our threshing?'

With that some of them abode to hear no more; but the most part remained, sorely perplexed and downcast. When the King saw how it was with them, he sweated.

'Hear me, men,' he said. 'If I should build a sea-wall, would I set a single line of stones to guard the land?'

A man of Romney shouted: 'No, but a rampart, King.'

'Aye,' said Harold, 'behind the dressed stones an earthen rampart. Both must hold, or else the sea bursts in and the land drowns. I set you here, Housecarles and Thegns and fyrd, to stem this flood. Mailed warriors and levies, ye are one; the wall and rampart of this Kingdom. Stand then, have patience. Those that fled shall hear your glory and find courage. It is not William's horsemen or his archers that shall save him then. He fears us now. His ships are beached, lest his men fly. This day is a beginning.'

When the noise abated, he said again: 'By all that you hold dear, I bid you stand. He will feign flight and try to draw you down. By that alone can he succeed; for if you go, what can you do against mailed horsemen? Can stones and earth unjoined hold back the sea? Whether the days of Ethelred must come again, or whether we shall leave our children peace and a proud memory, it lies upon the issue of this field.'

They heard him grimly, but they saw him smile.

'We gave the Northmen four-and-twenty ships,' he said. 'How many for the Normans?'

They answered with a roar of laughter: 'Let the bastards swim.'

'Aye, let them swim,' said Harold. 'God be with you. Stand fast, cleave where you can. Do not be tender with them, Danes. My Men of Kent, first blood to you. York, let this be a greater Stamford Bridge. Housecarles, we have the Duke himself against us. Teach him what his Knights are worth. Stand, my fyrd-men, stand fast, my rampart. What says the proverb? "He that seeks trouble, it were a pity he should miss it."'

He rode back amidst laughter and cheering to his Standard. There he alighted. His chiefs came to him with eager praise. Harold wiped his brow and said: 'Pass the word round. Tell it again.'

His messengers went through the host, bidding all men stand firm. The captains were in good heart.

Ansgar said to the King: 'You could not have done better. Now they know the issue.'

'Aye, they know it now,' said Harold. 'Poor devils, will they know it when his darts sting them and they have no answer?'

Ansgar and Elfwy and the King's captains and his brothers began to pray him that he would be content to hold command and would have no part in the fighting.

'We shall see,' he said.

Their hearts sank.

'It is past reason, brother,' said Gyrth.

Harold said: 'It is past reason that we stand here.'

When he began to mock, they saw that they but wasted breath, yet Abbot Elfwy still pleaded with him. The old man stood there, mail-clad. His face was pinched and blue with cold and weariness. When Harold said that he was all unfit to fight, he answered: 'I was never brisker. I would you were as hale.'

'We are a sorry crew, uncle,' said the King, 'but they will rue the day they met us.'

The host stood waiting. It was yet early, very cold. They stamped, and blew upon their fingers, and saw their breath rise up like steam. It seemed to them that half the day went by.

The King said to Elfwy: 'Uncle, I would that I had stayed.'

'You have a good precedent, my child,' said Elfwy, 'Alfred left his Mass before the victory of Ashdown.'

Harold smiled and gave him thanks.

'God Almighty,' said Leofwin, 'where is the fellow? He must be on shipboard.'

Earl Waltheof had brought ivory dice. He and Leofwin sat them down and fell to play. The King and those around watched the game, yawning; sometimes their lids fell and they were near slumber.

At last they heard Duke William's trumpets and saw a stir across the valley. When the hosts saw each other, a mighty shout went up. Then the Duke's first battle came down from the heights in good array, marching to music, at a foot pace. Archers and cross-bow men came first. They wore no mail, but jerkins of boiled leather and quilted coats. Then came the mail-clad foot, spear-men with shields and swords; and after them the Knights, pennons and banners flying. This force wheeled to face the English left. King Harold and his men watched them and spoke among themselves.

A second host followed. These men halted over against the English right. Last came a third battle, greater than the others. The King saw before him William's gold and scarlet banner, and many more that he had known in Normandy. There too, borne next the Duke himself, he saw a mighty Standard, azure and gold and silver, the sign of the Cross. He looked and his eyes widened. A murmur rose among the English.

'God save us,' they said. 'It is the Holy Cross.'

Even among the Housecarles such words passed. The King looked at Gyrth, as though he would have spoken.

'Can you name the captains, brother?' said Earl Gyrth.

After a moment, Harold said: 'Yonder in their right battle, Eustace of Boulogne commands, as the Duke's foremost ally. With him I see Ivo of Ponthieu, and lords from Flanders and from France. I see Burgundian banners and a Spanish standard. Some of the Duke's countrymen from Italy are yonder, and Normans from the Isle of Sicily. There are men too from Normandy with Eustace, the great FitzOsbern captains them. William has set them with the Count for that Eustace is an unsure warrior, bold enough in hope of victory and gain, but one that loves life above honour.'

'Who is on the left?' said Gyrth.

The King said: 'Alan the Red commands the Breton men. They fight as the Welsh, brother; brave as lions, but they will not stand. He has set to stiffen them with the good men of Maine and those of Poitou. Haimer of Thouars is their captain, and no bad one. It was well done to set him by the Bretons.'

'What of the centre battle?' said Earl Gyrth.

Harold did not answer.

'One good man I can spy yonder, brothers,' said Leofwin. 'I can see Malet's banner. It is a shame to see him in that pack.'

'Who else is there?' said Waltheof.

Harold said 'William's half-brothers ride with him, Mortain and the Bayeux Bishop. Robert is a good fellow, but no captain. Odo could teach the Duke himself. He is as valiant too, but a foul fighter. Would I might meet him.'

With that he named Neal of St. Sauveur who led the men of the Cotentin, Hugh the Constable, and many more.

'It is a famous chivalry,' he said, 'but take away the captain and one might liefer deem them wolves. By that I measure him.'

He mused and said: 'It is as though we looked upon the coast of France. Do you see, my lords, what he has done? On the right eastward, Flanders and Boulogne and Ponthieu; then the Normans of the centre, Lisieux and Caen and Bayeux, then the Cotentin; and on the West the Bretons. So shall his men fight by their neighbours and egg each other on.'

Ansgar said: 'The Bastard is a captain plainly, but I think he has a task before him.'

The King answered: 'If it please God to help us, we shall hold him.'

Earl Gyrth looked on the ordered ranks, the banners and the lances. His eyes rested on St. Peter's Cross and dwelt upon it; a light came into them like fire.

Leofwin chafed and fretted, and could not be still.

'I would the Duke would fall to work,' he said. 'My stomach comes and goes.'

Earl Waltheof bade him keep his tally when the sport began.

'Look to it, cousin,' he said. 'I mean to beat you.'

'What odds?' said Leofwin.

They laid a wager.

Harold passed his tongue over his lips. He looked up at the sun. The day shone clear and fair. The woods were bright with many hues. They heard far off the old bell of Our Lady's chapel, ringing the Hour of Tierce. The sound came stilly through the trees and died away. The King and his chiefs signed themselves and spoke a prayer. Harold kissed the silver ring and said to them: 'Sirs, may God keep you. Let the trumpets sound.'

### Of the First Onslaughts

Some of the Duke's men had been so faint-hearted that he had bidden them depart. Now he spoke to the soldiers once again.

'Slay everyone you can,' he said, 'for if we conquer we shall all be rich.'

They cheered at that. The English answered, yelling in mockery: 'Out, out!'

'Hark,' said Odo, 'the dogs are barking.'

William reined his horse and looked up at the hill. The sun dazzled upon the Standard and the Dragon. The spear-points burned like flames. Beyond the painted shields the banners shone with silver, gold and scarlet, sky-blue and green; the bright helms winked and glittered. The hill was steep and grown with gorse and brambles and yellow bracken. The rough grass was beset with molehills. Marshy ground and water-courses, the Asten and the river Brede, lay upon either flank; before him lay the miry valley. The Duke looked and rubbed his chin.

'He has made it like a castle,' said Count Robert. 'I never saw such an array of battle.'

'The nut has a hard rind,' said Odo. 'We shall need good teeth.'

'Brother,' said William, 'I will build my church where Harold stands.'

A monk of St. Martin of Marmoutiers cried out: 'Sire, name it for the soldiers' Saint.'

'I grant it,' said the Duke.

He cantered down the ranks of bowmen, giving counsel. He called on God and raised his mace. The host took up the cry: 'God help!'

The first ranks of the bowmen began to go forward.

Those who stood at the back of the English array could not see what passed in the valley. When they heard the trumpets, they stood a-tiptoe and craned their necks.

'Are they coming?' they said. 'Are they coming?'

Suddenly the shouting was hushed. They heard a whistling like the sound of wings. Then it seemed as though a hail-storm beat against the shield-wall. The shouting broke out again, mingled with shrieks and cries. So it went twice and three times and again, and still continued. The Housecarles stood unmoving.

When the archers fell back, the Duke's heavy armed foot came to the assault, launching their throwing-weapons, pressing on with spears and swords.

A man in the last rank of Harold's host, seeing an old crab-tree hard by, climbed up to know what might be doing.

'Can you see them?' said his comrades.

'By God,' he said, 'they are half-way up the hill. Our men are snoring. What ails the fellows?'

They began to shout rudely to the Housecarles, bidding them make a show of manhood. The Housecarles answered: 'Hold your peace, you midden-cocks. What do you know of warfare?'

When the enemy drew near, the thralls waited for no command, but every man let fly with what he had.

'Shoot, shoot,' they cried to the Housecarles.

The Duke's men came on, hurling their darts. On a sudden the King's trumpets spoke. The captains shouted. There was a stir and flash down the whole line of battle. The French battle-cry wavered and died away. A fearful shrieking rose. The English yelled in triumph.

Those who stood by the crab-tree pulled the man down and fought each other for his place. Clarions rang across the valley. A cry was made: 'The Knights, the Knights are coming! Stand fast. Keep your ranks.'

The men who had swarmed up into the tree stared breathless, seeing a sight of splendour and of terror beyond their dreams. Those who could see nothing heard a man's voice begin a battle-chant. The chorus swelled, awesome and terrible and ever louder. The ground trembled beneath the English, as though they stood above sea-caverns on a day of storm. A single horseman charged the shield-wall singing, tossing his lance on high. Then came a shock that made the whole host reel. The noise of battle roared and thundered and died away at last as a great surf that breaks upon a rock-bound shore. There remained only the sound of crying, more woeful than the voice of sea-birds.

The men of the shield-wall shouted their battle-cry: 'God Almighty! Holy Cross!'

They heard no answer.

The levies whooped and hooted their delight, and cried to those in front: 'Well fought, well fought, axe-men. You made the bastards skip.'

'What did you look for?' said the Housecarles.

They wiped their weapons without haste and took their talk up where they had left it. Anschill of Ware said to his comrade Burchard: 'Finn should have wed the wench.'

This first onslaught was scarcely beaten back, when the Duke marshalled his ranks again and sent archers and foot to the attack. Then for the second time came the great charge of horsemen. The heaps of dead before the shield-wall grew, and with them lay the lopped and mangled living. The King's few bowmen, scattered through the host and hidden in the woods on either flank, aimed their shafts at the horses, and as each assault was ended picked off the stragglers toiling down the hill. It went thus till high noon was past, and then a pause came in the battle. None had seen harder fighting than this day. A cold fear struck the Frenchmen at the heart.

King Harold ordered now that all sorely wounded men should go out of the fight. The ranks had stood so close that neither slain nor wounded men could fall.

Some of the wounded jested with the shire-men as they passed, and cursed their luck, that they must leave the work half-done.

'God's truth,' said the country fellows, 'your luck is more than ours. We have stood here all day like wethers in a pen.'

Ansgar the Marshal went out of the battle now. He had been stricken, wounded in the loins. The King bade him command the camp and send the captain to take his place. Ansgar besought him to have no more part himself in the close fighting, saying: 'Sire, my heart stood still to see you.'

Harold said he had not come there to be idle.

'My dear lord,' said Ansgar, 'have you not said it is the harder part? We need your head more than your hands.'

Before the next assault, the King rode round his array. Many of the shire-men had been stricken by the hail of weapons that passed the shield-wall. They chafed that they had had no revenge. He saw a young lad laid on the grass, dying. The lad wept. When Harold spoke to him, he answered: 'Lord King, I never struck a blow for you. What will they say at home?'

'Aye,' said an old man, 'it is not the dying, King. It is the manner of it.' So they spoke on every side, yet at his words they quietened.

When the attack began, Harold took his place among them, idle with the rest. No toil seemed to him harder. The valour of the House-carles seemed to him a lesser thing than this endurance. He spoke his thoughts. His neighbour, Stanwin, grinned, and said: 'King, we be slow to rise, but when we rise up, we be something.'

Stanwin offered the King half his bread and cheese.

Harold gave him thanks and said: 'Your wife bakes bravely.'

'Oh, ah,' said Stanwin, 'bravely as a Queen, but 'tis her tongue that's heavy.'

The King laughed. A little man called Breme, upon the other side, offered him drink from a great leathern bottle and pledged him, saying: 'I drink your health, King Harold.'

With that he wiped his hand across his mouth and passed the bottle.

'Drink hail,' said Harold. He drank a thin sour beer, and did as Breme had done. The clarions rang. The King looked over the heads of those before him and forgot his neighbours. He muttered words unknowingly and gripped his weapon. The Knights of Brittany and Poitou charged the shield-wall with lowered lances, shouting in their own speech and calling on their Saints. He saw beyond his battle-line the wild heads of the horses scattering foam, the flash of sword and lance, and the white glaring faces. The line stood firm. The first rank knelt, their bills pointed against the horses' breasts, the second stood close and set their points against the riders. He glanced up at the sun. The day was three-parts spent. He smiled.

Breme shouted up to him: 'How do we fare?'

'Better than well,' said Harold.

When the first shock of the charge was broken and the lances shivered, the English used both bills and axes. The Knights were hard warriors, but they had never found themselves so straitened. The axemen fought left-handed, so that no shield availed. Mail was shorn through like silk, swords shattered at a blow. Men saw their comrades hewn asunder. They saw their horses headless while they yet bestrode them. The ground grew slippery as in a marsh. Among the fallen the chargers plunged and screamed in a red mire. The axes rose and fell and rose again, scarlet and terrible. The Knights saw themselves weaponless before their slaughterers. They turned and fled, horror upon them.

A cry was raised: 'The Duke is slain. Each for himself!'

The flight grew frenzied. The whole host heard the word and wavered. A roar rose from the English. On either wing the levies burst the shield-wall, yelling. The King himself was borne away, as by a flood, down the hillside.

When the close pressure of the throng released him, Harold stood still and looked about him, panting. Where the ditch spanned the field below, the Breton horse had over-ridden their foot; chargers and men struggled and choked together in the foul water. Thralls were hard at work with bill-hooks, clubs and hatchets. He looked towards the centre and saw the matchless chivalry of Normandy in headlong flight. Beyond them the French banners were borne backward faster yet.

'Oh, God, if it could be!' he said. 'Where are the Earls?'

He heard his trumpets sounding the recall unheeded. A standard-bearer of the fyrd leapt down the hill towards him, yelling. Harold seized the staff and felled him. More levies rushed past. He heard the winding of a hunting-horn. A lad hulloed.

'Stand, men,' he shouted. 'Stand!'

His voice was lost. He saw a trumpeter and roared to him: 'Recall, recall. Sound the recall.'

The man stopped, staring. The King snatched the trumpet from his hands, and sounded. The shire-men were deaf. He saw that in the centre the flight was checked. The clarions rang. Duke William's banner turned to meet the fleeing Bretons, the Duke himself, bare-headed, galloping before, shouting in fury. The Norman Knighthood massed in wedge array behind him, bearing down upon the hurly-burly at the ditch.

Housecarles and Thegns had gathered to the King. Godric of Fifhide ran up with Ethelnoth of Canterbury.

Godric shouted something and pointed to the valley.

Harold cried: 'Back.'

They saw the horsemen drive across the field, the levies all unheeding.

'Sire, my men,' said Godric.

The King turned. Godric followed with the rest, sobbing forth curses. They heard the sounds of battle change behind them.

The English trumpets up and down the field blared the recall. Upon the left the lines were formed again. The centre stood unshaken. On the right many men were cut off. The King drew on the centre and the left, so that the front ranks yet appeared as strong. The axemen watched, bleak-faced, the bloody struggle in the valley.

A knoll stood out from the hill no great way from the summit on the right. Thurkill of Kingston Bagpuize had fought his way thither with a band of fyrd-men, Stanwin and Breme among them. Before they could win to their comrades the Knights came against them. There was an oak tree on the knoll and round it they made their stand. Even thralls held their own like giants, fighting without helm or mail. They stood within spear-cast of the King's lines and shouted to their side for help. But now no throwing-spears were left, nor stones nor arrows, save those that could be gleaned. Harold forbade any man to leave his place.

'Sire, for the love of Christ,' said Godric.

The King said: 'Be still.'

Before the shire-men were beaten down, Duke William led a new attack against the shield-burgh. This onslaught was more terrible than all, and this too failed.

King Harold had fought on the right. He mounted now and rode round his array. Then he came to his own place. He alighted slowly and leant against his horse. There was a hush like death upon the field. Harold's brothers and his captains had thought him lost. They swore he should not go from them again.

'Are you not wounded, Sire?' they said. 'Are you not hurt?'

He shook his head. Earl Leofwin began to curse the headstrong levies. Harold turned on him in fury. Seeing his brother's stricken look, he checked himself. Gyrth brought him water. He drank and said: 'Where is the messenger I sent to Ansgar?'

The man came to him. He asked if there were news yet of the Earls, but there was none. Then he asked if the baggage-wagons had been found.

'Sire,' said the man, 'the Marshal hears they have turned back to London.'

All those around stood silent, casting anxious glances on King Harold. He began to laugh.

'Well, sirs,' he said, 'we have worked for our glory, and we will not share it. If we have no help, neither has the Duke. I dare swear he remembers Rouen kindly.'

Seeing that he could jest, their hearts were lightened. The sun was westering, and they reckoned it was not more than three hours till nightfall.

As they were speaking, someone called out that the Knights charged again. They took their posts in haste. They saw, as in the first attack, a single horseman riding on alone, but they beheld no chivalry behind him. Brihtric of Gloucester said: 'It is a herald. He will sue for peace.'

But as they watched, they could see no white shield or flag of truce. The Knight rode furiously, leaping over furze and brambles, trampling the dead. As he drew near they heard him crying out and calling on his horse.

'Hola, hola,' he cried. They saw his bridle broken. A roar of laughter went down the line.

'This way, Frenchman,' called the Housecarles. 'We will quiet him for you.'

The horse came on at full gallop. When he saw the lifted axes, he pricked his ears and snorted. Then he spread his fore-feet wide and slithered to a halt, his quarters under him. His rider rose up and clasped him round the neck. So doing, he lost his stirrups.

'Hola,' cried the Knight, 'God help! St. Michael, mercy!'

Two Housecarles sprang out of the line towards him, axes aloft. The stallion squealed and backed and whirled about. He hurtled down the hill faster than he had come. The Knight held on for his life, with stirrups flying.

The French observed this exploit in a wrathful silence. The English loudly cheered. The King laughed till he sobbed.

'God Almighty,' he said, 'one man has won his fame!'

He turned back from the shield-wall and went to see his wounded men. They asked him what had chanced, and when he told them, the story passed from mouth to mouth and made them merry. The tale of the Knight's charge heartened the whole host like good wine. They were still laughing when the archers came on to attack again.

## Of the House of Godwin

Abbot Leofric of Peterborough had been wounded by a lance-thrust in the thigh. He lay with other sorely wounded men on the high ground behind the line of battle, where the Dragon and the Standard crowned the hill.

Leofric bore himself bravely. When he heard the trumpets sound for a new onslaught, he said to Erwin, the King's leech, who tended him: 'Make haste, for I have three men's work to do.'

'Lord Abbot, you can do no more this day,' said Erwin.

Leofric said: 'By the Apostle, Harold shall not say that all our kindred failed him.'

He ground his teeth and said again: 'Make haste.'

Erwin did for him what he could. The Abbot stretched out his hands and clutched the grass. He lay still, staring up into a cloudless sky. He thought that the air darkened. On a sudden he cried out and strove to raise himself.

'Lie still, my lord,' said Erwin, 'I have done.'

The day grew loud, as with the flight of starlings. Men looked up. Then the arrow-storm came down upon them, falling from on high. Erwin sank forward across the Abbot and was still. A shrieking rose, as from the souls in hell. The Duke's bowmen had aimed upwards, against the Standard. Upon the Housecarles, upon the men of Middlesex and Essex fell that keen rain. The wounded and those who tended them lay, like St. Edmund, pierced in every limb. Between them the barbed shafts thrilled in the ground. Then suddenly as it began, the storm was ended. The host stood dazed.

Abbot Leofric had no hurt, for Erwin's body saved him. He lay a moment as though stunned, not knowing what befell him. He saw the Fighting Man glitter above him, pierced with shafts. As he sought to rise, Abbot Elfwy staggered to him, stricken through the jaws. Leofric would have helped him, but Elfwy tore his hands away, and pointed whence he had come, striving to speak.

Leif the Northman ran up, stumbling across the fallen. He snatched the salves and linen. The water-bowl lay shattered.

'Water,' he said, 'bring water. Find a leech.'

Leofric looked after him and saw where the King stood, bowed together, staying himself upon his shield. Elfwy sank down, groaning. Leofric knew not if he lived or died. His own soul failed within him.

A man ran past with water in a leaking bucket. The Abbot halted after him. The King's brothers and his chiefs pressed round him, and men cried out for a leech.

Leofric said to Gyrth: 'I am a leech.'

'In God's name then,' said Gyrth.

He spoke to Harold. The King held his head between his hands. Blood ran through his fingers and down the shield. He neither moved nor answered.

Earl Waltheof stood with Godwin's sons. The Abbot asked him: 'What is the wound?'

And when he heard, he said: 'Lord Jesus, he must go out of the battle.'

Leif said to Harold: 'Foster-son, you must go back.'

He did not answer. They took counsel together. Then they sought to lead him back. Harold raised his head and fought them, crying out for Erwin.

'God damn you, where is the leech?' he said.

They loosed him in despair. He staggered, reeling. Leif caught him in his arms and laid him down. They heard the trumpets sound for the onset of the heavy-armed foot following the archers. The King sought to rise. He fell back and spoke Gyrth's name.

'Take the command, lord Earl,' said Leif.

Gyrth kissed his brother. He took Harold's shield, that men might think he was the King, and called his chiefs. His calm was changed. They saw him like a lion. Leofwin stood staring upon Harold, his face ashen, Waltheof beside him.

'You too,' said Leif. 'Back to your work.'

When Leofwin would have kissed the King, Harold struck at him. Earl Leofwin followed Gyrth, sobbing. The noise of battle rose again at the shield-wall. The clash of steel on steel was like the clangour of a hundred smithies. The King called on the name of Christ.

Abbot Leofric began his task with shaking hands. He laid aside the helm and put back the coif of ring-mail. A shaft had stricken Harold above the right eye and destroyed it. He had drawn the arrow-head so strongly that the torn flesh hung down. When Leofric touched his hurt, he swooned.

'He gave the Duke good help who sent this gad-fly,' said Leif.

The Abbot laboured in silence, sweating as he toiled, for faintness came on him from his own wound. Before the work was done, they heard the coming of the Knights. Harold lay as the dead. Leofric put his hand on his breast.

'Please God he will live,' he said. 'He must be borne back to the camp when I have done, and the news hidden if may be. Nothing will hold the men if they get word.'

'It will be night ere long,' said Leif.

As they spoke, they heard the yelling of the levies, like hounds in cry. Upon the left the host surged forward.

'God help us,' said Leif, 'this is the end.'

He seized his weapons and sprang up, thrusting through the press towards Gyrth's banner. Trumpets sounded vainly.

The King came from his swoon and murmured something.

'Lie still, my son,' said Leofric. 'The day goes well.'

The trumpets rang again, loud as the crack of doom. Harold raised himself up, casting the Abbot from him with a madman's strength. He cried out to those around him: 'Get me to my feet.'

From the valley on the left the shouts of triumph died before the Norman battle-cry. William had drawn the shire-men down by a feigned flight. The King turned and strove to see how the fight went on his right wing. The sun was low and the light smote him. He groaned and said: 'How is it on the right? Do the men stand?'

One of the Housecarles answered: 'They stand firm, lord King.'

Harold said: 'Bid Godric shorten his line. Let him send half his levies. Take up the Standard.'

When the Duke led his Knights against the weakened left, he saw the Fighting Man over against him, where he had thought to breach the shield-wall. Sometimes a Knight broke through to find his death, but the line held. It was the hour of sunset when the Knighthood fell back. They rode down the hillside, a ragged band, horses and men forspent.

King Harold had kept his station by the Fighting Man, gripping the banner-staff. When he was told that the assault had failed, he asked men for his brothers.

Leif came to him, and Waltheof, with new wounds.

'Is it you, foster-father?' said the King. 'Where are my brothers?'

Seeing him there upon his feet, Leif swore.

'Before God,' he said, 'are there no men of yours with wits about them? You must be out of the fight, Harold. What do you here?'

'Where is Gyrth?' said the King. 'Where is Leofwin?'

When Leif saw that nothing would serve, he fell to praising Harold's brothers. The King had never heard such words from him.

'What would you tell me, Leif?' he said.

Leif told his tidings.

'Fallen?' said Harold. 'Leofwin too?'

Earl Waltheof said, weeping: 'Oh, cousin, Gyrth threw himself against the Duke and slew his horse. Then the Knights came between us. The Duke struck him down. I saw Leofwin fall.'

'What would you, foster-son?' said Leif. 'They died like warriors. "Old age gives us no quarter, though the spears may."'

'And the Duke lives?' said Harold.

Leif said: 'The devil guards his own. The man was twice unhorsed. Haveloc's son dealt him a blow that might have felled an ox, yet the Duke slew him. Three times we thought the Bastard ours. He stood alone and fought us like a demon.'

The King said: 'Is he so great a warrior?'

He bade them bring his brothers' bodies to the Standards, and they brought them, bloody and trampled. The Duke's mace had fallen on Earl Gyrth, crushing both helm and head. A spear had stricken Leofwin through. He lay as though in wonder.

'Give me to drink,' said Harold.

He would not go out of the fight, or yield up the command to any man.

In the next attack, Duke William sent foot-soldiers before the archers. While they cast their spears, the bowmen loosed their arrows upwards. A roof of shields covered the English host. The closed ranks did not part. The dead fell, but the living never stirred. The House-carles stood like men of iron. The Duke beheld no opening for his horse. Seeing that silent and unmoving host, he signed himself.

When the archers and foot fell back, no clarions sounded. There came a great lull in the battle. Now men on both sides felt themselves spent past endurance. Many were dead of weariness alone. Those that lived could scarcely wield their weapons. The very reason of their warfare was forgotten in the thought of rest. The sun had set behind the western hills, and but an hour of daylight yet remained.

## Of the Fighting Man

Duke William summoned his captains to him in the valley. They came in silence, wounded, bone-weary, haggard-eyed. Their stallions trembled with drooped crests and bloody sides lathered with foam and sweat.

The Barons saw no praise in their lord's looks. When they had gathered, he looked round upon them in such a silence that they quailed.

At last he said: 'My lord and Barons, you were called warriors once. What shall I call you now? Our bowmen have done better service. Is this the valour of your chivalry? Look yonder. See your victors. A few wounded axe-men and a rabble of peasantry without a captain.'

They heard him, shamed.

The Duke raged.

'By God's splendour, sirs,' he said, 'must I win this day for you single-handed? Have I not fought with Harold, foot to foot, and given him the crown he earned? On foot I fought. I struck the tyrant down. Must I destroy them all? By the Apostle, if you forgo the spoils of victory now, you are the laughing-stock of Christendom.'

They were silent, with bowed heads.

'Very good,' he said. 'Fly if you will. It will not save you. I have destroyed the ships.'

At that they looked on him wild-eyed.

'Ye fools,' he said, 'when have you seen me worsted? I tell you the day is won. Harold is dead.'

As he was speaking, they heard from the hill a ragged shout, the sound of one man's name.

They hearkened, unbelieving. They heard that name again, and a third time.

'It cannot be,' said William. 'With mine own hand I slew him.'

Count Eustace cried out: 'Lord have mercy on us.'

Despair took them anew.

'My lords,' said Odo, 'it seems to me our arrow-storm was on the mark. It must have been his brother who bore Harold's shield. If the King be not dead, then he is wounded.'

William threw back his head and laughed.

'Good hearing, sirs,' he said. 'I feared before. I never yet knew men stand fast when such a captain fell. Now but one life stands between us and triumph.'

Eustace said: 'Cold comfort. He will not come into the battle, being wounded. And for those Knights of his that fight on foot, we shall not come at him while they are living.'

The Duke knitted his brows and said to Odo: 'Give us of your cunning counsel, brother. You are the man to help us now.'

'Why do you call on me?' said Odo. 'Call on Harold.'

When the council was ended, the Duke's lords rode back, each man to his own post. Hugh of Montfort, the Constable, upon the right of William's centre battle, had the King's Standard now before him. He called his chiefs and gave them his lord's command.

'We are to seek none but the King himself,' he said.

Duke William led his Knights again to the attack. As soon as the horsemen drew near the shield-wall, they began to shout King Harold's name. Some cried in their own tongue, some few in English, taunting the King with cowardice, mocking him that he hid behind his men.

Robert of Vieux Pont rode with the Constable, and with them William Malet. Hugh and Robert shouted loudly. Malet rode in silence.

The Constable cried to him: 'Take up the word, Sir Knight. The Duke commands.'

'I promised him my sword,' said Malet, 'not a woman's weapon.'

Robert of Vieux Pont answered: 'My faith, Malet, you will need all weapons, if you would see Greville again.'

Malet said: 'I was a Knight before I held Greville.'

As they charged, the Knighthood shouted to the Housecarles: 'Axe-men, where is your King, he that was perjured to the Duke? Does Harold hide himself? He is a dead man if we find him.'

The taunts sounded like an unending chant of shame. The King heard them where he stood. He gasped as though he fell into an ice-cold flood.

Leif said, raging: 'Give them no heed, my fosterling. This is their guile.'

The Knights hurled themselves against the shield-wall. As they fought and as they fell, they cried shame on the King: 'Coward, Usurper, Perjurer; show yourself, Harold, if you dare.'

He said to those around him: 'I will not bear it. Better die.'

They laid hands on him and held him back by force.

Patric of La Lande, fighting beside Duke William, shouted: 'Where do you hide, Harold FitzGodwin? You were bold enough in Brittany. Come out, Earl Harold. Hear me name you "perjurer".'

William roared, as he fought: 'Harold, your liege-lord calls you. Traitor, show yourself.'

The wounded Housecarles by the Standard dragged themselves up and seized their weapons, stumbling back into the battle. The King struggled, sobbing, cursing those who held him.

'Loose me,' he said; 'shall these go back and I stand here?'

Leif answered: 'Did your brothers die, that he should win this day with words?'

Thereafter Harold was still. He bade them give him his great axe. The keen edge was unturned. He signed the blood-stained steel as though he prayed.

The hue and cry continued. At the sound of it, King Harold's men grew battle-mad. This one thing wrought what the Duke's power could not. Axe-men rushed out slaughtering. Housecarles threw away their shields. The Men of Kent and London hurled themselves forward, the shire-men behind them. William saw his Knights go down, his bravest warriors fall.

Patric shouted to him: 'Eustace feigns flight again to draw them down.'

The Duke saw Count Eustace going back and all his right wing wavering, FitzOsbern shouting to the men in vain.

'By God,' he said, 'if they fly now, they will not turn to-day.'

When Count Eustace saw him coming, with the thousand knights who followed him, he cried: 'God help!' And he and his turned back to face the axes.

Duke William fought now beside Count Eustace and his men. Young Robert of Beaumont fought there also, leading a band of horsemen. The

Duke marked him. The lad fought like a hero, crying: 'Englishmen, where is your dastard King?'

William called to him: 'Beaumont, my Knight, your spurs are won this day.'

Robert laid on like three men, gasping forth his cry.

The weight of horsemen breached the English line in many places when the ranks were thinned. The fighting was back and forth on the hill-top. The Duke's men thought the day was won. Many turned back to plunder. Then the English drew together round the Dragon and the Standard, and fought more strongly. The battle grew yet harder. Men trod not on the ground, but on the fallen. Those that fell were trampled under foot and stifled. The light began to fail. A spear struck William's horse. The Duke fell headlong and rose dazed. Eustace horsed him, seizing a Knight's charger. Fury came on William. He fought despairing. His sole strength upheld them.

Hugh of Montfort pressed the attack against the Standard with all his might. Twenty Knights took a vow to win the Fighting Man. Robert FitzErneis was their leader. The Men of London broke before them and fell back, fighting like berserks. Robert alone lived till he reached the Standard. A great axe struck him down, but the breach widened. More Knights pressed on. The Housecarles heard a voice they knew, and saw their lord beside them. From either host a shout went up.

William looked westward. Against the after-glow he saw an axe-man mightier than his fellows. The Knighthood broke and fled before him, as though the tide of battle turned, now and for ever. The Duke wheeled his horse.

'Eustace,' he shouted, 'Ponthieu, Giffard, Normans, to me!'

They heard that call above the tumult, loud as at morning.

They drew off and threw themselves into a wedge array, and all together charged the Standard.

The King heard the thunder of their coming as he fought. He turned his head and saw the Cross. A sword struck him across the brow unseen. His axe fell from his hands. He sank down on his knee. His foemen yelled. They heard his battle-cry and saw him rising. A Knight bent from the saddle and hewed him to the thigh-bone before the shields could close, crying: 'God help!'

The Duke drove home his spurs and rode the ranks of Housecarles under foot. He saw his quarry. His lance struck down through shield and mail and breast into the ground. The ash-wood splintered. The weight of the charge carried William on. Men fell before the splintered lance. With his own hands he cast the Standard down.

Duke William's brothers drew rein at his side. Toustain the White bore after him the banner with the Cross. His bodyguard swept round. His Barons gathered. About them the strife yet raged, disordered, masterless. Where the King fell, Count Eustace and his men wheeled, howling, stabbing down with swords and lances. A man bore to the Duke a broken helm, an arm-ring wet with blood.

William turned and snatched the banner-staff from Toustain's hands. He stood up in his stirrups. Beyond the fury he saw the still woods, the dark heights of Telham. He shouted, weeping, to his men: 'Victory, victory with the help of God!'

But when the stars shone they were fighting still.

## Of The End

In the camp on Caldbec Hill the wounded heard the uproar of the fighting. Ansgar the Marshal had sent down all who could strike a blow, the boys and the camp-servants. None was left save maimed and dying men, the priests who tended them, and the flock of wives and children and old folk drawn from the country round. The sunset glory faded and yet none knew how the battle went.

As the twilight deepened there came a hush at last. Out of it rose a hoarse shout. It seemed to them the army cried King Harold's name.

'What shout is that?' said Ansgar. 'Is the day ours?'

He sent monks to the field. While they were gone the noise arose more hideously, the endless din of battle. Suddenly they heard a very yell of triumph. A Norman cry.

Ansgar said: 'Oh, Christ, what is it?'

He raised himself upon his elbow. When he looked down, he saw men running northward; at first a few, then more, then a great rush of the shire-levies. He looked about him as a man distraught.

'A trumpeter,' he said, 'find me a trumpeter.'

As they fled the shire-men heard the trumpet-calls ring out. They thought the Earls were come. They turned from flight and toiled up the steep hill with a new hope. When they beheld no more than Ansgar and his band of wounded and the lone trumpeter sounding his call, many fell down and wept.

Ansgar shouted to them. He had some of the men dragged before him.

'You dogs,' he said, 'why do you fly? Your orders were to stand.'

'The King,' they said, 'the King is gone. Harold is fallen.'

'Harold gone?' said Ansgar. 'What man commands?'

'Fly, fly,' they said, 'there is no host, no captain.'

'There is a captain here,' said Ansgar. 'I command. Hold fast. The Earls are coming.'

Seeing him so unshaken they began to know themselves again. Ansgar had men bear him to and fro. He ordered the defence as he was able. The stones for the engines lay there. He bade them carry them to the hill's edge, that they might roll them down upon the foe. He bade the trumpets sound as though a host were come. More levies gathered to him. He sent word to the field that he would hold the camp and ordered that all should fall back.

Sebricht had gone down with the other servants when the fight grew desperate. He was no warrior, yet he pressed on, clutching a dead man's sword. For the first time men fell before him. He heard the cry of the King's death, and Ansgar's bidding reached him. In the same instant he heard a shout of 'Holy Cross.' A sudden hope made his heart beat. He saw a rush of axe-men. He took up the battle-cry and fought beside them. Horsemen came against them and were beaten back. They came again. A third time they rode against the axes and drew off.

Sebricht cried: 'The King, is the King with you, Housecarles?'

Leif's voice answered him: 'What man is that?'

'It is I, Sebricht,' he said. 'Where is the King?'

'Gone,' said Leif. 'There is no joy in living after this day.'

Sebricht sobbed out: 'Ansgar the Marshal will defend the camp. He sends word to fall back.'

Abbot Leofric caught his arm and cried: 'Sebricht, are my kinsmen come? Was it their trumpets?'

'What should they do now?' said Leif. 'Better to die with Harold than to live without him.'

Earl Waltheof was with them.

'You are a Northman, Leif,' he said. 'We have our land yet. We can live to fight.'

'Aye, to fight,' said Leofric.

They heard the trumpets loud from the hill.

'Hark, they are come,' said Waltheof. 'Back, my lords.'

Brihtric of Gloucester joined them with other men. They fought their way towards the camp. There were many such small bands upon the field. Some few had Ansgar's word. Some turned. The rest fought on. It grew so dark that only by their voices could foes know each other. Godric of Fifhide and Edric the Deacon had joined Alfric of Gelling. He was Waltheof's warrior. Two Hampshire men were with them, Ednoth and Edwy, and others all unknown. A freeman of St. Edmundsbury bore them Ansgar's bidding.

Alfric answered: 'Harold did not fly.'

No man would turn away.

Godric the Sheriff said: 'Give us a song, Edric. Let the bastards know where to find Englishmen.'

Edric began to croak forth the words of the old warrior Brihtwold, in the Song of Maldon:

> 'Soul shall be stronger, spirit be keener,
> Mind shall be mightier as our might lessens.'

Godric and his men took up the battle-chant, hewing as they sang:

> 'Here lies our captain cut all to pieces,
> Good and gone under; aye may he groan for it,
> He that now from this warfaring would turn homeward.'

At the sound of that grim singing in the darkness, the Duke's men muttered spells against witchcraft and gave ground. The English staggered forward, seeking them. Edric led the chanting still. The freeman fought beside him with a club, Godric with his great axe. Their words came in gasps:

'I am grown grey-hair'd; go hence I will not,
But I here abiding with my bread-giver,
By so loved a man look to perish.'

It was near midnight and the moon had risen when the fighting on the hill was at an end.

*1948*

THE TEMPLE

One of Edward Bawden's illustrations for *London is London*, an anthology edited by D. M. Low

# DOUGLAS LE PAN

## *Rider on the Sands*

O WANDERER from an antique shore
Delighting in the glory of the morning,
With hair flowing and a crimson saddle-bow
And reins held lightly in a supple hand,
Stay in this defeated land,
Stay ever so,
Stay as a wonder and a warning,
Let your great chestnut rear and prance,
Rebuke the dancers in the arrested dance.

Here by the ocean evermore
Challenge the waves. Whether by luck you roamed
From fountained Delphi or the lacquered East,
As random in the woods a prince might ride
Who sought adventure far and wide
Or some rich feast;
Here where the pale green waves are combed
Gallop past tresses of starry rain,
Gallop and dazzle the waves with sun-bright mane.

And blazon the forgotten lore,
Bravado echoing to the strident clouds.
Though you have lost the country poets sung,
Stay here. Where could you ever be a stranger,
Bearing your own delight and danger
And always young?
How could you ever melt in crowds,
Roistering, laughing, scandalous, free,
Drinking the sun's strong immortality?

*1948*

# BASIL WILLEY

## *Arnold and the Lake District*

### FROM 'NINETEENTH CENTURY STUDIES'

Be thankful, thou; for if unholy deeds
Ravage the world, tranquillity is here!

WORDSWORTH

SO Thomas Arnold might have written of Fox How; so, in other language, he constantly did. For his life was not all 'unhasting, unresting diligence'; like nearly all the Christian (and other) Pilgrims of the nineteenth century, he turned periodically for solace to Beulah and the Delectable Mountains. Near the banks of the Rothay, and in close neighbourhood to Wordsworth at Rydal Mount, Arnold built his holiday home; and there, in that incomparable valley, he (and his family long after him) found rest and regeneration. I speak deliberately of this in a book devoted mainly to other themes, for I think that the whole course of English thought and letters in the nineteenth century would have been different if this island had not contained the mountain paradise of Westmorland and Cumberland. The Lake District was part of its religious creed; as Mr. Aldous Huxley has said, for good Wordsworthians a tour through Westmorland was 'as good as a visit to Jerusalem'. The Alps, indeed, offered their rarer ecstasies to the leisured and the adventurous, but the Lakeland mountains, linking heaven with home, spoke more healingly and intimately to the heart. Throughout that 'iron time of doubts, disputes, distractions, fears', they remained, for the dweller on the darkling plain, a silent and constant symbol of possible sublimity. Amidst the shaking of creeds and the crumbling of foundations, 'Nature' had already, in the previous century, attracted to itself much religious feeling, but it was in the nineteenth century that this particular geographical region became part of the national mythology. Doubtless Wordsworth had much to do with this, but I suspect that even without him the clear streams, the exquisite grass and flowers, the bog-scented air, the silence and the solitude of the district would have supplied their tonic and anodyne to the townsman and the inhabitant of Doubting Castle. For an England becoming steadily smokier and more hideous, and becoming less and less assured of its spiritual foundations and direction, it was (as it still is) of momentous importance that there should remain a region owing nothing to human contrivance and undesecrated by human hand, which could symbolize permanence, grandeur and joy, and convey

Authentic tidings of invisible things;
Of ebb and flow, and ever-during power;
And central peace, subsisting at the heart
Of endless agitation.

Arnold's passion for Fox How was all the more intense because the lines had not fallen to him in pleasant places; he speaks of the 'unsurpassable dulness of Rugby', and gazes with 'humorous despair' across the fields and hedgerows east of the town, reflecting that 'there is nothing fine between us and the Ural mountains'. Sensitive, like a true son of his century, to every nuance of landscape, he feels the spell of Oxfordshire, and concludes from this that Warwickshire, like Cambridgeshire and most of the eastern counties, is genuinely 'uninteresting', and has not merely suffered in comparison with Westmorland. But Westmorland delighted him not merely because of its beauty, freedom and repose, not merely because of its running streams—'the most beautiful object in nature'—or its wild flowers, which affected him like music. He valued it also as a retreat from the crudities of school life, and from the sad preoccupations of his working days. When he was at Fox How, the problems of Church and State, rich and poor, faith and reason, and

what we feel of sorrow and despair
From ruin and from change, and all the grief
That passing shows of Being leave behind,
Appeared an idle dream, that could not live
Where meditation was.

And so, even in the 'cool, flowery lap of earth', his unsleeping conscience felt the nettle danger; was it, perhaps, ignoble ease that he found in Easedale, 'most delicious of vales'? He looks at the mountains which shut in the valley, and thinks he could be content never to wander beyond them any more, and to take rest in a place he loves so dearly. But then he feels ashamed of the wish; Fox How is 'a home so peaceful and delightful that it would not be right to make it one's constant portion'. Christians must seek not yet repose, and even natural beauty may become a temptation, luring the pilgrim into enchanted gardens and bowers of Acrasia. 'Really, in these most troublous times, it seems more than is allowable to be living, as we are here, in a place of so much rest and beauty.' And yet his normal life was such a 'perpetual turmoil' that surely it could not be amiss to retire at rare intervals to the mount of transfiguration, and stand there with the Lord? Mountain joy can be sacred, not profane; from the days of Moses and the Psalmist to the time of Christ himself and onwards, great things have been when men and mountains met.

I often used to think of the solemn comparison in the Psalm, 'the hills stand round about Jerusalem; even so standeth the Lord about his people'. The girdling in of the mountains round the valley of our home is as apt an image as any earthly thing can be of the encircling of the everlasting arms, keeping off evil and showering all good.

No, the truly fatal lure was not the mountains, but the beckoning shadow of the High Church reaction, tempting us into the medieval maze—'like that phantom which Minerva sent to Hector to tempt him to his fate, by making him think that Deiphobus was at hand to help him'. From the hills comes real help:

Early had he learned
To reverence the volume that displays
The mystery, the life that cannot die;
But in the mountains did he *feel* his faith.
All things, responsive to the writing, there
Breathed immortality, revolving life,
And greatness still revolving; infinite:
There littleness was not; the least of things
Seemed infinite; and there his spirit shaped
Her prospects, nor did he believe,—he *saw*.

Besides, these joys, and this communion, were not tasted in selfish isolation; they were shared with his family and many friends, and above all with Rugby boys.

I find Westmorland very convenient in giving me an opportunity of having some of the Sixth Form with me in the holidays; not to read, of course, but to refresh their health when they get knocked up by the work, and *to show them mountains and dales, a great point in education*, and a great desideratum to those who only know the central or southern counties of England.

Arnold's sudden death, at the age of forty-seven, sent a wave of sorrow and consternation throughout the whole country. Newman had once asked with affected incredulity 'Is *he* a Christian?' But when he died, not only his devoted pupils and disciples, but men of all creeds and parties, recognized that a great spirit had departed from their midst.

*1949*

Jacket vignette by Lynton Lamb for *God's Eyes A-Twinkle* by T. F. Powys, 1947

## PETER YATES

### *A Morning*

ABOVE the mind in search of meaning
  The trees' bird-flashing branches shake
And spill the overflowing morning
  Light-fingering on the lake.

The webs of thought are snapped and broken
  And washed into the singing blue
As I stride through the emerald bracken
  And kick the diamonds of dew.

The morning tempts with rainbow dazzle
  And spills its sharpest fall of light
For me to swing my wand of hazel
  And cut the whisperings of night.

Yet while I feel all sunlight's teaching
  Blaze on my back and burn the cloth,
It will not break the restless twitching
  Of thought's wild midnight moth.

*1951*

# F. R. LEAVIS

## *The Dunciad*

FROM 'THE COMMON PURSUIT'

YES, one concedes grudgingly, overcoming the inevitable revulsion, as one turns the pages of this new edition (The 'Twickenham'), in which the poem trickles thinly through a desert of apparatus, to disappear time and again from sight—yes, there has to be a *Dunciad* annotated, garnished and be-prosed in this way. A very large proportion of the apparatus, after all, comes down from the eighteenth century with the poem, and the whole, though to read it all through will be worth no one's while, is enlightening documentation of the age that produced Pope and of which Pope made poetry. Yet, as the editor in his Introduction insists—'It has never sufficiently been recognized that in the *Dunciad* one of the greatest artists in English poetry found the perfect material for his art', he did make poetry, and it is the poetry that matters; so that one has to follow up one's concession with the remark that, though this new monument of scholarship will have to go into all the libraries for reference, it is not the edition in which the *Dunciad* should be read. The material is one thing, the poetry another. In fact, the sufficient recognition won't come except in company with the recognition that notes are not necessary: the poetry doesn't depend upon them in any essential respect.

'The art', says Professor Sutherland, 'which Pope lavished upon this poem has too often been obscured by an unnecessary concern for his victims'. Yes; and more generally, by an unnecessary concern *with* his victims—a concern of a kind that notes, especially obtrusive ones, inevitably encourage. The 'fading of its personalities', remarked by Professor Sutherland as something that appreciation of the *Dunciad* suffers from, is really an advantage, and one we ought not to refuse. For eighteenth-century readers it must have been hard not to start away continually from the poetry to thinking about the particular historical victim and the grounds of Pope's animus against him; for modern readers it should be much easier to appreciate the poetry as poetry—to realize that Pope has created something the essential interest of which lies within itself, in what it is. Yet where satire is concerned there appear to be peculiar difficulties in the way of recognizing the nature of art and of the approach to it, as Professor Sutherland bears inadvertent witness in the last sentence of his Introduction:

the criticism of the nineteenth and twentieth centuries has been far too much concerned with the moral issues raised by Pope's satire, and too little interested in its purely aesthetic values.

'Aesthetic' is a term the literary critic would do well to deny himself. Opposed to 'moral', as it is in this sentence, it certainly doesn't generate light. Moral values enter inevitably into the appreciation of the *Dunciad*, if it is judged to be a considerable work; the problem is to bring them in with due relevance, and the bringing of them in is the appreciation of Pope's art. How are malice, resentment, spite, contempt, and the other negative attitudes and feelings that we can't doubt to have played a large part in the genesis of his poetry, turned in that poetry into something that affects us as being so very different?

We don't feel the personalities as personal. More than that, we don't, for the most part, even in places where animus is very apparent, feel the total effect to be negative, expressing a hostile and destructive will. The force of this judgment comes out when we look by way of comparison at Swift. The final impression that Swift, in any representative place, leaves us with is one of having been exposed to an intense, unremitting and endlessly resourceful play of contempt, disgust, hatred, and the will to spoil and destroy. The contrast brings home to us the sense in which Pope, in practising his art of verse, is engaged, whatever his materials, in positive creation. It is Swift's prose I am thinking of in the first place, but the contrast is no less striking and significant when made between verse and verse. In verse, in fact, Swift is more barely and aridly negative (the air is 'thoroughly small and dry'), and more summarily destructive, than in prose; he never achieves anything approaching the complexity characteristic of the *Digression Concerning the Use of Madness in a Commonwealth*. In the following we have the richest, in the way of organization, that his verse yields:

When Celia in her glory shews,
If Strephon would but stop his nose,
(Who now so impiously blasphemes
Her ointments, daubs, and paints, and creams,
Her washes, slops, and every clout,
With which he makes so foul a rout;)
He soon would learn to think like me,
And bless his ravish'd sight to see
Such order from confusion sprung,
Such gaudy tulips raised from dung.

Effects like that of the closing couplets are not common in Swift's verse, but the sourly nagging meanness, the sawing meagreness, of the movement in general is representative. No one, of course, would carry out a solemn comparison of Swift and Pope as poets. My point is simply, by the contrast with Swift, who is not positively an Augustan—though he is nothing else positive—to bring out what is meant by saying that Pope, in practising his art of verse, is being an Augustan of a most positive kind. Against any of Swift's verse (if you want decasyllabics take the close of *A City Shower*) set this:

> This labour past, by Bridewell all descend,
> (As morning-pray'r and flagellation end)
> To where Fleet-ditch with disemboguing streams
> Rolls the large tribute of dead dogs to Thames,
> The King of Dykes! than whom, no sluice of mud
> With deeper sable blots the silver flood.

It is not enough to talk in the usual way (I have just seen a Sunday review that quotes the passage, which I had already marked) about the beauty of that last couplet. That beauty is inseparable from the whole habit of the versification. And in saying this one recognizes that 'versification' here involves more than the term is generally felt to convey. When Pope is preoccupied with the metrical structure, the weight, and the pattern of his couplets, he is bringing to bear on his 'materials' habits of thought and feeling, and habits of ordering thought and feeling. The habits are those of a great and ardent representative of Augustan civilization. The result is that even when he is closest to Swift he remains very un-Swiftian in effect: what we note at once as the characteristic movement (no simple metrical matter, of course) makes a radical difference:

> Like the vile straw that's blown about the streets
> The needy Poet sticks to all he meets,
> Coach'd, carted, trod upon, now loose, now fast,
> In the Dog's tail his progress ends at last.

The part of Augustan civilization in Pope's creative triumph is peculiarly apparent in the Fourth Book of the *Dunciad*. The pre-eminence of this book doesn't seem to be at all generally recognized. There is no sign, for instance, that the present editor recognizes it any more than Leslie Stephen did, writing his 'English Men of Letters' *Pope* before 1880. There can, then, be no harm in reiterating that the Fourth Book stands, not only (so much later in date as it is) apart from the other books, but much above them: it is a self-sufficient poem. The opening has an obvious relevance to my immediate argument:

> Yet, yet a moment one dim Ray of Light
> Indulge, dread Chaos, and eternal Night!
> Of darkness visible so much be lent,
> As half to shew, half veil the deep Intent.
> Ye Pow'rs! whose Mysteries restor'd I sing,
> To whom Time bears me on his rapid wing,
> Suspend a while your Force inertly strong,
> Then take at once the Poet and the Song.

This astonishing poetry ought to be famous and current for the unique thing it is. Consider how triumphantly it enlists Milton into an Augustan sublime. Faced with this passage as a detached fragment, and forgetting (if that can be granted as credible) where one had read it, what would one make of it? It could have been written, one would have to conclude, only by Pope, but one would hardly guess that it belonged to a satire. Yet within ten lines the poem breaks out into a most lively play of imaginative wit, overtly satirical, and the transition is irresistibly sure:

> Now flam'd the Dog-star's unpropitious ray,
> Smote ev'ry Brain, and wither'd ev'ry Bay;
> Sick was the Sun, the Owl forsook his bow'r,
> The moon-struck Prophet felt the madding hour:
> Then rose the Seed of Chaos, and of Night,
> To blot out Order, and extinguish Light,
> Of dull and venal a new World to mold,
> And bring Saturnian days of Lead and Gold.
> She mounts the Throne: her head a Cloud conceal'd,
> In broad Effulgence all below reveal'd,
> ('Tis thus aspiring Dulness ever shines)
> Soft on her lap her Laureat son reclines.
> Beneath her foot-stool, Science groans in Chains,
> And *Wit* dreads Exile, Penalties and Pains.
> There foam'd rebellious *Logic*, gagg'd and bound,
> There, stript, fair *Rhet'ric* languish'd on the ground;
> His blunted Arms by *Sophistry* are born,
> And shameless Billingsgate her Robes adorn.
> *Morality*, by her false Guardians drawn,
> *Chicane* in Furs, and *Casuistry* in Lawn,
> Gasps as they straiten at each end the cord,
> And dies, when Dulness gives her Page the word.
> Mad *Mathesis* alone was unconfin'd,
> Too mad for mere material chains to bind,
> Now to pure Space lifts her extatic stare,
> Now running round the Circle, finds it square.

The key to Pope's command of the sublime, and to his mastery of transition, presents itself in the couplet:

> Then rose the Seed of Chaos, and of Night,
> To blot out Order, and extinguish Light. . . .

'Order' for Pope is no mere word, but a rich concept imaginatively realized: ideal Augustan civilization. It is his greatness as a poet that he can relate the polite Augustan social culture always present in Augustan idiom and movement with something more profound than a code of manners: a code adequate to being thought of as the basis and structure of a great civilization. We have him doing it in this book of the *Dunciad*. 'Order' (associated with 'Light') imparts its grandeur to the opening, and it is the comprehensive positive from which the satire works (in ways I discuss in *Revaluation*, c. III). It is everywhere implicitly there, or within easy recall, and it explains the mastery of transition that goes with Pope's astonishing variety. As the antithesis of triumphant Chaos it informs the prophetic vision of the close with that tremendously imaginative and moving grandeur.[1]

That close, of course, with its reminders of the century of Marvell and Donne, gives us a Pope who is more than Augustan. And in so doing it serves as an admonition against leaving an over-simplifying account of him uncorrected. Though it is his creativeness—for all his satiric bent, he is an essentially creative spirit—that puts Pope in so different a relation to Augustan culture from Swift's, his creativeness is not merely a matter of his being able to realize an ideal Augustan order. The contrast with Swift comes out in another way. The respect in which the two writers (who were closely associated in the brewing of the *Dunciad*) have most affinity is represented by the characteristic piece of Swift's prose which I quote at the foot of p. 79. Nowhere does the habit of mind and expression illustrated here come nearer, in Swift, to producing an effect in which the satisfaction of the creative impulse plainly predominates. Very often the negative and destructive functions of the play of images and analogies are much more insistent: the strangeness—'the most heterogeneous ideas are yoked by violence together'—is intensely malevolent, and the surprise is brutally shocking. How essentially negative, in this sense, the passage just quoted is comes out when we set it by any of Pope's in which his kindred habit asserts itself. Take this, for instance:

> And now had Fame's posterior Trumpet blown,
> And all the Nations summon'd to the Throne.
> The young, the old, who feel her inward sway,
> One instinct seizes, and transports away.
> None need a guide, by sure Attraction led,
> And strong impulsive gravity of Head:
> None want a place, for all their Centre found,
> Hung to the Goddess, and coher'd around.
> Not closer, orb in orb, conglob'd are seen
> The buzzing Bees about their dusky Queen.

The formal attitude here is one of satiric antipathy, but plainly the positive satisfaction taken by the poet in creating this marvellously organized complexity of surprising tropes, felicitously odd images, and profoundly imaginative puns, determines the predominant feeling,

[1] Cf. Leslie Stephen (*Pope*, p. 132): 'There are some passages marked by Pope's usual dexterity, but the whole is awkwardly constructed, and has no very intelligible connexion with the first part. It was highly admired at the time, and, amongst others, by Gray. He specially praises a passage which has often been quoted as representing Pope's highest achievement in his art. At the conclusion the goddess Dulness yawns, and a blight falls upon art, science and philosophy. I quote the lines, which Pope himself could not repeat without emotion, and which have received the highest eulogies from Johnson and Thackeray.'

which, in fact, might fairly be called genial. So again here in a simpler instance (the first that presents itself at a turn of the page):

> Ah, think not, Mistress! more true Dulness lies
> In Folly's Cap, than Wisdom's grave disguise.
> Like buoys, that never sink into the flood,
> On Learning's surface we but lie and nod.
> Thine is the genuine head of many a house.
> And much Divinity without a *Nous*.
> Nor could a BARROW work on ev'ry block,
> Nor has one ATTERBURY spoil'd the flock.
> See! still thy own, the heavy Canon roll,
> And Metaphysic smokes involve the Pole.

And in general, the same predominance of creativeness, delighting in the rich strangeness of what it contemplates, is to be found whenever Pope devotes himself to 'expressing' or 'ridiculing' (as we are expected to say, considering him as a satirist) the varied absurdities of the human scene.

> A Nest, a Toad, a Fungus, or a Flow'r

—here we have, typified in brief, the kind of effect he so obviously loves; and the line serves as a reminder that 'human scene' is too limiting in suggestion.

> The common Soul, of Heav'n's more frugal make,
> Serves but to keep fools pert, and knaves awake:
> A drowsy Watchman, that just gives a knock,
> And breaks our rest, to tell us what's a clock.
> Yet by some object ev'ry brain is stirr'd;
> The dull may waken to a Humming-bird;
> The most recluse, discreetly open'd, find
> Congenial matter in the Cockle-kind;
> The mind, in Metaphysics at a loss,
> May wander in a wilderness of Moss;
> The head that turns at super-lunar things,
> Pois'd with a tail, may steer on Wilkins' wings.

Pope's interest in the objects of absorbing contemplation which he ascribes to the 'virtuosi' he is satirizing may not be precisely theirs, but it is unmistakably a positive interest. What fascinates him are effects of fantastic incongruity; effects that at the same time seem to evoke a more exciting reality than that of common sense. And in creating these effects he is undoubtedly registering certain insistent qualities of experience as it came, good Augustan though he was, to him.

The relation between his interest in these qualities and his concern for Augustan order constitutes one of the most striking aspects of his genius. There is no hostility between them; they associate together harmoniously in a perfect creative alliance. What we find in the part, in the relation between vivid nightmare absurdity and the decorous Augustanism of the verse, we find in large in the totality of the poem.

Worked pregnantly in between the Augustan sublimities of the opening and the close, we have, not an ordered development of a corresponding theme, argument or action, but a packed heterogeneity that corresponds in the large to

A Nest, a Toad, a Fungus, or a Flow'r.

Into this can go with perfectly congruous incongruity a satirically straightforward piece of Augustan 'Sense':

> Then thus. 'Since Man from beast by Words is known,
> Words are Man's province, Words we teach alone.
> When Reason doubtful, like the Samian letter,
> Points him two ways, the narrower is the better.
> Plac'd at the door of Learning, youth to guide,
> We never suffer it to stand too wide.
> To ask, to guess, to know, as they commence,
> As Fancy opens the quick springs of Sense,
> We ply the Memory, we load the brain,
> Bind rebel Wit, and double chain on chain.
> Confine the thought, to exercise the breath;
> And keep them in the pale of Words till death.
> Whate'er the talents, or howe'er designed,
> We hang one jingling padlock on the mind.

Such a passage comes in so naturally and easily because of the pervasive rationality of the Augustan versification and idiom. And that Pope can use these as he does in evoking his fantastic incongruities shows that there is nothing repressive about the Order that commands his imagination. His sense of wonder has been richly and happily nourished, and can invest what offers itself as satiric fantasy with the enchantment of fairy-tale:

> Wide, and more wide, it spread o'er all the realm;
> Ev'n Palinurus nodded at the Helm. . .

His ability to unite Augustan with seventeenth-century Wit has profound concomitants.

*1952*

# PÄR LAGERKVIST

## *Barabbas*

EVERYONE knows how they hung there on the crosses, and who they were that stood gathered round him: Mary his mother and Mary Magdalene, Veronica, Simon of Cyrene, who carried the cross, and Joseph of Arimathea, who shrouded him. But a little further down the slope, rather to one side, a man was standing with his eyes riveted on the dying man in the middle, watching his death-throes from the first moment to the last. His name was Barabbas. This book is about him.

He was about thirty, powerfully built, with a sallow complexion, a reddish beard and black hair. His eyebrows also were black, his eyes too deep-set, as though they wanted to hide. Under one of them he had a deep scar that was lost to sight in his beard. But a man's appearance is of little consequence.

He had followed the mob through the streets all the way from the governor's palace, but at a distance, somewhat behind the others. When the exhausted rabbi had collapsed beneath his cross, he had stopped and stood still for a while to avoid catching up with the cross, and then they had got hold of that man Simon and forced him to carry it instead. There were not many men in the crowd, except the Roman soldiers of course; they were mostly women following the condemned man and a flock of urchins who were always there when anyone was led out along their street to be crucified—it made a change for them. But they soon tired and went back to their games, pausing a moment to glance at the man with the long scar down his cheek who was walking behind the others.

Now he was standing up here on the gallows hill looking at the man on the middle cross, unable to tear his eyes away. Actually he had not wanted to come up here at all, for everything was unclean, full of contagion; if a man set foot in this potent and accursed place part of him would surely remain, and he could be forced back there, never to leave it again. Skulls and bones lay scattered about everywhere, together with fallen, half-mouldering crosses, no longer of any use but left to lie there all the same, because no one would touch anything. Why was he standing here? He did not know this man, had nothing to do with him. What was he doing at Golgotha, he who had been released?

The crucified man's head hung down and he was breathing heavily, it would not be long now. There was nothing vigorous about the fellow. His body was lean and gaunt, the arms slender as though they had never been put to any use. A queer man. The beard was sparse and the chest quite hairless, like a boy's. He did not like him.

From the first moment he had seen him in the courtyard of the palace, he had felt there was something odd about him. What it was he could not say: it was just something he felt. He didn't remember ever having seen anyone like him before. Though it must have been because he came straight from the dungeon and his eyes were still unused to the glare. That is why at first glance the man seemed to be surrounded by a dazzling light. Soon afterwards the light vanished of course and his sight grew normal again and took in other things besides the figure standing out there alone in the courtyard. But he still thought there was something very strange about him and that he was not like anyone else. It seemed quite incredible that he was a prisoner and had been condemned to death, just as he himself had been. He could not grasp it. Not that it concerned him—but how could they pass a sentence like that? It was obvious he was innocent.

Then the man had been led out to be crucified—and he himself had been unshackled and told he was free. It was none of his doing. It was their business. They were quite at liberty to choose whomever they liked, and it just turned out that way. They had both been sentenced to death, but one of them was to be released. He was amazed himself at their choice. As they were freeing him from his chains he had seen the other man between the soldiers disappear through the archway, with the cross already on his back.

He had remained standing looking out through the empty arch. Then the guard had given him a push and bellowed at him:—What are you standing there gaping for, get out of here, you're free! And he had woken up and gone out through the same archway, and when he saw the other dragging his cross down the street he had followed behind him. Why, he did not know. Nor why he had stood here hour after hour watching the crucifixion and the long death agony, though it was nothing whatever to do with him.

Those standing round the cross up there surely need not have been here? Not unless they had wanted to. Nothing was forcing them to come along and defile themselves with uncleanness. But they were no doubt relations and close friends. Odd that they didn't seem to mind being made unclean.

That woman must be his mother. Though she was not like him. But who could be like him? She looked like a peasant woman, stern and morose, and she kept wiping the back of her hand across her mouth and nose, which was running because she was on the brink of tears. But she did not cry. She did not grieve in the same way as the others, nor did she look at him in the same way as they did. So it was evidently his mother. She probably felt far more sorry for him than they did, but even so she seemed to reproach him for hanging there, for having let himself be crucified. He must have done something to let himself in for it, however pure and innocent he was, and she just could not approve of it. She knew he was innocent because she was his mother. Whatever he had done she would have thought so.

He himself had no mother. And no father either for that matter; he had never even heard one mentioned. And he had no relations, as far as he knew. So if he had been the one to be crucified there would not have been many tears shed. Not like this. They were beating their breasts and carrying on as though they had never known the like of such grief, and there was an awful weeping and wailing the whole time.

He knew the one on the right-hand cross quite well. If by any chance the fellow saw him standing down here he probably thought it was because of him, in order to see him suffer well and truly. He wasn't, he was not here because of that at all. But he had nothing against seeing him crucified. If anyone deserved to die it was that scoundrel. Though not because of what he had been sentenced for, but because of something quite different.

But why was he looking at him and not at the one in the middle, who was hanging there in his stead? It was because of him he had come. This man had forced him up here, he had a strange power over him. Power? If anyone looked powerless, he did. Surely no one could look more wretched hanging on a cross; the other two didn't look a bit like that and didn't seem to be suffering as much as he was. They obviously had more strength left. He hadn't even the strength to hold his head up; it had flopped right down.

Now he did raise it a bit, all the same; the lean, hairless chest heaved with panting, and his tongue licked his parched lips. He groaned something about being thirsty. The soldiers who were sprawled over a game of dice a little further down the slope, bored because the men hanging there took so long to die, did not hear. But one of the relations went down and told them. A soldier got up reluctantly and dipped a sponge in a pitcher, passing it up to him on a stick, but when he tasted the fusty, tainted liquid offered him he did not want it. The wretch just stood there grinning, and when he rejoined his companions they all lay grinning at what had happened. The bastards!

The relations or whoever they were looked despairingly up at the crucified man, who was panting and panting; it was clear that he would soon give up the ghost. And just as well if the end came soon, Barabbas thought, so that the poor man would not have to suffer any more. If only the end would come! As soon as the end came he would hurry away and never think of this again! . . .

But all at once the whole hill grew dark, as though the light had gone out of the sun; it was pitch-dark, and in the darkness above, the crucified man cried out in a loud voice:

— My God, my God, why hast thou forsaken me?

It sounded horrible. Whatever did he mean? And why had it grown dark? It was the middle of the day. It was quite unaccountable.

The three crosses were just faintly visible up there, it looked weird. Something terrible was surely going to happen. The soldiers had leapt to their feet and grabbed their weapons—whatever happened they always rushed for their weapons. They stood there round the crosses with their lances, and he heard them whispering together in alarm. Now they were frightened! Now they were not grinning any longer! They were superstitious of course.

He was afraid himself. And glad when it began to get light and everything became a little more normal. It got light slowly, as it does at dawn. The daylight spread across the hill and the olive trees round about, and the birds that had been silent started twittering again. It was just like dawn.

The relations up there were standing so still. There was no longer any sound of weeping and lamentation from them. They just stood looking up at the man on the cross—even the soldiers did so. Everything had grown so still.

Now he could go whenever he liked. For it was all over now, and the sun shone again and everything was just as usual. It had only been dark for a while because the man died.

Yes, he would go now. Of course he would. He had nothing to stay for, not now that he, that other one, was dead. There was no longer any reason. They took him down from the cross—he saw before he went. The two men wrapped him in a clean linen cloth—he noticed. The body was quite white and they handled it so carefully, as if they were afraid they might hurt it however slightly, or cause it pain of any kind; they behaved so strangely. After all, he was crucified and everything. They were queer people, to be sure. But the mother stood with dry eyes looking at what had been her son, and the rough, dark-complexioned face seemed unable to express her sorrow, only the fact that she could not grasp what had happened and would never be able to forgive it. He understood her better.

As the sorry procession moved past some little distance from him, the men carrying the shrouded body and the women walking behind, one of the women whispered to the mother—pointing to Barabbas. She stopped short and gave him such a helpless and reproachful look that he knew he could never forget it. They went on down towards the Golgotha road and then turned off to the left.

He followed far enough behind for them not to notice him. In a garden a short distance away they laid the dead man in a tomb that was hewn out of the rock. And when they had prayed by the tomb they rolled a large stone in front of the entrance and went away.

He walked up to the tomb and stood there for a while. But he did not pray, for he was an evil-doer and his prayer would not have been accepted, especially as his crime was not expiated. Besides, he did not know the dead man. He stood there for a moment all the same.

Then he too went in towards Jerusalem.

INSIDE the Gate of David and a little way along the street he met the girl with the hare-lip. She was hugging the walls of the houses and pretended not to see him, but he noticed that she had done so and that she had not expected to see him again. Perhaps she thought he had been crucified.

He walked along behind her and then caught up with her,—and so it was they met. It need not have happened. He need not have spoken to her, and was himself surprised that he had done so. She too, from what he could make out. She glanced at him shyly when necessary.

They did not speak of what was in their minds, he merely asked her where she was going and if she had heard anything from Gilgal. She answered no more than was necessary and slurred her words as usual so that it was hard to catch what she said. She was not going anywhere, and when he asked where she lived she made no reply. He saw that her skirt hung in tatters round the hem and that her broad, dirty feet were bare. Their conversation lapsed and they walked on beside each other without a word.

From an open doorway like a black hole came the sound of loud voices, and just as they passed, a large fat woman came rushing out and shouted at Barabbas. She was tipsy and waved her fat arms with excitement and joy at seeing him, wanting him to come in without further ado. He hesitated and also seemed rather embarrassed by the presence of his strange companion, but she merely tugged at him and shoved them both inside. He was greeted with shouts by two men and three women whom he could not see at first, until his eyes had got used to the semi-darkness. They eagerly made room for him at the table, pouring out wine for him and all talking at once: about his having been let out of prison and being discharged and how damned lucky he was that the other one had been crucified in his place! They overflowed with wine and desire to share his good fortune, touching him to transfer it to themselves, and one of the women stuck her hand in under his body garment and touched his hairy chest, which made the fat woman roar with laughter.

Barabbas drank with them, but said little. He sat for the most part gazing in front of him with the dark brown eyes that were too deep-set, as though they wanted to hide. They thought he was a little queer. Though of course he was like that sometimes.

The women poured out more wine for him. He went on drinking and let them talk, joining very little in the conversation himself.

At last they began asking what was the matter with him, why he was like that. But the large fat woman put her arm round his neck and said that it wasn't any wonder he seemed a bit queer after lying chained up in a dungeon for so long, very nearly dead; if a man is sentenced to death, then he's dead, and if he's let out and reprieved he's still dead, because that's what he has been at any rate and he's only risen again from the dead, and that's not the same as living and being like the rest of us. And when they grinned at what she said, she lost her temper and said she would throw them all out except Barabbas and the girl with the hare-lip whom she knew nothing about but who looked good-natured she thought, though a bit simple. The two men nearly split their sides laughing at a woman who talked to them like that, but then they quietened down and began a whispered conversation with Barabbas, saying that they were going up into the mountains again tonight as soon as it was dark; they had only been down here to sacrifice a kid they had brought. It had not been accepted, so they had sold it and sacrificed two stainless doves instead. Then, having some money to spare, they had spent it on a good time at this fat woman's. They wondered when he would be back up there again and told him where their den was now. Barabbas nodded in understanding but made no answer.

One of the women had begun talking about the man who had been crucified in Barabbas's place. She had seen him once, though only as he was walking past, and people had said that he was a man learned in the scriptures who went about prophesying and performing miracles. There was no harm in that and there were many who did it, so of course it must have been something else he was crucified for. He was a skinny fellow, that was all she remembered. Another woman said that she had never seen him but had heard he was supposed to have said that the temple would collapse and Jerusalem be destroyed by an earthquake and then both heaven and earth would be consumed by fire. It sounded crazy, and it was not surprising that he had been crucified because of it. But the third said that he had mixed mostly with the poor and used to promise them that they would enter the kingdom of God; even the harlots, and that greatly amused them all, though they thought it was very nice provided it were true.

Barabbas listened to them and no longer seemed to be so far away, though he never so much as smiled. He gave a start when the fat woman again put her arm round his neck and said that she didn't care a fig who that other man was, he was dead now anyway. Anyway, it was he who had been crucified and not Barabbas, and that was the main thing.

The girl with the hare-lip had at first sat huddled up, to all appearances inattentive. She had then listened tensely to the description of that other man, and now acted rather strangely. Getting up, she stared at her companion from the street with an expression of horror in her pale, emaciated face, and exclaimed in her queer, snuffling voice:

— Barabbas!

It was nothing remarkable in itself, she only called him by his name, but they looked at her in amazement, unable to grasp what she meant by crying out like that. Barabbas too seemed strange, and his eyes kept shifting about as they did sometimes when he wanted to avoid looking at anyone. Why it was, they didn't understand; anyway it didn't matter, and it was best not to take any notice. For whatever one might say about Barabbas's being a good comrade and all that, he was a bit odd—one never really knew where one was with him.

She huddled up again on her bit of matting over on the earthen floor, but still went on looking at him with her burning eyes.

The fat woman went and got food for Barabbas. It struck her he must be starving; those dirty swine probably gave their prisoners nothing to eat. She set in front of him bread and salt and a piece of dried mutton. He ate but little, soon handing what was left across to the girl with the hare-lip, as though he were already satisfied. She threw herself on it and devoured it like an animal, then rushed out of the house: quite suddenly she was not there.

They ventured to ask what sort of woman she was, but of course got no answer. That was typical of him. He was always like that, secretive about his own affairs.

— What sort of miracles did he perform, that preacher, he said, turning to the women, and what did he preach about for that matter?

They said that he healed the sick and drove out evil spirits; he was supposed to have raised people from the dead too, but nobody knew if it was true, it couldn't be of course. What he preached about they had no idea. But one of them had heard a story he was supposed to have told about someone who arranged a big feast, a wedding or something, but no guests arrived, so they had to go out into the streets and invite just anybody, and all they could get were beggars and poor starving wretches who scarcely had a rag to their backs, and then the great lord got angry, or at any rate he said that it didn't matter—no she couldn't remember properly how it was. Barabbas seemed to be listening intently the whole time, as though they had related something quite extraordinary. And when one of the women said that he must have been one of those who believed themselves to be the Messiah, he stroked his great red beard and sat lost in thought. — The Messiah? . . . No, he wasn't the Messiah, he mumbled to himself.

— No of course he couldn't be, said one of the men, for then they would never have been able to crucify him, then those bastards themselves would have been struck to the ground. Didn't she know what a Messiah was!

— No of course! In that case he would have come down from the cross and slain the lot of them!

— A Messiah who lets himself be crucified! Did you ever hear the like!

Barabbas remained sitting with his beard in his big hand, looking down at the earthen floor. — No, he wasn't the Messiah. . . .

— Oh drink up now, Barabbas, and don't sit there muttering, said one of his confederates, poking him in the ribs—it was strange his daring to do so, but he did. And Barabbas actually took a draught from the earthenware beaker, putting it down again abstractedly. The women quickly filled it up again and got him to swallow another draught. The wine must have had some effect, but his thoughts still seemed to be elsewhere. The man gave him another prod with his elbow.

— Come now, have a drink and cheer up! Aren't you glad you're out of it and sitting here enjoying yourself among friends instead of hanging rotting on a cross? Isn't this better, eh? Aren't you having a good time here, eh? Think of that, Barabbas! You've saved your skin, you're alive! You're *alive*, Barabbas!

— Yes. Yes, of course, he said. Of course. . . .

In this way they gradually got him to stop staring into space like that and to become more normal. They sat drinking and talking for a while about one thing and another, and there was nothing queer about him any longer, they thought.

But in the middle of discussing this and that he asked a strange question. He asked them what they thought about the darkness today, when the light had gone out of the sun for a time.

— Darkness? What darkness? They looked at him in astonishment. It hadn't been dark had it? When?

— About the sixth hour?,

— Pshaw . . . what rubbish. No one had seen anything like that!

He looked incredulously from one to the other, quite bewildered. They all assured him they had not noticed any darkness, nor had anyone else in the whole of Jerusalem. Had he really thought it got *dark*? In the middle of the day! How very peculiar. But if he really had thought so, then it must be because there was something wrong with his eyes after lying shut up in the dungeon for so long. Yes, that's probably what it was. The fat woman said that of course it must be due to that, to the fact that his eyes had not got used to the light: that he had been blinded by the light for a while. And no wonder either.

He looked at them doubtfully—and then appeared relieved in some way. He straightened himself a little and reached out his hand for the beaker—took a deep draught out of it. And then instead of putting it back on the table, kept it in his hand and held it out for more. It was given to him instantly; they all drank, and he was clearly beginning to relish the wine in quite a different way. He drank as he normally did when it was offered and they could see it put him in a better mood. He did not grow especially communicative, but he did tell them something about what it had been like in prison. Yes, he'd had a hell of a time of course, no wonder he was a bit light-headed. But to think he had got out, eh! It wasn't so easy once they got their claws into you. What luck, eh! First that he had been there waiting to be crucified just at the Passover, when they usually release somebody. And then that it should have been he of all people! What infernal good luck! He thought so too, and when they pushed him and thumped him on the back and sprawled over him with their heated breath he smiled and drank with them, one after the other. He thawed as the wine rose to his head, and became more and more lively, loosening his body garment because of the heat, and lying down and making himself comfortable like the others. He was obviously enjoying himself. He even put his arm round the woman nearest him and pulled her towards him. She laughed and hung round his neck. But the fat woman took him from her and said that now her darling was really himself again, now he was as he should be and quite well again after that dreadful prison. And never again was he to go imagining things about any silly darkness, nonono, tuttuttut—she pulled him to her and made little caressing noises all over his face with her pouted lips, fondling the back of his neck with her fat fingers and playing with his red beard. They were all pleased at the change in him and that he was more himself, more like he could be sometimes when he was in a good mood. And now they all let themselves go wholeheartedly. They drank and gabbled and agreed about everything and found they were having a good time together, lying there inflaming themselves with the wine and with each other. The men, who had not tasted wine or seen a woman for several months, made up for it now; soon they would be going back to their mountains, they hadn't much time left—now they must really celebrate being in Jerusalem, and celebrate Barabbas's release! They got drunk on the strong, sour wine and amused themselves with all the women except the fat one, pulling them in one after the other behind a curtain further inside and coming back flushed and panting to resume their drinking and noise. They did everything thoroughly, as was their wont.

They continued in this way until it began to grow dark. Then the two men got up and said it was time they were going. Throwing their goat-skins over their shoulders and hiding their weapons under them, they said good-bye and crept out into the street, where it was already nearly dark. Soon afterwards the three women went and lay down behind the curtain, tipsy and utterly exhausted, and fell fast asleep. When the fat woman and Barabbas were thus left alone she asked if he didn't think it was about time they too enjoyed themselves together, if he wasn't in need of it after having been treated so badly. She for her part greatly fancied one who had languished so long in prison and so nearly been crucified. She took him up on to the roof, where she had a little arbour made of palm leaves for the hot time of the year. They lay down and she fondled him a little and he grew quite wild, wallowing in her fat body as though he never wanted to leave it. Half the night passed by without their being conscious of anything round them.

When at last they were quite spent she turned over on her side and fell asleep at once. He lay awake beside her sweaty body, looking up at the roof of the arbour. He thought of the man on the middle cross and of what had happened up there on the gallows hill. Then he began to wonder about that darkness, and whether it had really happened. Could it be as they said, merely something he had imagined? Or perhaps it was just something up there at Golgotha, as they had noticed nothing here in the city? Up there anyway it had been dark, the soldiers had been scared and one thing and another—or had he imagined that too? Had he just imagined the whole thing? No, he could not work it out, didn't know what to make of it. . . .

He thought of him again, the man on the cross. Lay with his eyes open, unable to sleep, feeling her fleshy body against him. Through the dry leaves in the roof he could see up into the sky—it must be the sky, although no stars were to be seen. Nothing but the darkness.

For now it was dark both at Golgotha and everywhere else.

NEXT day Barabbas walked about the city and met many whom he knew, both friend and foe. Most of them seemed surprised to see him, and one or two started as though they had seen a ghost. It gave him a nasty feeling. Didn't they know he had been released? When would they realize it—that it was not he who had been crucified?

The sun beat down, and it was extraordinary how hard it was to accustom his eyes properly to the glare. Perhaps something really had gone wrong with them during his time in prison? He preferred to keep in the shade, anyway. As he passed the colonnade in the street leading up to the temple he went in and sat under the arches to rest his eyes for a while. It felt good.

One or two men were already sitting huddled along the wall. They were talking in an undertone and seemed to resent his arrival, looking sideways at him and lowering their voices still more. He caught a word here and there but could make no sense of it; what of it anyway, he didn't care what secret dealings they had. One of them was a man of about his own age and with a red beard, too; the hair, also red, was long and tousled and joined the beard. The eyes were blue, which gave a curious, simple appearance, and the face was large and fleshy. Everything about him was large. He was a real rough diamond, an artisan judging from his hands and clothes. It didn't matter to Barabbas who he was or what he looked like, but he was the kind of man one couldn't help noticing, even though there was nothing whatever remarkable about him. Except that he had blue eyes of course.

The big man was upset, in fact they all were. They were evidently talking about someone who was dead; it seemed like it anyhow. Now and then they would all sigh heavily, men though they were. If that was really the case, if they were mourning someone, why didn't they leave the lamenting to women, to professional mourners?

Suddenly Barabbas heard that the dead man had been crucified, and that it had happened yesterday. Yesterday . . .?

He strained his ears to hear more, but they lowered their voices again and he could catch nothing.

Who was it they were talking about?

People were walking past out in the street and it was quite impossible to hear a word. When it was more or less quiet again, he made out enough to know it was as he thought—it was *him* they were talking about. He who . . .

How strange. . . . He had been thinking about him a while ago himself. He had happened to pass the archway leading into the courtyard, and this had brought him to mind. And when passing the spot where the cross had been too much for the man, he had also thought of him. And here they were sitting talking about that very man. . . . Strange. What had they to do with him? And why did they whisper the whole time? The big red-haired man was the only one who was audible occasionally; his body didn't seem suited to whispering.

Were they saying anything about . . . about the darkness! About its having grown dark when he died! . . .

He listened tensely, so eagerly that they must have noticed it. They suddenly fell completely silent, not uttering a word for a long time, merely sitting and looking at him out of the corners of their eyes. Then they whispered something amongst themselves which he couldn't catch. And after a while they took leave of the big man and went away. There were four of them; there was not one he liked the look of.

Barabbas was left sitting alone with the big man. He had half a mind to speak to him, but could not think how to begin. The man sat there pursing his lips, and now and then shaking his big head. As is the way with simple folk, he gave bodily expression to his troubles. At last Barabbas asked him outright what was worrying him. He looked up in perplexity with his round blue eyes without answering. But after gazing frankly at the stranger for a moment he asked if Barabbas was from Jerusalem. No, he wasn't. — But you seem to be from your speech? Barabbas replied that his home was not so far from here—away in the mountains to the east. The man evidently found this more reassuring. He didn't trust these people here in Jerusalem, not an inch, he made no bones about it; he was sure most of them were downright robbers and scoundrels. Barabbas gave a smile and quite agreed with him. And what about himself? Himself? Oh, his home was a long long way from here. His childlike eyes tried to express just how far away it was. And he wanted very much to be where he belonged, he confided ingenuously to Barabbas, not in Jerusalem or anywhere else in the world. But he didn't suppose he would ever get back to his native soil and live and die there as he had meant to do, as he had once imagined. Barabbas thought it sounded queer. Why not? he asked. Who was to stop him? Isn't every man his own master?

— Oh no, the big man replied musingly. That is not so.

What was he doing here then? Barabbas could not help asking. The big man did not answer at once, but then said uncertainly that it was because of his Master.

— Master?

— Yes. Had he not heard about the Master?

— No.

— Oh. About the one who was crucified yesterday on the hill of Golgotha?

— Crucified? No, he had not heard about it. Why?

— Because it was ordained that such a thing must come to pass.

— Ordained? Was it *ordained* that he was to be crucified?

— Yes indeed. It said so in the scriptures, and besides the Master himself had foretold it.

— Had he? And it said so in the scriptures? Well, personally he was not so familiar with them that he knew of it.

— No, nor am I. But that's how it is.

Barabbas did not doubt it. But how was it that his Master had to be crucified and what was the point of it anyway? It was all very strange.

— Yes . . . that's what I think. I can't see why he had to die. And in such a horrible way. But it had to be as he had prophesied. It must all come to pass as it was ordained. And he used to say so many times, the man added, bowing his great head, that he must suffer and die for us.

Barabbas glanced up at him.

— Die for us!

— Yes, in our stead. Suffer and die, innocent, in our stead. For you have to admit that we are the guilty ones, not he.

Barabbas sat gazing out into the street and asked no more for a time.

— It is easier now to understand what he meant, the other man said to himself.

— Did you know him well? Barabbas enquired.

— Yes indeed. Indeed I did. I was with him from the very first moment he began up there amongst us.

— Oh, did he come from the same part as you?

— And since then I've been with him the whole time, wherever he went.

— Why?

— Why? What a question. It's easy to see you don't know him.

— What do you mean?

— Well you see, he had power over one. A remarkable power. He would merely say to one: follow me! and one had to follow. There was nothing else to be done. Such was his power. If you had known him you would have experienced it. You too would simply have followed him.

Barabbas sat for a moment in silence. Then he said:

— Yes, he must have been an extraordinary man, if all you say is true. But surely the fact that he was crucified proved that he had no special power?

— Oh no, you're wrong there. I thought so too at first—and that's what is so terrible. That I could believe such a thing for one moment! But now I think I understand the meaning of his shameful death, now that I've thought things over a bit and talked to the others, who are more at home with the scriptures. You see, it's like this, he had to suffer all this, although he was innocent, he even had to descend into hell for our sakes. But he shall return and manifest all his glory. He is to rise again from the dead! We are quite sure of it.

— Rise again from the dead! What nonsense!

— It's not nonsense. Indeed he will. Many even think it will be tomorrow morning, for that is the third day. He is supposed to have said that he would remain in hell for three days—though *I* never heard him say so. But that's what he is supposed to have said. And at sunrise tomorrow . . .

Barabbas gave a shrug.

— Don't you believe it?

— No.

— No, no . . . how can you? . . . You who have never known him. But many of us believe. And why shouldn't he rise again himself when he has raised so many from the dead?

— Raised from the dead? That he never did!

— Yes indeed. I've seen it with my own eyes.

— Is it really true?

— Of course it's true. Indeed it is. So he has power all right. He has power to do anything, provided he wants to. If only he had used it for his own sake, but that he has never done. And why did he let himself be crucified if he had so much power . . .? Yes, yes, I know. . . . It's not easy to grasp, I grant you. I am a simple man, you see, it's not easy to understand all this, you may be sure.

— Are you not sure that he will rise again?

— Yes, yes, of course I am. I am quite sure it's true what they say. That the Master is to return and reveal himself to us in all his power and glory. I am quite certain of that—and they know the scriptures much better than I do. It will be a great moment. They even say that then the new age will begin, the happy age when the Son of Man will reign in his kingdom.

— The Son of Man?

— Yes. That's what he called himself.

— The Son of Man . . .?

— Yes. So he said. But some believe . . . No, I can't say it.

Barabbas moved closer to him.

— What do they believe?

— They believe . . . that he is God's own son.

— God's son!

— Yes. . . . But surely that can't be true, it's almost enough to make one afraid. I would really much rather he came back as he was.

Barabbas was quite worked up.

— How can they talk like that! he burst out. The son of God! The son of God crucified! Don't you see that's impossible!

— I said that it can't be true. And I'll gladly say it again if you like.

— What sort of lunatics are they who believe that! Barabbas went on, and the scar under his eye turned dark red, as it always did when there was anything the matter. The son of God! Of course he wasn't! Do you imagine the son of God comes down on to the earth! And starts going round preaching in your native countryside!

— Oh . . . why not? It's possible. As likely there as anywhere else. It's a humble part of the world, to be sure, but he had to begin somewhere.

The big fellow looked so ingenuous that Barabbas was inclined to smile, but he was far too worked up. He twisted and turned and twitched at his goat-hair mantle the whole time as though it had slipped off one shoulder, which it hadn't.

— And the wonders that occurred at his death, the other man said, have you thought of them?

— What wonders?

— Don't you know that it grew dark when he died?

Barabbas glanced away and rubbed his eyes for a moment.

— And that the earth quaked and the hill of Golgotha was rent asunder where the cross stood.

— It certainly was not! You've just made all that up! How do you know it was rent asunder? Were you there?

A sudden change came over the big man. He looked uncertainly at Barabbas and then down on the ground.

— No, no, I know nothing about it. I cannot testify to it, he stammered. And for a long time he sat silent, sighing deeply.

At last, laying his hand on Barabbas's arm, he said:

— You see . . . I was not with my Master when he suffered and died. By then I had taken to my heels. Forsaken him and fled. And before that I had even denied him. That is the very worst of all—that I *denied* him. How can he forgive me, if he returns? What shall I say, what shall I answer when he asks me about it?

And hiding his great bearded face in his hands, he rocked to and fro.

— How could I do such a thing? how is it possible for one to do such a thing? . . .

The bright-blue eyes were full of tears when at last he raised his head again and looked at the other man.

— You asked what was troubling me. Now you know. Now you know the kind of man I am. And my Lord and Master knows even better. I am a poor miserable wretch—do you think he can forgive me?

Barabbas answered that he thought so. He was not particularly interested in what the other man told him, but he said it all the same, partly by way of assent and partly because he could not help liking this man who sat there accusing himself like any criminal, though he had done nothing. Who hasn't let somebody else down in one way or another?

The man gripped his hand and held it tightly in his.

— Do you think so? Do you think so? he repeated in a thick voice.

At that moment a group of men walked past outside in the street. When they caught sight of the big red-haired man and saw who it was he sat talking to and holding by the hand, they started as though unable to believe their eyes. They hurried forward, and although approaching the shabbily dressed man in a curiously respectful way they burst out:

— Don't you know who that man is!

— No, he answered truthfully, I don't know. But he is a kind-hearted man and we have had a good talk together.

— Don't you know that it was in place of him that the Master was crucified!

The big man released Barabbas's hand and looked from one to the other, unable to conceal his dismay. The newcomers showed their feelings even more plainly, breathing violently in agitation.

Barabbas had got to his feet and was standing with his back turned so that his face was no longer visible.

— Get thee hence, thou reprobate! they said to him fiercely.

And pulling his mantle about him, Barabbas walked off down the street alone without looking back.

THE girl with the hare-lip was unable to sleep. She lay looking up at the stars and thought of what was soon to come to pass. No, she did not want to fall asleep, she wanted to keep watch this night.

She was lying on some twigs and straw she had gathered in a hollow outside the Dung Gate, and round her she could hear the sick groaning and moving restlessly in their sleep and the tinkle of the leper's bells, the one who sometimes got up and walked about because of the pain. The stench of the large refuse-heaps filled the whole valley and made it difficult to breathe, but she was so used to it that she no longer noticed it. No one here noticed it any longer.

Tomorrow at sunrise . . . Tomorrow at sunrise . . .

What a strange thought—soon all the sick would be well and all the starving be fed. It was almost beyond belief. How would it all come about? But soon the heavens would open and the angels descend and feed them all—at least all the poor. The rich would no doubt continue to eat in their own houses, but the poor, all those who were really hungry, would be given food by angels, and here by the Dung Gate cloths would be spread out over the ground, white linen cloths, and food of all kinds would be laid out on them and everyone would lie down and eat. It wasn't really so very hard to imagine if one just thought that everything would be completely different from what it was now. Nothing would be like anything one had seen or experienced before.

Perhaps she too would be in other clothes, one never knew. White possibly. Or perhaps in a blue skirt? Everything would be so different because the son of God was risen from the dead and the new age had dawned.

She lay thinking of it all, of how it would be.

Tomorrow . . . Tomorrow at sunrise . . . She was glad she had been told about it.

The leper's bells sounded closer at hand. She recognized them; he usually made his way up here of a night, though it was not allowed; they had to keep inside their enclosure at the very bottom of the valley, but now in the night-time he took the risk. It was as if he sought human companionship and for that matter he had once said that was the reason. She saw him picking his way between the sleepers in the starlight.

The realm of the dead . . . what was it like there really? They said that he was now wandering about in the realm of the dead. . . . What did it look like? No, she had no idea. . . .

The old blind man moaned in his sleep. And a little further away the emaciated young man lay panting, the one who could always be heard. Quite near her lay the Galilean woman, whose arm twitched because she had someone else's spirit in her. There were many round her who thought they would be made whole by the mud in the spring, and there were poor wretches who lived on refuse from the tip-heaps. But tomorrow no one would go rooting about there any more. They lay twisting in their sleep, but she was not sorry for them any more.

Perhaps the water would be purified by an angel breathing on it? And they would really be healed when they stepped down into it? Perhaps even the lepers would be healed? But would they be allowed to step down into the spring? Would they really? One didn't know for sure how it would be. . . . No, one knew very little really. . . .

Perhaps nothing would happen to the spring and no one even bother about it. Perhaps the angelic hosts would float along through the whole Ge-Hinnom valley and over all the earth, sweeping away disease and sorrow and misfortune with their wings!

She lay thinking that perhaps that was how it would be.

Then she thought of that time when she met the son of God. Of how kind he had been to her. Never had anyone been so kind to her. She might well have asked him to cure her of her deformity, but she didn't want to. It would have been easy for him to do so, but she didn't want to ask him. He helped those who really needed help; his were the very great deeds. She would not trouble him with so little.

But it was odd, very odd, what he had said to her as she knelt there in the dust by the wayside, when he had turned and walked back to her.

— Do you too expect miracles of me? he asked.

— No, Lord, I don't. I only watched you as you passed.

Then he had given her such a tender yet sorrowful look, and he had stroked her cheek and touched her mouth without anything at all happening to it. And then he had said: You shall bear witness for me.

How strange. What did he mean? Bear witness for me? She? It was incredible. How could she?

He had had no difficulty at all in understanding what she said, as everyone else did, he had understood at once. But it was not surprising, seeing that he was the son of God.

All kinds of thoughts came to her as she lay there. The expression of his eyes as he spoke to her and the smell of his hand as he touched her mouth. . . . The stars were reflected in her wide-open eyes, and she thought how strange it was that there were more and more the longer she gazed up into the sky. Since she had stopped living in a house she had seen so many stars . . . just what were stars anyway? She didn't know. They were created by God of course, but what they were she didn't know. . . . Out in the desert there had been a lot of stars. . . . And up in the mountains . . . in the mountains at Gilgal. . . . But not *that* night; no, not *that* night. . . .

Then she thought of the house between the two cedar-trees. . . . Her mother standing in the doorway looking after her as she walked down the hill with the curse over her. . . . Oh yes, naturally they had to turn her out and she had to live like the animals in their lairs. . . . She remembered how green the fields were that spring, and her mother standing looking after her just inside the darkened doorway to avoid being seen by the man who had uttered the curse. . . .

But it didn't matter now. Nothing mattered now.

The blind man sat up and listened, he had woken up and heard the tinkling of the leper's bells.

— Be off with you! he shouted, shaking his fist at him in the darkness. Go away! What are you doing here!

The sound of the bells died away in the night and the old man lay down again, mumbling, with his hand over his vacant eyes.

Are children who are dead also in the realm of the dead? Yes, but surely not those who die before they leave the womb? It was not possible, surely? They couldn't suffer there in torment, it couldn't be like that surely? Though she didn't know for certain. . . . Didn't know for certain about anything. . . . —Cursed be the fruit of thy loins. . . .

But now with the dawning of the new age perhaps all curses were lifted of themselves? It might well be. . . . Though one couldn't be sure. . . .

Cursed . . . be . . . the fruit of thy loins. . . .

She shivered, as though with the cold. How she longed for the morning! Wouldn't it be soon now? She had been lying here for so long; was not the night nearly over? Yes, the stars above her were no longer the same, and the crescent moon had long since gone down behind the hills. The guard had been changed for the last time—three times now she had seen the torches up on the city walls. Yes, the night must be over. The last night. . . .

Now the morning star was rising over the Mount of Olives! She recognized it at once, it was so big and clear, much bigger than all the others. Never before had she seen it shine like this. Folding her hands across her sunken breast, she lay looking up at it for a while with her burning eyes.

Then she got up swiftly and hurried away into the darkness.

He was lying crouched behind a tamarisk bush on the other side of the road, opposite the sepulchre. When it grew light he would be able to see across to it. He would have a good view of it from here. If only the sun would rise!

True, he knew that the dead man would not rise from the dead, but he wanted to see it with his own eyes to make quite sure. That was why he had got up very early, long before sunrise, and lain in wait here behind the bush. Though up to a point he was rather surprised at himself for having done so, for being here. Why was he bothering his head so much about it anyway? What had it really got to do with him?

He had expected several to be here to witness the great miracle. That was why he had hidden himself, to avoid being seen by them. But there was obviously no one else here. It was odd.

Yes, now he could make out someone kneeling a little in front of him, in the very road it seemed. Who could it be, and how had it happened; he had not heard anyone come. It looked like a woman. The grey figure was hardly discernible as it knelt there in the dust it resembled.

Now it was getting light, and soon the first rays of the sun were thrown on to the rock out of which the sepulchre was carved. It all happened so quickly that he couldn't quite follow it—now of all times when he really should have had his wits about him! The sepulchre was empty! The stone was rolled away on the ground below and the carved-out space in the rock empty!

At first he was so amazed that he merely lay staring at the opening into which he had himself seen them put the crucified man, and at the great stone which he had seen them roll in front of it. But then he realized what it was all about. Nothing had happened in actual fact. The stone had been rolled away the whole time, before ever he came, and the sepulchre had been empty even then. Who had rolled it aside and who had made off with the dead man was not hard to guess. The disciples had of course done it some time during the night. Under cover of darkness they had carried off their adored and beloved Master so as to be able to say later that he had risen from the dead just as he had predicted. It wasn't hard to work that out.

That was why there was no sign of them here this morning, at sunrise, when the miracle should really have happened. Now they were keeping out of the way!

Barabbas crept out of his hiding-place and went to inspect the sepulchre properly. As he passed the grey kneeling figure in the road he glanced down and saw to his amazement that it was the girl with the hare-lip. He stopped short—remained standing, looking down at her. Her starved ashen face was turned towards the empty sepulchre and her ecstatic eyes saw nothing else. Her lips were parted but she scarcely breathed; the disfiguring scar in her upper-lip was quite white. She did not see him.

It gave him a peculiar feeling, almost of shame, to see her like this. And he recalled something, something he didn't want to recall—that was how her face had looked then. Just as he had also had a feeling of shame then. . . . He shook himself free of it.

At last she noticed him. She too seemed surprised at the meeting, that he should be here. It wasn't to be wondered at—he was surprised himself at his being here. What business was it of his?

Barabbas would have liked to pretend that he had simply been walking along the road, that he had been passing by pure chance and had no idea what place this was and that there was a sepulchre here. Could he pretend? It would seem rather far-fetched perhaps, she might not believe him, but he said all the same:—Why are you kneeling there like that?

The girl with the hare-lip neither looked up nor moved, just went on kneeling as before with her eyes turned towards the opening in the rock. He barely heard her whisper to herself:

— The son of God is risen. . . .

It gave him a queer feeling to hear her say it. Against his will he felt something—he couldn't make out what. He stood there for a moment not knowing what to say or do. Then he went up to the sepulchre, as he had thought of doing, and made sure it was empty—but he knew that already and it meant nothing one way or the other. Then he went back to where she was kneeling. Her face was so reverent and full of rapture that he really felt sorry for her. There was no truth at all in this thing that made her happy. He could have told her all about this resurrection—but hadn't he done her enough harm already? He could not bring himself to tell her the truth. He asked her cautiously how she thought it had come to pass, how the crucified man had risen from the grave.

She looked up at him for a moment in surprise. Didn't he know? But then in her snuffling voice she described rapturously and in detail how an angel in a mantle of fire had come rushing down from heaven with arm outstretched like the point of a spear. And the spear had been thrust in between the stone and the rock and parted them. It sounded as simple as could be and it was too, although it was a miracle. That's how it had happened. Had he not seen it?

Barabbas looked down and said that he had not, and deep down inside he thought how very pleased he was not to have seen it. It showed that his eyes were all right now, like everybody else's eyes, that he no longer saw any visions but only reality itself. That man had no power over him any more; he had not witnessed any resurrection or anything. But the girl with the hare-lip still knelt there, her eyes radiant with the memory of what she had seen.

When at last she got to her feet to move away, they walked together some of the way in towards the city. They said little, but he did find out that after they had left each other that time, she had come to believe in this man she called the son of God and whom he just called the dead man. But when he asked what it was this man really taught, she was reluctant to answer. She looked away and avoided his glance. When they reached the parting of the ways—she was evidently going to take the road leading down to the valley of Ge-Hinnom while he thought of going on to the Gate of David—he asked her again what the doctrine was that he preached and which she believed in, though actually it was no concern of his. She stood for a moment looking down on the ground; then giving him a shy look she said in her slurring voice:

— Love one another.

And so they parted.

Barabbas stood for a long time gazing after her.

BARABBAS kept asking himself why he stayed on in Jerusalem when he had nothing to do there. He merely drifted about the city to no purpose, without turning his hands to anything. And he supposed that up in the mountains they were wondering why he was so long. Why did he stay? He didn't know himself.

The fat woman thought at first that it was because of her, but she soon realized it wasn't. She felt rather piqued, but heavens above, men are always ungrateful when they get what they want all the time, and she did have him sleeping with her and she liked that. It was lovely to have a real man for a bit and one it was nice to fondle. And there was one thing about Barabbas, even if he didn't care for you, he didn't care for anyone else either, you could always be sure of that. He didn't care for anybody. He never had. And besides—up to a point she was rather glad he didn't care for her. At any rate, while he was making love to her. Afterwards she sometimes felt a bit miserable and had a little cry all to herself. But actually she didn't mind that either. Even that could feel nice. She had great experience of love and did not disdain it in any form.

But why he mooned about here in Jerusalem was more than she could imagine. Or what he found to do all day long. It wasn't as if he were one of those good-for-nothings who stood loafing about the streets, he was a man who had always been used to an active, dangerous life. It wasn't like him to dawdle round doing nothing in this way.

No, he wasn't really himself since that happened—since he was nearly crucified. He seemed to find it hard somehow to get used to the fact that he hadn't been, she told herself with a loud laugh as she lay during the worst of the midday heat with her hands across her big belly.

Barabbas could not avoid sometimes running into the followers of the crucified rabbi. No one could say that he did so deliberately; but there were a number of them here and there in the streets and market-places, and if he encountered them he liked to stop and talk for a while and ask them about him and that queer doctrine which he couldn't make head or tail of. Love one another? . . . He steered clear of the temple square and the fashionable streets round about and kept to the alley-ways of the lower city, where the craftsmen sat working in their shops and the hawkers cried their wares. There were many believers among these simple folk and Barabbas liked them better than those he had met up in the colonnade. He got to know something of their peculiar ideas, but he never seemed to get anywhere with them personally or understand them properly—it may have been because they expressed themselves so foolishly. They were firmly convinced that their Master had risen from the dead and that he would soon come at the head of the heavenly hosts and establish his kingdom. They all said the same, it was evidently what they had been taught. But they were not all equally sure that he was the son of God. Some thought it strange if he really were, because they themselves had both seen and heard him, even spoken to him for that matter. And one of them had made a pair of sandals for him and taken his measurements and everything. No, they found that hard to imagine. But there were many who declared that he was, and that he would sit on the heavenly throne beside the Father. But first this sinful and imperfect world would be destroyed.

What kind of queer people were they?

They noticed that he didn't for a moment believe as they did, and were on their guard against him. Some were downright suspicious and they nearly all showed that they didn't particularly like him. Barabbas was used to that, but oddly enough this time he took it to heart—which he had never done before. People had always kept out of his way and shown that they would rather not have anything to do with him. Perhaps it was because of his appearance, perhaps the knife-wound deep down into his beard which no one knew the cause of, perhaps the eyes that were so deep-set that no one could see them properly. Barabbas was quite well aware of all that, but it didn't matter to him what people thought! He had never bothered about it.

He had not known until now that it rankled.

They for their part kept together in every way through their common faith, and were very careful not to let anyone in who did not belong. They had their brotherhood and their love feasts, when they broke bread together as if they were one big family. It was probably all part and parcel of their doctrine, with their 'love one another'. But whether they loved anyone who was not one of themselves was hard to say.

Barabbas had no wish to take part in such a love feast, not the slightest; he was put off by the very thought of such a thing, of being tied to others in that way. He wanted always to be himself and nothing else.

But he sought them out all the same.

He even pretended that he wanted to become one of them—if only he could understand their faith properly. They answered that it would make them happy and that they would gladly try to explain their Master's doctrine to him as well as they could, but in point of fact they did not appear glad. It was most odd. They reproached themselves for not being able to feel any real joy at his advances, at perhaps gaining a new fellow-believer—a thing which normally made them so happy. What could be the reason for it? But Barabbas knew why. Getting up suddenly, he strode away, the scar under his eye crimson.

Believe! How could he believe in that man he had seen hanging on a cross! That body which was long ago quite dead and which he had proved with his own eyes had not been resurrected! It was only their imagination! The whole thing was only their imagination! There wasn't anyone who rose from the dead, either their adored 'Master' or anyone else! And besides, he, Barabbas, could hardly be blamed for their choice! That was their business! They could have chosen anyone at all, but it just turned out that way. The son of God! As if he could be the son of God! But supposing he were, there was surely no need for him to have been crucified if he had not wanted to be. He must have wanted it himself! There was something weird and horrid about it—he must have *wanted* to suffer. For if he really was the son of God, it would have been the easiest thing in the world to get out of it. But he didn't *want* to get out of it. He wanted to suffer and die in that dreadful way and not be spared; and so it had been, he had got his own way about not being let off. He had let him, Barabbas, go free, instead. He had commanded: Release this man and crucify me.

Though of course he was not the son of God, that was obvious. . . .

He had used his power in the most extraordinary way. Used it by not using it, as it were; allowed others to decide exactly as they liked; refrained from interfering and yet had got his own way all the same, to be crucified instead of Barabbas.

They spoke of his having died for *them*. That might be. But he really had died for Barabbas, no one could deny it! In actual fact he was closer to him than they were, closer than anyone else, was bound up with him in quite another way. Although they didn't want to have anything to do with him! He was chosen, one might say—chosen to escape suffering, to be let off. He was the real chosen one, acquitted instead by the son of God himself—at his command, because he wished it. Though they suspected nothing!

But he didn't care for their 'brotherhood' and their 'love feasts' and their 'love one another'. He was himself. In his relationship to that crucified man they called the son of God he was also himself, as always. He was no serf under him as they were. Not one of those who went round sighing and praying to him.

How can one *want* to suffer: when there's no need, when one's not forced to? That sort of thing is beyond belief and the mere thought of it almost enough to turn the stomach. When he thought of it he could see before him the lean, miserable body with arms hardly strong enough to hang by and the mouth that was so parched that it was all it could do to ask for a little water. No, he didn't like anyone who sought out suffering in that way, one who hung himself up on a cross. He didn't like him at all! But they adored their crucified one and his suffering, his pitiable death, which could probably never be pitiable enough for them. They adored death itself. It was horrid, it filled him with disgust. It put him right off both them and their doctrine and the one they said they believed in.

No, he didn't like death, not one bit. He loathed it and would much rather never die. Perhaps that was why he didn't have to? Why he had been chosen to be let off it? Supposing the crucified man really was the son of God, why then he knew everything and was quite well aware that he, Barabbas, did not want to die, either suffer or die. And so he had done so in his stead! And all Barabbas had had to do was to go with him up to Golgotha and see him crucified. That was all that was asked of him and even that he had thought difficult, disliking death as he did and everything connected with it.

Yes, he was indeed the one the son of God had died for! It was of him and no other that it had been said: Release this man and crucify me!

Such were Barabbas's thoughts as he walked away after trying to be one of them, as he strode away from the potter's workshop in Potters' Lane, where they had so plainly shown that they did not want him among them.

And he decided to go and see them no more.

But next day, when he turned up again notwithstanding, they asked what it was in their faith that he didn't understand; showing clearly that they felt sorry and reproached themselves for not having welcomed him properly and been glad to give him the knowledge for which he was thirsting. What was it he wanted to ask them about? That he didn't understand?

Barabbas was on the point of shrugging his shoulders and replying that the whole thing was a mystery to him and in fact he couldn't be bothered with it. But then he mentioned that a thing like the resurrection, for instance, he found hard to grasp. He didn't believe that there was anyone who had risen from the dead.

Glancing up from their potters' wheels, they looked first at him and then at each other. And after whispering amongst themselves the eldest among them asked if he would like to meet a man whom their Master had raised from the dead? If so they could arrange it, but not till the evening, after work, as he lived some little way outside Jerusalem.

Barabbas was afraid. This was not what he had expected. He had imagined they would argue about it and put forward their point of view, not try to prove it in such a pushing way. True, he was convinced that the whole thing was some queer fancy, a pious swindle, and that actually the man had not been dead. He was afraid all the same. He didn't in the least want to meet the man. But he couldn't very well say so. He must pretend he was grateful for the chance of convincing himself of their Lord and Master's power.

He put in time by walking about the streets in a state of mounting agitation. When he returned to the workshop at closing-time, a young man accompanied him out through the city gates and up towards the Mount of Olives.

The man they sought lived on the outskirts of a little village on the slopes of the mountain. When the young potter drew aside the straw mat over the doorway they saw him sitting inside with his arms in front of him on the table and gazing straight out into the room. He seemed not to notice them until the young man greeted him in his clear voice. Then he slowly turned his head towards the door and returned their greeting in a curiously flat tone. The young man having given him a message from the brethren in Potters' Lane and stated their errand, they were invited with a movement of the hand to sit down at the table.

Barabbas sat opposite to him and was drawn to examine his face. It was sallow and seemed as hard as bone. The skin was completely parched. Barabbas had never thought a face could look like that and he had never seen anything so desolate. It was like a desert.

To the young man's question the man replied that it was quite true that he had been dead and brought back to life by the rabbi from Galilee, their Master. He had lain in the grave for four days and nights, but his physical and mental powers were the same as before, nothing had altered as far as they were concerned. And because of this the Master had proved his power and glory and that he was the son of God. He spoke slowly in a monotone, looking at Barabbas the whole time with his pale, lack-lustre eyes.

When he had finished, they continued talking for a while about the Master and his great deeds. Barabbas took no part in the conversation. Then the young man got up and left them to go and see his parents, who lived in the same village.

Barabbas had no wish to be left alone with the man, but he could think of no pretext for abruptly taking his leave. The man looked steadily at him with the queer opaque eyes that expressed nothing at all, least of all any interest in him, but which nevertheless pulled Barabbas towards him in some inexplicable way. He would have liked to make his escape, tear himself away and escape, but he could not.

The man sat for some time without speaking. Then he asked Barabbas if he believed in their rabbi, that he was the son of God. Barabbas hesitated, then answered no, for it felt so odd to lie to those vacant eyes which didn't seem to mind in the least whether one lied or not. The man took no offence, merely said with a nod:

— No, there are many who don't. His mother, who was here yesterday, doesn't believe either. But he raised me from the dead because I am to witness for him.

Barabbas said that in that case it was only natural he should believe in him, and that he must be eternally grateful to him for the great miracle he had wrought. The man said, yes, he was, he thanked him every day for having brought him back to life, for the fact that he belonged to the realm of the dead no longer.

— The realm of the dead? Barabbas exclaimed, noticing that his voice trembled slightly. The realm of the dead? . . . What is it like there? You who have been there! Tell me what it's like!

— What it's like? the man said, looking at him questioningly. He clearly didn't quite understand what the other meant.

— Yes! What *is* it? This thing you have experienced?

— I have experienced nothing, the man answered, as though disapproving of the other's violence. I have merely been dead. And death is nothing.

— Nothing?

— No. What should it be?

Barabbas stared at him.

— Do you mean you want me to tell you something about the realm of the dead? I cannot. The realm of the dead isn't anything. It exists—but it isn't anything.

Barabbas could only stare at him. The desolate face frightened him, but he could not tear his eyes away from it.

— No, the man said, looking past him with his empty gaze, the realm of the dead isn't anything. But to those who have been there, nothing else is anything either.

— It is strange your asking such a thing, he went on. Why did you? They don't usually.

And he told him that the brethren in Jerusalem often sent people there to be converted, and indeed many had been. In that way he served the Master and repaid something of his great debt for having been restored to life. Almost every day someone was brought by this young man or one of the others and he testified to his resurrection. But of the realm of the dead he never spoke. It was the first time anyone had wanted to hear about it.

It was growing dark in the room, and getting up he lighted an oil lamp that hung from the low ceiling. Then he got out bread and salt, which he placed on the table between them. He broke the bread and passed some to Barabbas, dipping his own piece in the salt and inviting Barabbas to do the same. Barabbas had to do likewise, though he felt his hand shaking. They sat there in silence in the feeble light from the oil lamp, eating together.

*This* man had nothing against eating a love feast with him! He was not so particular as the brethren in Potters' Lane, and made but little distinction between one man and another! But when the dry, yellow fingers passed him the broken bread and he had to eat it, he imagined his mouth was filled with the taste of corpse.

Anyway, what did it mean, his eating with him like this? What was the hidden significance of this strange meal?

When they had finished, the man went with him to the door and bade him go in peace. Barabbas mumbled something and hastily took his leave. He strode rapidly out into the darkness and down the mountain-side, thoughts pounding in his head.

The fat woman was joyously surprised at his violence as he took her; it was with no little zest he did it this evening. What caused it she didn't know, but tonight it seemed as if he really needed something to hold on to. And if anyone could give that to him, she could. She lay dreaming she was young again, and that someone loved her. . . .

Next day he kept clear of the lower part of the city and Potters' Lane, but one of them from the workshop there ran into him up in Solomon's colonnade and immediately asked how it was yesterday, whether it was not true what they had said? He answered that he did not doubt that the man he had visited had been dead and then resurrected, but that to his way of thinking their Master had had no right to raise him from the dead. The potter was dumbfounded, his face turning almost ashen at this insult to their Lord, but Barabbas merely turned his back and let him go.

It must have become known not only in Potters' Lane, but in the oil-pressers', the tanners', the weavers' lanes, and all the others; for when Barabbas, as time went on, went there again as usual, he noticed that the believers he usually talked to were not at all as before. They were taciturn, and looked at him suspiciously the whole time out of the corners of their eyes. There had never been any intimacy between them, but now they openly showed their mistrust. In fact, a wizened little man whom he didn't even know tugged at him and asked why he was for ever mixing with them, what he wanted of them, whether he was sent by the temple guard or the high priest's guard or perhaps by the Sadducees? Barabbas stood there speechless, looking at the little old man, whose bald head was quite red with rage. He had never seen him before and had no idea who he was, except that he was obviously a dyer, judging from the red and blue strands of wool stuck through holes in his ears.

Barabbas realized that he had offended them and that their feelings towards him were quite changed. He was met with snubs and stony faces wherever he went, and some stared hard at him as if to make clear to him that they intended finding out who he was. But he pretended to take no notice.

Then one day it happened. It ran like wildfire through all the lanes where the faithful lived, suddenly there was not one who didn't know it. It is *he*! It is *he*! He who was released in the Master's stead! In the Saviour's, in God's son's stead! It is Barabbas! It's Barabbas the acquitted!

Hostile glances pursued him, hate gleamed from smouldering eyes. It was a frenzy which did not even abate after he had vanished from their sight, never to show himself there again.

— Barabbas the acquitted! Barabbas the acquitted!

HE crept into his shell now and didn't speak to a soul. For that matter, he hardly ever went out; just lay inside the curtain at the fat woman's or in the arbour up on the roof when there was too much of a hubbub in the house. Day after day he would spend in this manner, without occupying himself in any way whatsoever. He scarcely bothered about eating, at least he wouldn't have done if food had not been put before him and his attention drawn to it. He seemed utterly indifferent to everything.

The fat woman could not make out what was wrong with him, it was beyond her. Nor did she dare ask either. It was best to leave him in peace, which was what he seemed to want. He barely answered when spoken to, and if one peeped cautiously inside the curtain now and again, he merely lay there staring up at the ceiling. No, it was quite beyond her. Was he going off his head? Losing his reason? It was more than she could say.

Then she hit on it. It was when she overheard that he had been mixing with those lunatics who believed in the fellow who had been crucified when Barabbas himself should have been! Then it dawned on her! No wonder he had grown a bit queer. They were the cause of it. They of course had been filling his head with their crazy notions. It was enough to make anyone touched, going about with half-wits like them. They thought that that crucified man was some sort of saviour or whatever it was, who was to help them in some way and give them everything they asked for, and wasn't he to be king in Jerusalem too and send the beardless devils packing; oh she didn't really know what it was they taught and she didn't care either, but they were barmy, everyone knew that. How in heaven's name could he go and get tied up with them? What had he to do with them? Yes! Now she had it! He himself was to have been crucified, but then he hadn't been, their saviour had been instead, and that was terrible of course, he had to try to explain it and so on, that it wasn't his fault and so on, and then they had kept on talking of how remarkable that fellow was that they believed in, how pure and innocent and what an important person if you please and how awful it was to treat such a great king and lord in that way, had in fact filled his head with all sorts of stuff and nonsense, until he had gone quite daft because he wasn't dead, because it wasn't he who was dead. That was it of course, that's what had happened of course!

She might have known it was because he had not been crucified! The simpleton! She really had to laugh, laugh outright at her silly old Barabbas. He was too funny for words. Yes, that's what it was all about of course.

But even so it was about time he pulled himself together and listened to reason. She'd have a talk to him, that she would. What's all this nonsense?

But she didn't have a talk to him. She meant to, but nothing ever came of it. For some reason one didn't start talking to Barabbas about himself. One meant to perhaps, but could never bring oneself to do it.

So things went on as before, with her going round wondering what on earth was the matter with him. Was he ill? Perhaps he was ill? He had got thin, and the scar from the knife-wound that that Eliahu had given him was the only spot of colour in the wan, hollow face. He was a sorry sight, not at all his usual self. Not at all his usual self in any way—it wasn't like him to go mooning about like this, to lie staring up at the ceiling. Barabbas! A man like Barabbas!

Supposing it was not *he*? Supposing he'd become someone else, was possessed by someone else, by someone else's spirit! Just think if he were no longer himself! It certainly seemed like it! By that other man's spirit! He who really had been crucified! And who certainly wished him no good. Fancy if that 'saviour' when he gave up the ghost breathed it into Barabbas instead, so as not to have to die and so as to be avenged for the wrong that had been done him, be avenged on the one who was acquitted! It was quite possible! And when one came to think of it, Barabbas had been queer like this ever since then! yes, she remembered his strange behaviour when he had come in here just after his release. Yes, that's what it was all right, and that explained everything. The only thing that wasn't quite clear was how the rabbi had managed to breathe his spirit into Barabbas, for he had given up the ghost at Golgotha and Barabbas had not been there. But then if he was as powerful as they made out, he could probably do even that, could make himself invisible and go wherever he wanted. He no doubt had the power to get exactly what he wanted.

Did Barabbas himself know what had happened to him, that he had someone else's spirit in him? That he himself was dead but that the crucified man was alive in him? Did he?

Perhaps he suspected nothing; but it was easy to see he was the worse for it. And no wonder either, it was someone else's spirit and it wished him no good.

She felt sorry for him, she could hardly bear to look at him she felt so sorry for him. He for his part never looked at her at all, but that was because he couldn't be bothered. He took no notice of her at all, not the slightest, so it was no wonder he didn't look at her. And he never wanted her any more at nights, that was the worst of all; it showed more than anything else that he couldn't be bothered with her. It was only she who was stupid enough to cling to this poor wretch. She would lie crying to herself of a night, but now it didn't feel a bit nice. Strange . . . She never thought to experience anything like that again.

How was she to get him back? How was she to cast out the crucified man and get Barabbas to be Barabbas again? She had no idea how you cast out spirits. She knew nothing at all about it, and this was a powerful and dangerous spirit, she could see that; she was almost afraid of it, though normally she was not of a timid nature. You only had to look at Barabbas to see how powerful it was, how it just took complete control of a big strong man who was alive himself until a short time ago. It was beyond her. No wonder she felt a bit scared. It was sure to be specially powerful having belonged to a crucified man.

No, she wasn't afraid exactly. But she didn't like crucified people. It was not in her line. She had a large, generously proportioned body, and the one that suited her was Barabbas. Barabbas as he was *himself*. Such as he was before he had got it into his head that it was he who should have been crucified. What she relished was the very fact that he had *not* been crucified, that he had got off!

Such were the fat woman's thoughts in her great loneliness. But at last it came to her that in actual fact she knew nothing at all about Barabbas. Neither what was wrong with him nor whether he was possessed by that crucified man's spirit or not. Nothing at all. All she knew was that he took no notice of her and that she was foolish enough to love him. The thought of this made her cry, and she lay there feeling dreadfully unhappy.

Barabbas was about in the city once or twice during the time he lived with her, and on one occasion it happened that he found himself in a house that was merely a low vault with vent-holes here and there to let in the light, and with a pungent smell of hides and acids. It was evidently a tannery, though it was not in Tanners' Lane but down below the temple hill towards the Vale of Kedron. Presumably it was one of those that tanned the hides of the sacrificial animals from the temple; but it was no longer in use, the vats and tubs along the walls were empty, though they still retained all their fumes and smells. The floor was littered with oak-bark, refuse and filth of all kinds that one trod in.

Barabbas had slunk in unobserved and was huddled in a corner near the entrance. There he squatted, looking out over the room full of praying people. Some he couldn't see; in fact the only ones discernible were those who happened to be lying where the light filtered through the vent-holes in the arched roof; but there must have been people lying everywhere praying, even in the semi-darkness, for the same mumbling could be heard from there too. Now and then the murmur would rise and grow stronger in one part, only to subside again and mingle with the rest. Sometimes everyone would begin praying much more loudly than before, with more and more burning zeal, and someone would get up and begin witnessing in ecstasy for the resurrected Saviour. The others would then stop speaking instantly and all turn in that direction, as though to draw strength from him. When he had finished they would all start praying together again, even more fervently than before. In most cases Barabbas could not see the witness's face, but once when it was someone quite close to him he saw that it was dripping with sweat. He sat watching the man in his transports, and saw how the sweat ran down the hollow checks. He was a middle-aged man. When he had finished he threw himself down on the earthen floor and touched it with his forehead, as everyone does in prayer; it was as though he had suddenly remembered there was also a God, not only that crucified man he had been talking about the whole time.

After him a voice could be heard a long way off which Barabbas seemed to recognize. And when he peered in that direction he found it was the big red-bearded man from Galilee standing there in a ray of light. He spoke more calmly than the others and in his native dialect, which everyone in Jerusalem thought sounded so silly. But all the same they listened more tensely to him than to anyone else, they hung on his words—though as a matter of fact there was nothing in the least remarkable about what he said. First he spoke for a while about his dear Master, never referring to him as anything else. Then he mentioned that the Master had said that those who believed in him would suffer persecution for his sake. And if this did happen, they would endure it as well as they could and think of what their Master himself had suffered. They were only weak, miserable human beings, not like him, but even so they would try to bear these ordeals without breaking faith and without denying him. That was all. And he seemed to say it as much to himself as to the others. When he had finished it was almost as if those present were rather disappointed in him. He noticed it, evidently, and said that he would say a prayer which the Master had once taught him. This he did, and they appeared more satisfied, some in fact were really moved. The whole room was filled with a kind of mutual ecstasy. When he came to the end of the prayer, and those nearest him turned as if to 'congratulate' him, Barabbas saw that he was surrounded by the men who had said 'Get thee hence, thou reprobate!'

One or two others then witnessed and were so filled with the spirit that the congregation continued in its exaltation and many rocked their bodies to and fro as though in a trance. Barabbas watched them from his corner, sitting and taking note of everything with his wary eyes.

All at once he gave a start. In one of the beams of light he saw the girl with the hare-lip standing with her hands pressed against her flat chest and her pallid face turned up to the light that was streaming down on it. He had not seen her since that time at the sepulchre and she had become even more emaciated and wretched, clad only in rags and her cheeks sunken in from starvation. Everyone present was looking at her and wondering who she was, no one knew her apparently. He could see that they thought there was something odd about her, though they couldn't say what; except that she had nothing on but rags of course. They were evidently wondering what her evidence would be.

What did she want to witness for! What was the point! exclaimed Barabbas within himself. Surely she realized she wasn't fitted for it! He was quite worked up, though it was nothing whatever to do with him. What did she want to witness for!

It didn't seem as though she herself were so very happy about it either; she stood with her eyes closed, as if unwilling to look at anyone round her and anxious to get it over. What did she want to do it for then! When there was no need!

Then she began to witness. She snuffled out her faith in her Lord and Saviour, and no one could possibly think there was anything moving about it, as there was presumably meant to be. On the contrary, she spoke even more absurdly and thickly than usual, because of standing in front of so many people and being nervous. And they showed clearly that they were ill at ease, that they thought it was embarrassing; some turned away in shame. She finished by snivelling something about 'Lord, now I have witnessed for thee, as thou didst say I should do,' and then sank down again on the earthen floor and did her best to make herself inconspicuous.

They all looked self-consciously at one another, it was as if she had ridiculed what they were about. And perhaps she had! Perhaps they were quite right! Their only thought after this seemed to be to put an end to their meeting as soon as possible. One of the leaders, one of those who had said 'Get thee hence, thou reprobate', got up and announced that they would disperse now. And he added that everyone knew why they had met here this time and not right in the city, and that next time they would meet somewhere else, none as yet knew where. But the Lord would be sure to find a refuge for them where they could be safe from the world's evil, he would not desert his flock, he was their shepherd and . . .

Barabbas heard no more. He had crept out before the others and was glad to be well away from it all.

The mere thought of it made him feel sick.

WHEN the persecutions began, the old blind man, led by the youth who was always panting, went to one of the prosecutors in the sanhedrin and said:

— Among us out at the Dung Gate there is a woman who is spreading heresies about a saviour who is to come and change the whole world. All that exists shall be destroyed and another and better world arise, where only his will shall be done. Should she not be stoned?

The prosecutor, who was a conscientious man, told the blind man to give more detailed reasons for his accusation. First and foremost, what kind of saviour was he? The old man said that it was the same one that those others had been stoned for believing in, and if there was any justice then she ought to be stoned too. He himself had heard her say that her lord would save all people, even the lepers. He would heal them and make them just as clean as the rest of us. But what would happen if the lepers became like other people? If they went about all over the place—perhaps even without having to carry bells any longer—so that no one would know where they were, at least no one who was blind. Was it lawful to spread such heresies?

Some little way from him in the darkness he could hear the councillor stroking his beard. He was then asked if there were any who believed in what she proclaimed?

— Indeed, there are, he answered. Among that scum out there by the Dung Gate there are always those who are ready to listen to such things. And the lepers down in the valley like it best of all of course. She hob-nobs with them, what is more; several times she has been inside the enclosure and taken the most shameful interest in them, it is said. She may even have had intercourse with them, for all I know. I wouldn't know anything about that. But she's no virgin anyway, from what I hear. And she is supposed to have had a child which she killed. But I don't know. I just hear what's said. There's nothing wrong with my hearing; it's only my eyes that are missing, so I am blind. And that is a great misfortune, noble Lord. A great misfortune to be blind like this.

The councillor asked if that 'saviour' as she called him—who should really be called the crucified man—had gained many adherents out there amongst them through her?

— Yes, he had. They all want to be healed, you see, and he heals them all, she says—lame, moonstruck and blind—so that there will be no more misery left in the world, either at the Dung Gate or anywhere else. But latterly they have started getting angry out there because he never comes. She's been saying for so long now that he will come, but when he never does they get annoyed of course and mock her and abuse her, and it's not to be wondered at either and nothing to lie and snivel about at night so that a body can't sleep. But the lepers still cling to it, and it's not surprising the way she has dinned it into them. She has even promised them that they shall be allowed into the temple square and go up into the Lord's house.

— The lepers!

— Yes.

— How can she promise anything so absurd?

— Well, she 's not the one who does the promising, but her lord, and he is so powerful that he can promise anything at all and change anything at all. He sees to everything, for he is the son of God.

— The son of God!

— Yes.

— Does she say that he is the son of God!

— Yes. And that 's sheer blasphemy, because everyone knows he was crucified, and I shouldn't think there 's any need to find out any more. Those who sentenced him surely knew what they were doing, didn't they?

— I myself was one of those who sentenced him.

— Oh well then, you know all about him!

There was silence for a while; all the old man heard was the councillor there in the darkness stroking his beard again. Then the voice declared that the woman would be summoned before the council to answer for her faith and defend it if she could. The old man expressed his thanks and withdrew, bowing meekly; then began scrabbling on the wall to find the doorway by which he had come in. The councillor sent for his attendant to help him out, but while they were waiting he asked the blind man, for safety's sake, if he bore a grudge against the woman in question.

— Bear her a grudge? No, how could I? I have never borne anyone a grudge, why should I? I have never even seen them. Not a single soul have I ever seen.

The attendant helped him out. In the street outside the entrance stood the youth from the Dung Gate, panting in the darkness; the blind man groped for his hand and they went home together.

When the girl with the hare-lip had been sentenced she was led out to the stoning-pit that lay a little to the south of the city. A whole crowd of yelling people went with her and a subordinate officer of the temple guard with his men; they, with their plaited hair and beards, were stripped to the waist and had iron-studded ox-hide whips with which to maintain order. When they reached the pit the inflamed mob spread out along the edge, while one of the soldiers led her down into it. The whole pit was full of stones, which down at the bottom were dark with old blood.

The commanding officer called for silence and a deputy of the high priest pronounced sentence and the reasons for it, saying that he who had accused her was to cast the first stone. The old blind man was led forward to the edge and told what it was all about, but he would not hear of it.

— Why should I cast stones at her? What have I to do with her, I have never even seen her!

But when at last they made him understand that such was the law and that he couldn't get out of it, he muttered crossly that he supposed he'd have to. A stone was put into his hand and he threw it out into the darkness. He tried again, but there was no point in it, as he had no idea where the target was; he merely threw straight out into the darkness which was the same in all directions. Barabbas, who was standing beside him and who up till now had had eyes only for the girl down there whom the stones were going to hit, now saw a man step forward to help the blind man. The man had a stern, aged, withered face and on his forehead he wore the law's commandments enclosed in leather capsules. He was presumably a scribe. Taking the blind man's arm he tried to aim for him, so that they could get on with the stoning. But the result was the same as before. The stone went wide of the mark. The sentenced woman was still standing down there with wide, shining eyes waiting for what was to happen.

The true believer grew so impatient at last that he bent down and picked up a large sharp stone, which he hurled with all his senile might at the hare-lipped girl. It did in fact hit her, and she staggered and raised her spindly arms in a rather helpless way. The mob gave a wild shriek of approval and the true believer stood looking down at his work, clearly well pleased with it. Barabbas, stepping right up to him, lifted his mantle slightly and stuck a knife into him with a deft movement that told of long practice. It happened so quickly that no one noticed anything. And besides, they were all so busy casting their stones down on to the victim.

Barabbas pushed his way through to the edge, and there, down in the pit, he saw the girl with the hare-lip stagger forward a step or two with outstretched hands, crying out:

— He has come! He has come! . . . I see him! I see him! . . .

Then she fell to her knees, and it was as though she seized hold of the hem of someone's garment as she snuffled:

— Lord, how can I witness for thee? Forgive me, forgive . . .

Then sinking down on the blood-stained stones she gave up the ghost.

When it was all over, those immediately round about discovered that a man lay dead amongst them, while another man was seen to run off between the vineyards and disappear into the olive-groves over towards the Vale of Kedron. Several of the guard gave chase, but were unable to find him. It was as if the earth had swallowed him up.

WHEN darkness fell, Barabbas crept back to the stoning-pit and climbed down into it. He could see nothing, and had to grope his way. Right at the bottom he found her lacerated body, half buried under stones that had been cast quite needlessly, long after she was dead. It was so small and light that he hardly felt it in his arms as he carried it up the steep slope and away into the darkness.

He carried it hour after hour. Now and then he would stop and rest for a while, with the dead girl lying in front of him on the ground. The clouds had blown away and the stars were shining; after a time the moon rose too, so that everything was visible. He sat looking at her face, which oddly enough was very little hurt. Nor was it much paler than when she was alive, for this was hardly possible. It was quite transparent, and the scar in the upper-lip had become so small, as though it didn't in the least matter. And it didn't either, not now.

He thought of the time when he had hit on the idea of saying that he loved her. When he had taken her—no, he put that out of his mind. . . . But the time when he had said that he loved her, so that she would not give him away but do just as he wanted—how her face had lighted up. She was not used to hearing that. It seemed to make her happy in some way to hear it, though she must have known it was a lie. Or hadn't she known? In any case he had got things the way he wanted them; she had come every day with what he needed to keep himself alive, and he had got her of course—more than he wanted really. He had made do with her because there was no other woman to hand, though her snuffling voice had got on his nerves and he had told her not to talk more than she had to. And when at last his leg was healed he had gone off again of course. What else was he to do?

He looked out across the desert opening up before him, lifeless and arid, lit by the moon's dead light. It extended like this in all directions, he knew. He was familiar with it without having to look about him.

Love one another . . .

He glanced at her face again. Then lifting her up he resumed his way on over the mountains.

He was following a camel- and mule-track that led from Jerusalem across the Desert of Judah to the land of the Moabites. There was nothing to be seen of the track itself; but droppings from animals, and occasionally the skeleton of one of them picked clean by the vultures, showed where it twisted and turned. When he had been walking for more than half the night the path began to lead downwards and he knew that he had not much further to go. He made his way down through one or two narrow clefts and then out as though into another desert, but even wilder and more desolate. The track continued across it, but he sat down to rest for a while first, tired after the strenuous descent with his burden. Anyway, he was nearly there now.

He wondered whether he would be able to find it himself or whether he would have to ask the old man? He would much prefer not to look him up, would rather do all this alone. The old man might not understand why he had brought her here. Did he understand himself for that matter? Was there any point in it? Yes, she belonged here, he thought. That is if she belonged anywhere at all. Down in Gilgal she would never be allowed to rest, and in Jerusalem she would have been thrown to the dogs. He didn't think she ought to be. Though what did it matter really? What difference did it make to her? What good did it do her to be brought here where she had lived as an exile and where she could find rest in the same grave as the child? None at all. But he felt he wanted to do it all the same. It is not so easy to please the dead.

What was the use of her having gone off like that to Jerusalem? Of joining those crazy desert fanatics who raved about the coming of a great Messiah and said they must all make their way to the Lord's city? Had she listened to the old man instead, this would never have happened to her. The old man wasn't going to unsettle himself, he said he had done it so many times for nothing, that there were so many who made out they were the Messiah but who weren't at all. Why should it be the right one this particular time? But she listened to the madmen.

Now here she lay, battered and dead for his sake. The right one?

Was he the right one? The saviour of the world? The saviour of all mankind? Then why didn't he help her down there in the stoning-pit! Why did he let her be stoned for his sake! If he was a saviour, why didn't he save!

He could have done that all right if he'd wanted to. But he liked suffering, both his own and others'. And he liked people to witness for him. 'Now I have witnessed for thee, as thou didst say I should do.'... 'Risen from hell in order to witness for thee.'...

No, he didn't like that crucified man. He hated him. It was he who had killed her, had demanded this sacrifice of her and seen to it that she didn't escape it. For he had been present down there, she had seen him and gone towards him with outstretched hands for help, had snatched at his mantle—but not a finger had he lifted to help her. And he was supposed to be the son of God! God's loving son! Everyone's saviour!

He himself at any rate had knifed that man who had cast the first stone. He, Barabbas, had done that much at least. True, it meant nothing. The stone was already cast, it had already hit her. There was absolutely no point in it. But all the same. He had knifed him all the same!

He wiped his hand across his wry mouth and smiled scornfully to himself. Then he shrugged and got to his feet. Lifted up his burden, impatiently, as though he had begun to tire of it, and started off again.

He passed the old man's hermit's-cave, which he easily recognized from that time when he had come here by chance. Then he tried to remember where they had gone when the old man showed him the way to the child's grave. They had had the lepers' caves on their right and the desert fanatics' straight in front, but they hadn't gone as far as that. Yes, he recognized it quite well, though it looked different now in the moonlight. They had been walking down here towards the hollow while the old man told him that the child was still-born because it had been cursed in the womb and that he had buried it at once as everything still-born is unclean. Cursed be the fruit of thy loins. . . . The mother had not been able to be present, but later on she had often sat there by the grave. . . . The old man had talked the whole time. . . .

It should be somewhere here surely? Shouldn't it? Yes, here was the stone slab. . . .

Lifting it up he laid her down beside the child, who was already completely withered. Arranged her torn body, as though to make sure she would be comfortable, and finally threw a glance at the face and the scar in the upper-lip which didn't matter any more. Then he replaced the slab and sat down and looked out over the desert. He sat thinking that it resembled the realm of death, to which she now belonged; he had carried her into it. Once there, it made no difference really where one rested, but now she lay beside her withered child and nowhere else. He had done what he could for her, he thought, stroking his red beard and smiling scornfully.

Love one another . . .

WHEN Barabbas came back to his own people he was so changed that they scarcely recognized him. Their companions who had been down in Jerusalem had said that he seemed a bit queer; and no wonder either, being in prison for so long and then so nearly crucified. It would soon wear off, they thought. But it had not done so, not even now, so long afterwards. What lay at the back of it all was more than they could say, but he was no longer himself.

He had always been queer of course. They had never really understood him or known just where they were with him, but this was something else. He was just like a stranger to them and he too must have thought they were strangers he had never seen before. When they explained their plans he paid hardly any attention, and he never offered any opinion himself. He seemed completely indifferent to it all. He took part of course in their beats along the caravan routes and the raids down the Jordan Valley now and then, but rather half-heartedly and without being of much use. If there was any danger he didn't exactly keep out of the way, but very nearly. Perhaps even this was due to sheer apathy; there was no telling. He didn't seem in the mood for anything. Only once, when they plundered a wagon with tithes from the Jericho region for the high priest, did he run completely amuck and cut down the two men from the temple guard who were escorting it. It was quite unnecessary, as they made no resistance and gave in the minute they saw they were outnumbered. Afterwards he even outraged their bodies, behaving so incredibly that the others thought it was going too far and turned away. Even if they did hate all those guards and the whole of the high priest's pack, the dead belonged to the temple and the temple belonged to the Lord. It almost frightened them, his violating them like that.

But otherwise he never showed any desire to join in and do his bit, as they all had to do; what they were up to was somehow no concern of his. Not even when they attacked a Roman picket at one of the ferry-stations by the Jordan did he show any particular enthusiasm; though it was the Romans who had wanted to crucify him and all the rest of them had been in a state of savage excitement, cutting the throats of every single soldier and flinging the bodies into the river. Not that they doubted that his hatred of the oppressors of the Lord's people was as great as theirs, but had they all been as half-hearted as he, things would have gone very badly for them that night.

The change that had come over him was quite unaccountable, for if any of them had been daring it was Barabbas. He it was who used to plan most of their ventures and be the first to carry them out. Nothing seemed impossible for him, and he used to pull it off too. Because of his boldness and cunning they were quite willing to let him have his way and devise plans for them, and they had grown used to relying on everything turning out well. He became a kind of leader, though they didn't recognize leaders among them and no one really liked him. Perhaps it was for that very reason; because he was queer and moody and different from themselves, so that they never quite made him out and he remained a kind of stranger. They knew what they were like themselves, but where he was concerned they knew hardly anything; and oddly enough it gave them confidence. Even the fact that they were actually a little afraid of him secretly gave them confidence. Though of course it was chiefly because of his mettle and craftiness and success in what he undertook.

But now—what did they want with a leader who showed not the slightest wish to lead, who didn't even seem to want to do his share, as they all must? Who preferred to sit by the mouth of the cave staring down over the Jordan Valley and away across the sea that was called the Dead. Who looked at them with his curious eyes and in whose company they always felt ill at ease. He never really spoke to them, or if he did they only felt more than ever that there was something odd about him. He seemed to be somewhere else entirely. It was almost unpleasant. Perhaps it was part and parcel of what he had been through down in Jerusalem, of being so nearly crucified. In fact, it was almost as if he really had been crucified and had then come back here again just the same.

He spread unease around him. They weren't at all pleased at having him there, at his return. He didn't belong here any longer. As leader he was impossible—and he was hardly fitted for anything else! In that case he wasn't anything at all then? No, it was curious—he wasn't anything at all!

Now that they came to think of it, he had not always been the one who led and made decisions, not always the bold, reckless Barabbas who snapped his fingers at danger and death and everything. He had not been like that until Eliahu had given him that cut under the eye. Before then he had been anything but a dare-devil—rather the reverse. They remembered that very well as a matter of fact. But after this he had suddenly become a man. After that treacherous thrust, which had really been aimed to kill, and after the savage death-struggle that followed, which had ended by Barabbas hurling the terrible but already senile and clumsy Eliahu down the precipice below the mouth of the cave. The younger man was so much more lithe and agile; despite all his strength the old warrior could not hold his own against him, and that fight was his doom. Why did he provoke it? Why did he always hate Barabbas? They had never been able to find out. But they had all noticed that he had done so from the first moment.

It was after this that Barabbas had become their leader. Up till then there had been nothing special about him. He had not become a real man until he had got that knife-wound.

So they sat talking, whispering amongst themselves.

But what they did not know, what nobody at all knew, was that this Eliahu, who now stood out so clearly and vividly in their minds, was Barabbas's father. No one knew that; no one could know. His mother was a Moabite woman whom the band had taken prisoner many years before when they plundered a caravan on the Jericho highway and with whom they had all amused themselves before selling her to a brothel in Jerusalem. When it became obvious that she was pregnant, the proprietress wouldn't keep her there any longer and sent her packing, and she gave birth in the street and was found dead afterwards. Nobody knew whom the child belonged to, and she couldn't have said herself; only that she had cursed it in her womb and borne it in hatred of heaven and earth and the Creator of heaven and earth.

No, nobody knew the ins and outs of it. Neither the whispering men right at the back of the cave nor Barabbas as he sat at the opening, gazing out into the void across to the burnt-up mountains of Moab and the endless sea that was called the Dead.

Barabbas was not even thinking of Eliahu, although he was sitting just where he had flung him down the rock-face. He was thinking instead, for some reason—or rather for no reason at all—of the crucified Saviour's mother, of how she had stood looking at her nailed-up son, at him she had once borne. He remembered her dry eyes and her rough peasant's face which couldn't express the grief she felt, and perhaps didn't want to either among strangers. And he remembered her reproachful look at him as she passed. Why just at him? There were surely plenty of others to reproach!

He often thought of Golgotha and what had happened there. And often of her, that other man's mother.

He looked away again over the mountains on the other side of the Dead Sea, and saw how the darkness came down over them, over the land of the Moabites.

THEY wondered greatly how they could get rid of him. They longed to be free of this useless and irksome encumbrance and to be spared the sight of his gloomy face, which depressed them and made everything so joyless. But how were they to go about it? How could it be done, how could they say to his face that he didn't fit in here any longer and that they would be glad if he took himself off? Who was going to tell him? None of them was particularly keen—to be quite honest, none of them dared. For no reason, they were still possessed by a kind of absurd fear.

So they continued with their whispering; saying how fed up with him they were and how they disliked him, and always had done; and that it was perhaps his fault that they were starting to be dogged by such bad luck and had recently lost two men. They could hardly expect much luck with a Jonah like that amongst them. A sultry and menacing feeling of tension filled the cave, and eyes that were almost malevolent glittered in the semi-darkness at the man who sat brooding alone out by the precipice, as though bound to an evil destiny. How were they to get rid of him!

And then one morning he had simply disappeared. He just wasn't there. They thought at first that he had lost his reason and thrown himself over the cliff, or that an evil spirit had entered into him and flung him into space. Perhaps Eliahu's spirit, to be avenged on him? But when they searched down below in the same spot where they had once found Eliahu's battered body, he was not there, nor could they find the slightest trace of him anywhere. He had simply disappeared.

Feeling greatly relieved, they returned to their eyrie up on the steep mountain-side, which was already burning-hot from the sun.

OF Barabbas's fate, where his haunts were and what he did with himself after these events and during the rest of his manhood, no one knows anything for certain. Some think that after his disappearance he retired into complete solitude somewhere in the desert, in the desert of Judah or the desert of Sinai, and devoted himself to the contemplation of the world of God and mankind; while others think that he joined the Samaritans, who hate the temple in Jerusalem and the priesthood and the scribes there, that he is supposed to have been seen during the Passover on their holy mountain at the sacrificing of the lamb, kneeling waiting for the sunrise at Gerizim. But some regard it as proven that for the greater part of the time he was simply the leader of a robber band on the slopes of Lebanon, towards Syria, and as such showed cruelty to both Jews and Christians who fell into his hands.

As has been said, no one can know which of these is true. But what is definitely known is that when well into his fifties he came as a slave to the Roman governor's house in Paphos after having spent several years in the Cyprian copper mines which were subject to the latter's administration. Why he had been seized and condemned to the mines, to the most ghastly punishment imaginable, is not known. But more remarkable than the fact that such a thing could happen to him is that once having descended to this hell he was ever able to return to life again, though still a slave. There were, however, special circumstances connected with this.

He was now a grey-haired man with a furrowed face but otherwise remarkably well preserved in view of all he had gone through. He had recovered amazingly soon and regained much of his strength. When he left the mines he resembled a dead man rather than a living one; his body was quite emaciated and his eye-sockets expressionless, like wells that had been drained dry. When the expression in his eyes returned, it became even more restless than before, and uneasy, dog-like, as though cowed; but it also glittered occasionally with the hatred his mother felt for all creation when she gave birth to him. The scar under his eye, which had faded right away, once more dug down into the grey beard.

Had he not been of such tough material he would never have survived. He had Eliahu and the Moabite woman to thank for this, they had once again given him life. And this despite their both having hated, not loved, him. Nor had they loved each other. That is how much love means. But he knew nothing of what he owed them and their malevolent embrace.

The house to which he came was large, with many slaves. Among them was a tall, lanky, very lean man, an Armenian called Sahak. He was so tall that he always walked with a slight stoop. His eyes were large, a trifle protuberant, and his dark, wide-eyed gaze made him glow in some way. The short white hair and the burnt-up face made one think he was an old man, but actually he was only in his forties. He too had been in the mines. Barabbas and he had spent their years there together, and together had succeeded in getting away. But he had not recovered like the other one; he was still just as incredibly emaciated, and the snow-white hair and seemingly fire-ravaged face gave him a branded and scorched appearance that made him look quite different. He seemed to have undergone something which Barabbas in spite of everything had not endured. And this was indeed so.

The other slaves were very curious about these two who had managed to escape from something which normally no one got out of alive, and they would have liked very much to hear all about it. But they did not get much out of them regarding their past. The two kept to themselves, though they did not speak much to each other, nor did they seem to have very much in common. Yet even so they appeared inseparable in some way. It was strange. But if they always sat next to each other during meals and their time off, and always lay beside each other in the straw at night, it was only because they had been chained together in the mines.

This had been done the moment they arrived in the same transport from the mainland. The slaves were shackled together in twos and then the same pair always worked together side by side in the depths of the mine. Neither was ever separated from his fellow-prisoner, and these twin slaves did everything in common and grew to know one another inside out, sometimes to the point of frenzied hatred. They had been known to hurl themselves at each other in savage fury for no reason other than that they were welded together like this in hell.

But these two seemed to suit each other and even to help each other endure their servitude. They got on well together and were able to talk, in this way diverting themselves during the heavy work. Barabbas was not very communicative of course, so the other did most of the talking, but he liked to listen. They did not speak of themselves to begin with, neither of them seemed to want to; they both evidently had their secrets which they were unwilling to reveal, so it was some time before they really knew anything about each other. It was more by chance one day that Barabbas happened to mention he was a Hebrew and born in a city called Jerusalem. Sahak was extraordinarily interested when he heard this, and began asking about one thing and another. He seemed to be quite familiar with this city, although he had never been there. At last he asked if Barabbas knew of a rabbi who had lived and worked there, a great prophet in whom many believed. Barabbas knew who was meant and answered that he had heard about him. Sahak was eager to know something about him, but Barabbas replied evasively that he did not know so very much.—Had he himself ever seen him? Yes . . . he had as a matter of fact. Sahak attached great importance to the fact that Barabbas had seen him, for after a while he asked once more if it were really true that he had done so. And Barabbas again replied, though rather half-heartedly, that he had.

Sahak lowered his pick and stood deep in thought, stood there completely absorbed by what had happened to him. Everything had become so different for him; he could scarcely realize it. The whole mine-shaft was transfigured and nothing was the same as before. He was chained together with one who had seen God.

As he stood there he felt the lash of the slave-driver's whip whine across his back. The overseer had just happened to pass by. He crouched down under the blows, as if thereby to avoid them, and began zealously swinging the pointed pick. When his tormentor finally passed on he was covered in blood and the whole of his long body was still quivering from the lashes. Some time elapsed before he could speak again, but when he did he asked Barabbas to tell him how it was he had seen the rabbi. Was it in the temple, in the sanctuary? Was it one of the times when he spoke of his future kingdom? Or when was it? At first Barabbas would not say, but at last he answered reluctantly that it was at Golgotha.

— Golgotha? What is that?

Barabbas said that it was a place where they crucified criminals.

Sahak was silent. He lowered his eyes. Then he said quietly:

— Oh, it was *then*. . .

This is what happened the first time they talked about the crucified rabbi, which they were often to do later on.

Sahak wanted very much to hear about him, but especially about the holy words he had uttered and about the great miracles he had performed. He knew of course that he had been crucified, but he would rather Barabbas told him about something else.

Golgotha . . . Golgotha . . . Such a strange, unfamiliar name for something that was nevertheless so well known to him. How many times had he not heard of how the Saviour had died on the cross and of the wondrous things that had happened then. He asked Barabbas if he had seen the veil of the temple after it had been rent? And the rock too had been cleft asunder—he must have seen that since he was standing there at that very moment?

Barabbas replied that it might well have happened, though he had not seen it.

— Yes, and the dead who had got up out of their graves! Who had risen from the realm of death in order to witness for him, for his power and glory!

— Yes . . . Barabbas said.

— And the darkness that descended over all the earth when he gave up the ghost?

Yes, Barabbas had seen *that*. He had seen the darkness.

It seemed to make Sahak very happy to hear this, though at the same time he did appear to be worried by the thought of that place of execution; he could almost see in front of him the cleft rock and the cross standing upon it, with the son of God hung up to be sacrificed. Yes, of course the Saviour had to suffer and die, he had to do that in order to save us. That's how it was, though it was hard to understand. He preferred to think of him in his glory, in his own kingdom, where everything was so different from here. And he wished that Barabbas, to whom he was fettered, had seen him another time and not at Golgotha. How was it he saw him there of all places?

— That you should see him just then, he said to Barabbas, wasn't that rather strange? Why were you there?

But to this Barabbas made no reply.

Once Sahak asked if he really had not seen him at some other time as well? Barabbas did not answer at once. Then he said that he had also been present in the courtyard of the palace when the rabbi was condemned, and described all that had happened. He also mentioned the extraordinary light that he had seen surrounding him on that occasion. And when he noticed how happy it made Sahak to hear about this light, he did not bother to mention that it was only because he had been dazzled by the sun, coming straight out into it from the dungeon. Why should he mention it? It was of no interest to the other—it was of no interest to anyone. By not bothering to give an explanation of the miracle, he made Sahak so happy that he wanted to hear all about it over and over again. His face shone and even Barabbas felt something of his happiness—it was as though they shared it. Whenever Sahak asked him, he would tell him about his wonderful vision, now so long ago, imagining he saw it clearly in front of him.

Some time later he confided to Sahak that he had also witnessed the master's resurrection. No, not so that he had seen him rise from the dead, no one had done that. But he had seen an angel shoot down from the sky with his arm outstretched like the point of a spear and his mantle blazing behind him like a flame of fire. And the point of the spear had rolled away the stone from the tomb, pushing in between the stone and the rock and parting them. And then he had seen that the tomb was empty. . . .

Sahak listened in amazement, his large ingenuous eyes fastened on the other. Was it possible? Was it really possible that this wretched, filthy slave had seen this happen? That he had been present when the greatest of all miracles occurred? Who was he? And how was it he himself was so favoured as to be shackled to one who had experienced this and been so close to the Lord?

He was beside himself with joy at what he had heard, and felt that now he must confide his secret to the other, he could no longer contain it. Glancing round cautiously to make sure that no one was coming, he whispered to Barabbas that he had something to show him. He led him over to the oil-lamp burning on a ledge in the rock-face, and by its flickering light showed him the slave's disk which he wore round his neck. All slaves wore a similar disk, on which their owner's mark was stamped. The slaves here in the mine bore the mark of the Rome State on their disks, for it was to this they belonged. But on the reverse of Sahak's disk they could together make out several strange, mysterious signs which neither of them could interpret but which Sahak explained meant the name of the crucified one, the Saviour, God's own son. Barabbas looked in wonderment at the curious notches which seemed to have a magic significance, but Sahak whispered that they meant he belonged to the son of God, that he was *his* slave. And he let Barabbas himself touch it. Barabbas stood for a long time holding it in his hand.

For a moment they thought they heard the overseer coming, but it was not so, and they leant against each other once more to look at the inscription. Sahak said that it had been done by a Greek slave. He was a Christian, and had told him about the Saviour and his kingdom that was soon to come; he it was who had taught him to believe. Sahak had met him at the smelting-furnaces, where none can survive for more than a year at the very most. The Greek had not survived so long, and as he breathed his last there in the glowing heat Sahak had heard him whisper:—Lord, do not forsake me. They had chopped off his foot to remove the shackles more easily and thrown him into the furnace, as they always did in such cases. Sahak had expected to end his life in the same way; but not long afterwards a number of slaves, Sahak amongst them, had been removed here, where more were needed.

Now Barabbas knew that he too was a Christian and that he was God's own slave, Sahak finished, looking at the other man with his steadfast eyes.

Barabbas was very reticent and quiet for several days after this. Then he asked Sahak in a curiously faltering voice if he would not engrave the same inscription on his disk too.

Sahak was only too pleased, provided he could. He did not know the secret signs, but he had his own disk to copy from.

They waited their chance until the overseer had just gone by, and with a sharp splinter of stone Sahak, by the light of the oil-lamp, began engraving the signs as well as he could. It was not easy for him with his unpractised hand to copy the strange outlines, but he took pains to do his very best and make it as similar as possible. Many times they had to break off because someone was coming, or because they fancied so, but at last it was finished, and they both thought it was really quite like. Each stood looking in silence at his inscription, at the mysterious signs which they understood nothing at all about, but which they knew signified the crucified man's name—that they belonged to him. And suddenly they both sank down on their knees in fervent prayer to their Lord, the Saviour and God of all oppressed.

The overseer saw them from some distance away, lying as they were right up near the lamp, but they themselves noticed nothing, so engrossed were they in their prayer. He rushed up and flayed them half to death. When at last he moved on Sahak sank to the ground, but the man then turned back and forced him up again with further lashes. Staggering against each other, they resumed their work.

This was the first time Barabbas suffered for the crucified man's sake, for that pale-skinned rabbi with no hair on his chest who had been crucified in his stead.

So the years passed. Day after day. They would not have been able to tell one day from another had they not been shoved away every evening to sleep together with hundreds of others who were equally exhausted, and from this realized that it was night. They were never allowed to leave the mine. Like shadows, bloodless, they lived perpetually, year after year, in the same semi-darkness down there in their realm of death, guided by the flickering lamps and here and there by a log-fire. Up by the mouth of the pit a little daylight forced its way down, and there they could look up towards something that might be the sky. But they could see nothing of the earth, of the world to which they had once belonged. There, too, at the mouth of the mine, food was lowered to them in baskets and dirty troughs, from which they fed like animals.

Sahak had a great sorrow. Barabbas no longer prayed with him. He had done so once or twice after wanting to have the Saviour's name engraved on his slave's disk, but then never again. He had merely become more and more reserved and strange, impossible to understand. Sahak understood nothing. It was a complete mystery to him. He himself continued to pray, but Barabbas would only turn away, as though he did not even want to watch. He used to place himself so that he screened the other while he prayed, in case someone came along, so that Sahak would not be disturbed during his prayers. It was as though he wanted to help him pray. But he himself did not pray.

Why? What was the reason? Sahak had no idea. It was all a riddle, just as Barabbas himself had become a riddle to him. He had thought he knew him so well and that they had come so close to one another down here in the underworld, in their common place of punishment, especially when they lay and prayed together those few times. And all at once he found that he knew nothing about him, nothing at all really, although he was so attached to him. Sometimes he even felt that this strange man at his side was utterly foreign to him in some way.

Who was he?

They continued talking to each other, but it was never the same as before, and Barabbas had a way of half turning his back when they spoke together. Sahak never again managed to see his eyes. But had he ever really seen them? Now that he thought of it—had he ever really done so?

Just whom was he chained to?

Barabbas never again spoke of his visions. The loss of this to Sahak, the emptiness, is not hard to understand. He tried to recall them as well as he could, tried to see them in front of him, but it was not easy. And it was not the same—how could it be. He had never stood by the side of the Loving One and been dazzled by the light around him. He had never seen God.

He had to content himself with the memory of something wonderful he had once seen with Barabbas's eyes.

He especially loved the vision of Easter morning, the burning angel flashing down to set the Lord free from hell. With that picture really clear before him, Sahak knew that his Lord was undoubtedly risen from the dead, that he was alive. And that he would soon return to establish his kingdom here on earth, as he had so often promised. Sahak never doubted it for a moment, he was quite certain that it would come to pass. And then they would be called up out of the mine, all who languished here. Yes, the Lord himself would stand at the very pit-head and receive the slaves and free them from their fetters as they came up, and then they would all enter his kingdom.

Sahak longed greatly for this. And each time they were fed he would stand and look up through the shaft to see if the miracle had occurred. But one could not see anything of the world up there, nor know what might have happened to it. So many wonderful things might have taken place about which one had not the faintest idea. Though they would surely have been brought up if something like that really had happened, if the Lord really had come. He would surely not forget them, not forget his own down here in hell.

Once when Sahak was kneeling at the rock-face saying his prayers something extraordinary happened. An overseer who was fairly new in the mine, and who had replaced their former tormentor, approached them from behind in such a way that Sahak neither saw nor heard him. But Barabbas, who was standing beside the praying man without praying himself, caught sight of him in the semi-darkness and whispered urgently to Sahak that someone was coming. Sahak immediately rose from his knees and his prayer and began working busily with his pick. He expected the worst, all the same, and cowered down in advance as though he already felt the lash across his back. To the great amazement of them both, however, nothing happened. The overseer did in fact stop, but he asked Sahak quite kindly why he had been kneeling like that, what it meant. Sahak stammered that he had been praying to his God.

— Which God? the man asked.

And when Sahak told him, he nodded silently as though to say that he had thought as much. He began questioning him about the crucified 'Saviour', whom he had heard spoken of and had obviously pondered over a great deal. Was it really true that he had let himself be crucified? That he suffered a slave's base death? And that he was nevertheless able to make people worship him afterwards as a god? Extraordinary, quite extraordinary . . . and why was he called the Saviour? A curious name for a god. . . . What was meant by it? . . . Was he supposed to save us? Save our souls? Strange . . . Why should he do that?

Sahak tried to explain as well as he could. And the man listened willingly, though there was but little clarity and coherence in the ignorant slave's explanation. Now and then he would shake his head, but the whole time he listened as though the simple words really concerned him. At last he said that there were so many gods, there must be. And one ought to sacrifice to them all to be on the safe side.

Sahak replied that he who had been crucified demanded no sacrifices. He demanded only that one sacrifice oneself.

— What's that you say? Sacrifice oneself? What do you mean?

— Well, that one sacrifice oneself in his great smelting-furnace, Sahak said.

— In his smelting-furnace . . .?

The overseer shook his head.

— You are a simple slave, he said after a moment, and your words match your wits. What strange fancies! Where did you pick up such foolish words?

— From a Greek slave, Sahak answered. That is what he used to say. I don't really know what it means.

— No, I'm sure you don't. Nor does anyone else. Sacrifice oneself . . . In his smelting-furnace . . . in his smelting-furnace . . .

And continuing to mumble something which they could no longer catch, he disappeared into the darkness between the sparsely placed oil-lamps, like one losing his way in the bowels of the earth.

Sahak and Barabbas puzzled greatly over this striking event in their existence. It was so unexpected that they could scarcely grasp it. How had this man been able to come down here to them? And was he really an ordinary overseer? Behaving like that! Asking about the crucified one, about the Saviour! No, they could not see how it was possible, but of course they were glad about what had happened to them.

After this the overseer often stopped to speak to Sahak as he passed by. Barabbas he never spoke to. And he got Sahak to tell him more about his Lord, about his life and his miracles, and about his strange doctrine that we should all love one another. And one day the overseer said:

— I too have long been thinking of believing in this god. But how can I? How can I believe in anything so strange? And I who am an overseer of slaves, how can I worship a crucified slave?

Sahak replied that his Lord had admittedly died a slave's death but that in actual fact he was God himself. Yes, the only God. If one believes in him one can no longer believe in any other.

— The only god! And crucified like a slave! What presumption! Do you mean that there is supposed to be only *one* god—and that people crucified him!

— Yes, Sahak said. That is how it is.

The man gazed at him, dumbfounded. And shaking his head, as was his habit, he went on his way, vanishing into the dark passage of the mine.

They stood looking after him. Caught a glimpse of him for a second by the next oil-lamp, and then he was gone.

But the overseer was thinking of this unknown god who merely became more incomprehensible the more he heard about him. Supposing he really were the only god? That it was to him one should pray and none other? Supposing there were only one mighty god who was master of heaven and earth and who proclaimed his teaching everywhere, even down here in the underworld? A teaching so remarkable that one could not grasp it? 'Love one another . . . love one another' . . . No, who could understand that? . . .

He stopped in the darkness between two lamps in order to consider it better in solitude. And all at once it came like an inspiration to him what he was to do. That he was to get the slave who believed in the unknown god away from the mine here, where all succumbed in the end, and have him put to some other work, something up in the sun. He did not understand this god, and still less his teaching; it was not possible for him to understand it, but that is what he would do. It felt just as though this were the god's will.

And when he was next above ground he sought out the overseer in charge of the slaves who worked on the landed property belonging to the mine. When the latter, who was a man with a fresh peasant's face but a large, coarse mouth, realized what it was all about, he showed clearly that the idea did not appeal to him. He had no wish for a slave from the mines. In point of fact he needed several slaves, especially now with the spring ploughing, for as usual there were not nearly enough oxen to do the draught work. But he did not want anyone from the mines. They were quite useless, had no strength at all, and besides, the other slaves would have nothing to do with them—what did they want up here above ground? But in the end he let himself be persuaded by the older man, who had a strange capacity for getting his own way. And the latter returned to the mine.

The following day he talked to Sahak about his god for longer than he had ever done before. And then he told him what he had arranged for him. He was to present himself to the guard at the bottom of the shaft to be freed from his shackles and separated from his fellow-prisoner. And then he would be taken up out of the mine and put in the charge of the man under whom he was to work from now on.

Sahak looked at him, unable to believe his ears. Could it be true? The overseer said that it was, and that this had evidently been shown to him by Sahak's god in order that his will might be done.

Sahak pressed his hands to his breast and stood for a moment in silence. But then he said that he would not be separated from his fellow-prisoner, for they had the same God and the same faith.

The overseer looked at Barabbas in astonishment.

— The same faith? He? But he never kneels and prays as you do!

— No, Sahak replied, somewhat uncertainly, that may be. But he has been close to him in quite a different way, he has stood by his cross while he suffered and died on it. And he has seen a bright light round him once and an angel of fire who rolled away the stone from his tomb in order that he could rise ırom hell. He it is who has opened my eyes to his glory.

All this was beyond the overseer, who shook his head in a puzzled way and looked sideways at Barabbas, at the man with the scar under his eye who always avoided meeting one's glance and who even now was standing there with averted eyes. Did he belong to Sahak's god? It was not possible, surely? He did not like him.

Nor had he any wish to let him also out of the mine. But Sahak said again:

— I cannot be separated from him.

The overseer stood mumbling to himself and looking at Barabbas out of the corner of his eye. At length he agreed very reluctantly that it should be as Sahak wished and that they should keep each other company as before. Then he walked away from them into his solitude.

When Sahak and Barabbas presented themselves to the guard at the appointed time, they were both freed from their chains and taken up out of the mine. And when they came up into the daylight and saw the spring sun shining across the mountain-side that smelt of myrtle and lavender, and the green fields in the valley below and the sea beyond, Sahak fell down on his knees and cried out in ecstasy:

— He has come! He has come! Behold, his kingdom is here!

The slave-driver who had come to fetch them looked at him agape as he knelt there. Then he prodded him with his foot as a sign to get up.

— Come now, he said.

THEY were well suited for harnessing together to the plough, for they had already been coupled for so long that they were as used to each other as a pair of mules. They were gaunt and scraggy of course, and with their half-shaven heads they were a laughing-stock among the other slaves; it was obvious at a glance where they came from. But one of them at any rate picked up again fairly soon, he was a robust fellow by nature, and after a while they pulled together quite well. The overseer was reasonably satisfied with them; they were not so bad considering that they were prisoners from the mine.

They themselves were full of gratitude for what had happened to them. Even though they had to toil like oxen from morning till night, it was still so different from before. Just being out in the air, being able to breathe it, made everything so much easier. They delighted in the sun, though their lean bodies dripped with sweat and they were treated just like cattle and really no better than before. The lash whined over them as it had done in the mine, especially over Sahak, who was not as strong as Barabbas. But they had nevertheless returned to life, as it were; they lived on the earth like other beings and not down in perpetual darkness. Morning and evening came, day and night, and they were there to see it and know the joy of it. But they were well aware that God's kingdom had not yet come.

By degrees the other slaves changed their attitude towards them and ceased to regard them as some curious kind of animal. Their hair grew again and they became like all the others, and less notice was taken of them. The remarkable thing about them really was not that they had been prisoners in the mine, but that they had been able to escape from the hell to which they were condemned. In actual fact it was this that had, from the very beginning, aroused the others' curiosity and a kind of reluctant admiration, though they wouldn't own to it. They tried to get out of the other two how it had all come about, but were not very successful. The newcomers were not talkative, and regarding this miracle they didn't seem to want to talk at all. They were a bit odd and kept mostly to themselves.

They need not have done so now. They were no longer chained together. They could have made friends with some of the others if they had wanted to, and there was no further need to eat and sleep beside each other. But they still stuck together and always walked close beside each other as if inseparable. It was all the more strange as in point of fact they had grown shy of one another and found talking more difficult now. They acted as inseparables, though they had drifted apart.

While working they had to go side by side. But not at other times, when they could have mixed with the other slaves. Feeling out of it as they did, however, perhaps it was not really so odd that they held aloof. They had grown so used to keeping together, and used to the chain that was no longer there. When they woke up in the dark at night and felt that they were not shackled together they were almost frightened, until it dawned on them that at least they were lying side by side as before. The knowledge was a relief.

To think that Barabbas should live to see such a thing! That it could be like that for *him*! It was most extraordinary. For if anyone was ill-suited to being hobbled together with another person, it was he. Against his will, however, he had been; with an iron chain, what is more. And even though the chain no longer existed he still retained it in one way; couldn't do without it, apparently. Though of course he tugged at it in an effort to break away. . . .

But not Sahak. On the contrary, he felt very hurt that things were not as before between them. Why weren't they?

Of their miraculous rescue from the mines, from hell, they never spoke. The first day or two they had done so, but not after that. Sahak had said then that they had been rescued by the son of God, everyone's Saviour. Yes, they had. . . . Of course they had. . . . Though in actual fact it was Sahak who had been rescued by his Saviour, by the son of God, but Barabbas had been rescued by Sahak. Wasn't that right? Wasn't that how it was?

Hm, it was hard to say.

Barabbas had in any case thanked Sahak for saving him. But had he thanked God? Yes, surely he had? But it wasn't certain. One couldn't be sure.

It grieved Sahak that he knew so infinitely little about Barabbas, whom he was so fond of. And it hurt him so much that they were unable to pray together, as they had done down in the mine, in hell. How he would have loved to do it. But he didn't reproach him. He just didn't understand.

There was so much about Barabbas that one didn't understand. But anyway it was he who had seen the Saviour die, and rise again from the dead; and the heavenly light all round him he had seen too. Though they never talked about that any more. . . .

Sahak grieved—but not for his own sake. His gaunt, burnt-up face beneath the snow-white hair was scarred by sparks from the smelting-furnaces and the lash had wealed his emaciated body. But for his own part he did not grieve. For his own part he was, on the contrary, a happy man. Especially now, since his Lord had worked this miracle for him, brought him up here into the sun and up to the lilies of the field, which he himself had spoken of so beautifully.

He had worked the same miracle for Barabbas too. But Barabbas gazed uneasily about him in the world that lay again before his eyes, and none knew what he was thinking.

Such was their relationship during the first part of their time up there.

When the spring ploughing was finished they were put to work on the water-wheels which must be set going as soon as the heat began, if everything was not to get dried up. This too was heavy work. And later, when the harvest had been got in, they were moved down to the corn-mill, one of the many buildings which surrounded the Roman governor's residence and made, together with the dirty native village, an entire little town round the shipping-port. In this way they had come right down to the sea.

It was there, inside the mill, that they met the little one-eyed man.

He was a thick-set slave with short-cropped head and a grey, wrinkled face with a shrivelled mouth. His one eye had a furtive look, the other had been gouged out because he had once stolen some bushels of flour. For this reason too he had a large wooden frame round his neck. His job was to fill the sacks with flour and carry them into the store-room, and neither this simple task nor his mouse-coloured, insignificant appearance was in the least remarkable. For some reason he was more conspicuous than most of the others all the same, perhaps because one felt so strangely insecure and ill at ease in his presence. One always knew if he were there or not, and even without turning round his one-eyed stare could be distinctly felt. It was seldom one came face to face with him.

He paid no attention whatever to the two newcomers, he didn't even appear to see them. It passed quite unnoticed that he observed with a slight sneer that they were assigned to the heaviest millstone. No one could possibly see that he smiled, that his grey, withered-up mouth meant to smile. There were four mills and each was worked by two slaves. It was customary for asses to be used, but they were less plentiful here than humans of whom there were more than enough and who were also cheaper to keep. But Sahak and Barabbas thought that the food here was almost plentiful compared with what they had been used to, and that by and large they were better off now than before, in spite of the heavy work. The slave-driver did not treat them so badly; he was a stout, rather easy-going man who mostly went about with his whip over his back without using it. The only one to whom he used to give a taste of it was an old blind slave who was practically on his last legs.

The whole building inside was white with flour which had settled everywhere in the course of the years, on the floor and the walls and on all the cobwebs in the ceiling. The air was thick with flour-dust and filled with the hollow rumble of the millstones as they were revolved in all four mills at once. All the slaves worked naked, except the little one-eyed man, who wore a loin-cloth of sacking and sneaked about inside the flour-mill like a rat. The wooden frame round his neck gave him the appearance of having been trapped but of having broken loose in some way. It was said that he ate flour out of the sacks when he was alone in the store-room, though the wooden frame was supposed to prevent this. And that he did it not from hunger but in defiance, because he knew that if he were caught he would have the other eye put out and would be set to pull the millstone, just like the old blind man—work that he knew was more than he could manage and which filled him with almost as great a horror as the darkness which awaited him if they caught him stealing again. But how much of this was true it was hard to say.

No, he was not specially interested in the two newcomers. He watched them on the sly, as he watched all the others, and waited to see what would happen. He had nothing special against them. Nothing *special*. They were prisoners from the mine, he had heard. He had never come across any before. But he had nothing special against mine-prisoners. He had nothing special against anybody.

Seeing that they had been in the copper mines they must be dangerous criminals, though one of them hardly looked like it. By comparison the other did, and was evidently anxious to conceal it. He was a contemptible type and the other was a simpleton, but how had they got out of the mine? Up out of hell? Who had helped them? That was the point. But it was nothing to do with him.

If one waits long enough something always turns up. An explanation is always forthcoming in one way or another. Everything explains itself, so to speak. One has to keep an eye open of course. And this he did.

So it was that he saw the tall lean one with the big cow-eyes kneel down at night in the darkness and pray. Why did he do that? He was praying to a god of course, but which? What sort of god did one pray to in that way?

The little one-eyed man knew of many gods, though it would never have occurred to him to pray to them. And had the idea by any chance struck him, he would naturally have done as everyone else did, prayed before their image in the temple to which they belonged. But this curious slave prayed to a god who, he obviously thought, was there in the darkness in front of him. And he spoke to him just as he would to a living being, who, he imagined, took notice of him. It was most peculiar. He could be heard whispering and praying earnestly there in the dark, but anybody could see that there was no god there. It was all imagination.

One can't very well be interested in what doesn't exist, but after making this discovery the one-eyed man began talking to Sahak now and then to find out more about this extraordinary god. And Sahak explained it all to him as well as he could. He said that his god was everywhere, even in the dark. One could call on him anywhere at all and feel his presence. Why, one could even feel him inside one's own breast, and that was the most blissful of all. The one-eyed man answered that it was really a remarkable Lord he had.

—Yes, it is indeed, said Sahak.

The one-eyed man seemed to ponder a while over what he had heard, over Sahak's invisible but obviously very powerful god, and then he asked if it was he who had helped them to get out of the mine?

— Yes, Sahak said. It was.

And he added that he was the God of all the oppressed and was going to free all slaves from their chains and redeem them. For Sahak wanted to proclaim his faith and felt that the other was longing to hear this.

— Oh? said the one-eyed man.

Sahak realized more and more that the little slave, whom no one could be bothered with and whose eye had been put out, wanted to hear about his and everyone's salvation, and that it was the Lord's will that he should speak to him about it. He therefore did so as often as possible, though Barabbas looked askance at them and seemed to disapprove. And at last, one evening when they were sitting by themselves on one of the millstones after the day's work, he showed him his secret, the inscription on the back of his slave's disk. It all really came about through the one-eyed man's asking the unknown god's name—provided this might be uttered—and then Sahak had told it to him, and to prove his Lord's power and greatness had let him see the actual secret signs that stood for the holy name. The one-eyed man regarded the inscription with great interest and listened to Sahak's story of the Greek slave who had engraved it and had understood the meaning of every stroke. It was incredible how anyone in this way could know the sign of God.

Sahak looked once more at the inscription and then turned it inwards again. And as he held it to his breast he said joyously that he was God's own slave, that he belonged to him.

— Oh, said the one-eyed man.

And after a while he asked if the other one from the mines also had this inscription on his slave's disk.

Why yes, said Sahak.

And the little man nodded and said yes of course, though actually he had not been at all sure that they had quite the same faith and the same god, for this criminal with the gash under his eye never prayed. They went on talking of this strange god, and did so several more times after this conversation, which Sahak felt had brought them very close to one another. He had done right in confiding his great secret to the other and it was surely the Lord himself who had inspired him to do so.

Great was the amazement in the mill when the slave-driver one morning announced that Sahak and Barabbas were summoned to appear before the governor himself at a certain time during the day. It was the first time such a thing had happened, at any rate in this slave-driver's day, and he was just as amazed as any of the others and was quite at a loss to know what lay behind it all. Two wretched slaves in the actual presence of the Roman governor! He was to conduct them there and seemed a little anxious himself, as he had never before set foot inside the mighty one's residence. However, it was hardly likely that he could have anything to do with the matter: he was only responsible for their getting there. At the appointed time they set off, and everyone in the mill stood gazing after them, even the little slave who resembled a rat and who couldn't smile because he had a shrivelled-up mouth—he too stood gazing after them with his one eye.

Sahak and Barabbas would not have been able to find their own way through the narrow streets, which were completely strange to them. They followed immediately behind their slave-driver and kept close together, just as before. It was as if they had been chained together again.

Arrived at the great house, they were admitted through the carved cedar-wood doors by a magnificent black slave who was fettered to the door-post. He merely showed them into the vestibule and handed them over to an officer on duty, who led them across a sunny courtyard to a medium-sized room that opened on to it. There they suddenly found themselves face to face with the Roman.

All three flung themselves down on their faces and touched the floor with their foreheads, as the slave-driver had dinned into them, though both Sahak and Barabbas considered it shameless to humble oneself like that in front of one who, after all, was only a human being. Not until they were told did they dare get up. The Roman, who was leaning back in a chair on the far side of the room, beckoned them to approach, which they did hesitantly, venturing by degrees to look up at him. He was a powerfully built man of about sixty with a plump but not flabby face, broad chin and a mouth that they quickly saw was wont to command. The eyes were sharply observant but not actually unfriendly. Oddly enough, there was nothing really frightening about him.

He enquired of the slave-driver first how the two slaves had conducted themselves, if he was satisfied with them. The man stammered out that he was, adding for safety's sake that he always treated his slaves very severely. It was impossible to know whether his noble lord appreciated this; he threw a quick glance at the man's fat body and dismissed him with a light wave of the hand—he could go. The man was far from having anything against this and instantly took his leave; in fact in his hurry he was so lacking in respect that he nearly turned his back on his lord.

The latter then turned to Sahak and Barabbas and began asking them where they came from, what they had been punished for and how they had come up out of the mine, who had arranged it. The whole time he spoke quite kindly. Then getting up, he walked across the floor, and they were surprised to find that he was so tall. Going up to Sahak, he took hold of his slave's disk, looked at the stamp on it and asked if he knew what it meant. Sahak replied that it was the stamp of the Roman State. The governor said with a nod that that was quite right, and that it therefore showed that Sahak belonged to the State. Then turning the metal disk over, he looked with evident interest, but with no sign of surprise, at the secret inscription on the back. 'Christos Iesus . . .' he read, and both Sahak and Barabbas were filled with wonder that he could read the signs, decipher God's holy name.

— Who is that? he asked.

— It is my God, Sahak answered with a slight tremor in his voice.

— Aha. It is a name I cannot remember having heard before. But then there are so many gods, one can't keep track of them all. Is it the god of your native province?

— No, Sahak answered. It is everybody's God.

— Everybody's? You don't say so? That's not at all bad. And I have never even heard of him. He keeps his renown somewhat secret, if I may say so.

— Yes, said Sahak.

— Everybody's god. In that case he must have more than a little power. What does he base it on?

— On love.

— Love? . . . Well, why not. Anyway, it's no concern of mine, you may believe as you like about it. But tell me, why do you bear his name on your slave's disk?

— Because I belong to him, Sahak said, again with a slight tremor.

— Indeed? Belong to him? How can you do that? Do you not belong to the State, just as this stamp signifies? Are you not a State slave?

Sahak made no reply. He merely stood looking down at the floor. At last the Roman said—but not at all unkindly:

— You must answer this. We must be quite clear on this point, don't you see. Do you belong to the State? Tell me now.

— I belong to the Lord my God, said Sahak without looking up.

The governor stood regarding him. Then he lifted Sahak's head and looked into his burnt-up face, the face that had been at the smelting-furnaces. He said nothing, and after a time, when he had seen what he wanted, he let go the other man's chin.

Then he went and stood in front of Barabbas, and as he turned over his slave's disk in the same way he asked:

— And you? Do you also believe in this loving god?

Barabbas made no reply.

— Tell me. Do you?

Barabbas shook his head.

— You don't? Why do you bear his name on your disk then?

Barabbas was silent as before.

— Is he not your god? Isn't that what the inscription means?

— I have no god, Barabbas answered at last, so softly that it could hardly be heard. But Sahak and the Roman both heard it. And Sahak gave him a look so full of despair, pain and amazement at his incredible words that Barabbas felt it pass right through him, right into his inmost being, even though he did not meet the other's eyes.

The Roman too seemed surprised.

— But I don't understand, he said. Why then do you bear this 'Christos Iesus' carved on your disk?

— Because I want to believe, Barabbas said, without looking up at either of them.

The Roman looked at him, at his ravaged face and the gash under the eye; at the hard, coarse mouth, which still retained much of its strength. There was no expression in the face and he was not sure that he would find any there even if he lifted up the head as he had done with the other. Besides, it would never have occurred to him to do so with this man. Why? He didn't know.

He turned again to Sahak.

— Do you grasp fully the implication of what you have said? That it means you are setting yourself up against Cæsar? Do you not know that he too is a god and that it is to him you belong, his stamp you bear on your disk? And you say that you belong to another, unknown god, whose name you have carved on your disk to show that you are not Cæsar's but his. Is that not so?

— Yes, Sahak answered in a shaking voice, but it did not tremble as much as before.

— And you stick to this?

— Yes.

— But don't you understand what you are letting yourself in for by doing so?

— Yes. I understand.

The Roman paused, thinking of this slave's god, whom as a matter of fact he had heard spoken of quite a lot recently, this madman in Jerusalem who had himself died a slave's death. 'Loose all chains' . . . 'God's own slave, whom he will set free' . . . Anything but a harmless doctrine in fact . . . And faces such as that slave's had no appeal for a slave-owner. . . .

— If you renounce your faith no harm shall come to you, he said. Will you do it?

— I cannot, Sahak replied.

— Why not?

— I cannot deny my God.

— Extraordinary man. . . . Surely you must be aware of the punishment you force me to sentence you to. Are you really so brave that you can die for your faith?

— That is not for me to decide, said Sahak quietly.

— That doesn't sound so very brave. Is life not dear to you?

— Yes, answered Sahak. It is.

— But if you do not forswear this god of yours, nothing can save you. You will lose your life.

— I cannot lose the Lord my God.

The Roman shrugged his shoulders.

— Then there is nothing more I can do for you, he said, going over to the table at which he had been sitting when they came. He struck its marble top with a little ivory hammer.

— You are just as crazy as your god, he added half to himself.

While they were waiting for the guard to come the governor went up to Barabbas, turned his slave's disk over, drew out his dagger and scratched the point of it across the words 'Christos Iesus'.

— There's really no need, as you don't believe in him in any case, he said.

While this was happening Sahak looked at Barabbas with an expression that seared through him like fire and which he was never to forget.

And so Sahak was led away by the guard and Barabbas was left standing there. The governor commended him for his sensible behaviour and said that he wished to reward him for it. He was to report to the foreman of the slaves here in the house and have other and better work assigned to him.

Barabbas gave him a quick look and the Roman found that the man's eyes did in fact have an expression, harmless though it was. Hatred was quivering there like the point of an arrow that would never be shot.

And so Barabbas went to do as he had been commanded.

WHEN Sahak was crucified Barabbas stood concealed behind some hibiscus bushes a little distance away, so that his friend on the cross should not be able to see him. But Sahak had already been tortured so much beforehand that he was unlikely in any case to have been aware of him. This had been done from force of habit and because they had thought that the governor had simply forgotten to give the order. Actually the governor had not meant anything like that, though he had not bothered either to give an order to the contrary. And so for safety's sake they had done as usual. What the slave was sentenced for they had no idea, nor did they care. They were doing this sort of thing continually.

Half of his head had been shaved again and the white hair was stained with blood. The face expressed nothing really, but Barabbas who knew it so well understood what it would have expressed had it been able. He stood gazing at it the whole time with burning eyes, if it can be said that eyes such as Barabbas's are burning, and it could be said now. He also gazed at the emaciated body; he could not have torn himself away even if he had wanted to, and he didn't want to. The body was so scraggy and feeble that it was hard to imagine what crime it could have committed. But on the chest, where every rib was visible, the State's insignia were branded, to show that it was a case of high treason. The slave's disk, on the other hand, had been removed for the sake of the metal and because it was no longer needed.

The place of execution was a small rise outside the town, surrounded here and there at the foot by one or two bushes and thickets. Behind one of these stood Barabbas the acquitted. Apart from him and those who had charge of the crucifixion there was not a soul there, no one had bothered to witness Sahak's death. Otherwise people often collected, especially when the victim was guilty of a heinous crime. But Sahak had committed neither murder nor anything else, and nobody knew him or what he had done.

It was spring again now, just as it had been when they came up out of the mine and Sahak had fallen on his knees and exclaimed 'He has come!' The earth was green and even the execution-hill was full of flowers. The sun was shining on the mountains and across the sea that lay not far below. But it was the middle of the day, the heat was already oppressive and big swarms of flies rose up the moment anyone moved on the befouled slope. They were all over Sahak's body, and he was past being able to move sufficiently to drive them away. No, there was nothing great or uplifting about Sahak's death.

It was all the more curious, therefore, that Barabbas could be so moved by it. But he was. He followed it with eyes that were resolved to remember every detail—the sweat that ran down the forehead and from the deep, hollow armpits; the heaving chest with its marks from the State's branding-irons; the flies that no one chased away. The head hung down and the dying man groaned heavily; Barabbas heard every breath right down where he was standing. He too breathed jerkily and heavily, and his mouth was half-open like his friend's up there. He even thought he felt thirsty, as the other undoubtedly did. It was remarkable that Barabbas could feel as he did, but he had been shackled together with him for so long. He thought he still was, for that matter, that he and the crucified man were united again with their iron chain.

Sahak was now trying to get something out, there was something he wanted to say; perhaps he wanted a drink, but no one could catch what it was. Nor could Barabbas hear what he was saying, in spite of straining his ears. Besides, he was standing much too far away. He could of course have rushed up the slope, up to the cross, and cried out to his friend up there, asked what he wanted, if there was something he could do for him—and he could at the same time have chased away the flies. But he didn't. He stood there hidden behind his bush. He did nothing. He merely gazed at him the whole time with burning eyes and his mouth half-open from the other's pain.

No so very long after this it was clear that the crucified man would not have to suffer much more. His breath came faintly, it was no longer audible down where Barabbas stood, and the chest was hardly moving. After a while it stopped altogether and one could take it that Sahak was dead. Without any darkness descending over the earth and without any miracles at all, he quietly and unobtrusively gave up the ghost. None of those who were waiting for him to die noticed anything, they lay playing dice just as they had done that time so long ago. But this time they did not start up and were not in the least alarmed that the man on the cross had died. They didn't even notice it. The only one who did was Barabbas. And when he realized what had happened, he gave a gasp and sank down on his knees as though in prayer.

Strange . . . And to think how happy Sahak would have been if he had lived to see it. Unfortunately he was already dead.

And anyway, even though Barabbas was kneeling, he was not in fact praying. He had no one to pray to. But he knelt there for a while all the same.

Then he hid his ravaged, grey-bearded face in his hands and seemed to cry.

Suddenly one of the soldiers uttered an oath, on discovering that the crucified man was dead and that all they had to do was to take him down and go home. And so they did.

Thus it was when Sahak was crucified and Barabbas the acquitted stood looking on.

WHEN the governor retired from his governorship and returned to Rome to spend his remaining years there, he had amassed a fortune which was greater than that of any previous ruler of the island; but at the same time he had administered the mines and the whole province with a profit to the State unknown before. Innumerable overseers and slave-drivers had contributed to this success by their sense of duty, severity and perhaps even cruelty; thanks to them it had been possible to exploit fully the natural resources and squeeze both population and slaves to the utmost. But he himself was far from cruel. It was only his rule that was hard, not himself; if anyone blamed him for such a thing it was due to ignorance, to the fact that one didn't know him. And to most people he was an unknown, half-mythical person. Thousands of human wrecks down in their mine-pits and at their ploughs out in the sun-baked fields gave a sigh of relief when they heard that he thought of going away; in their simplicity they hoped that a new ruler would be better. But the governor himself left the beautiful island with sadness and regret. He had been very happy there.

He was particularly aware that he would miss his work, for he was a vigorous and active man who liked to have plenty to do. But he was also a highly cultured person and therefore looked forward at the same time to the possibilities Rome offered of a refined way of living and intercourse with cultivated equals. As he reclined in his comfortable easy chair on the shady poop deck of the ship his thoughts lingered on this with pleasure.

He had taken with him the slaves he thought he would need for his own use, and among them Barabbas. He had, however, put him down on the list more out of consideration and sentiment, for a slave of his age was not likely to be of much use to him. But he liked this sensible slave who had loyally allowed his god's name to be crossed out, and decided that he should come too. No one could believe that Barabbas's master was so considerate and unforgetful.

The voyage took longer than usual as the ship was greatly becalmed, but after several weeks' continuous rowing it glided into the port of Ostia with the galley-slaves bleeding, and the governor arrived in Rome the very next day, followed within a day or two by his retinue and possessions.

The palace which he had arranged to buy was in the most fashionable quarter and in the very heart of the city. It was several storeys high and decorated inside with multi-coloured marble and in every way furnished with excessive luxury. Barabbas, who lived in the basement like all the other slaves, never saw much more of it than this, but he realized that it must be a very sumptuous and magnificent house. It was quite immaterial to him. He was given light work to do, odd jobs of various kinds, and each morning he and several of the other slaves went with the superintendent of the kitchen, a haughty freedman, when the latter made his purchases in the market. In this way he got to see quite a lot of Rome.

Perhaps it cannot be said that he really saw it. It merely flitted past his eyes without seeming to affect him. When jostled by the crowd in the narrow streets or walking about the clamorous market-places, which were so full of people that one could hardly push one's way through, it all reached him as something extraneous and as though through a mist. The mighty, tumultuous capital never in fact became a reality to him, and he went about absently in the midst of it, engrossed in his own thoughts. Men and women from every country and of every race were mixed higgledy-piggledy, and anyone but Barabbas would probably have been fascinated by this seething mass and by all the wealth and splendour, by the stately buildings and the innumerable temples to every imaginable god, to which the nobility had themselves carried in costly, gilded litters to worship each his own—when they did not prefer the luxury shops in the Via Sacra or one of the resplendent baths. Eyes other than his would no doubt have reflected all this enraptured. But Barabbas's eyes reflected nothing; perhaps they were too deep-set to do so, and what they saw merely glided past like something that did not concern them. No, he didn't care a straw for this world. He was indifferent to it. So he thought himself at any rate.

But he could not have been quite so indifferent to it as he thought, all the same. For he hated it.

Among the other things that seemed unreal to him were the many processions that passed through the streets, with their priests and believers and sacred emblems. To him who had no god it must have felt strange to be meeting them continuously and to have to make way for them. Pressed against the house walls, he watched them with a stealthy, averted look. Once he even followed one of these processions into a remarkable temple which he had never seen before, and when inside he, like the others, stopped in front of a picture of a mother with her boy-child in her arms; and when he asked who it was they said that it was the most blessed Isis with the child Horus. But then they began looking at him suspiciously, at someone who did not know the Holy Mother's name, and a temple guard came and turned him out; by the copper portal the guard made a secret sign to protect himself and the temple. Perhaps he saw that Barabbas was conceived and born in hatred of all things created in heaven and earth and of the Creator of heaven and earth.

With the scar down his cheek flaming red and the pupils of his fierce, hidden-away eyes quivering like arrow-heads, Barabbas rushed away, and then through street after street and lane after lane. Get thee hence, thou reprobate! He lost his bearings and hadn't the faintest idea where he was, and when at last he found his way home he only narrowly escaped being punished—but this they dared not do as they knew that he was in favour with the master of the house. And besides, they believed his muddled explanation that he had lost his way in the city that was still so strange to him. He crouched in his corner in the slave-cellar and as he lay there in the darkness he felt the crossed-out 'Christos Iesus' burn like fire against his heaving chest.

That night he dreamt that he was shackled to a slave who lay beside him praying, but whom he could not see.

— What are you praying for? he asked him. What is the use?

— I am praying for you, the slave answered out of the darkness in a well-known voice.

Then he lay quite still so as not to disturb the praying man and felt his old eyes filling with tears. But when he awoke and fumbled about on the floor for the chain, it was not there, nor the slave either. He was not bound together with anyone. Not with anyone at all in the whole world.

On one occasion when he was alone in one of the cellars underneath the palace he found the sign of the fish carved into the wall in an out-of-the-way place. It was clumsily done but there was no doubt as to what it was intended to be and the meaning of it. He stood wondering which of the slaves could be a Christian. He wondered greatly over it during the days and weeks that followed and observed each one of them carefully to try to find out. But he asked no one. He made no enquiries as to whether there was anyone who knew. In that case it would not have been so difficult. But he did nothing like that.

He did not associate with them, with the other slaves, more than was absolutely necessary. He never spoke to any of them and therefore didn't know them. And for this reason no one knew him or bothered about him.

There were many Christians in Rome, that he knew. He knew that they assembled in their prayer-houses, in their brotherhoods in different parts of the city. But he made no effort to go along. It may have crossed his mind once or twice, but he never went. He bore the name of their god carved on his disk, but it was crossed out.

Latterly they had apparently had to meet in secret, in other places, as they were afraid of persecution. Barabbas had heard about it in the market-place from several who had spaced out their fingers after them by way of protection, just as the temple guard in the Holy Mother's temple had done to him. They were abhorred, hated, suspected of witchcraft and goodness knows what. And their god was a notorious malefactor who had been hanged a long time ago. Nobody wanted to have anything to do with them.

One evening Barabbas overheard two of the slaves standing whispering together in the darkness of the cellar; they could not see him and believed themselves alone. Barabbas could not see them either, but he recognized them by their voices. They were two newly-bought slaves who had not been many weeks in the house.

They were speaking of a meeting of the brethren that was to be held the following evening in Marcus Lucius' vineyard on the Appian Way. After a while Barabbas realized that it was not in the vineyard they were all to meet but in the Jewish catacombs that had their beginning there.

Curious place at which to meet. . . . Among the dead. . . . How could they want to meet there . . . ?

On the evening of the next day, in good time before the slave-cellar was shut for the night, he slipped away from the palace at the risk of his life.

When he came out on the Via Appia it was nearly dusk and there was scarcely any longer a soul to be seen. He found the vineyard by asking a shepherd who was driving his flock home along the road.

Once down under the earth he groped his way along in the narrow, sloping passage. The daylight from the opening still guided him as he made his way down into the first burial gallery and saw how it extended into the darkness. He groped his way along in it, feeling with his hands against the cold, damp stone slabs of the walls. They were to gather in the first big burial chamber, he had understood from the two slaves. He went on.

Now he thought he could hear voices. He stopped and listened—no, there wasn't a sound. He continued. He had to go very warily the whole time as there were often steps, one or several steps, that always led still deeper down into the earth. He went on and on.

But he didn't come to any burial chamber. It was still the same narrow gallery. Now it was branching off, he could feel, and he didn't know which way to choose. He stood hesitating, utterly at a loss. Then he saw a gleam of light in the distance—quite a long way off. Yes, it was a gleam of light! He hurried towards it. That's where it must be!

But suddenly there was no longer any light to be seen. It had vanished—perhaps because without his knowing he had turned into another passage-way, a side-passage to the first. He hurried back to see the light again. But it had disappeared; it was not there any more!

He stood there completely dazed. Where were they? Where was he to find them? Were they not here then?

And where was he himself? Oh yes, he knew how he had got here, he could always find his way back to the entrance. And he decided to return as he had come.

But as he was making his way back along the gallery which he knew he had followed the whole time and where he recognized every step up, he suddenly caught sight of the gleam of light again. A strong, unmistakable glow, but in a side-passage which he had evidently not noticed previously, and not in the same direction as before. It must be the same glow, however, and he hurried towards it—that's where it must be! The glow became brighter and brighter. . . .

Until all at once it went out. Just wasn't there.

He put his hand to his head. To his eyes. Whatever kind of light was it he had seen? *Wasn't* it a light? Was it only imagination . . . or something funny with his eyes . . . like that time long, long ago. . . . He rubbed them and looked about him. . . .

No, there was no light here at all! Not anywhere, in any direction! Only an endless, icy darkness surrounding him, in which he was quite alone—for they were not here at all, there wasn't a soul here, a single human being other than himself, only the dead! . . .

The dead! . . . He was surrounded by the dead. Everywhere, in every direction, in every passage and gallery, whichever way he turned. Where was he to go! He had no idea which way he was to go in order to get out again, to get away from here, out of the realm of the dead. . . .

The realm of the dead! . . . He was in the realm of the dead! He was shut up inside the realm of the dead! . . .

He was filled with terror. A suffocating terror. And suddenly he rushed away, senselessly, panic-stricken, in any direction at all, stumbling over unseen steps, into one passage after the other, trying to find the way out, the way out of the realm of the dead. . . . He strayed about down there like a man crazed, panting and gasping for breath. . . . At last he simply swayed along the passages, bumping against the walls where all the dead lay walled up, against the walls of death, outside which he could never come. . . .

At last he felt a warm current of air from up on the earth, from another world. . . . Half insensibly he dragged himself up the slope and came out among the grape-vines.

There he lay resting on the ground and looking up at the dark void of heaven.

It was dark now everywhere. In heaven as well as on earth. Everywhere . . .

As Barabbas made his way back to the city along the nocturnal Via Appia he felt very much alone. Not because no one walked beside him on the road and no one passed him, but because he was alone in the endless night that rested over the whole earth, alone in heaven and on earth and among the living and the dead. This he had always been, but it wasn't until now that he realized it. He walked there in the darkness, as though buried in it, walked there with the scar in his lonely old face, the scar from the blow his father had dealt him. And among the grey hairs on his wrinkled chest hung his slave's disk with God's crossed-out name. Yes, he was alone in heaven and on earth.

And he was immured in himself, in his own realm of death. How could he break out of it?

Once and once only had he been united to another, but that was only with an iron chain. Never with anything else but an iron chain.

He heard his own footsteps against the stone surface of the road. Otherwise the silence was complete, as though there were not another living soul in all the world. On all sides he was surrounded by the darkness. Not a light. Not a light anywhere. There were no stars in the heavens and all was desolate and void.

He breathed heavily, for the air was sultry and hot. It felt feverish—or was it he who was feverish, who was ill, who had got death into him down there? Death! He always had that inside him, he had had that inside him as long as he had lived. It hunted him inside himself, in the dark mole's passages of his mind, and filled him with its terror.

Although he was so old now, although he had no wish to live any longer, it still filled him with its terror just the same. Although he wanted so much . . . just wanted . . .

No, no, not to die! Not to die! . . .

But they gathered down there in the realm of the dead to pray to their God, to be united with him and with each other. They were not afraid of death, they had vanquished it. Gathered for their fraternal meetings, their love feasts . . . Love one another . . . Love one another . . .

But when he came they were not there, not a single one of them was there. He simply wandered round alone in the dark, in the passages, in his own mole's passages. . . .

Where were they? Where were they who made out that they loved one another?

Where were they this night, this sultry night—now that he had entered the city it felt even more oppressive—this night that was brooding over the whole world—this night of fever in which he could scarcely breathe—which was stifling him. . . .

As he turned a street corner he felt the smell of smoke strike against him. It was coming from the cellar of a house not far away; the smoke was billowing out of the basement and from one or two vent-holes tongues of flame came licking out. . . . He hurried towards it.

As he ran he heard cries all round him from other running people:

— Fire! Fire!

At a street-crossing he found that it was also burning in a side-street, burning even more fiercely there. He grew bewildered, couldn't understand. . . . Then suddenly he heard shouts some distance away:

— It's the Christians! It's the Christians!

And from one side after the other:

— It's the Christians! It's the Christians!

At first he stood there dumbfounded, as if unable to take in what they said, what they meant. The Christians . . .? Then he understood, then he got it.

Yes! It's the Christians! It's the Christians who are setting fire to Rome! Who are setting fire to the whole world!

Now he knew why they had not been out there. They were here to set this odious Rome, to set the whole of this odious world on fire! Their hour had come! Their Saviour had come!

The crucified man had returned, he of Golgotha had returned. To save mankind, to destroy this world, as he had promised. To annihilate it, let it go up in flames, as he had promised! Now he was really showing his might. And he, Barabbas, was to help him! Barabbas the reprobate, his reprobate brother from Golgotha, would not fail. Not now. Not this time. Not now! He had already rushed up to the nearest blaze, snatched up a brand and run and flung it down into the window of a cellar in another house. He fetched one brand after the other and ran and flung them down in new places, in new cellars. He did not fail!

Barabbas did not fail! He set light well and truly. No half measures! The flames leapt out of one house after the other, scorching all the walls; everything was burning. And Barabbas rushed on, to spread the fire still more, rushed round panting with God's crossed-out name on his chest. He did not fail. He did not fail his Lord when he really needed him, when the hour was come, the great hour when everything was to perish. It was spreading, spreading! Everything was one vast sea of fire. The whole world, the whole world was ablaze!

Behold, his kingdom is here! Behold, his kingdom is here!

IN the prison underneath the Capitol all the Christians who had been accused of the fire were collected, and among them Barabbas as well. He had been caught red-handed and after interrogation had been taken there and thrown together with them. He was one of them.

The prison was hewn out of the actual rock and the walls dripped with moisture. In the prevailing half-light they could not see each other very distinctly and Barabbas was glad of it. He sat by himself in the rotting straw rather to one side, and the whole time with his face averted.

They had spoken a lot about the fire and the fate that awaited them. Their having been accused of starting the fire must have been merely a pretext to arrest and sentence them. Their judge knew perfectly well that they had not done it. Not a single one of them had been there; they had not gone outside their doors after they had had warning that there was to be a persecution and that their meeting-place in the catacombs had been betrayed. They were innocent. But what did that matter. Everyone wanted to believe them guilty. Everyone wanted to believe what had been shouted out in the streets by the hired mob: 'It's the Christians! It's the Christians!'

— Who hired them? said a voice from out of the darkness. But the others took no notice.

How could the Master's followers be guilty of such a thing as arson, of setting Rome on fire? How could anyone believe such a thing? Their Master set human souls on fire, not their cities. He was the Lord and God of the world, not a malefactor.

And they began speaking of him who was Love and the Light and of his kingdom which they were awaiting according to his promise. Then they sang hymns with strange and lovely words which Barabbas had never heard before. He sat with bowed head listening to them.

The iron-studded bar outside the door was drawn aside, there was a squeaking of hinges and a gaoler came in. He left the door open to admit more light during the prisoners' feeding, of which he had charge. He himself had clearly just had his dinner and regaled himself liberally with wine, for he was red-faced and talkative. Uttering coarse words of abuse he tossed them the food they were to have: it was almost uneatable. He didn't mean any harm with his swearing, however, he was merely speaking the language of his trade, the one that all gaolers used. He sounded almost good-natured as a matter of fact. On catching sight of Barabbas, who happened to be sitting full in the light from the doorway, he gave a bellow of laughter.

— There's that crazy loon! he shouted. The one who ran round setting fire to Rome! You half-wit! And then you all say it wasn't you who set light to everything! You're a pack of liars! He was caught in the act of hurling a brand down into Caius Servius' oil-store.

Barabbas kept his eyes lowered. His face was rigid and expressed nothing, but the scar under his eye was burning red.

The other prisoners turned to him amazed. None of them knew him. They had thought he was a criminal, one who didn't belong to them, he had not even been interrogated or put into prison at the same time as they had.

— It's not possible, they whispered among themselves.

— What isn't possible? asked the gaoler.

— He can't be a Christian, they said. Not if he has done what you say.

— Can't he? But he has said so himself. Those who caught him told me so, they told me everything. And he even confessed it at the interrogation.

— We do not know him, they mumbled, uneasy. And if he belonged to us, then surely we ought to know him. He's an utter stranger to us.

— You're all a nice lot of humbugs! Wait a minute, you'll soon see!

And going up to Barabbas he turned over his slave's disk.

— Take a look at this—isn't that your god's name all right? I can't make out this scrawl, but isn't it, eh? Read for yourselves!

They crowded round him and Barabbas, gaping in astonishment at the inscription on the back of the disk. The majority of them couldn't decipher it either, but one or two whispered in a subdued and anxious tone:

— Christos Iesus . . . Christos Iesus . . .

The gaoler flung the disk back against Barabbas's chest and looked round triumphantly.

— Now what do you say, eh? Not a Christian, eh? He showed it to the judge himself and said that he didn't belong to the emperor but to that god you pray to, the one who was hanged. And now he'll be hanged too, that I can swear to. And all the rest of you for that matter! Though you were all much more cunning about it than he was. It's a pity that one of you was stupid enough to go running straight into our arms saying he was a Christian!

And grinning broadly at their bewildered faces, he went out, slamming the door behind him.

They crowded again round Barabbas and began plying him furiously with questions. Who was he? Was he really a Christian? Which brotherhood did he belong to? Was it really true that he had started the fire?

Barabbas made no answer. His face was ashen grey and the old eyes had crept in as far as possible so as not to be seen.

— Christian! Didn't you see that the inscription was crossed out?

— Was it crossed out! Was the Lord's name crossed out!

— Of course it was! Didn't you see?

One or two had seen it but hadn't given it a second thought. What did it mean anyway?

One of them snatched at the slave's disk and peered at it once more; even though the light was worse now, they could still see that the inscription was scratched out with a clear, rough cross apparently made with a knife by some powerful hand.

— Why is the Lord's name crossed out? they asked, one after the other. What does it mean? Don't you hear—what does it mean?

But Barabbas didn't answer even now. He sat with his shoulders hunched and avoided looking at any of them, let them do what they liked with him, with his slave's disk, but made no answer. They grew more and more agitated and amazed at him, at this strange man who professed to be a Christian but who couldn't possibly be. His curious behaviour was beyond them. At last some of them went over to an old man who was sitting in the dark further inside the dungeon and who had not taken any part in what had been going on among them. After they had spoken to him for a while the old man got up and walked over with them to Barabbas.

He was a big man with a broad back who, despite a slight stoop, was still unusually tall. The powerful head had long but thinning hair, quite white like his beard, which came right down over his chest. He had an imposing but very gentle expression; the blue eyes were almost childishly wide and clear though full of the wisdom of age.

He stood first looking for a long time at Barabbas, at his ravaged old face. Then he seemed to recollect something and nodded in confirmation.

— It's so long ago, he said apologetically, sitting down in the straw in front of him.

The others, who had gathered round, were very surprised. Did their greatly revered father know this man?

He evidently did, as they could see when he began talking to him. He asked him how he had got on during his life. And Barabbas told him what had happened to him. Not all, far from it, but enough for the other man to be able to understand or divine most of it. When he understood something Barabbas was unwilling to say, he merely nodded in silence. They had a good talk together, although it was so foreign to Barabbas to confide in anyone and though he didn't really do so now. But he answered the other's questions in a low, tired voice and even looked up now and again into the wise, childish eyes and at the furrowed old face, which was ravaged like his own but in quite a different way. The furrows were engraved deep into it, but it was all so different, and it radiated such peace. The skin in which they were engraved seemed almost white and the cheeks were hollow, probably because he had but few teeth left. But actually he had altered very little. And he still spoke his confident and ingenuous dialect.

The venerable old man gradually got to know both why the Lord's name was crossed out and why Barabbas had helped to set fire to Rome —that he had wanted to help them and their Saviour to set this world on fire. The old man shook his white head in distress when he heard this. He asked Barabbas how he could have thought it was they who had started the fire. It was Cæsar himself who had had it done, the wild beast himself, and it was him Barabbas had helped.

— It was this worldly ruler you helped, he said, him to whom your slave's disk says you belong, not the Lord whose name is crossed out on it. Without knowing it, you served your rightful lord.

— Our Lord is Love, he added gently. And taking the disk that hung on Barabbas's chest amongst the grey hairs, he looked sorrowfully at his Lord and Master's crossed-out name.

He let it drop from his old fingers and sighed heavily. For he realized that this was Barabbas's disk, the one he had to bear, and that there was nothing at all he could do to help him. And he realized that the other knew this too, saw it from his timid and solitary eyes.

— Who is he? Who is he? they all shouted when the old man got to his feet again. At first he didn't want to answer them, tried to get out of it. But they kept on at him until at last he was forced to do so.

— He is Barabbas, he who was acquitted in the Master's stead, he said.

They stared at the stranger, dumbfounded. Nothing could have astounded or upset them more than this.

— Barabbas! they whispered. Barabbas the acquitted! Barabbas the acquitted!

They didn't seem able to grasp it. And their eyes gleamed fierce and threatening in the semi-darkness.

But the old man quietened them.

— This is an unhappy man, he said, and we have no right to condemn him. We ourselves are full of faults and shortcomings, and it is no credit to us that the Lord has taken pity on us notwithstanding. We have no right to condemn a person because he has no god.

They stood with downcast eyes, and it was as though they didn't dare to look at Barabbas after this, after these last terrible words. They moved away from him in silence to where they had been sitting before. The old man sighed and followed them with heavy steps.

Barabbas sat there again alone.

He sat there alone day after day in the prison, on one side apart from them. He heard them sing their songs of faith and speak confidently of their death and the eternal life that awaited them. Especially after sentence had been pronounced did they speak of it a great deal. They were full of trust, there was not the slightest doubt amongst them.

Barabbas listened, deep in his own thoughts. He too thought of what was in store for him. He remembered the man on the Mount of Olives, the one who had shared his bread and salt with him and who was now long since dead again and lay grinning with his skull in the everlasting darkness.

Eternal life . . .

Was there any meaning in the life he had led? Not even that did he believe in. But this was something he knew nothing about. It was not for him to judge.

Over there sat the white-bearded old man among his own people, listening to them and talking to them in his unmistakable Galilean dialect. But occasionally he would lean his head in his big hand and sit there for a moment in silence. Perhaps he was thinking of the shore of Genesaret and that he would have liked to die there. But it was not to be. He had met his Master on the road and he had said 'Follow me.' And this he had had to do. He looked ahead of him with his childlike eyes, and his furrowed face with the hollow cheeks radiated a great peace.

And so they were led out to be crucified. They were chained together in pairs, and as they were not an even number Barabbas came last in the procession, not chained to anyone. It just turned out like that. In this way, too, it happened that he hung furthest out in the rows of crosses.

A large crowd had collected, and it was a long time before it was all over. But the crucified spoke consolingly and hopefully to each other the whole time. To Barabbas nobody spoke.

When dusk fell the spectators had already gone home, tired of standing there any longer. And besides, by that time the crucified were all dead.

Only Barabbas was left hanging there alone, still alive. When he felt death approaching, that which he had always been so afraid of, he said out into the darkness, as though he were speaking to it:

— To thee I deliver up my soul.

And then he gave up the ghost.

*1952*

# PATRIC DICKINSON

## *Song*

WHEN you are young<br>
You never notice the seasons,<br>
In an unbroken dream<br>
They pour from the crystal fountain,<br>
Barefoot summer<br>
Deep in the starfish pools,<br>
Woollen winter<br>
On the hollow ringing pond<br>
And stars in the squeaking ice:<br>
In an unbroken dream<br>
The first and the last firelight<br>
Crocus and robin song.

There is no time<br>
But the dandelion in the meadow<br>
To blow away in a breath,<br>
No love but a cherrystone enchantment—<br>
Sometime, Never.<br>
O curled in the question of delight<br>
A living answer<br>
You move in a vivid world<br>
Where death is drifting seed<br>
To blow away in a breath—<br>
Till the first kiss breaks the dream,<br>
You awake to be young, to be old.

*1952*

# ELSPETH HUXLEY

## *Gambia*

FROM 'FOUR GUINEAS'

THE whole crew of the *Mansa Kila Kuta* is African: quiet, blue-sweatered men who work with the smooth, easy calm of the altogether competent. They know the river as a herdsman his cattle, every bar and current of it, and the river is not easy to know. The banks are flat beyond belief, and for the first 150 miles or so, where salt tides run, lined with a dark belt of mangroves lacking totally in landmarks; yet the quartermaster can pick up a buoy at midnight correctly to within 100 yards of his reckoning.

These men are local aristocrats, elevated by wealth and the prestige of office. The quartermaster in command, a tall, grizzled sailor with an admiral's dignity, has served for nearly thirty years in the Gambia Marine and has acquired the solidity of an oak tree. Africans of this kind, who have accepted and discharge responsibility, arouse great confidence. They grow to full stature when pruned by discipline and fertilized by trust.

Despite a sparkle on the water, a clear sun-bleached sky, grey herons flying, this salty Gambia might prove a dull river were it not for all the little creeks that wind inland, their mouths hidden among the mangroves. In a native fishing-craft fitted with a motor, we wove our way first through mud-banks gripped by the mangroves' black talons, then through flat fields of paddy or of grass so long and thick-stemmed that the stalks all but met overhead. Posts mark the channel, which disappears under-water at the spring tides, and a-top each post sits one pied kingfisher. Squacca herons, reef herons and another small kind, buff not grey, fly ahead slowly; spur-wing geese circle at a distance; egrets encrust the foliage of bushes; ring-doves coo.

A bird-adorned, gentle, placid scene that reminded me of East Anglia; this might almost have been a giant Alde

> 'that flows
> Quietly through green level lands,
> So quietly it knows
> Their shape, their greenness and their shadows well;
> And then undreamingly for miles it goes.
> And silently, beside the sea.'

Save for the crocodiles, of course, dozing on mudbanks, and rice, and the mosquitoes. . . . Foreign parts seem often to provoke in English people the most inappropriate comparisons. Driving through the rain-forest of Eastern Nigeria, on every side tangles of creepers, giant mahoganies and oil-palms, passing an occasional mud village full of coal-black occupants, a man observed: 'This reminds me so much of Warwickshire.' And a Yorkshireman once remarked in the Celebes, gazing at Javanese in huge soup-plate hats driving water-buffaloes harnessed to wooden ploughs through liquid mud: 'This is just like the country round Hull.'

We came here and there to a narrow bund ending at the water's edge. The Government have chivvied the people into building these bunds, to enable them to penetrate more easily into the swamps to transplant rice, using money from the Farmers' Fund, derived from official profits on the groundnut crop. Transplanting obliges people to wade all day in mud and water up to their knees, living bait for mosquitoes and leeches, bent double under the hot sun. This, needless to say, is women's work. If you see a man in the paddy-fields he is usually one of the 'strange farmers' who come from French territory in their thousands to grow a season's crop on land provided by Gambians, in return for a rent consisting of about half the tenant's working time.

It is uphill work, getting people to help themselves. They would rather starve, not as a matter of choice, but because their wish for leisure is even stronger than their wish for food—just as we go on having wars not because anyone wants them, but because some men's wish for power is stronger than their wish for peace. Here in Gambia you do not die of hunger, or not often. Hang on, and the rains will come to put a little flesh back on your ribs. So you do no more work than your wife can manage.

Our boat chugged underneath a bund that spanned the narrow channel and we watched the women file across, yellow rice-ears piled on their heads in great golden cones like an oriental head-dress. They walked with a smooth, easy glide, their bodies gleaming, feet bare, a cotton cloth twisted round the waist, arms swinging loose. They were bringing in the rice to a village raised a few feet above the flooded flats, like all villages neatly encased in screens of *krinting*, a kind of reed. And like all villages, pullulating with children—flocks, droves, packs of little ones.

At Geneiri, some way up this creek, the Medical Research Council had an experimental village. They still have large laboratories outside Bathurst for work on human nutrition.

Fifty per cent. at least of all Gambian children, their scientists estimate, die before they are ten. That is so all over Africa—in some places the figure is a good deal higher. (Curiously enough, the Gambia is relatively free from gut parasites like hookworm.) Under Dr. B. S. Platt, a Professor in the London School of Hygiene and Tropical Medicine, a team is experimenting on how to cut down this mortality and at the same time improve a grievously low standard of nutrition.

A village called Keneba is being systematically cleared of malaria infection by repeated spraying with insecticides. Already infant mortality has tumbled in a spectacular fashion. At another village, Sekuta, every other new-born baby has received a dose of chloroquin (which kills the parasite) and not a single dosed baby has died of malaria. Moreover, the dosed infants look twice as well and plump as their undosed companions. One would of course expect malaria to keep a child back, but Dr. Platt and his colleagues are asking 'why?' and, out of this question, new lines of enquiry are opening up. For instance, malaria parasites in the blood need nourishment. So do the antibodies which the blood makes to fight the parasites. All these organisms perhaps use valuable proteins which the body needs to build its tissues, and of which it is thus deprived. African diets are notoriously short of proteins, so short that probably few Europeans could live healthily on them. Has the African managed to adapt his body to extract more nitrogen from his diet and to make better use of it, just as he has adapted his body, through pigmentation, better to resist the sun?

All this laboratory work is deep and fascinating, and will add new facts to the sum of knowledge. But the consequences are as pregnant with threat and promise as the discovery of nuclear fission. Every baby inherits the necessity to fill its belly twice a day for sixty, seventy, eighty years to come. Consider this little black infant, mewling and puking, at Keneba or Geneiri: if all goes well, it will need before it dies at least twenty tons of rice, the flesh of several bullocks, two or three tons of fish, and vegetables, grain, fruit, spices besides. Say that in one small village, twenty babies are born this year. Ten that would otherwise die are saved by doctors, and the next year ten more, and the year after that. In twenty years, that means 200 extra people: each year, 4,000 extra tons of rice, the flesh of a dozen bullocks, seven or eight tons of fish. By now the saved ones have in their turn started breeding, and soon the process gets out of hand, as threatening as a cancerous tumour. Where will all this rice come from, this corn, those fish and beasts? Who will grow them, on what land?

Already, perhaps nine Africans out of ten are under-nourished. How can under-nourishment be swept away at the same time as people multiply? Do the doctors not see that they are chasing simultaneously a fox running north and a hare running south? Doctors, bearers of mercy though they be, must yet be seen as the gravest threat to the future peace of Africa. They decline responsibility for the results of what they do. 'That's for politicians and administrators to settle,' they say. '*Our* job is to save life.' How can the poor politicians find a solution when the doctors present them with something quite insoluble? With the needle that repels smallpox, bubonic plague and yaws they have upset the balance set up by Nature to match our human population to the resources which must support it. All over Africa, in hundreds of thousands of villages like Sekuta, babies that would formerly have died now stay alive. Here and there, new farms are won from bush and forest to feed them. But new land cannot be bred like people and Africa is running out of new land. In places it has run out already and famine has begun to come back. If malaria is conquered, the doom of millions by starvation will almost certainly be sealed.

Doctors worship exclusively the god of life, and to him make innumerable sacrifices. Indians know better, and render homage to Siva, the Destroyer, no less than to Vishnu, the Preserver, and Brahma, Creator of all.

*1954*

# JULIAN HUXLEY

## *Transhumanism*

AS a result of a thousand million years of evolution, the universe is becoming conscious of itself, able to understand something of its past history and its possible future. This cosmic self-awareness is being realized in one tiny fragment of the universe—in a few of us human beings. Perhaps it has been realized elsewhere too, through the evolution of conscious living creatures on the planets of other stars. But on this our planet it has never happened before.

Evolution on this planet is a history of the realization of ever new possibilities by the stuff of which earth (and the rest of the universe) is made—life; strength, speed and awareness; the flight of birds and the social polities of bees and ants; the emergence of mind, long before man was ever dreamt of, with the production of colour, beauty, communication, maternal care, and the beginnings of intelligence and insight. And finally, during the last few ticks of the cosmic clock, something wholly new and revolutionary, human beings with their capacities for conceptual thought and language, for self-conscious awareness and purpose, for accumulating and pooling conscious experience.

Do not let us forget that the human species is as radically different from any of the microscopic single-celled animals that lived a thousand million years ago, as they were from a lifeless fragment of stone or metal.

The new understanding of the universe has come about through the new knowledge amassed in the last hundred years—by psychologists, biologists and other scientists, by archaeologists, anthropologists and historians. It has defined man's responsibility and destiny—to be an agent for the rest of the world in the job of realizing its inherent potentialities as fully as possible.

It is as if man had been suddenly appointed managing director of the biggest business of all, the business of evolution—appointed without being asked if he wanted it, and without proper warning and preparation. What is more, he can't refuse the job. Whether he wants to or not, whether he is conscious of what he is doing or not, he *is* in point of fact determining the future direction of evolution on this earth. That is his inescapable destiny, and the sooner he realizes it and starts believing in it, the better for all concerned.

What the job really boils down to is this:—the fullest realization of man's possibilities, whether by the individual, by the community, or by the species in its processional adventure along the corridors of time. Every man-jack of us begins as a mere speck of potentiality, a spherical and microscopic egg-cell. During the nine months before birth, this automatically unfolds into a truly miraculous range of organization: after birth, in addition to continuing automatic growth and development, the individual begins to realize his mental possibilities—by building up a personality, by developing special talents, by acquiring knowledge and skills of various kinds, by playing his part in keeping society going. This post-natal process is not an automatic or a predetermined one. It may proceed in very different ways according to circumstances and according to the individual's own efforts. The degree to which capacities are realized can be more or less complete. The end-result can be satisfactory or very much the reverse; in particular, the personality may grievously fail in attaining any real wholeness. One thing is certain, that the well-developed, well-integrated personality is the highest product of evolution, the highest realization we know of in the universe.

The first thing that the human species has to do to prepare itself for the cosmic office to which it finds itself appointed is to explore human nature, to find out what are the possibilities open to it (including, of course, its limitations, whether inherent or imposed by the facts of external nature). We have pretty well finished the geographical exploration of the earth; we have pushed the scientific exploration of nature, both lifeless and living, to a point at which its main outlines have become clear; but the exploration of human nature and its possibilities has scarcely begun. A vast new world of uncharted possibilities awaits its Columbus.

The great men of the past have given us glimpses of what is possible in the way of personality, of intellectual understanding, of spiritual achievement, of artistic creation. But these are scarcely more than Pisgah glimpses. We need to explore and map the whole realm of human possibility, as the realm of physical geography has been mapped and explored. How to create new possibilities for ordinary living. What can be done to bring out the latent capacities of the ordinary man and woman for understanding and enjoyment. To teach people the techniques of achieving spiritual experince (after all, one can acquire the technique of dancing or tennis, so why not of mystical ecstasy or spiritual peace?). To develop native talent and intelligence in the growing child, instead of frustrating or distorting them. Already we know that painting and poetry, music and mathematics, acting and science, can come to mean something very real to quite ordinary average boys and girls—provided only that the right methods are adopted for bringing out the children's hidden possibilities. We are beginning to realize that even the most fortunate people are living far below capacity; and most human beings develop not more than a small fraction of their potential mental and spiritual efficiency. The human race, in fact, is surrounded by a vast area of unrealized possibilities, a challenge to the spirit of exploration.

The scientific and technical explorations have given the Common Man all over the world a notion of physical possibilities. Thanks to science, the under-privileged are coming to believe that no one need be underfed or chronically diseased, or deprived of the benefits of its technical and practical applications. The world's unrest is largely due to this new belief. People are determined not to put up with a subnormal standard of physical health and material living, now that science has revealed the possibility of raising it. The unrest will produce some unpleasant consequences before it is dissipated; but it is in essence a beneficent unrest, a dynamic force which will not be stilled until it has laid the physiological foundations of human destiny.

Once we have explored the possibilities open to consciousness and personality, and the knowledge of them has become common property, a new source of unrest will have emerged. People will realize and believe that if proper measures are taken, no one need be starved of true satisfaction, or condemned to sub-standard fulfilment. This process too will begin by being unpleasant, and end by being beneficent. It will begin by destroying the ideas and the institutions that stand in the way of our realizing our possibilities (or even deny that the possibilities are there to be realized), and will go on by at least making a start with the actual construction of true human destiny.

Up till now, human life has generally been, as Hobbes described it, 'nasty, brutish and short'; the great majority of human beings (if they have not already died young) have been afflicted with misery in one form or another—poverty, disease, ill-health, over-work, cruelty, or oppression. They have attempted to lighten their misery by means of their hopes and their ideals. The trouble has been that the hopes have generally been unjustified, the ideals have generally failed to correspond with reality.

The zestful but scientific exploration of possibilities and of the techniques for realizing them will make our hopes rational, and will set our ideals within the framework of reality, by showing how much of them are realizable.

Already, we can justifiably hold the belief that these lands of possibility exist, and that the present limitations and miserable frustrations of our existence could be in large measure surmounted. We are already justified in the conviction that human life as we know it in history is a wretched makeshift, rooted in ignorance; and that it could be transcended by a state of existence based on the illumination of knowledge and comprehension, just as our modern control of physical nature based on science transcends the tentative fumblings of our ancestors that were rooted in superstition and professional secrecy.

To do this, we must study the possibilities of creating a more favourable social environment, as we have already done in large measure with our physical environment. We shall start from new premisses. For instance, that beauty (as something to enjoy and something to be proud of) is indispensable, and therefore that ugly or depressing towns are immoral; that quality of people, not mere quantity, is what we must aim at, and therefore that a concerted policy is required to prevent the present flood of population-increase from wrecking all our hopes for a better world; that true understanding and enjoyment are ends in themselves, as well as tools for or relaxations from a job, and that therefore we must explore and make fully available the techniques of education and self-education; that the most ultimate satisfaction comes from a depth and wholeness of the inner life, and therefore that we must explore and make fully available the techniques of spiritual development; above all, that there are two complementary parts of our cosmic duty: one to ourselves, to be fulfilled in the realization and enjoyment of our capacities, the other to others, to be fulfilled in service to the community, and in promoting the welfare of the generations to come and the advancement of our species as a whole.

The human species can, if it wishes, transcend itself—not just sporadically, an individual here in one way, an individual there in another way, but in its entirety, as humanity. That is our dawning belief.

We need a name for this new belief. Perhaps *transhumanism* will serve: man remaining man, but transcending himself, by realizing new possibilities of and for his human nature.

'I believe in transhumanism'; once there are enough people who can truly say that, the human species will be on the threshold of a new kind of existence, as different from ours as ours is from that of Pekin man. It will at last be consciously fulfilling its real destiny.

*1955*